Structure of High-Resolution NMR Spectra

Structure of High-Resolution NMR Spectra

P. L. CORIO

MOBIL OIL CORPORATION
Central Research Division Laboratory
Princeton, New Jersey

1966

ACADEMIC PRESS NEW YORK · LONDON

ACADEMIC PRESS INC.
111 Fifth Avenue, New York, New York 10003

United Kingdom Edition published by
ACADEMIC PRESS INC. (LONDON) LTD.
Berkeley Square House, London W.1

LIBRARY OF CONGRESS CATALOG CARD NUMBER: 65-26393

PRINTED IN THE UNITED STATES OF AMERICA

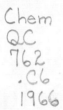

TO

MARGARET, ELIZABETH, AND PAUL

Preface

This book represents an expansion of an article published several years ago in *Chemical Reviews*. The preparation of the book was prompted by the continuing response to that article, and at the request of many readers to prepare an expanded version treating the mathematical and physical ideas in greater detail. The attempt to accommodate these readers, together with my own predilections in the matter, have imparted something of a mathematical character to the book. It would be a mistake, however, to suppose that the book is a collection of abstract mathematical theorems. With few exceptions, the theorems developed are repeatedly used in the theory and interpretation of complex spectra. The mathematics itself should pose no problem to anyone who has completed an introductory course in quantum mechanics. Readers who deem themselves insufficiently prepared in linear algebra will find a brief survey of the subject in Appendix I. Group theory and the theory of product spaces are treated in the text; mathematical questions of a somewhat secondary nature are discussed in Appendices II through V.

The book is primarily addressed to students and research workers whose main interests lie in the field of high-resolution nuclear magnetic resonance. The book could also be used by research workers whose interest in the subject stems from its utility in other areas of research. There are numerous tables giving formulas for the resonance frequencies and intensities of important spin systems, numerical tables of frequencies and intensities for commonly occurring two-group systems, figures of experimental and theoretical spectra, and a number of general theorems on multispin systems, all of which are most useful in expediting the interpretation of observed spectra. The book could also be used in a course in high-resolution nuclear magnetic resonance spectroscopy, or for supplementary reading in an elementary course in quantum mechanics.

The first chapter presents a more or less standard introduction to the subject and is intended for readers approaching the subject for the first time. Chapter 2 develops the quantum mechanical theory of angular momentum which is applied in Chapter 3 to the study of magnetic moments in external fields. The angular momentum of multispin systems is discussed in Chapter 4. Chapter 5 develops the general theory of steady state spectra, with special reference to the concept of a group of magnetically equivalent nuclei and the concept of an irreducible component of a multispin system. These concepts are applied in Chapter 6 to the $A_{n_A}B_{n_B}$ systems, and in Chapter 7 to the $A_{n_A}BX_{n_X}$ systems. Chapter 7 also includes a general discussion of perturbation theory and moment calculations. The theory of groups is discussed in Chapter 8, with particular reference to projection operators and their use in the construction of symmetrized bases. These developments, together with the concept of an irreducible component, provide the theoretical basis for the subsequent discussion of symmetrical systems. The concluding chapter presents an introduction to multiple quantum transitions, double resonance and spin echo experiments.

I am indebted to many friends and colleagues whose generous assistance materially lightened my task. However, precedence must be given to a more fundamental debt. I refer to my indebtedness to the corporate management of the *Mobil Oil Corporation*—especially to Dr. R. W. Schiessler, General Manager of the Research Department—for placing time and the facilities of the Central Research Division Laboratory at my disposal. I also wish to express my gratitude to Dr. P. D. Caesar, Mr. M. L. Deutsch, Dr. J. P. McCullough, and Dr. C. D. Prater for their continued interest and encouragement which were positively demonstrated on many occasions.

I have benefited by the advice and suggestions of Dr. R. A. Albert, Professor B. P. Dailey, Dr. R. C. Hirst, and Professor P. C. Lauterbur, who read all or some part of the manuscript. I am particularly grateful to Dr. R. A. Albert, Dr. R. C. Hirst, and Mr. B. Wichnoski for assisting with the proofreading. I wish to thank Dr. L. G. Alexakos for providing the spectrum of chlorine trifluoride, Dr. R. C. Hirst for providing the spectrum of 2,6-dichlorofluorobenzene, and Mr. P. Yajko for the double resonance spectra of trimethylphosphite and formamide. I am indebted to Dr. G. C. Finger of the Illinois State Geological Survey for providing a sample of 2-fluoro-4,6-dichlorophenol, to Dr. P. S. Landis for synthesizing a number of thiophene derivatives, and to Dr. W. O. Haag for synthesizing 1,1-di-neopentyl-2-*t*-butylethylene. I am also indebted to Dr. W. A. Anderson, Dr. R. Freeman, Professor E. L. Hahn, Dr. D. H. Whiffen, the American Chemical Society, the American Institute of Physics, The Institute of Physics and The Physical Society, for permission to reproduce material originally published in *Chemical Reviews*, *Journal of Chemical Physics*, *Physical Review*, and *Proceedings of The Physical Society*. Finally, I wish to thank Mrs. Eugenie Cox, who typed most of the manuscript.

Rocky Hill, New Jersey P. L. CORIO

Contents

Chapter 6. Systems with Two Groups of Magnetically Equivalent Nuclei

Chapter 7. Perturbation and Moments Calculations

Chapter 8. The Analysis of Symmetrical Spin Systems

Chapter 9. Multiple Quantum Transitions, Double Resonance and Spin Echo Experiments

CHAPTER 1

Elementary Theory of Magnetic Resonance

1. The Physical Background

The historical roots of nuclear magnetic resonance spectroscopy can be traced back to the old quantum theory, which flourished during the 12-year period (1913–1925) immediately preceding the discovery of modern quantum mechanics. Indeed, the Stern-Gerlach experiment (1921)—unquestionably the precursor of all magnetic resonance experiments—was originally designed (*1*) to detect the space quantization of orbital magnetic moments; but modified versions of the experiment were later used to provide the first reliable determinations of nuclear magnetic moments. The experimental technique was vastly improved by the introduction of the resonance method (1938), and subsequent improvements led to precise determinations of nuclear moments by atomic and molecular-beam magnetic resonance experiments (*2*, *3*). However, it was not until 1946 that nuclear magnetic resonances were detected in bulk matter (*4*, *5*).

This introductory chapter presents a qualitative discussion of the physical basis for magnetic resonance experiments and a brief account of Bloch's phenomenological theory (*4*). The relevant quantum mechanical theory—the theory of spin angular momentum and the quantum mechanics of magnetic moments in magnetic fields—will be discussed in Chapters 2 and 3. The greater part of the discussion presented in this chapter will be couched in the language of classical mechanics.

A. Angular Momentum

The motion of a classical point particle, relative to a suitably chosen coordinate system, is determined by Newton's laws of motion (*6*) together with an initial specification of the position vector $\mathbf{r}$ and the velocity vector[1]

$$\mathbf{v} = \frac{d\mathbf{r}}{dt} = \dot{\mathbf{r}}.$$

If the particle is subjected to a force field $\mathbf{F}$, the position vector at any time is given by the solution of the equation of motion

$$\mathbf{F} = \frac{d}{dt}(m\mathbf{v}) = \dot{\mathbf{p}}, \tag{1.1}$$

where m is the mass of the particle (assumed constant) and $\mathbf{p} = m\mathbf{v}$ its *linear momentum*.

For some purposes, the motion of the particle is more appropriately described in terms of the vector moments of $\mathbf{F}$ and $\mathbf{p}$, computed with respect to the origin. The moment of force is called the *torque* and denoted $\boldsymbol{\tau}$; the moment of linear momentum is called the *angular momentum* and denoted $\mathbf{P}$:

$$\boldsymbol{\tau} = \mathbf{r} \times \mathbf{F}, \qquad \mathbf{P} = \mathbf{r} \times m\mathbf{v}. \tag{1.2}$$

Evidently, $\boldsymbol{\tau}$ is perpendicular to the instantaneous plane determined by $\mathbf{r}$ and $\mathbf{F}$, while $\mathbf{P}$ is perpendicular to the instantaneous plane of $\mathbf{r}$ and $\mathbf{v}$.

An important relation between the torque and the angular momentum may be deduced by computing the vector moments of the first two members of (1.1):

$$\mathbf{r} \times \mathbf{F} = \mathbf{r} \times \frac{d}{dt}(m\mathbf{v}) = \frac{d}{dt}(\mathbf{r} \times m\mathbf{v}).$$

The last equality follows from the rule for the differentiation of a vector product and the fact that the vector product of any vector with itself vanishes identically. Thus the torque acting on a particle is equal to the time rate of change of the angular momentum:

$$\boldsymbol{\tau} = \frac{d\mathbf{P}}{dt}. \tag{1.3}$$

The importance of the angular momentum in classical mechanics is based upon the fact that $\mathbf{P}$ is a *constant of the motion* whenever the torque vanishes identically.[2] For, according to (1.3), the vanishing of $\boldsymbol{\tau}$ implies

---

[1] Here, and subsequently, a dot over any symbol denotes differentiation with respect to time.

[2] In general, any physical quantity is said to be a constant of the motion if its total time derivative vanishes identically.

that $\mathbf{P}$ is constant in magnitude and direction. Thus the plane determined by $\mathbf{r}$ and $\mathbf{v}$ is invariable, and the motion of the particle is necessarily confined to this plane. The path traced out by the terminus of $\mathbf{r}$ is called the *orbit*, and $\mathbf{P}$ is called the *orbital angular momentum*.

An example of a force field which results in the conservation of angular momentum is the so-called *central force* (*6*), where $\mathbf{F}$ is always collinear with $\mathbf{r}$, so that $\mathbf{r} \times \mathbf{F} \equiv 0$. In the particular case of a particle whose orbit passes through the origin, conservation of angular momentum requires that $\mathbf{P} = \mathbf{r} \times m\mathbf{v} \equiv 0$, which implies that $\mathbf{v} = \dot{\mathbf{r}}$ is collinear with $\mathbf{r}$. In this circumstance, the force is proportional to $\mathbf{r}$ and the orbit degenerates to a straight line through the origin. In the case of a central force whose magnitude varies as the inverse square of the distance from the origin, the orbit is always a conic section.

The concept of angular momentum is of fundamental importance in quantum mechanics, but the orbital angular momentum of a quantum mechanical particle possesses properties that are remarkably different from those of a classical particle. Let $\mathbf{P}$ denote the orbital angular momentum of a classical particle with respect to an arbitrary origin, and let $\mathbf{n}$ denote a unit vector specifying the direction of a variable line through the origin. If $\mathbf{P}$ is a constant of the motion, then, according to classical mechanics, the projection of $\mathbf{P}$ along $\mathbf{n}$ varies continuously from $+|\mathbf{P}|$ to $-|\mathbf{P}|$ as the angle between $\mathbf{n}$ and $\mathbf{P}$ varies continuously from 0 to π. On the other hand, the quantum mechanical theory of angular momentum asserts that a measurement of a component of angular momentum in *any* direction must yield some member of the sequence

$$-\hbar L, \quad -\hbar(L-1), \ldots, \hbar(L-1), \quad \hbar L, \tag{1.4}$$

where $\hbar$ is Planck's constant[3] divided by 2π,

$$\hbar = \frac{h}{2\pi} = 1.0544 \times 10^{-27} \quad \text{erg-sec},$$

and L is a nonnegative integer called the *orbital quantum number*.

The discrete nature of the sequence (1.4) is described by saying that in quantum mechanics the angular momentum is *quantized*. It is convenient to express the quantization in terms of a discrete variable K whose domain consists of the $2L + 1$ integers: $-L$, $-(L-1)$, ..., $L-1$, L. A generic member of the sequence (1.4) is denoted $\hbar K$.

[3] The numerical values of the fundamental physical constants follow the recommendations of the International Committee on Weights and Measures (*Natl. Bur. Std.* (*U.S.*) *Tech. News Bull.*, Oct. 1963).

It is important to recognize that although an experimental measurement of the angular momentum in a given direction **n** must yield one of the $2L + 1$ possible values of $\hbar K$, the probability of observing a particular value $\hbar K'$ will not, in general, be unity. The probabilities of the several values of $\hbar K$ are theoretically calculable (cf. Chapter 3) and, in principle, may be experimentally determined by measuring the angular momentum of a large number of identical systems $S_1, S_2, \ldots, S_N$ $(N \gg 2L + 1)$. These experiments yield a set of N values $\hbar K_1, \hbar K_2, \ldots, \hbar K_N$, where each K_i is an integer in the closed interval $(-L, L)$. From these data one can compute the probability distribution associated with the sequence (1.4) for the direction **n**. If the value $\hbar K$ is observed in each of the N experiments (i.e., the probability of $\hbar K$ is unity), the direction **n** is called the *axis of quantization.*

Another distinction between the classical and quantum mechanical conceptions of orbital angular momentum is provided by the relation of the square of the maximum component of angular momentum to the square of the total angular momentum in the two theories. According to classical mechanics, the component of **P** in a direction **n** is a maximum when **n** is parallel to **P**, so that $(\mathbf{n} \cdot \mathbf{P})^2_{\text{max}} = |\mathbf{P}|^2$. According to quantum mechanics, the square of the angular momentum is $\hbar^2 L(L + 1)$, not $(\hbar K)^2_{\text{max}} = \hbar^2 L^2$.

The quantization of the angular momentum is a consequence of the quantum mechanical interpretation of the angular momentum as a *vector operator* (cf. Chapter 2), rather than an ordinary vector composed of three scalar components. The $2L + 1$ quantities $-\hbar L, -\hbar(L - 1), \ldots, \hbar L$ are the eigenvalues associated with the component of the angular momentum operator in any specified direction, and $\hbar^2 L(L + 1)$ is the eigenvalue associated with the square of the angular momentum operator. However, the quantum mechanical properties of the orbital angular momentum approach those of a classical angular momentum in the limit as quantum mechanics approaches classical mechanics, that is, as $\hbar \to 0$. For the orbital quantum number L may, in principle, become arbitrarily large, so that it is possible for $\hbar \to 0$ and $L \to \infty$ in such a way that the product $\hbar L$ remains finite. In the limit, the sequence (1.4) approaches a continuous range of values, and the square of the angular momentum $\hbar^2 L(L + 1) = \hbar^2 L^2(1 + 1/L) \to \hbar^2 L^2$, as $L \to \infty$.

Since the possible components of a quantum mechanical angular momentum are always integral (or half-integral) multiples of $\hbar$, and the square of the angular momentum is proportional to $\hbar^2$, it is convenient to introduce a dimensionless "vector" which "measures" the angular momentum in units of $\hbar$. In the particular case of an orbital angular momentum, this vector is denoted **L**, so that $\hbar\mathbf{L}$ represents the orbital angular momentum. The component of $\hbar\mathbf{L}$ in the direction $\mathbf{n}$ is denoted $\hbar\mathbf{n} \cdot \mathbf{L}$. The eigenvalues of $\mathbf{L}^2$ are $L(L+1)$; those of $\mathbf{n} \cdot \mathbf{L}$ are $-L$, $-(L-1), \ldots, L$.

B. Orbital Magnetic Moments

The quantization of orbital angular momentum requires the quantization of any physical quantity that is functionally related to the angular momentum. Perhaps the most familiar textbook example is the deduction of the quantization of the energy from the postulated quantization of orbital angular momentum in Bohr's theory of the hydrogen atom. A second example is the quantization of the orbital magnetic moment generated by the orbital motion of a charged particle.

The relation between the orbital magnetic moment and the orbital angular momentum may be derived by considering a classical point particle of mass M and electric charge Q moving with respect to a fixed origin. The motion of the charge generates an orbital magnetic moment (7), defined by

$$\boldsymbol{\mu} = \frac{Q}{2c}\mathbf{r} \times \mathbf{v}, \tag{1.5}$$

where c is the speed of light. But the orbital angular momentum of the particle is $\mathbf{r} \times M\mathbf{v}$, so that

$$\boldsymbol{\mu} = \frac{Q}{2Mc}\mathbf{P}. \tag{1.6}$$

The scalar factor $Q/2Mc$ is called the *gyromagnetic ratio*[4] and denoted γ.

Equation (1.6) is valid in both classical and quantum mechanics, but in the classical case it is to be interpreted as a relation between ordinary vectors, whereas in a quantum mechanical context it relates the vector operator for the orbital magnetic moment to the vector operator for the orbital angular momentum. In the case of an electron, the quantum mechanical magnetic moment operator is usually expressed in the form

$$\boldsymbol{\mu} = -\frac{e\hbar}{2m_e c}\mathbf{L} = -\mu_B\mathbf{L}, \tag{1.7}$$

where

$$\mu_B = 9.2732 \times 10^{-21} \quad \text{ergs G}^{-1}$$

[4] The electromagnetic units are gaussian cgs, so that the dimensions of γ and $\boldsymbol{\mu}$ are: $[\gamma]$ = rad sec^{-1} G^{-1}, $[\boldsymbol{\mu}]$ = ergs G^{-1}.

is the so-called *Bohr magneton.* From the quantization of **L**, it follows that an observation of the component of the orbital magnetic moment in any direction must yield some member of the sequence

$$-\mu_B L, \quad -\mu_B(L-1), \ldots, \mu_B(L-1), \quad \mu_B L.$$

The maximum observable component of the orbital magnetic moment operator, $\mu_B(K)_{\max} = \mu_B L$, is defined as the orbital magnetic moment of the electron. Thus an electron in a state with $K = L = 1$ is said to possess an orbital magnetic moment of 1 Bohr magneton. Obviously, an electron in a state with $L = 0$ does not generate an orbital magnetic moment. Atomic states with $L = 0$ are called *S states.* The ground states of ${}_1H^1$ and ${}_{47}Ag^{107}$, for example, are S states.

Equation (1.6) also holds for a system of particles with charges $q_1, q_2, \ldots$, and masses $m_1, m_2, \ldots$, such that $q_i = km_i$, where k is a constant. The angular momentum and magnetic moment are defined as

$$\mathbf{P} = \sum_i m_i \mathbf{r}_i \times \mathbf{v}_i, \qquad \boldsymbol{\mu} = \frac{1}{2c} \sum_i q_i \mathbf{r}_i \times \mathbf{v}_i,$$

and the condition $q_i = km_i$ shows that $\boldsymbol{\mu} = (k/2c)\mathbf{P}$. The constant k is just the ratio of the total charge to total mass, as one may verify by summing $q_i = km_i$ over all particles.

An analogous argument can be used to establish (1.6) for the case of a rigid body with charge density $q(x, y, z)$ and mass density $\rho(x, y, z)$ such that $q(x, y, z)/\rho(x, y, z)$ is a constant. The only difference in the calculation is that summations over particles are replaced by integrations over the volume of the body.

C. The Electron Spin

The hypothesis that electrons possess an internal angular momentum was introduced into modern physics (*8, 9*) during the last hours of the old quantum theory (1925) to explain structural details of atomic spectra that were inexplicable on the basis of the quantization of the electronic orbital angular momentum alone. The internal angular momentum of the electron was assumed to arise from a circulation of the electronic mass brought about by an actual rotation of the electron, which was visualized as a small sphere with charge $-e$ and mass m_e. Because of the evident analogy of this classical model to spinning tops, the internal angular momentum is often described as the *electron spin.*

In the absence of a definitive theory, the classical description of the electron spin was at best heuristic; the ultimate justification of the hypothesis depended upon its agreement with experiment. It was found that the electron-spin hypothesis was compatible with the results of experimental observations if the following conditions were satisfied:

(1) The component of the electron spin in *any* direction is of the form $s\hbar$, where s is the discrete *spin variable* whose range consists of two points: $s = +\frac{1}{2}$ and $s = -\frac{1}{2}$.

(2) The spin magnetic moment is related to the internal angular momentum by the equation

$$\boldsymbol{\mu} = -\frac{e\hbar}{m_e c}\,\mathbf{s}, \tag{1.8}$$

where $\hbar\mathbf{s}$ is the quantum mechanical angular momentum of the electron.

The first condition demands the quantization of the internal angular momentum, but this was not an innovation in physics, since the old quantum theory had enjoyed many successes in quantizing orbital angular momentum. The significant aspects of the quantization were the half-integral quantum numbers and the fact that the absolute magnitude of a component of the electron spin could not exceed $\hbar/2$. The maximum value of the spin variable is called the *spin* or *spin quantum number*. Since the spin is fixed at $\frac{1}{2}$, $\hbar/2$ tends to zero as $\hbar \rightarrow 0$, so that the electron spin has no analog in classical mechanics.

The second condition asserts that the electron gyromagnetic ratio is $-e/m_e c$ rather than $-e/2m_e c$, as might be expected from classical considerations. However, conditions (1) and (2) together imply that a measurement of a component of the magnetic moment in any direction would yield the values $-\mu_B$ for $s = +\frac{1}{2}$ and $+\mu_B$ for $s = -\frac{1}{2}$. Hence the factor of $\frac{1}{2}$ removed from the classical expression for the gyromagnetic ratio by (2) is replaced by (1) in an experimental determination of the electron's magnetic moment. Thus a free electron has a magnetic moment of 1 Bohr magneton.

The new quantum mechanics (1926) did not include the electron spin in its theoretical structure, so that it was necessary to fit the electron spin into the theory. The absence of a classical model led to some difficulties (*10*), but eventually (1927) a satisfactory theoretical framework was developed (*11*) which provided a basis for the quantitative interpretation of the alkali doublets (spin-orbit interaction), the anomalous Zeeman effect, and the Stern-Gerlach experiment (*12*).

The theoretical problem of the electron spin was considerably clarified by the relativistic quantum mechanics of Dirac (1928). According to the special theory of relativity, the space and time coordinates must enter into the theory in a symmetrical way, whereas the (second)

Schrödinger equation prescribes that the time development of the wave function is governed by an equation that is linear only in the time derivative. The synthesis of these conditions into the principle that the space and time derivatives appear linearly in a relativistic quantum mechanics (*13*) requires the introduction of a new variable. The new variable was not specified initially, but upon developing the theory it turned out to be an angular momentum of spin $\frac{1}{2}$. The theory also predicts that a particle of mass m and charge $-e$ possesses a spin magnetic moment with gyromagnetic ratio $-e/mc$.

The spin and magnetic moment of the electron are now well-established properties which are as characteristic of the electron as its mass or charge. The internal angular momentum is a property built into the electron by Nature; hence, the spin of the electron is often described as an *intrinsic angular momentum.*

D. The Stern-Gerlach Experiment

The conceptual differences in the classical and quantum mechanical descriptions of angular momentum were put to a crucial test in the Stern-Gerlach experiment. This experiment provided unambiguous evidence confirming the quantization of angular momentum. At the same time, however, the experiment revealed an anomaly which was subsequently explained by the electron-spin hypothesis.

The physical basis of the Stern-Gerlach experiment rests on an elementary theorem concerning the behavior of a magnetic moment in an inhomogeneous magnetic field. Let $\mathbf{H}(x, y, z)$ denote a stationary external magnetic field[5] and $\boldsymbol{\mu}$ the magnetic moment of a microscopic physical system. In the presence of the field, the magnetic moment experiences a torque

$$\boldsymbol{\tau} = \boldsymbol{\mu} \times \mathbf{H}, \tag{1.9}$$

which tends to align $\boldsymbol{\mu}$ with the direction of the field at the point occupied by $\boldsymbol{\mu}$ (Fig. 1.1). The energy of orientation may be obtained from the torque-energy relation

$$\frac{\partial E}{\partial \theta} = |\boldsymbol{\tau}| = \mu H \sin \theta, \tag{1.10}$$

where θ is the angle between $\boldsymbol{\mu}$ and $\mathbf{H}$. For a fixed, but otherwise arbitrary point in the field, it follows that

$$E = -\boldsymbol{\mu} \cdot \mathbf{H}, \tag{1.11}$$

[5] An external magnetic field is a field set up in an otherwise homogeneous region of space which does not include the sources of the field. The curl of an external magnetic field is zero.

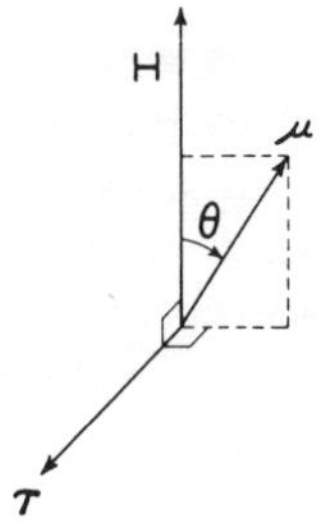

FIG. 1.1. The geometric relations between **μ**, **H**, and **τ**.

where the reference level for the energy has been set at zero field. Since **μ** does not depend upon x, y, or z, the force exerted on **μ** is given by[6]

$$\mathbf{F} = -\nabla E = (\boldsymbol{\mu} \cdot \nabla)\mathbf{H} = \mu_x \frac{\partial \mathbf{H}}{\partial x} + \mu_y \frac{\partial \mathbf{H}}{\partial y} + \mu_z \frac{\partial \mathbf{H}}{\partial z} . \tag{1.12}$$

For the particular case where **H** is a uniform field, the force vanishes and the moment does not change its position.

The Stern-Gerlach experiment is performed (Fig. 1.2) by heating a source of silver atoms in an oven O and allowing the thermally emitted atoms to pass from the oven into an evacuated chamber where they are collimated by slits S_1 and S_2 ; the atomic beam thus formed is passed through an inhomogeneous magnetic field and deposited on a plate P. If the atoms in the beam possess a magnetic moment, by virtue of a nonvanishing angular momentum, the nature of the silver deposit will depend upon whether the angular momentum obeys classical or quantum mechanical laws.

For simplicity, let the field and its gradient be in the z direction, so that the force on an atom is

$$F_z = \mu_z \frac{\partial H_z}{\partial z} .$$

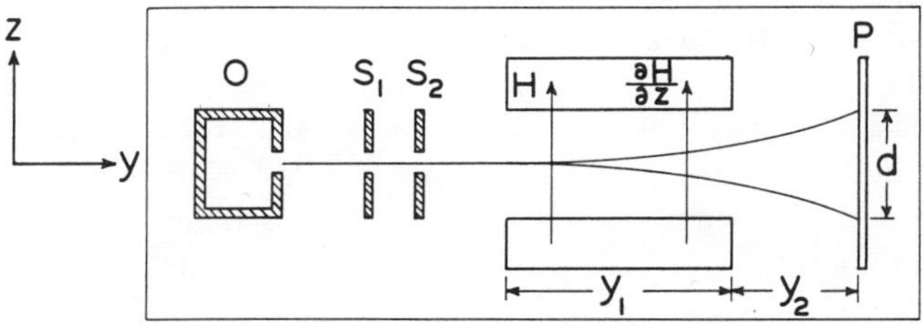

FIG. 1.2. Schematic representation of the Stern-Gerlach experiment.

[6] Equation (1.12) follows from the vector identity $\nabla(\boldsymbol{\mu} \cdot \mathbf{H}) = (\boldsymbol{\mu} \cdot \nabla)\mathbf{H} + (\mathbf{H} \cdot \nabla)\boldsymbol{\mu} + \boldsymbol{\mu} \times (\nabla \times \mathbf{H}) + \mathbf{H} \times (\nabla \times \boldsymbol{\mu})$ and the fact that $\nabla \times \mathbf{H} = 0$ for an external field.

According to classical theory, an atom whose magnetic moment makes an angle θ with the z direction will be deflected an amount proportional to $\mu_z = \mu \cos \theta$. Now the incoming beam includes all values in the range of θ, so that classically one expects the beam to be drawn out and deposited as a continuous band on the plate. On the other hand, if the z component of the magnetic moment is a function of a discrete variable, the beam should be split into several components and deposited as discrete bands on the plate. In the original experiment the beam was split into two components. The observed splitting was attributed to an orbital magnetic moment whose discrete orientations had to be an odd number, namely, $2L + 1$, where L is an integer. If one assumes that $L = 1$, and that the atoms enter the field with the most probable velocity, measurements of y_1, y_2, d, and $\partial H_z/\partial z$ permit computation of the magnetic moment. The original calculation showed that the observed splitting was consistent with a magnetic moment of 1 Bohr magneton. However, if $L = 1$, the theory predicts that the beam should be split into $2L + 1 = 3$ components, corresponding to $K = 1, 0, -1$. The two beams observed were assumed to correspond to $K = \pm 1$, but the theory was unable to account for the absence of the unperturbed ($K = 0$) beam.

The results of the Stern-Gerlach experiment are completely explained by the electron-spin hypothesis. The silver atom is normally in a $^2S_{1/2}$ state; that is, the resultant angular momentum is just the intrinsic spin of the 5s electron. Applying conditions (1) and (2) of Section 1.C, one concludes that the beam should be split into two components with the upper and lower beams corresponding to atoms whose valence electrons are described by $s = \mp\frac{1}{2}$ and $\mu_z = \pm\mu_B$.

The Stern-Gerlach experiment is analogous to the polarization of light waves by doubly refracting crystals. The direction of the magnetic field defines an axis of reference for the two independent states of spin orientation, and corresponds to the polarizer in optical experiments. The gradient of the magnetic field separates the silver atoms into two groups, one with $s = +\frac{1}{2}$, the other with $s = -\frac{1}{2}$, and corresponds to an optical analyzer. This analogy helps to clarify the essential quantum mechanical properties of intrinsic spin angular momentum. For convenience, let the beam consist of spin-$\frac{1}{2}$ particles with a positive gyromagnetic ratio. All particles in the upper-beam component are then described by $s = +\frac{1}{2}$ and are said to be polarized in the positive z direction. It must be emphasized, however, that the z direction is arbitrary. Before the beam enters the field region there is no preferred direction of quantization—the direction of quantization is established by the direction of the applied field **H**.

If the magnet is rotated through an angle θ about the direction of the incoming beam, the unpolarized beam will again be split into two components corresponding to $s = \pm \frac{1}{2}$; but these states of quantization are referred to the new direction of the field. This result emphasizes the fact that if a particle has spin $\frac{1}{2}$, the measurement of a component of its angular momentum in *any* direction can yield only $\pm\hbar/2$. The experiment is illustrated in Fig. 1.3(a), where the common direction of

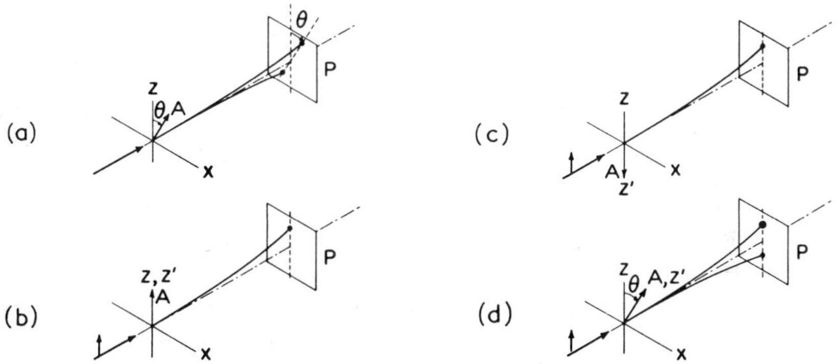

FIG. 1.3. Schematic representations of Stern-Gerlach experiments for an unpolarized incident beam (a), and z-polarized beams (b), (c), and (d). The vector **A** indicates the direction of the Stern-Gerlach analyzer.

the field and its gradient are represented by a vector **A** issuing from the origin of an arbitrarily chosen coordinate system. To clarify the drawing, the beam components have been represented as geometric rays and the beam deposits as two points on the plate.

If the incident beam has been selectively polarized in some direction (for example, by selecting one of the components of an initial Stern-Gerlach experiment), then the experimental results depend upon the angle θ which the direction of the polarization makes with the Stern-Gerlach analyzer **A**. If $\theta = 0$, and the incident beam consists entirely of particles with $s = +\frac{1}{2}$ [Fig. 1.3(b)], then all particles in the beam are deflected in the positive z direction. If the experiment is repeated with $\theta = \pi$ [Fig. 1.3(c)], the beam is again deflected in the positive z direction. In this case, the Stern-Gerlach analyzer **A** defines a new z axis, and relative to this axis the beam particles all appear to be in a spin state characterized by $s = -\frac{1}{2}$.

For $0 < \theta < \pi$, an incident z-polarized beam will be split into two components [Fig. 1.3(d)], but the deposits on the plate will not be of equal intensity. This result is best analyzed by considering the problem from a coordinate system whose z' axis is parallel to **A**. Consider first a single particle of the beam. The incoming particle is polarized in the z direction, but from the point of view of z', the particle appears to have a mixture of the $+z$ and $-z$ polarizations. Upon interacting with the Stern-Gerlach analyzer, the particle exhibits one or the other of the two states of polarization, but which state of polarization will be observed for a single particle cannot be predicted. If the experiment is repeated many times, as indeed it is with a beam, one can ask for the probabilities P_+ and P_- of observing the positive or negative states of polarization. Clearly, the intensity ratio of the two beam deposits is P_+/P_- and

$$P_+ + P_- = 1.$$

The functional dependence of P_+ and P_- on θ may be determined from the special cases already considered. When z coincides with z', a beam polarized in the $+z'$ direction is not split by **A** [Fig. 1.3(b)], so that $P_+ = 1$ when $\theta = 0$. When $\theta = \pi$, as in Fig. 1.3(c), $P_- = 1$. From these particular results, one can conclude that

$$P_+ = \cos^2 \frac{\theta}{2}, \qquad P_- = \sin^2 \frac{\theta}{2}.$$

In optical polarization the intensities are proportional to $\cos^2 \theta$ and $\sin^2 \theta$; the half angles appear in the above equations because the two independent states of polarization of a spin-$\frac{1}{2}$ particle differ in phase by 180°.

E. Nuclear Spins

The electron-spin hypothesis was quickly followed (1927) by the suggestion (*14*) that the proton also possesses an intrinsic spin angular momentum characterized by the spin quantum number $\frac{1}{2}$. Somewhat surprisingly, the spin of the proton was not inferred from an analysis of the structure of spectral lines, but from the anomalous behavior of the specific heat of molecular hydrogen. On the other hand, it had been noted by Pauli (*15*), before the electron-spin hypothesis, that a non-vanishing nuclear angular momentum could explain the hyperfine structure observed in atomic spectra. Pauli's suggestion referred to the angular momenta of complex nuclei which, at the time, were presumed to consist of A protons and A-Z electrons, where A and Z are, respectively, the nuclear mass and charge numbers. Thus the proposed nuclear angular momentum did not represent an intrinsic angular momentum—the latter is an attribute of a single particle (*16*). However, as long as the internal structure of the nucleus is not at issue, the distinction between the angular momenta of "simple" and complex particles is an academic one, and *intrinsic* is frequently used as a modifier in either case.

The first determinations of the spins of complex nuclei were based upon analyses of atomic hyperfine structure which showed that a nuclear angular momentum could be characterized as a general quantum mechanical angular momentum. In particular, the spin quantum number I may be integral or half-integral, and a component of the angular momentum in any direction is of the form $m\hbar$, where m is the discrete spin variable whose range consists of $2I + 1$ values: $-I, -I + 1, ..., I - 1, I$.

Significant experimental results on the spins and quantum statistics of complex nuclei were obtained from studies of the band spectra of homonuclear diatomic molecules (*17*). In fact, the experimentally determined quantum statistics played a prominent part in the rejection of a nuclear model consisting of electrons and protons. According to quantum statistics (*18*), all spin-$\frac{1}{2}$ particles follow Fermi-Dirac statistics, and systems of spin-$\frac{1}{2}$ particles obey Fermi-Dirac or Bose-Einstein statistics, accordingly as the number of particles is odd or even. Experimentally, it was found that the statistics depended only on the mass number. On the electron-proton model, the mass number is equal to the number of protons, so that the nuclear electrons appeared to lose their identity as fermi particles. For example, ${}_7N^{14}$ was found to satisfy Bose-Einstein statistics, whereas quantum statistics demands Fermi-Dirac statistics for a system of 21 fermi particles. The difficulty was resolved with the discovery of the neutron (1932). For it was immediately pointed out (*19*) that if the neutron is a spin-$\frac{1}{2}$ particle, a nucleus consisting of Z protons and A-Z neutrons would satisfy the requirements demanded by experiment. On this model, the mass number is determined by the total number of nucleons, which in turn determines the quantum statistics.

The total angular momentum of a complex nucleus (*20*) is the sum of the intrinsic and orbital angular momenta of the protons and neutrons and may be written

$$\hbar\mathbf{I} = \hbar(\mathbf{L} + \mathbf{S}),$$

where $\mathbf{I}$ is the dimensionless nuclear spin vector and $\hbar(\mathbf{L} + \mathbf{S})$ denotes the sum of the orbital and spin angular momenta of the nucleons. Since the orbital angular momentum is described by integral quantum numbers, the nuclear-spin quantum number is expected to be integral or half-integral, accordingly as A is even or odd, and this conclusion is confirmed by experiment. Furthermore, no exception has as yet been found which violates the empirical rule that the nuclear spin is zero whenever A and Z are even integers. These results are illustrated in Table 1.1, which lists the spins of some common nuclei.[7] It should be recognized that the nuclear spins given in Table 1.1 refer to the nuclear ground state. In excited nuclear states, the spin quantum number may be different from that observed for the ground state (*20*). All subsequent references to nuclear spin will refer to the ground-state spin.

TABLE 1.1

SPINS AND MAGNETIC MOMENTS OF SOME COMMON NUCLEI

Nucleus	I	μ/μ_0
$_1H^1$	$\frac{1}{2}$	2.79270
$_1H^2$	1	0.85738
$_5B^{10}$	3	1.8006
$_5B^{11}$	$\frac{3}{2}$	2.6880
$_6C^{12}$	0	0
$_6C^{13}$	$\frac{1}{2}$	0.70216
$_7N^{14}$	1	0.40357
$_7N^{15}$	$\frac{1}{2}$	−0.28304
$_9F^{19}$	$\frac{1}{2}$	2.6273
$_{15}P^{31}$	$\frac{1}{2}$	1.1305

F. Nuclear Moments

A nucleus with a nonvanishing spin angular momentum also possesses a magnetic moment. Indeed, it is the interaction of the nuclear moment(s) with internal and applied fields which permits the observation of effects attributed to the nuclear angular momentum.

The proton has intrinsic spin $\frac{1}{2}$ and one expects, according to the Dirac relativistic theory, that a measurement of the proton magnetic moment would yield an absolute value of 1 *nuclear Bohr magneton*, namely,

$$\mu_0 = \frac{e\hbar}{2M_p c} = 5.0500 \times 10^{-24} \quad \text{ergs G}^{-1},$$

where e and M_p are the charge and mass of the proton. Furthermore, since the neutron carries no charge, the Dirac theory predicts a zero moment for the neutron. Experimentally it is found that

$$\mu_p = 2.79278\mu_0\,, \qquad \mu_n = -1.9130\mu_0\,.$$

[7] A complete tabulation is available on request from Varian Associates, Palo Alto, California.

These results may be expressed in terms of a dimensionless g factor by the equation

$$\boldsymbol{\mu} = g\mu_0\mathbf{I}, \tag{1.13}$$

where the components of $\mathbf{I}$ are $m = +\frac{1}{2}$, $m = -\frac{1}{2}$. The magnetic moment is defined as the maximum component of $\boldsymbol{\mu}$ in any direction, so that g has the values 5.58556 and -3.8260 for the proton and neutron, respectively.

Since the Dirac theory does not correctly predict the magnetic moments of the neutron or proton, it comes as no surprise to learn that the nuclear moments of complex nuclei must be determined experimentally.[8] It is found that the magnetic moment can be expressed in the form (1.13), where the value of g depends upon the nucleus. Nuclear g values may be positive or negative; their absolute values usually range from 1 to 6.

If the nuclear spin is greater than $\frac{1}{2}$, the absolute magnitudes of the components of $\boldsymbol{\mu}$ in a given direction will range over several distinct values. The magnetic moment is defined as that component for which the spin variable has the value I:

$$\mu = g\mu_0 I. \tag{1.14}$$

Tabulated values of the magnetic moment usually give the magnetic moment in units of the nuclear Bohr magneton, that is, $\mu/\mu_0 = gI$. However, for the description of nuclear magnetic resonance experiments it is preferable to express the relation between the magnetic moment and angular momentum vectors in terms of the nuclear gyromagnetic ratio defined by

$$\boldsymbol{\mu} = \gamma\hbar\mathbf{I}. \tag{1.15}$$

Comparing this relation with (1.13), it follows that

$$\gamma = \frac{g\mu_0}{\hbar} = g\frac{e}{2M_pc} = 4.78948 \times 10^3 g \quad \text{rads sec}^{-1}\ \text{G}^{-1}.$$

The absolute values of nuclear gyromagnetic ratios usually range from 10^2 to 10^4 rads sec^{-1} G^{-1}. For example, the gyromagnetic ratio of the proton is

$$\gamma_p = 2.67519 \times 10^4 \quad \text{rads sec}^{-1}\ \text{G}^{-1}.$$

---

[8] In this connection, it should be noted that the Dirac theory predicts that the electronic g value is exactly 2, whereas the experimental value is actually 2.002292.

Equation (1.15) expresses the collinearity of μ and **I**, but it should be pointed out that μ represents the time-averaged nuclear moment in the direction of **I**. That the magnetic moment is not collinear with **I** at all times may be made plausible by assuming that the magnetic moment is the vector sum of the orbital and spin magnetic moments. Since the neutron carries no charge, it cannot generate an orbital magnetic moment; hence the orbital part of the assumed decomposition contains no contribution from the neutrons, and μ cannot be proportional to **I**.

From a classical point of view (*21*), Eq. (1.15) may be justified by noting that the magnetic moment rotates rapidly about the direction of the angular momentum. The time interval required for an experimental observation of the magnetic moment includes many periods of the rotation of μ about **I**, so that one observes the time-averaged value of μ in the direction of **I**.

A nucleus whose spin quantum number is greater than $\frac{1}{2}$ possesses a nuclear electric quadrupole moment which arises from a charge distribution within the nucleus that is not spherically symmetric (*3*). The nuclear electric quadrupole moment interacts with the gradient of the electric field set up at the nuclear centroid by the surrounding electrons. This interaction vanishes identically for spin-$\frac{1}{2}$ nuclei, and is zero for nuclei with spins $I > \frac{1}{2}$ whenever the electronic charge distribution is spherically symmetric. Since the following chapters will be primarily concerned with spin-$\frac{1}{2}$ nuclei, the theory of the quadrupole interaction will not be considered here.

2. Classical Dynamics of Magnetic Moments in Applied Fields

A. The Equation of Motion

The dynamics of nuclear magnetic moments in applied magnetic fields can be profitably discussed from the point of view of quantum mechanics or that of classical mechanics. This somewhat paradoxical circumstance is brought about by a remarkable correspondence between the equation of motion for a classical magnetic moment and the quantum mechanical equation of motion for the magnetic moment operator. The precise formulation of this correspondence must be deferred to Chapter 3, but the implications of this correspondence will be anticipated in the present chapter through the frequent consideration of the nuclear magnetic moment as an ordinary classical vector. The particular advantage of this interpretation is that the solution of the classical equation of motion leads to an elegant geometric description of the resonance phenomenon.

The classical equation of motion for a magnetic moment results upon eliminating the torque and the nuclear angular momentum from the equations

$$\boldsymbol{\mu} = \gamma\hbar\mathbf{I}, \qquad \boldsymbol{\tau} = \boldsymbol{\mu} \times \mathbf{H}, \qquad \boldsymbol{\tau} = \frac{d}{dt}(\hbar\mathbf{I}).$$

Thus

$$\dot{\boldsymbol{\mu}} = -\gamma\mathbf{H} \times \boldsymbol{\mu}, \tag{2.1}$$

where $\boldsymbol{\mu}$ is now interpreted as an ordinary vector.

In general, the classical motion has six degrees of freedom—three of translation and three of rotation. The three translational degrees of freedom will be removed by assuming that $\mathbf{H}$ is not a function of position, although it may depend upon the time. The initial point of $\boldsymbol{\mu}$ is then fixed in space, and this point will be taken as the origin.

Two additional conditions on the motion of $\boldsymbol{\mu}$ may be derived from (2.1) by taking the scalar product on both sides of the equation with $\boldsymbol{\mu}$ and $\mathbf{H}$:

$$\boldsymbol{\mu} \cdot \dot{\boldsymbol{\mu}} = 0, \tag{2.2}$$

$$\mathbf{H} \cdot \dot{\boldsymbol{\mu}} = 0. \tag{2.3}$$

Condition (2.2) is equivalent to

$$\frac{d}{dt}(\boldsymbol{\mu} \cdot \boldsymbol{\mu}) = 0,$$

which may be immediately integrated to give

$$|\boldsymbol{\mu}| \equiv \mu = \text{constant}.$$

This result, which is valid for any time dependence of $\mathbf{H}$, expresses the conservation of the magnitude of $\boldsymbol{\mu}$ and reduces the problem to one with two degrees of freedom. It follows that the terminus of $\boldsymbol{\mu}$ is constrained to move on the surface of a sphere of radius μ.

The second condition is not directly integrable when $\mathbf{H}$ is a function of t, but its differential form suffices for a geometric description of the motion. Consider first the special case where $\mathbf{H}$ does not change with the time, so that (2.3) is equivalent to

$$\frac{d}{dt}(\boldsymbol{\mu} \cdot \mathbf{H}) = 0.$$

This equation expresses the conservation of the energy

$$E = -\boldsymbol{\mu} \cdot \mathbf{H} = \text{constant}.$$

Since μ, E, and H are constant, it follows that the angle between $\boldsymbol{\mu}$ and $\mathbf{H}$ is also constant. The dynamic problem is thus reduced to a single degree of freedom, so that the motion of $\boldsymbol{\mu}$ consists of a rotation about the direction of $\mathbf{H}$ [Fig. 1.4(a)]. The sense of the rotation is

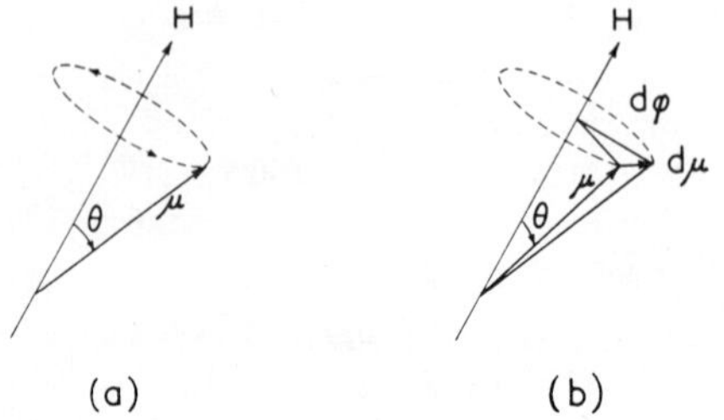

FIG. 1.4. (a) Precession of $\boldsymbol{\mu}$ about the direction of a stationary uniform field $\mathbf{H}$; (b) the infinitesimal change in $\boldsymbol{\mu}$ during a time interval dt.

determined by the sign of γ. For given any initial orientation of $\boldsymbol{\mu}$, say $\boldsymbol{\mu}(t_0)$, the direction in which $\boldsymbol{\mu}$ rotates, relative to the initial plane of $\boldsymbol{\mu}(t_0)$ and $\mathbf{H}$, is determined by (2.1); hence the sense of the rotation is positive or negative, accordingly as the sign of γ is negative or positive.

The angular frequency of rotation about $\mathbf{H}$ is, by definition,

$$\omega = \frac{d\varphi}{dt},$$

where $d\varphi$ is an element of angle between successive radii on the instantaneous circle of rotation [Fig. 1.4(b)]. From the figure it is clear that

$$\mu \sin\theta \, d\varphi = d\mu = | \gamma\boldsymbol{\mu} \times \mathbf{H} | \, dt;$$

hence

$$\omega = | \gamma | H. \tag{2.4}$$

Rotational motions that evolve with time are often described as precessions, and more specifically as Larmor precessions if the motions are induced by the application of a magnetic field to a system of magnetic moments or moving charged particles. The frequency $\omega = | \gamma | H$ is called the (angular) *nuclear Larmor precession frequency* when γ is interpreted as the nuclear gyromagnetic ratio. In stationary fields of the order of 10,000 G, the nuclear Larmor frequency is in the megacycle range. For example, the Larmor frequency of the proton in a field of 10,000 G is

$$\frac{\omega}{2\pi} = \frac{\gamma_p H}{2\pi} = \frac{2.67519 \times 10^8}{2\pi} = 42.577 \quad \text{Mcps}.$$

When the applied field is a function of the time, the motion of **μ** is quite complicated and, excepting special cases, its analytical description cannot be expressed in terms of the elementary transcendental functions. However, (2.4) is still valid, provided that ω and H are interpreted as instantaneous values. Indeed, the motion of **μ**, over a small time interval dt, may be described as an infinitesimal rotation about the instantaneous direction of $\mathbf{H}(t)$. The motion of **μ** over a finite time interval is compounded from an infinite sequence of such infinitesimal rotations.

B. Integration of the Equation of Motion

An analytical description of the motion requires the integration of the system of three equations obtained from the expansion of (2.1). The integration of this system can be reduced to the integration of a single first-order equation. For this purpose, let

$$\boldsymbol{\mu} = \mu(u, v, w), \tag{2.5}$$

where u, v, and w are the components of a unit vector in the direction of **μ**. The motion of $\boldsymbol{\mu}/\mu$ is simply the radial projection of the motion of **μ** onto the unit sphere about the origin. From (2.1) and (2.5) it follows that

$$\dot{u} = \gamma(H_z v - H_y w), \qquad \dot{v} = \gamma(H_x w - H_z u), \qquad \dot{w} = \gamma(H_y u - H_x v). \tag{2.6}$$

Now

$$u^2 + v^2 + w^2 = 1, \tag{2.7}$$

and this relation admits the following factorization:

$$(u + iv)(u - iv) = (1 + w)(1 - w).$$

Thus one can introduce two complex parameters defined by the equations

$$\zeta = \frac{u + iv}{1 + w} = \frac{1 - w}{u - iv}, \qquad -\zeta' = \frac{u + iv}{1 - w} = \frac{1 + w}{u - iv}. \tag{2.8}$$

These parameters are not independent, since

$$\zeta' \zeta^* = -1. \tag{2.9}$$

The definitions (2.8), when solved for u, v, and w, yield

$$u = \frac{\zeta\zeta' - 1}{\zeta' - \zeta}, \qquad v = -i\,\frac{\zeta\zeta' + 1}{\zeta' - \zeta}, \qquad w = \frac{\zeta' + \zeta}{\zeta' - \zeta}. \tag{2.10}$$

These relations identically satisfy (2.3) and (2.7), and one may readily verify that ζ and ζ' satisfy the same Riccati equation,

$$\dot{\zeta} = \frac{i\gamma}{2}\{H_x + iH_y - 2H_z\zeta - (H_x - iH_y)\zeta^2\}. \tag{2.11}$$

The geometric interpretation of this reduction is simple. The unit sphere about the origin is stereographically projected onto the complex ζ plane ($\zeta = \xi + i\eta$) with the south pole of the sphere as the center of the projection. The correspondence established by the projection is one-to-one and maps all points in the northern hemisphere onto the points of the ζ plane which lie inside the equatorial circle, while all points in the southern hemisphere are mapped onto the points of the ζ plane outside this circle. The north pole, for example, is mapped onto the point $\zeta = 0$, while the south pole is mapped onto the point at infinity ($\zeta = \infty$). Thus the path traced out by (u, v, w) is mapped onto a corresponding path in the ζ plane, and (2.11) is the equation of motion for the projected locus.

The geometry of the stereographic projection is shown in Figs. 1.5 and 1.6, from which one may easily deduce the projection formulas:

$$\frac{\rho'}{1+w} = \frac{1-w}{\rho'} = \frac{\rho}{1}, \qquad \frac{\rho'}{\rho} = \frac{u}{\xi} = \frac{v}{\eta}.$$

From these ratios, one obtains, since $\rho^2 = \xi^2 + \eta^2$,

$$\xi = \frac{u}{1+w}, \qquad \rho^2 = \frac{1-w}{1+w}, \qquad \eta = \frac{v}{1+w}, \qquad \zeta = \xi + i\eta. \tag{2.12}$$

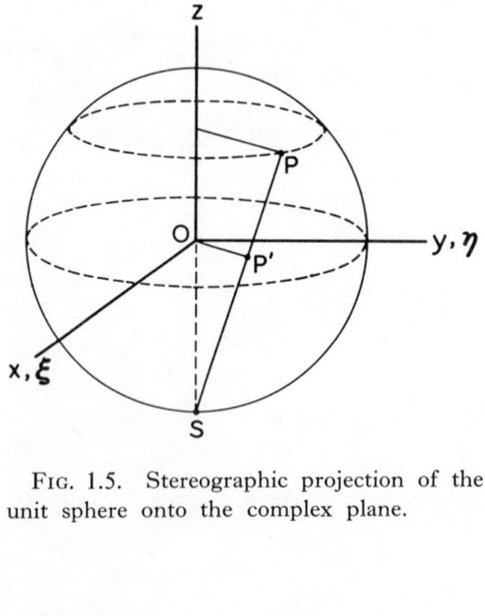

FIG. 1.5. Stereographic projection of the unit sphere onto the complex plane.

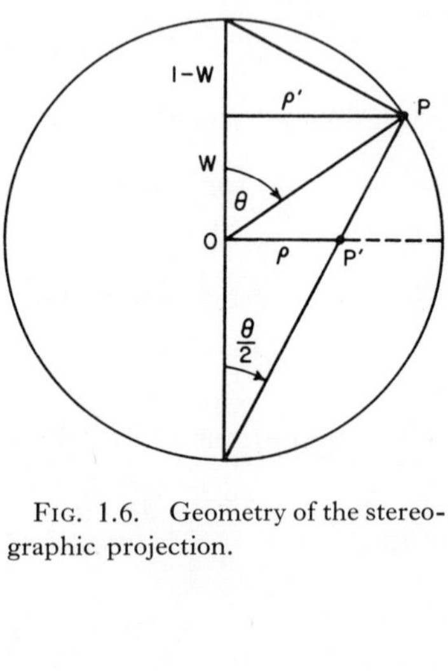

FIG. 1.6. Geometry of the stereographic projection.

If u, v, and w are expressed in terms of the polar angles φ and θ,

$$u = \sin\theta\cos\varphi, \qquad v = \sin\theta\cos\varphi, \qquad w = \cos\theta; \tag{2.13}$$

then

$$\begin{aligned} \xi &= \cos\varphi\tan\frac{\theta}{2}, & \rho &= \tan\frac{\theta}{2}, \\ \eta &= \sin\varphi\tan\frac{\theta}{2}, & \zeta &= e^{i\varphi}\tan\frac{\theta}{2}. \end{aligned} \tag{2.14}$$

Note that if ζ is the image of a point $P(u, v, w) = P(\varphi, \theta)$ on the unit sphere, the image of the diametrically opposite point $P(-u, -v, -w) = P(\varphi + \pi, \pi - \theta)$ is

$$-\frac{1}{\zeta^*} = \zeta' = -e^{i\varphi}\cot\frac{\theta}{2}. \tag{2.15}$$

The solution of (2.11) can be made to depend upon the solution of a second-order linear differential equation. For if one introduces a variable y by

$$\zeta = \frac{2}{i\gamma(H_x + iH_y)}\frac{\dot{y}}{y} \tag{2.16}$$

then

$$\ddot{y} + \left\{ i\gamma H_z - \frac{\dot{H}_x - i\dot{H}_y}{H_x - iH_y} \right\}\dot{y} + \frac{\gamma^2}{4}(H_x^2 + H_y^2)y = 0. \tag{2.17}$$

If y_1 and y_2 are two independent solutions of (2.17), then

$$\zeta = \frac{2}{i\gamma(H_x + iH_y)}\frac{c_1\dot{y}_1 + c_2\dot{y}_2}{c_1 y_1 + c_2 y_2}. \tag{2.18}$$

Equation (2.18) depends only upon the ratio of the constants c_1 and c_2, and so contains only one arbitrary (complex) constant of integration.

The solution of (2.17) for magnetic fields that vary with time is normally a problem of some difficulty. However, in the particular case where the components of $\mathbf{H}(t)$ are

$$H_x = H_1\cos\omega t, \qquad H_y = \mp H_1\sin\omega t, \qquad H_z = H_0 \tag{2.19}$$

($\dot{H}_1 = \dot{\omega} = \dot{H}_0 = 0$), then (2.17) has constant coefficients and is easily integrated to

$$y = c_1\exp(-i\Omega_1 t) + c_2\exp(-i\Omega_2 t),$$

where

$$\Omega_1 = \gamma H_0 \mp \omega + [(\gamma H_0 \mp \omega)^2 + \gamma^2 H_1{}^2]^{1/2},$$
$$\Omega_2 = \gamma H_0 \mp \omega - [(\gamma H_0 \mp \omega)^2 + \gamma^2 H_1{}^2]^{1/2}.$$

From these results it is not difficult to trace back through the preceding definitions and obtain explicit expressions for the components of $\boldsymbol{\mu}$ as functions of the time. A more direct method of obtaining these results will be given in Section 3 along with a geometric description of the motion.

The fields defined by (2.19) are called *precessing* or *rotating fields*, since they rotate about the z axis with frequency ω and a sense of rotation given by the sign of H_y. The rotation of the full field $\mathbf{H}(t)$ stems from the rotation of $H_{xy} = (H_x, H_y, 0)$, which is said to be circularly polarized. In magnetic resonance experiments, the frequency of H_{xy} is in the megacycle range, so that H_{xy} is frequently described as a (circularly polarized) radiofrequency (rf) field.

C. Adiabatic Change of Field

When the magnetic field is a function of t, the angle between $\boldsymbol{\mu}$ and $\mathbf{H}(t)$ will also be a function of t. However, if the time rate of change of $\mathbf{H}$ is sufficiently slow, $\boldsymbol{\mu}$ will maintain a given orientation relative to $\mathbf{H}$.

A simple criterion for the approximate conservation of $\angle(\boldsymbol{\mu}, \mathbf{H})$ may be obtained by examining the second derivative of $\boldsymbol{\mu}$:

$$\ddot{\boldsymbol{\mu}} = \gamma^2(\boldsymbol{\mu} \times \mathbf{H}) \times \mathbf{H} + \gamma\boldsymbol{\mu} \times \dot{\mathbf{H}}. \tag{2.20}$$

The right side of this relation differs from the second derivative of $\boldsymbol{\mu}$ when $\mathbf{H}$ is constant, and $\angle(\boldsymbol{\mu}, \mathbf{H})$ is rigorously conserved, only by the presence of the term $\gamma\boldsymbol{\mu} \times \dot{\mathbf{H}}$. Hence the motion of $\boldsymbol{\mu}$ will approximately maintain $\angle(\boldsymbol{\mu}, \mathbf{H})$ if

$$|\boldsymbol{\mu} \times \dot{\mathbf{H}}| \ll |\gamma| |(\boldsymbol{\mu} \times \mathbf{H}) \times \mathbf{H}|.$$

Now for any vectors $\mathbf{A}$ and $\mathbf{B}$, $|\mathbf{A} \times \mathbf{B}| \leqslant |\mathbf{A}| |\mathbf{B}|$, so that the above inequality will be satisfied if

$$|\boldsymbol{\mu}| |\dot{\mathbf{H}}| \ll |\gamma| |(\boldsymbol{\mu} \times \mathbf{H}) \times \mathbf{H}| \leqslant |\gamma| |\boldsymbol{\mu}| |\mathbf{H}|^2,$$

or

$$|\dot{H}| \ll |\gamma| H^2. \tag{2.21}$$

When (2.21) is satisfied, the time rate of change of $\mathbf{H}$ is said to be *adiabatic*.

3. The Resonance Phenomenon

A. Rotating Coordinate Systems

The classical motion of a magnetic moment in precessing fields of the form (2.19) admits a transparent geometric description when the problem is considered from a coordinate system which is initially coincident with the fixed laboratory coordinate system but subsequently rotates about the z axis with the same sense and frequency as the rf field (Fig. 1.7).

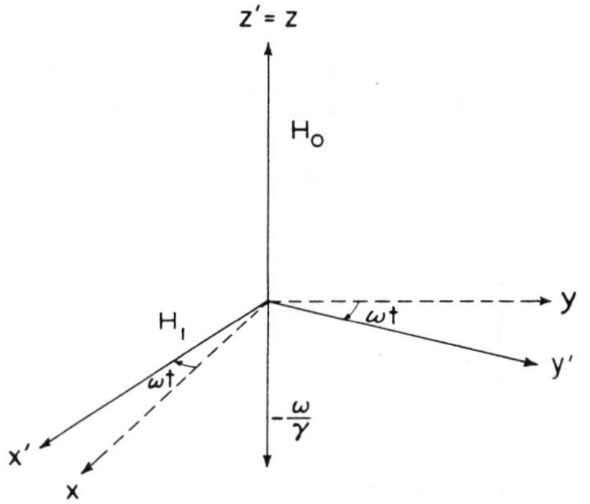

FIG. 1.7. Magnetic fields in the rotating coordinate system for $\gamma > 0$.

The motivation behind the introduction of the rotating coordinate system is that an observer in the rotating system does not observe that component of the motion generated by a uniform precession of $\boldsymbol{\mu}$ about the z axis with the sense and frequency of the rf field. If the equation for the time dependence of $\boldsymbol{\mu}$ in the rotating system can be solved, the motion of $\boldsymbol{\mu}$ relative to the laboratory coordinate system is obtained by superimposing the appropriately sensed rotation about the z axis.

The exploitation of this idea requires a simple but important relation connecting the time derivatives of an arbitrary vector, as observed from the stationary and rotating coordinate systems. Let K denote a cartesian-coordinate system fixed in the laboratory, and K' a second cartesian-coordinate system whose origin is always coincident with that of K but rotates relative to K with angular velocity $\boldsymbol{\omega}$.

The angular velocity $\boldsymbol{\omega}$ is measured with respect to K, and it will be assumed that observers in K and K' use the same system of units for all measurements. Furthermore, differentiation with respect to the time will be denoted d/dt relative to K, and $\delta/\delta t$ relative to K'.

If **U** denotes any fixed vector in K' (e.g., **U** could denote one of the unit vectors along the axes of K'), then, by definition

$$\frac{\delta \mathbf{U}}{\delta t} = 0.$$

However, the vector **U**, being fixed in K', rotates with angular velocity $\boldsymbol{\omega}$ relative to K; hence, an observer in K describes the motion of **U** by the equation

$$\frac{d\mathbf{U}}{dt} = \boldsymbol{\omega} \times \mathbf{U}.$$

Consider now a fixed vector **V** in the stationary system, so that

$$\frac{d\mathbf{V}}{dt} = 0.$$

An observer stationed in K' perceives a rotation of **V** with angular velocity $-\boldsymbol{\omega}$, and describes the motion of **V** by the equation

$$\frac{\delta \mathbf{V}}{\delta t} = -\boldsymbol{\omega} \times \mathbf{V} \qquad \left(\frac{d\mathbf{V}}{dt} = 0\right).$$

However, if **V** is a vector of K which is a function of time, then an observer in K' perceives not only the rotational motion $-\boldsymbol{\omega} \times \mathbf{V}$, but also the change of **V** brought about by its change of orientation relative to K. Thus

$$\frac{\delta \mathbf{V}}{\delta t} = -\boldsymbol{\omega} \times \mathbf{V} + \frac{d\mathbf{V}}{dt} \tag{3.1}$$

for any vector **V** in K.

B. Classical Description of Resonance

The application of (3.1) to the motion of a magnetic moment in an arbitrary magnetic field **H** yields

$$\frac{\delta \boldsymbol{\mu}}{\delta t} \equiv \dot{\boldsymbol{\mu}}_r = -\gamma \left\{\mathbf{H} + \frac{\boldsymbol{\omega}}{\gamma}\right\} \times \boldsymbol{\mu}, \tag{3.2}$$

where $-\gamma \mathbf{H} \times \boldsymbol{\mu}$ has been substituted for $d\boldsymbol{\mu}/dt$. All vectors in the last member of (3.2) are referred to the stationary coordinate system; the equation of motion for $\boldsymbol{\mu}_r$ relative to the rotating system is obtained by transforming these vectors into the rotating system. The transform of $\boldsymbol{\mu}$ is $\boldsymbol{\mu}_r$, and the rotating fields (2.19) are transformed into

$$\mathbf{H}_r = H_1 \mathbf{e}_{x'} + H_0 \mathbf{e}_{z'}\,, \tag{3.3}$$

where $\mathbf{e}_{x'}$ and $\mathbf{e}_{z'} = \mathbf{e}_z$ denote unit vectors along the x' and z' axes of the rotating system. The time dependence of $\mathbf{H}$ disappears in the rotating system by choice of $\boldsymbol{\omega}$ as

$$\boldsymbol{\omega} = -\frac{\gamma}{|\gamma|}\,\omega \mathbf{e}_{z'}\,. \tag{3.4}$$

Thus the equation of motion for $\boldsymbol{\mu}_r$ is

$$\dot{\boldsymbol{\mu}}_r = -\gamma \left\{ H_1 \mathbf{e}_{x'} + \left(H_0 - \frac{\omega}{|\gamma|}\right) \mathbf{e}_{z'} \right\} \times \boldsymbol{\mu}_r\,. \tag{3.5}$$

Comparing (3.5) with (2.1), it follows that $\boldsymbol{\mu}_r$ experiences an effective field (Fig. 1.7):

$$\mathbf{H}_e = H_1 \mathbf{e}_{x'} + \left(H_0 - \frac{\omega}{|\gamma|}\right) \mathbf{e}_{z'}\,. \tag{3.6}$$

It is convenient to define an angular velocity vector by the equation

$$\boldsymbol{\Omega} = |\gamma|\, \mathbf{H}_e = \omega_1 \mathbf{e}_{x'} + (\omega_0 - \omega)\mathbf{e}_{z'} \tag{3.7}$$

where

$$\omega_1 = |\gamma|\, H_1\,, \qquad \omega_0 = |\gamma|\, H_0\,.$$

The vector $\boldsymbol{\Omega}$ lies in the $x'z'$ plane and can be written in the form

$$\boldsymbol{\Omega} = \Omega \mathbf{n}, \tag{3.8}$$

where

$$\begin{aligned} \mathbf{n} &= \sin\theta\, \mathbf{e}_{x'} + \cos\theta\, \mathbf{e}_{z'}\,, \qquad \tan\theta = \omega_1/\Delta, \\ \Delta &= \omega_0 - \omega, \qquad \Omega = (\Delta^2 + \omega_1{}^2)^{1/2}. \end{aligned} \tag{3.9}$$

In this notation the equation of motion becomes

$$\dot{\boldsymbol{\mu}}_r = -\frac{\gamma}{|\gamma|}\, \boldsymbol{\Omega} \times \boldsymbol{\mu}_r\,. \tag{3.10}$$

From this equation the nature of motion can be deduced at once. For, since $\boldsymbol{\Omega}$ is independent of the time, the discussion of Section 2.A shows that the motion of $\boldsymbol{\mu}_r$ consists of a uniform precession about $\mathbf{n}$ with frequency Ω, and a sense of rotation determined by the sign of $-\gamma$ (Fig. 1.8). Furthermore, the angle θ_0 between $\mathbf{n}$ and $\boldsymbol{\mu}_r(t)$ is a constant of

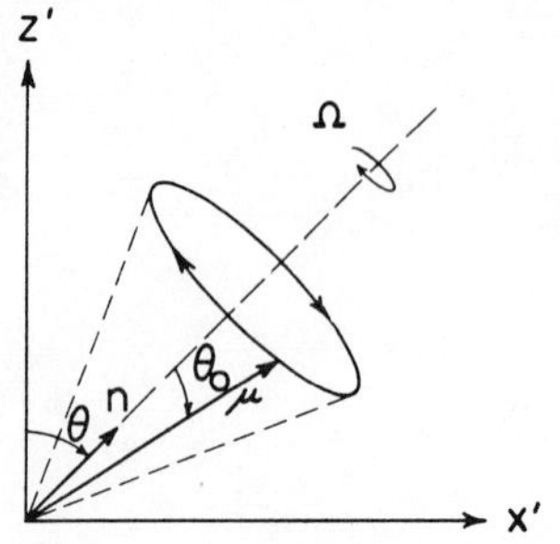

FIG. 1.8. Precession of a magnetic moment with $\gamma > 0$ as observed in the rotating coordinate system.

the motion which is, therefore, equal to the angle between $\mathbf{n}$ and $\boldsymbol{\mu}_r(0)$. But

$$\boldsymbol{\mu}_r(0) = \boldsymbol{\mu}(0), \tag{3.11}$$

so that

$$\cos \theta_0 = \boldsymbol{\mu}(0) \cdot \frac{\mathbf{n}}{\mu}.$$

During the course of the motion, $\boldsymbol{\mu}_r(t)$ traces out a cone of semiangle θ_0 ; this cone will be called the *body cone.*[9]

The motion of $\boldsymbol{\mu}(t)$ is now obtained by allowing $\boldsymbol{\mu}_r(t)$ to rotate about the z axis with frequency ω and with the sign of $-\gamma$. The vector $\mathbf{n}$ also rotates about the z axis and traces out a cone of semiangle θ (Fig. 1.9).

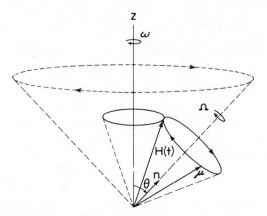

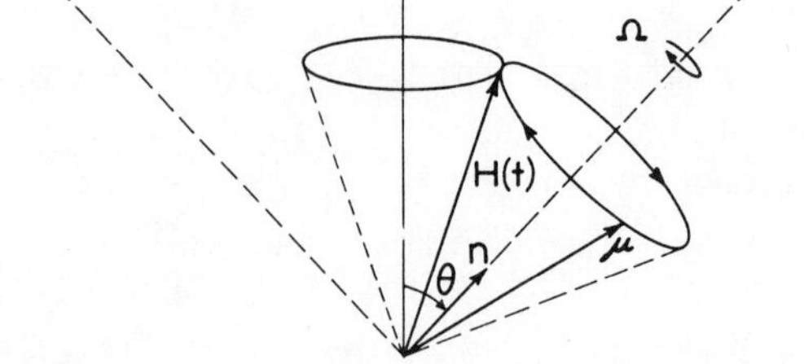

FIG. 1.9. Motion of a magnetic momen with $\gamma > 0$ as observed from the laboratory reference system.

[9] This terminology is suggested by rigid-body dynamics.

From a dynamic point of view, the cone of interest is the *space cone* defined by $\boldsymbol{\mu}(0)$ and the z axis, for the motion of $\boldsymbol{\mu}(t)$ may be simply described as a rolling, without slipping, of the body cone on the space cone (Fig. 1.9). At any instant, the points of tangency lie on the instantaneous axis of rotation, which is just the instantaneous direction of $\mathbf{H}(t)$.

From the definitions (3.9), it is clear that if $|\Delta| \gg \omega_1$, $\mathbf{n}$ is very nearly parallel (or antiparallel) to the z axis. Hence if $\boldsymbol{\mu}(0)$ is initially parallel to the z axis, the x and y components of $\boldsymbol{\mu}(t)$ will precess about the z axis with frequency $\approx\omega_0$. Although ω_0 will be in the megacycle range for fields of the order of 10,000 G, the x, y components of $\boldsymbol{\mu}(t)$ are small compared to $|\boldsymbol{\mu}(t)|$, since $\theta \approx 0$. However, as $\Delta \to 0, \mathbf{n} \to \mathbf{e}_{x'}$, and at resonance, that is, when $\Delta = 0$, $\boldsymbol{\mu}$ rotates about $\mathbf{e}_{x'}$ with frequency ω_1 and simultaneously rotates about the z axis with frequency ω.

The resonance condition is usually achieved by keeping the radiofrequency fixed and modulating the steady z field over a range which includes the resonant value. If the rate of change of the field satisfies the adiabatic condition, the description of the motion given above still holds. From (2.21) and (3.6), the adiabatic condition on $\mathbf{H}_e$ is

$$\left|\frac{dH_0}{dt}\right| \ll |\gamma| H_e^2 = |\gamma| \left\{H_1^2 + \left(H_0 - \frac{\omega}{|\gamma|}\right)^2\right\}.$$

The right side has a minimum at resonance, so that if

$$|\dot{H}_0| \ll |\gamma| H_1^2, \tag{3.12}$$

$\boldsymbol{\mu}_r$ will follow the field adiabatically.

C. Quantum Mechanical Description of Resonance

The quantum mechanical description of the resonance phenomenon is, qualitatively, quite simple. The rf field excites transitions between the $2I + 1$ quantum states with uniformly spaced energy levels $E_m = -|\gamma| \hbar H_0 m = -\hbar\omega_0 m$ (Fig. 1.10). The exchange of a single quantum of energy between the rf field and the spin system is said to be an *absorptive* or *emissive single quantum transition*, accordingly as $\Delta m = -1$ or $\Delta m = +1$. The frequency associated with an absorptive single quantum transition is

$$\frac{E_{m-1} - E_m}{\hbar} = -\omega_0(m-1) + \omega_0 m = \omega_0 .$$

Transitions for which $|\Delta m| > 1$ are called *multiple quantum transitions*. These transitions occur through the absorption or emission of se-

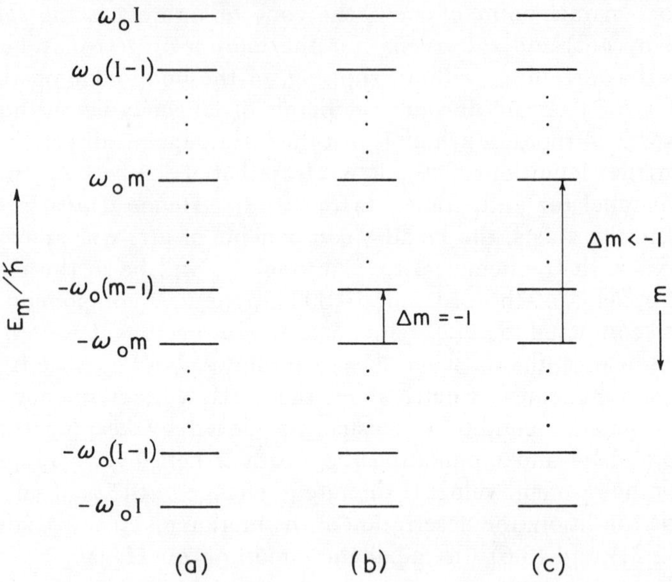

FIG. 1.10. (a) Energy levels of a nucleus with spin I in a uniform field; (b) absorptive single quantum transition; (c) absorptive multiple quantum transition.

veral rf quanta *via* intermediate states connecting the initial and final states. Multiple quantum transitions will be discussed at greater length in chapters 3, 5, and 9.

D. The Oscillating Field

The time-dependent field used to excite a nuclear resonance does not take the form of a circularly polarized field in an actual experimental arrangement. Instead, a linearly polarized field

$$H_x = 2H_1 \cos \omega t$$

is superimposed on the steady z field. A linearly polarized field can be decomposed into a pair of circularly polarized fields with equal amplitudes rotating about the z axis, as shown in Fig. 1.11. Algebraically, the decomposition is

$$(2H_1 \cos \omega t)\, \mathbf{e}_x = H_1(\mathbf{e}_x \cos \omega t - \mathbf{e}_y \sin \omega t) + H_1(\mathbf{e}_x \cos \omega t + \mathbf{e}_y \sin \omega t)\,.$$

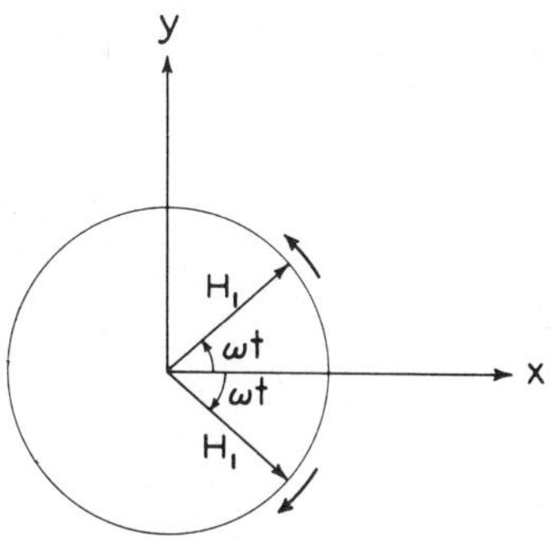

FIG. 1.11. The decomposition of a linearly polarized field into two circularly polarized components.

Only one of the rotating components has the same sense as the Larmor precession of μ about $\mathbf{H}_0$, and it is easy to show that the circularly polarized field whose sense of rotation is opposite to that of the Larmor precession produces relatively insignificant changes in the orientation of μ. However, this point alone does not warrant the rejection of the out-of-phase component of $2H_1 \cos \omega t$; it is necessary to stipulate further that

$$H_1 \ll H_0 .$$

A perturbation calculation (*22*) shows that the oscillating field changes the resonance frequency from $\omega = |\gamma| H_0$ to

$$\omega = |\gamma| H_0 \left\{ 1 + \frac{1}{4} \left(\frac{H_1}{H_0} \right)^2 \right\} .$$

In most high-resolution experiments, H_1 is of the order of milligauss and H_0 of the order of kilogauss, so that the shift in the resonance frequency is negligible. Henceforth, the perturbing radiofrequency field will be taken in the appropriate circularly polarized form.

The decomposition of a linearly polarized field into circularly polarized components is not unique. For example, if P denotes a plane containing the x axis, then the superposition of contrarotating fields with equal amplitudes and frequencies, rotating about an axis perpendicular to P, generates a field that is linearly polarized in the x direction. The particular choice of P as the xy plane when $H_1 \ll H_0$ is dictated by the expected importance of the Larmor precession about $H_0\mathbf{e}_z$.

E. Algebraic Analysis

The geometric analysis of the motion of a magnetic moment in a rotating magnetic field can be immediately transcribed into the language of matrix algebra. Indeed, the initial condition (3.11) and the discussion of Section 3.B lead at once to the matrix equation

$$\boldsymbol{\mu}(t) = Z(t)R(t)\boldsymbol{\mu}(0), \tag{3.13}$$

where $\boldsymbol{\mu}(t)$ and $\boldsymbol{\mu}(0)$ now denote 3×1 column matrices, while $Z(t)$ and $R(t)$ denote, respectively, 3×3 orthogonal matrices for rotations by ωt and Ωt about $\mathbf{e}_z$ and $\mathbf{n}$; the sense of both rotations is determined by the sign of $-\gamma$. Since $Z(t)$ and $R(t)$ are orthogonal,[10]

$$Z^{-1}(t) = \tilde{Z}(t), \qquad R^{-1}(t) = \tilde{R}(t).$$

The matrices for $Z(t)$ and $R(t)$ may be obtained by inserting the appropriate rotation angles and direction cosines of the axes of rotation into the general three-dimensional rotation matrix (Appendix II). One finds that

$$Z(t) = \begin{pmatrix} \cos \omega t & \sigma \sin \omega t & 0 \\ -\sigma \sin \omega t & \cos \omega t & 0 \\ 0 & 0 & 1 \end{pmatrix},$$

$$R(t) = \begin{pmatrix} \cos^2\theta \cos \Omega t + \sin^2\theta & \sigma \cos \theta \sin \Omega t & \sin \theta \cos \theta \, (1 - \cos \Omega t) \\ -\sigma \cos \theta \sin \Omega t & \cos \Omega t & \sigma \sin \theta \sin \Omega t \\ \sin \theta \cos \theta \, (1 - \cos \Omega t) & -\sigma \sin \theta \sin \Omega t & \sin^2\theta \cos \Omega t + \cos^2\theta \end{pmatrix},$$

where

$$\sigma = \frac{\gamma}{|\gamma|}. \tag{3.14}$$

With these matrices one may obtain explicit expressions for the components of $\boldsymbol{\mu}(t)$ by carrying out the matrix multiplications indicated in (3.13). If the initial time is taken as t_0, rather than $t = 0$, the initial condition (3.11) is changed to $\boldsymbol{\mu}(t_0) = \boldsymbol{\mu}_r(t_0)$, and t is to be replaced by $t - t_0$.

The derivation of the preceding results was based upon the geometric interpretation of the motion of a classical magnetic moment in a rotating field. It is very instructive, however, to consider (2.1) as a matrix differential equation, since the mathematical techniques used in its solution are quite analogous to those used in the analysis of the corresponding quantum mechanical problem (Section 3.A, Chapter 4). In fact, the solution of the matrix differential equation can be expressed in a

[10] The mathematical notation introduced here, and in all subsequent discussions, will be found in Appendix I.

form that is exactly analogous to the quantum mechanical solution.

The expanded matrix form of (2.1) is

$$\frac{d}{dt}\begin{pmatrix}\mu_x\\ \mu_y\\ \mu_z\end{pmatrix} = -\sigma\begin{pmatrix}0 & -\omega_0 & -\sigma\omega_1 \sin \omega t\\ \omega_0 & 0 & -\omega_1 \cos \omega t\\ \sigma\omega_1 \sin \omega t & \omega_1 \cos \omega t & 0\end{pmatrix}\begin{pmatrix}\mu_x\\ \mu_y\\ \mu_z\end{pmatrix}, \tag{3.15}$$

where $(H_1 \cos \omega t, \sigma H_1 \sin \omega t, H_0)$ has been taken for $\mathbf{H}(t)$. For brevity, the last equation will be written

$$\dot{\boldsymbol{\mu}} = -\sigma M(t)\boldsymbol{\mu}, \tag{3.16}$$

where $M(t)$ is the skew-symmetric matrix exhibited in (3.15).

The solution of (3.16) is facilitated by the transformation

$$\boldsymbol{\mu} = Z(t)\boldsymbol{\mu}_r$$

which leads to the matrix differential equation

$$\dot{\boldsymbol{\mu}}_r = \{-\sigma\tilde{Z}(t)M(t)Z(t) - \tilde{Z}(t)\dot{Z}(t)\}\boldsymbol{\mu}_r\,. \tag{3.17}$$

Carrying out the differentiation of $Z(t)$ and the indicated matrix multiplications, one finds that

$$\frac{d}{dt}\begin{pmatrix}\mu_{rx}\\ \mu_{ry}\\ \mu_{rz}\end{pmatrix} = -\sigma\begin{pmatrix}0 & -\Delta & 0\\ \Delta & 0 & -\omega_1\\ 0 & \omega_1 & 0\end{pmatrix}\begin{pmatrix}\mu_{rx}\\ \mu_{ry}\\ \mu_{rz}\end{pmatrix}. \tag{3.18}$$

The last equation can be written in the form

$$\dot{\boldsymbol{\mu}}_r = -\sigma\Omega A\boldsymbol{\mu}_r, \tag{3.19}$$

where

$$A = \begin{pmatrix}0 & -\cos\theta & 0\\ \cos\theta & 0 & -\sin\theta\\ 0 & \sin\theta & 0\end{pmatrix}. \tag{3.20}$$

The solution of (3.19) is

$$\boldsymbol{\mu}_r(t) = e^{-\sigma\Omega tA}\boldsymbol{\mu}_r(0), \tag{3.21}$$

where $e^{-\sigma\Omega tA}$ denotes the exponential function[11] of the matrix $-\sigma\Omega tA$.

[11] The properties of exponential operators are discussed in Appendix III.

It can be shown (cf. Appendix III) that

$$R(t) = e^{-\sigma\Omega tA} = I - (\sigma \sin \Omega t)A + (1 - \cos \Omega t)A^2, \tag{3.22}$$

$$Z(t) = e^{-\sigma\omega tB} = I - (\sigma \sin \omega t)B + (1 - \cos \omega t)B^2, \tag{3.23}$$

where

$$B = \begin{pmatrix} 0 & -1 & 0 \\ 1 & 0 & 0 \\ 0 & 0 & 0 \end{pmatrix}, \tag{3.24}$$

and I denotes the 3×3 identity matrix.

Thus the solution of (3.15) can be concisely written (*23*)

$$\boldsymbol{\mu}(t) = e^{-\sigma\omega tB} e^{-\sigma\Omega tA} \boldsymbol{\mu}(0). \tag{3.25}$$

4. The Phenomenological Theory

A. Static Nuclear Paramagnetism

The magnetic properties of matter may be described in terms of the macroscopic magnetization vector **M**, defined as the magnetic moment per unit volume of the sample. For isotropic, nonferromagnetic materials, the magnetization is directly proportional to the applied field

$$\mathbf{M} = \chi \mathbf{H}, \tag{4.1}$$

where χ is a dimensionless scalar, independent of **H**, called the *magnetic susceptibility*.

The experimental values of χ include positive and negative values, and this fact allows a convenient classification of matter into *paramagnetic* ($\chi > 0$) and *diamagnetic* ($\chi < 0$) substances. Paramagnetism is associated with those substances whose atoms or molecules possess permanent magnetic moments. Diamagnetism appears as the result of electronic motions induced by the field and does not require the presence of permanent magnetic moments. A second distinction is that paramagnetism is temperature-dependent, whereas diamagnetism is usually insensitive to temperature changes.

The temperature dependence of paramagnetism is a consequence of the thermal energy of the atomic or molecular systems containing the magnetic moments. In the case of nuclear paramagnetism, the form of the temperature dependence can be obtained by a simple statistical calculation. For this purpose, it will be assumed that the sample contains N_0 identical nuclear moments per unit volume, and that the magnetic interactions of the moments with each other are small compared to their interaction with the z field $H_0\mathbf{e}_z$. These assumptions permit the description of each nuclear moment as a quantized system whose energy levels are

$$E_m = -\boldsymbol{\mu} \cdot \mathbf{H} = -\gamma\hbar\mathbf{I} \cdot \mathbf{H} = -\gamma\hbar H_0 m. \tag{4.2}$$

The system of moments can be described by giving the occupation numbers N_m specifying the number of nuclei with the I_z eigenvalue m. When these numbers are known, the steady nuclear polarization along the z axis is given by the formula

$$M_0 = \sum_m N_m \mu_z = \gamma\hbar \sum_m m N_m, \tag{4.3}$$

where the summation extends from $m = -I$ to $m = +I$.

The occupation numbers satisfy the condition

$$N_0 = \sum_m N_m, \tag{4.4}$$

and, at thermal equilibrium, their ratios are given by the Boltzmann formula (*18*):

$$\frac{N_{m'}}{N_m} = \exp\left(\frac{E_m - E_{m'}}{kT}\right), \tag{4.5}$$

where k is the Boltzmann constant ($k = 1.38054 \times 10^{-16}$ ergs °K^{-1}) and T is the absolute temperature. Equations (4.4) and (4.5) can be combined to give

$$N_m = \frac{N_0\, e^{xm}}{\sum_{m'} e^{xm'}}, \qquad x = \frac{\gamma\hbar H_0}{kT}. \tag{4.6}$$

The evaluation of the summation in (4.6) is facilitated by changing the spin variable to $j = I + m'$ with $j = 0, 1, ..., 2I$. This substitution reduces the summation to the geometric series

$$\sum_{m'=-I}^{+I} e^{xm'} = e^{-xI} \sum_{j=0}^{2I} e^{jx} = \frac{\sinh[(I + \frac{1}{2})x]}{\sinh(x/2)}. \tag{4.7}$$

From (4.3), (4.6), and (4.7) it follows that

$$\frac{M_0}{\gamma\hbar N_0} = \frac{d}{dx} \ln\left(\sum_{m'} e^{xm'}\right) = \left(I + \frac{1}{2}\right) \coth\left[\left(I + \frac{1}{2}\right)x\right] - \frac{1}{2}\coth\frac{x}{2}. \tag{4.8}$$

When the thermal energy (kT) is numerically much larger than the magnetic energy ($| Ix | \ll 1$), one can use the expansion

$$\coth \theta = \frac{1}{\theta} + \frac{1}{3}\theta + \cdots$$

to obtain

$$M_0 = \frac{N_0 \mu^2}{3kT} \frac{I+1}{I} H_0 . \tag{4.9}$$

Hence the static nuclear susceptibility is

$$\chi_0 = \frac{N_0 \mu^2}{3kT} \frac{I+1}{I} . \tag{4.10}$$

Applying (4.9) to the protons in water at 300°K and 10,000 G, one finds $M_0 \approx 3 \times 10^{-6}$ G, which corresponds to $\chi \approx 3 \times 10^{-10}$.

In the opposite limit, that is, when $| Ix | \gg 1$, the hyperbolic cotangents in (4.8) are close to unity and

$$M_{\text{sat}} = N_0 \mu .$$

In this case, which occurs with very high fields or extremely low temperatures, all nuclei are in the state with $m = I$ and the system is said to be *saturated*. For the protons in water at 300°K, the saturation magnetization is about 0.9 G.

At ordinary temperatures the magnetic fields required to achieve the saturation magnetization are enormous. This can be illustrated by considering a collection of protons in thermal equilibrium at 300°K. For spin-$\frac{1}{2}$ nuclei, (4.8) simplifies to

$$M_0 = \frac{\gamma \hbar N_0}{2} \tanh \frac{x}{2} ,$$

so that

$$\frac{M_0}{M_{\text{sat}}} = \tanh \frac{x}{2} .$$

The static magnetization M_0 has a value equal to 1 per cent of the saturation value when $x = 0.02$, which requires a magnetic field of

$$H_0 = \frac{0.02kT}{\gamma \hbar} = \frac{6 \times 1.3805}{(2.6752)(1.0544)} \times 10^{11} = 2.94 \times 10^{8} \quad \text{G}.$$

The field strength required to achieve 99.99 per cent of the saturation value is 1.47×10^{11} G.

The calculation of the steady paramagnetism resulting from the orbital and spin magnetic moments of electrons is complicated by the coupling of the corresponding angular momenta (*24*). However, since μ_B is about a thousand times larger than μ_0, the electronic contribution to the total paramagnetism is expected to be much larger than the nuclear contribution whenever both occur in the same sample.

The determination of diamagnetic susceptibilities requires an analysis of the electronic motions induced by the magnetic field. In general, the problem must be treated by quantum mechanical perturbation theory, but for atoms with no unpaired electron spins, a simple classical argument (*24*) can be used to obtain the formula

$$\chi = -\frac{N_0 e^2}{6m_e c^2} \sum_i \langle r_i^2 \rangle_{\text{av}},$$

where N_0 is the number of atoms per unit volume, and r_i is the distance of the *i*th electron from the nucleus. Since r_i is of the order of 10^{-8} cm, the summation is of the order of $10^{-16}Z$, and $|\chi| \approx 10^{-6}$.

The preceding discussion shows that, at ordinary temperatures, the steady nuclear polarization established in a stationary magnetic field is completely masked by the presence of any electronic paramagnetism or by the ever-present electronic diamagnetism. In a magnetic resonance experiment, it is not the steady nuclear polarization that is detected but the emf induced in a suitably oriented receiver coil by a time variation of the nuclear magnetization. The time variation of the nuclear polarization is generated by a time-dependent magnetic field, and the induced emf is a consequence of Faraday's law of induction, which states that if the magnetic flux through a closed conducting loop (the receiver coil) changes with time, an emf appears in the circuit and is given by

$$\mathscr{E} = -\frac{1}{c}\frac{d\phi}{dt},$$

where $\mathscr{E}$ is the induced emf and ϕ the magnetic flux. The flux, by definition, is the integral of the normal component of the magnetic induction over any surface bounded by the perimeter of the conducting loop. If the magnetic induction is denoted by **B**, the flux will be given by

$$\phi = \int \mathbf{B} \cdot \mathbf{n}\, dA,$$

where **n** is a unit vector normal to an element of area dA. The magnetic induction associated with a variable magnetization is

$$\mathbf{B}(t) = 4\pi \mathbf{M}(t),$$

so that

$$\mathscr{E} = -\frac{4\pi}{c}\frac{d}{dt}\int \mathbf{M}\cdot\mathbf{n}\,dA.$$

In the usual experimental arrangement, the receiver coil is a tightly wound coil of N turns whose plane is perpendicular to the y axis. It follows that the induced emf is

$$\mathscr{E} = -\frac{4\pi NA}{c}\dot{M}_y,$$

where A is the cross-sectional area of the receiver coil. All other considerations aside, it is clear that a large time variation of **M** is necessary for a successful magnetic resonance experiment.

The required rapid changes in the orientation of the nuclear magnetization can be effected by precessing fields of the form (2.19). Whatever the specific form of $\mathbf{H}(t)$, the change with time of $\mathbf{M}(t)$ may be obtained by assuming that

$$\mathbf{M} = \sum_i \boldsymbol{\mu}_i, \tag{4.11}$$

where the summation is taken over all the magnetic moments in a unit volume of the sample. The time derivative of the macroscopic nuclear magnetization may be obtained by differentiating (4.11) and substituting $-\gamma\mathbf{H}\times\boldsymbol{\mu}_i$ for $\dot{\boldsymbol{\mu}}_i$:

$$\dot{\mathbf{M}} = -\gamma\mathbf{H}\times\mathbf{M}. \tag{4.12}$$

Equation (4.12) has the same form as the classical equation of motion for a single magnetic moment and expresses the driving influence of the external field. However, (4.12) does not take into account the changes in **M** caused by the internal electric and magnetic fields generated by charges and moments within the sample. The effects of these internal fields can be phenomenologically described in terms of the so-called *relaxation times* (*4, 5, 25*).

B. Relaxation Times

Consider an isotropic sample of bulk matter containing a collection of identical nuclear magnetic moments. In the absence of a steady magnetic field, the nuclear moments are randomly oriented and the average magnetization vanishes. This implies that the occupation numbers for the (degenerate) nuclear spin states are equal. Indeed, if $H_0 \to 0$ in the Boltzmann formula, it follows that $N_m/N_{m'} \to 1$. The equalities

$$N_I = N_{I-1} = N_{I-2} = \cdots = N_{-I} \tag{4.13}$$

provide, therefore, a set of conditions which must be satisfied by an initially unpolarized sample.

If the sample is placed in a steady magnetic field, the initial state defined by (4.13) does not correspond to an equilibrium state, since the occupation numbers for the equilibrium state must satisfy (4.5) when $\mathbf{H} \neq 0$; thermal equilibrium can be attained only by an adjustment of the initial values of the occupation numbers to the values demanded by the Boltzmann distribution. The adjustment or relaxation of the spin system to an equilibrium state requires that some of the nuclei undergo transitions to states of lower energy, with the emitted energy being transferred to the molecular surroundings.

The environment of a magnetic nucleus is often summarily described as the *lattice* and is assumed to include the magnetic moments of neighboring nuclei as well as the electronic moments of any paramagnetic species present in the sample. The thermal motions of the lattice set up fluctuating electric and magnetic fields at the nuclei, and the interaction of the nuclear moments with these fields provides a mechanism for the approach to thermal equilibrium (*5, 25*). During the approach to thermal equilibrium, M_z approaches the value $M_0 = \chi_0 H_0$, and Bloch (*4*) introduced the assumption that the change of M_z with time could be described by a first-order rate process:

$$\dot{M}_z = \frac{1}{T_1}(M_0 - M_z), \tag{4.14}$$

where T_1 is a constant variously described as the *thermal, longitudinal,* or *spin lattice* relaxation time. The time constant T_1 is a joint property of the spin system and its environment; its value reflects the extent to which the nuclear moments are coupled to their surroundings. A large value of T_1 corresponds to weak coupling and a slow approach to equilibrium, whereas a short value of T_1 indicates strong coupling and a rapid approach to equilibrium.

The thermal relaxation time may be taken as an approximate measure of the lifetime of a nuclear spin state or as a measure of the time lapse required before a magnetic resonance experiment can be performed upon an initially unpolarized sample. From the latter interpretation, it is clear that a large value of T_1 is not desirable. On the other hand, a very small value of T_1 is also undesirable. For if T_1 is taken as the lifetime of a spin state, the uncertainty principle gives an uncertainty $\Delta\omega \approx 1/T_1$ for the energy levels, which can no longer be represented as in Fig. 1.10. Instead, each of the $2I + 1$ levels is more properly represented by a large number of closely spaced levels spread over a frequency range of approximate width $1/T_1$. A small value of T_1 would thus result in a broad nuclear resonance signal.

The experimental values of T_1 are usually in the range 10^{-4} to 10^4 sec. The smallest values of T_1 are observed with liquids containing paramagnetic ions, whereas solid samples at low temperatures may exhibit relaxation times of the order of several hours or days. For liquids free of paramagnetic impurities, T_1 is usually of the order of seconds, which corresponds to a natural line width of the order of tenths of a cycle per second. For example, the relaxation times of oxygen-free samples of water and benzene are $T_1\,(H_2O) = 3.6$ sec, $T_1\,(C_6H_6) = 19.3$ sec.

The initial value of the nuclear polarization need not be zero. A nonzero initial magnetization can be obtained by first establishing a steady polarization $\mathbf{M}(0)$ in a field $\mathbf{H}(0)$ and then quickly transferring the sample into the steady z field $\mathbf{H}_0$. If $\mathbf{H}(0)$ is not parallel to $\mathbf{H}_0$, then at least one of the x, y components of $\mathbf{M}(0)$ will be nonzero. But from the assumed isotropic nature of the sample, the equilibrium values of M_x and M_y must be zero, so that decay processes are also associated with the x and y components of $\mathbf{M}$. Bloch (*4*) assumed that the decay of M_x and M_y could be described by first-order rate processes:

$$\dot{M}_x = -\frac{M_x}{T_2}, \qquad \dot{M}_y = -\frac{M_y}{T_2}, \tag{4.15}$$

where T_2 is the *transverse* relaxation time.

The decay of M_x and M_y is associated with those mechanisms which tend to distribute the μ_i in (4.11) randomly over a cone with symmetry axis $\mathbf{H}_0$, but negligibly affect the total magnetic energy. This random distribution of the μ_i about $\mathbf{H}_0$ occurs over a time interval of the order of T_2, so that if a magnetic resonance experiment is performed with the intention of observing $\dot{M}_y$, the observation must be carried out during a time interval $\tau \approx T_2$, since $M_x \approx M_y \approx 0$ for $\tau \gg T_2$. It follows that if T_2 is very small, the resonance frequency cannot be sharply defined, and the observed resonance will encompass a frequency range of the order of $1/T_2$. It is desirable, therefore, to have large values of T_2.

An important mechanism for the decay of M_x and M_y is the dipolar interaction between a nucleus and the surrounding nuclear dipoles. The nuclear dipoles add a local field to the steady z field, with the result that the nuclear Larmor frequencies are spread over a range γH_{loc}. The z component of a nuclear dipole at a point (r, θ) is given by[12]

$$\frac{\mu}{r^3}(1 - 3\cos^2\theta),$$

[12] The magnetic scalar potential is $\Psi = \mu \cos\theta/r^2$, and the field of the dipole may be determined from $\mathbf{H} = -\nabla\Psi$.

where $\theta = \angle(\boldsymbol{\mu}, \mathbf{r})$ and $\boldsymbol{\mu}$ has been taken parallel to the z axis. Thus the local field which one nuclear dipole sets up at the position of a second dipole is of the order of μ/r^3. For protons at a distance of 1.5 A, $H_{\text{loc}} \approx 7$ G, and line widths of this order are observed in solid samples (*26b*). In liquid systems, the nuclei change their relative orientations at a rate that often exceeds the Larmor frequency, and the random average value of H_{loc} is zero, since $\langle\cos^2 \theta\rangle_{\text{av}} = \frac{1}{3}$. It follows that the line widths in liquids are expected to be very much narrower than those observed with solid materials. Experimentally, T_2 is very small for solid materials (10^{-5} to 10^{-4} sec), and often much smaller than T_1. In pure liquids, however, T_2 is comparable with, and very often equal to, T_1.

The motional averaging of the dipolar fields in liquids is responsible for the narrow resonances observed in high-resolution nuclear magnetic resonance spectroscopy, but the natural line widths anticipated for liquid systems are rarely observed in high-resolution spectra, since the resonances are artificially broadened by field inhomogeneities ΔH which exceed the natural line width. For example, if $T_1 = T_2 = 5$ sec, the natural line width is approximately $1/\pi T_2 = 0.07$ cps, while observed line widths are seldom less than one- or two-tenths of a cycle per second. The contribution of the field inhomogeneity to the apparent line width is often taken into account by defining an effective transverse relaxation time as $(T_2{}^*)^{-1} = T_2^{-1} + |\gamma|\,\Delta H$.

C. The Bloch Equations

The relaxation of the nuclear magnetization in a stationary field $H_0\mathbf{e}_z$ may be described by the equation

$$\dot{\mathbf{M}}_{\text{relax}} = -\frac{1}{T_2}(M_x\mathbf{e}_x + M_y\mathbf{e}_y) - \frac{1}{T_1}(M_z - M_0)\mathbf{e}_z, \tag{4.16}$$

but this equation is not a valid expression for $\dot{\mathbf{M}}_{\text{relax}}$ when the system is subjected to time-dependent fields. In such instances (*27*), the relaxation of $\mathbf{M}$ takes place along and at right angles to the instantaneous field $\mathbf{H}(t)$. However, if the system experiences a field $H_0\mathbf{e}_z$ and a transverse rf field whose amplitude is very much smaller than H_0, (4.16) can be used to describe the relaxation of $\mathbf{M}$ in $\mathbf{H}(t)$. The total time rate of change of $\mathbf{M}$ is then given by the sum of the right-hand members of (4.12) and (4.16):

$$\dot{\mathbf{M}} + \gamma\mathbf{H}(t) \times \mathbf{M} + \frac{1}{T_2}(M_x\mathbf{e}_x + M_y\mathbf{e}_y) + \frac{1}{T_1}M_z\mathbf{e}_z = \frac{1}{T_1}M_0\mathbf{e}_z. \tag{4.17}$$

Equation (4.17) is the phenomenological equation of Bloch (*4*); its component equations are usually called the *Bloch equations*.

The solution of the Bloch equation for magnetic fields of the form (2.19) is facilitated by transforming the equation into the appropriate rotating coordinate system. The transformed nuclear magnetization will be denoted

$$\mathbf{M}_r = (M_{xr}, M_{yr}, M_{zr}) \equiv (u, v, M_z).$$

The vector differential equation satisfied by $\mathbf{M}_r$ is obtained by replacing $\mathbf{M}$ and $\mathbf{H}(t)$ in (4.17) with $\mathbf{M}_r$ and $\mathbf{H}_e$, where $\mathbf{H}_e$ is the effective field in the rotating coordinate system.[13] Alternatively, one may expand the cross product and introduce the transformation equations

$$\begin{aligned} M_x &= u \cos \omega t + \sigma v \sin \omega t, \\ M_y &= -\sigma u \sin \omega t + v \cos \omega t, \\ M_z &= M_{zr}. \end{aligned} \tag{4.18}$$

By either method one finds

$$\dot{\mathbf{M}}_r + \gamma \mathbf{H}_e \times \mathbf{M}_r + \frac{1}{T_2}(u\mathbf{e}_{x'} + v\mathbf{e}_{y'}) + \frac{1}{T_1} M_z \mathbf{e}_z = \frac{1}{T_1} M_0 \mathbf{e}_z. \tag{4.19}$$

The components of the angular velocity $\gamma \mathbf{H}_e$ are given by

$$\gamma \mathbf{H}_e = \sigma(\omega_1, 0, \Delta), \tag{4.20}$$

and, since $\mathbf{H}_e$ is independent of the time, (4.19) is equivalent to three simultaneous linear differential equations of the first order with constant coefficients.

The general solution of (4.19) can be written as the sum of a stationary solution $\mathbf{S} = (S_u, S_v, S_z)$, and a transient solution $\mathbf{T}(t) = (T_u, T_v, T_z)$:

$$\mathbf{M}_r = \mathbf{S} + \mathbf{T}.$$

By definition, $\mathbf{S}$ satisfies (4.19) with $\mathbf{M}_r = \mathbf{S}$ and $\dot{\mathbf{S}} = 0$; hence

$$\dot{\mathbf{T}} + \gamma \mathbf{H}_e \times \mathbf{T} + \frac{1}{T_2}(T_u \mathbf{e}_{x'} + T_v \mathbf{e}_{y'}) + \frac{1}{T_1} T_z \mathbf{e}_z = 0, \tag{4.21}$$

$$\gamma \mathbf{H}_e \times \mathbf{S} + \frac{1}{T_2}(S_u \mathbf{e}_{x'} + S_v \mathbf{e}_{y'}) + \frac{1}{T_1}(S_z - M_0)\mathbf{e}_z = 0. \tag{4.22}$$

1. *The Transient Solution.* If the relaxation terms in (4.21) are negligible, the first two terms show that the motion of $\mathbf{T}$ consists of a

[13] This statement is not correct if the relaxation times for the x and y components of $\mathbf{M}$ are different.

rotation of **T** about the direction of $\mathbf{H}_e$ with angular velocity $\gamma \mathbf{H}_e$. When the relaxation terms are not negligible, the motion consists of a rotation and a decay of **T**. The decay is governed by T_1 and T_2, but it cannot be described as a decay superimposed upon a rotation unless $T_1 = T_2$. For this particular case, the motion of $\mathbf{T}(t)$ is identical with the motion sketched in Fig. 1.9 except for a decay of $\mathbf{T}(t)$ through the exponential factor e^{-t/T_2}.

For times $\tau \gg T_1, T_2$, the contribution of $\mathbf{T}(t)$ to the nuclear magnetization is negligible, so that experiments designed to detect the decay of $\mathbf{T}(t)$ must be performed over time intervals that are comparable to the relaxation times. Experiments of this nature are called *transient experiments*; they include pulsed nuclear resonance experiments and the so-called *spin echo experiments* (*28*, *26*), which are especially useful for the determination of relaxation times. Experiments performed over time intervals that are long compared to the relaxation times can detect only the contribution of **S** to the nuclear magnetization and are called *steady-state experiments.*

2. *The Steady-State Solution.* The components of the steady-state solution may be obtained by expanding the cross product and solving the resulting linear algebraic equations. After some easy calculations one finds

$$
\begin{aligned}
S_u &= \frac{M_0 T_2^{\,2} \omega_1 \Delta}{1 + (\Delta T_2)^2 + T_1 T_2 \omega_1^{\,2}}, \\
S_v &= \frac{\sigma M_0 T_2 \omega_1}{1 + (\Delta T_2)^2 + T_1 T_2 \omega_1^{\,2}}, \qquad (4.23) \\
S_z &= \frac{M_0 (1 + T_2^{\,2} \Delta^2)}{1 + (\Delta T_2)^2 + T_1 T_2 \omega_1^{\,2}}.
\end{aligned}
$$

The description of **S** as the "steady-state" solution refers to the fact that $\dot{\mathbf{S}} = 0$ when observed from the rotating coordinate system. When observed from the (stationary) laboratory coordinate system, the steady-state vector **S** precesses about the z axis, and it is this precession of **S** which generates the induced voltage detected in steady-state experiments. Indeed, from (4.18) and (4.23) it follows that the contribution of **S** to the emf induced in a receiver coil whose plane is perpendicular to the y axis is

$$
\mathscr{E} = -\frac{4\pi N A}{c} \dot{M}_y = \frac{4\pi N A \omega}{c} (\sigma S_u \cos \omega t + S_v \sin \omega t). \qquad (4.24)
$$

Experimentally, one can observe either of the trigonometric components which are known as the u and v modes:

$$\mathscr{E}_u = \frac{4\pi NA\omega}{c}\sigma S_u \cos \omega t, \qquad \mathscr{E}_v = \frac{4\pi NA\omega}{c} S_v \sin \omega t. \tag{4.25}$$

From the equation for S_v, it is clear that both $\mathscr{E}_u$ and $\mathscr{E}_v$ are sensitive to the sign[14] of γ which is determined, in part (*4*), by the phase of the induced emf with respect to the rf field. Aside from this distinction, there is no compelling reason to discriminate further between $\gamma > 0$ and $\gamma < 0$; henceforth it will be assumed that $\gamma > 0$.

For $\omega_1^2 T_1 T_2 \ll 1$, the amplitude functions S_u and S_v are directly proportional to $\omega_1 = \gamma H_1$, so that the observed voltage is proportional to the amplitude of the rf field. However, the rate at which energy is absorbed from the rf field is proportional to the square of the rf-field amplitude. For the work done by a magnetic field in changing the magnetization from $\mathbf{M}$ to $\mathbf{M} + d\mathbf{M}$ is $dE = \mathbf{H} \cdot d\mathbf{M}$, so that

$$\frac{dE}{dt} = \mathbf{H} \cdot \frac{d\mathbf{M}}{dt}.$$

Thus the rate at which energy is absorbed from the rf field is

$$\frac{dE}{dt} = H_1(\mathbf{e}_x \cos \omega t - \mathbf{e}_y \sin \omega t) \cdot \frac{d\mathbf{M}}{dt} = H_1 \omega S_v .$$

From this equation it follows that the induced voltage is proportional to $H_1^{-1}(dE/dt)$.

The amplitudes of the u and v modes, considered as functions of Δ, possess markedly different properties, which are determined by S_u and S_v. The amplitude function S_u (cf. Fig. 1.12) is an odd function of Δ which vanishes at $\Delta = \pm\infty$. As $\Delta \to 0$ through negative values, S_u is negative and decreases to a minimum at

$$-\frac{1}{T_2}(1 + T_1 T_2 \omega_1^2)^{1/2}.$$

When $\Delta = 0$, $S_u = 0$, and as Δ increases through positive values, S_u increases to a maximum at

$$+\frac{1}{T_2}(1 + T_1 T_2 \omega_1^2)^{1/2}$$

[14] If the receiver coil is mounted on the x axis, the induced emf will be proportional to M_x, which is not sensitive to the sign of γ.

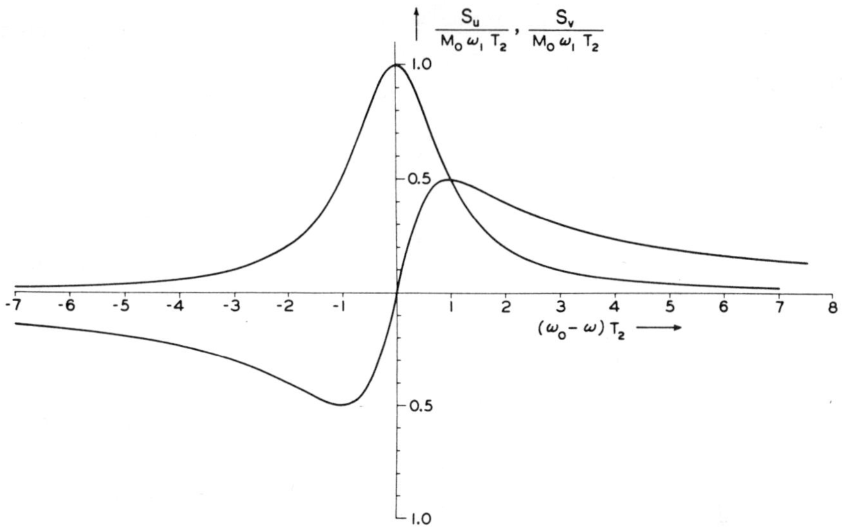

FIG. 1.12. The amplitude functions S_u and S_v for $\omega_1{}^2 T_1 T_2 \gg 1$.

and returns to zero at $\Delta = +\infty$. The maximum and minimum values of S_u are given by

$$|(S_u)_{\max}| = |(S_u)_{\min}| = \frac{M_0 T_2 \omega_1}{2(1 + T_1 T_2 \omega_1{}^2)^{1/2}} \tag{4.26}$$

and are separated by the frequency

$$\delta\omega = \frac{2}{T_2}(1 + T_1 T_2 \omega_1{}^2)^{1/2}. \tag{4.27}$$

The amplitude function S_v is a symmetric function of Δ which vanishes at $\Delta = \pm\infty$, and rises to a maximum of

$$(S_v)_{\max} = \frac{M_0 T_2 \omega_1}{1 + T_1 T_2 \omega_1{}^2} \tag{4.28}$$

at $\Delta = 0$. The frequency separation between the two points for which $S_v = \frac{1}{2}(S_v)_{\max}$ is equal to the separation of the maximum and minimum values of S_u, so that $\delta\omega$ may be taken as a common measure of the width of the S_u and S_v curves. Graphs of S_u and S_v are plotted in Fig. 1.12 for the special case $\omega_1{}^2 T_1 T_2 \ll 1$. From the figure it is evident that S_u has the character of a dispersion, while S_v represents an absorption.

The maximum and minimum values of S_u and S_v depend upon M_0, T_1, T_2, and ω_1. When $(S_u)_{\max}$ is considered as a function of $\omega_1(T_1T_2)^{1/2}$, it is easily shown that

$$(S_u)_{\max,\max} = \frac{M_0}{2}\left(\frac{T_2}{T_1}\right)^{1/2}, \tag{4.29}$$

and this occurs when $\omega_1(T_1T_2)^{1/2} \gg 1$. Thus, for given values of T_1 and T_2, the detection of $\mathscr{E}_u$ is facilitated by choosing $H_1 \gg 1/\gamma(T_1T_2)^{1/2}$. On the other hand,

$$(S_v)_{\max,\max} = (S_u)_{\max,\max},$$

and this occurs when

$$H_1 = \frac{1}{\gamma(T_1T_2)^{1/2}}. \tag{4.30}$$

Equation (4.30) gives the optimum value of H_1 for the detection of the absorption mode. For protons in liquid systems with $T_1 = T_2 = 5$ sec, the optimum value of H_1 is about 10^{-2} mG. In high-resolution experiments, H_1 usually ranges from a few hundredths to a few tenths of a milligauss.

For values of H_1 greater than the optimum value, $(S_v)_{\max,\max}$ decreases, and saturation of the absorption line sets in. Physically, saturation means that the nuclear spins are absorbing energy from the rf field at a rate that exceeds the rate of energy losses through relaxation processes.

The properties of the steady magnetization are easily visualized upon noting that the terminus of **S** lies on a second-degree surface. The equation of this surface may be obtained by taking the scalar product of (4.22) with **S**:

$$\frac{1}{T_2}(S_u^2 + S_v^2) + \frac{1}{T_1}(S_z^2 - S_zM_0) = 0.$$

The reduction of this equation to normal form shows that the terminus of **S** lies on the surface of an ellipsoid of revolution with semiaxes $a_u = a_v = (M_0/2)(T_2/T_1)^{1/2}$, $a_z = M_0/2$, and whose center of symmetry is at $(0, 0, \frac{1}{2}M_0)$.

D. Transient Oscillations

The equations for S_u and S_v were obtained on the assumption that Δ was a fixed quantity. However, these results remain valid if Δ is a slowly varying quantity. A simple criterion for the rate of change of Δ may be obtained as follows. The steady-state solution (S_u, S_v, S_z) is valid only for times long compared to T_1 and T_2, so that the resonance must be swept during a time interval

$$\tau_R \gg T_1, T_2. \tag{4.31}$$

When this condition is satisfied, a sweep through resonance is called a *slow passage*. Let Δ be a linear function of the time and let $\delta\omega$, as defined by (4.27), be taken as a measure of the width of the resonance. For slow passage $\tau_R \approx (\delta\omega)/|\dot{\Delta}| \gg T_1, T_2$. Since $T_2 \leqslant T_1$, this inequality will be satisfied if

$$\left| \frac{dH_0}{dt} \right| \ll \frac{2}{\gamma T_1 T_2} (1 + \omega_1{}^2 T_1 T_2)^{1/2}. \tag{4.32}$$

As a numerical example, consider the case of protons with $T_1 = T_2 =$ 5 sec, and suppose the v mode is observed with H_1 at its optimum value. For this case, $\dot{H}_0$ should be considerably less than 4×10^{-6} G sec^{-1} $\approx$ 0.02 cps sec^{-1}.

When $|\dot{H}_0|$ becomes comparable to the right side of (4.32), the transient term will not be damped out during the passage through resonance and can make a contribution to the observed signal. Again taking the v mode with H_1 at its optimum value, one finds that

$$|\dot{H}_0| \approx 2\sqrt{2}\,\gamma H_1{}^2.$$

But this means that the adiabatic condition

$$|\dot{H}_0| \ll \gamma H_1{}^2$$

is violated. Hence, $\mathbf{T}(t)$ not only contributes to the observed signal but also fails to follow the changing field adiabatically. The voltage induced in the receiver coil is proportional to $\dot{T}_y$, which, in the neighborhood of resonance, is alternately positive and negative, and decaying. Thus the observed transient appears as an oscillation on the tail of the absorption curve.[15] These transient oscillations are called "wiggles"; they appear after the resonance maximum because $\mathbf{T}(t)$ does not follow the changing field adiabatically (29) during the passage through resonance.

[15] For an example see the experimental spectrum of acetaldehyde shown in Chapter 5.

REFERENCES

1. (a) O. Stern, *Z. Physik* **7**, 249 (1921). (b) W. Gerlach and O. Stern, *ibid.* **8**, 110 (1921); **9**, 349, 353 (1922); *Ann. Physik* **74**, 673 (1924).
2. I. I. Rabi, J. R. Zacharias, S. Millman, and P. Kusch, *Phys. Rev.* **53**, 318 (1938).
3. (a) N. F. Ramsey, "Molecular Beams." Oxford Univ. Press, London and New York, 1956. (b) H. Kopfermann, "Nuclear Moments." Academic Press, New York, 1958.
4. F. Bloch, *Phys. Rev.* **70**, 460 (1946).
5. N. Bloembergen, E. M. Purcell, and R. V. Pound, *Phys. Rev.* **73**, 679 (1948).
6. H. Goldstein, "Classical Mechanics," Chaps. 1, 3; Chap. 5, p. 176. Addison-Wesley, Reading, Massachusetts, 1950.
7. J. A. Stratton, "Electromagnetic Theory," Chap. 4. McGraw-Hill, New York, 1941.
8. G. E. Uhlenbeck and S. Goudsmit, *Naturwiss.* **13**, 953 (1925); *Nature* **117**, 264 (1926).
9. For a general discussion of electron spin, see H. A. Kramers, "Quantum Mechanics," Chap. VI. Wiley (Interscience), New York, 1957.
10. See, for example, E. C. Kemble, "Fundamental Principles of Quantum Mechanics," Chap. XIII. McGraw-Hill, New York, 1937.
11. W. Pauli, *Z. Physik* **43**, 601 (1927); C. G. Darwin, *Proc. Roy. Soc.* (*London*) **A115 1**, (1927).
12. See, for example, (a) F. K. Richtmyer, E. H. Kennard, and T. Lauritzen, "Introduction to Modern Physics." McGraw-Hill, New York, 1955; (b) E. U. Condon and G. H. Shortley, "Theory of Atomic Spectra." Cambridge Univ. Press, London and New York, 1935.
13. P. A. M. Dirac, "The Principles of Quantum Mechanics," 4th ed., Chap. XI. Oxford Univ. Press, London and New York, 1958.
14. D. M. Dennison, *Proc. Roy. Soc.* (*London*) **A115**, 483 (1927).
15. W. Pauli, *Naturwiss.* **12**, 741 (1924).
16. For an interesting historical account of nuclear spin, see S. A. Goudsmit, *Phys. Today* **14**, 18, June (1961).
17. H. A. Bethe, "Elementary Nuclear Theory." Wiley, New York, 1947.
18. D. ter Haar, "Elements of Statistical Mechanics," Chap. IV. Holt, New York, 1960.
19. (a) W. Heisenberg, *Z. Physik* **77**, 1 (1932). (b) E. Majorana, *ibid.* **82**, 137 (1933).
20. M. G. Mayer and J. H. Jensen, "Elementary Theory of Nuclear Shell Structure." Wiley, New York, 1955.
21. For the quantum mechanical argument, see E. Feenberg and G. E. Pake, "Notes on the Quantum Theory of Angular Momentum," Chap. 5. Addison-Wesley, Reading, Massachusetts, 1953.
22. F. Bloch and A. Seigert, *Phys. Rev.* **57**, 522 (1940).
23. P. L. Corio, *J. Chem. Phys.* **38**, 979 (1963).
24. J. H. Van Vleck, "The Theory of Electric and Magnetic Susceptibilities." Oxford Univ. Press, London and New York, 1932.
25. N. Bloembergen, "Nuclear Magnetic Relaxation." Schotanus and Gens, Utrecht, 1948. Reprinted by Benjamin, New York, 1961.
26. General discussions of nuclear magnetic resonance may be found in the following references: (a) G. E. Pake, *Am. J. Phys.* **18**, 438, 473 (1950). (b) G. E. Pake, *in* "Solid State Physics" (F. Seitz and D. Turnbull, eds.), Vol. 2, pp. 1–91. Academic Press, New York, 1956. (c) E. R. Andrew, "Nuclear Magnetic Resonance." Cambridge Univ. Press, London and New York, 1955. (d) A. Abragam, "The Principles of Nuclear Magnetism." Oxford Univ. Press, London and New York, 1961. (e) Reference

3(b), Chap. III. (f) C. P. Slichter, "Principles of Magnetic Resonance: With Examples from Solid State Physics." Harper, New York, 1963.

27. (a) R. S. Codrington, J. D. Olds, and H. C. Torrey, *Phys. Rev.* **95**, 607 (1954). (b) A. G. Redfield, *Phys. Rev.* **98**, 1787 (1955). (c) G. E. Pake, "Paramagnetic Resonance," p. 23. Benjamin, New York, 1962.
28. E. L. Hahn, *Phys. Rev.* **80**, 580 (1950).
29. B. A. Jacobsohn and R. K. Wangsness, *Phys. Rev.* **73**, 942 (1948).

CHAPTER 2

Theory of Spin Angular Momentum

1. The Vector Character of Spin Angular Momentum

A. The Spin Operators

The spin angular momentum of a fundamental particle—or that of a complex nucleus—is associated with internal degrees of freedom that do not possess classical analogs. For this reason, the operators required for the description of a spin angular momentum cannot be obtained by applying the usual prescriptions for the construction of quantum mechanical operators (*1–3*). Indeed, the absence of an appropriate classical analog implies that explicit expressions for the spin operators cannot be obtained at all, so that they must be represented by abstract symbols whose properties are revealed by experiment. It is preferable, however, to develop the theory of spin angular momentum on the basis of a few plausible assumptions whose validity is established by the agreement of the theory with experiment.

The first assumption is that the spin angular momentum of a particle is represented by a *vector operator*. This means, in the first place, that the spin operators constitute a set of three linearly independent component operators. The component operators will be distinguished by subscripts referring to the three orthogonal axes of a right-handed cartesian-coordinate system K, and all three components will be collectively described as the spin vector $\mathbf{I}$:

$$\mathbf{I} = (I_x, I_y, I_z). \tag{1.1}$$

The physical interpretation of the component operators is that an observer O, in the coordinate system K, uses I_x, I_y, and I_z to compute quantum mechanical averages that are interpreted as the expectation values for the components of the spin angular momentum along the cartesian axes.[1] Since the component operators are identified with observable quantities, it follows from the general principles of quantum mechanics that I_x, I_y, and I_z are linear and hermitian.

In addition to the component operators, a fourth spin operator is defined by the equation

$$\mathbf{I}^2 = \mathbf{I} \cdot \mathbf{I} = I_x^2 + I_y^2 + I_z^2. \tag{1.2}$$

This operator is called the *square* of the spin vector, and its expectation value is interpreted as the square of the spin angular momentum. Since it is a sum of hermitian operators, $\mathbf{I}^2$ is also an hermitian operator.

B. Transformation Properties

A second requirement imposed by the vector character of spin angular momentum concerns the transformation properties of the component operators. To describe these properties, it is necessary to introduce a second right-handed coordinate system, K', whose origin is coincident with that of the original system K. The two coordinate systems are related by an orthogonal transformation[2] R, satisfying

$$R\tilde{R} = \tilde{R}R = 1, \qquad \det R = +1, \tag{1.3}$$

where 1 is the identity transformation. If the transformation R is represented by a 3×3 matrix (R_{ij}), the matrix elements of R are the nine direction cosines of the axes of K' with respect to the axes of K.

The relations between K and K' are conveniently described by an auxiliary notation which relabels the axes of both coordinate systems according to the prescription: $x, x' \leftrightarrow 1$, $y, y' \leftrightarrow 2$, $z, z' \leftrightarrow 3$. Quantities referred to different coordinate systems will be distinguished by primes. In this notation, the orthogonality relations satisfied by the direction cosines are

$$\sum_k R_{jk} R_{lk} = \delta_{jl},$$

where δ_{jl} is the Kronecker delta.

---

[1] The mean or expectation value of a quantum mechanical operator X, with respect to a system described by a state vector $\psi_n \equiv | n \rangle$, is defined as the scalar product $(\psi_n, X\psi_n) \equiv \langle n | X | n \rangle$.

[2] The properties of three-dimensional orthogonal transformations are discussed in Appendix II.

Consider now an observer O', stationed in K', who wishes to describe the same spin angular momentum that O describes by the vector operator $\mathbf{I} = (I_1, I_2, I_3) \equiv (I_x, I_y, I_z)$. For this purpose, O' introduces the vector operator

$$\mathbf{I}' = (I_1', I_2', I_3'), \tag{1.4}$$

whose components have the same physical interpretation with respect to the coordinate system of O' that I_1, I_2, and I_3 have in the coordinate system of O. The transformation properties of vector operators require the components of $\mathbf{I}'$ to be related to those of $\mathbf{I}$ by the orthogonal transformation R:

$$\begin{aligned} I_1' &= R_{11}I_1 + R_{12}I_2 + R_{13}I_3, \\ I_2' &= R_{21}I_1 + R_{22}I_2 + R_{23}I_3, \\ I_3' &= R_{31}I_1 + R_{32}I_2 + R_{33}I_3. \end{aligned} \tag{1.5}$$

Conversely, the components of $\mathbf{I}$ are related to $\mathbf{I}'$ by the inverse transformation $R^{-1} = \tilde{R}$:

$$\begin{aligned} I_1 &= R_{11}I_1' + R_{21}I_2' + R_{31}I_3', \\ I_2 &= R_{12}I_1' + R_{22}I_2' + R_{32}I_3', \\ I_3 &= R_{13}I_1' + R_{23}I_2' + R_{33}I_3'. \end{aligned} \tag{1.6}$$

Equations (1.5) and (1.6) may be interpreted as a means of obtaining quantum mechanical averages in one reference system from those computed in another system. Alternatively, equations (1.5) may be interpreted as the operators required by O for computing quantum mechanical averages along three orthogonal directions that are not parallel to any of his coordinate axes. In particular, the operator for the component of the spin angular momentum along a direction specified by the unit vector $\mathbf{n} = (n_x, n_y, n_z)$ is

$$\mathbf{n} \cdot \mathbf{I} = n_x I_x + n_y I_y + n_z I_z. \tag{1.7}$$

C. The Commutation Relations

The final assumption of the theory is that the components of the spin vector in the reference system K satisfy commutation relations identical with those satisfied by the components of the orbital angular momentum operators (*1*). In the (xyz) notation, and with $\hbar$ as the unit of angular momentum, the rules of commutation are

$$\begin{aligned} I_x I_y - I_y I_x &= iI_z, \\ I_y I_z - I_z I_y &= iI_x, \\ I_z I_x - I_x I_z &= iI_y, \end{aligned} \tag{1.8}$$

where i is the imaginary unit. The auxiliary notation permits concise expression of the commutation relations as

$$[I_j, I_k] = i \sum_l e_{jkl} I_l , \tag{1.9}$$

where e_{jkl} is the Levi-Civita tensor density defined as

$$e_{jkl} = \begin{cases} +1 & \text{if } (jkl) \text{ is an even permutation of } (123), \\ 0 & \text{if any two of } (jkl) \text{ are equal}, \\ -1 & \text{if } (jkl) \text{ is an odd permutation of } (123). \end{cases}$$

The commutation properties of the components of $\mathbf{I}$ imply that the square of the spin vector commutes with each component of $\mathbf{I}$:

$$[\mathbf{I}^2, I_j] = 0 \qquad (j = 1, 2, 3). \tag{1.10}$$

For example, the commutator of $\mathbf{I}^2$ and I_z is

$$[\mathbf{I}^2, I_z] = [I_x{}^2, I_z] + [I_y{}^2, I_z],$$

since an operator commutes with itself or with any integral power of itself. The right-hand member of this equality is equivalent to

$$\begin{aligned} &[I_x{}^2, I_z] + [I_y{}^2, I_z] + I_x I_z I_x - I_x I_z I_x + I_y I_z I_y - I_y I_z I_y \\ &\quad = I_x[I_x , I_z] + [I_x , I_z]I_x + I_y[I_y , I_z] + [I_y , I_z]I_y = 0. \end{aligned}$$

Similar calculations establish the commutation of I_x and I_y with $\mathbf{I}^2$.

D. Invariance of the Theory

The spin operators refer to internal degrees of freedom and cannot be assumed to commute with operators that also reflect internal properties of the particle—for example, the operators describing the magnetic moment or the nuclear electric quadrupole moment, if the latter exists. On the other hand, the components of $\mathbf{I}$ do commute with any operator that does not refer to internal properties—the matrix elements of the orthogonal transformation R, the position vector, the linear momentum, or any function of these operators, such as the orbital angular momentum. It follows, from (1.5) and (1.9), that the commutation relations satisfied by the components of $\mathbf{I}'$ are[3]

$$[I_j', I_k'] = i \sum_l e_{jkl} I_l'. \tag{1.11}$$

[3] The proof of equation (1.11) is obtained at once upon noting that

$$R_{ij} = (-1)^{i+j} \det M_{ij} ,$$

where M_{ij} is the 2×2 matrix obtained from the matrix of R by deleting the ith row and jth column. This relation follows from the fact that the unit vectors along the cartesian axes of K' satisfy $\mathbf{e}_j' \times \mathbf{e}_k' = \sum_l e_{jkl} \mathbf{e}_l'$.

Moreover, from (1.5) and the orthogonality relations satisfied by the R_{ij}, it follows that

$$\mathbf{I} \cdot \mathbf{I} = \mathbf{I}' \cdot \mathbf{I}'. \tag{1.12}$$

Hence, from (1.5), (1.10), and (1.11),

$$[\mathbf{I}' \cdot \mathbf{I}', I_j'] = 0 \qquad (j = 1, 2, 3). \tag{1.13}$$

By induction, it follows that for a given set of right-handed cartesian-coordinate systems $K, K', K'', \ldots$, related by the proper orthogonal transformations $R, R', R'', \ldots$, any relation satisfied by the operators $\mathbf{I}^2, I_x, I_y$, and I_z in K—or any property deduced from their commutation relations—is also true for the corresponding operators in $K', K'', \ldots$. This result establishes the invariance of the theory for all observers $O, O', O'', \ldots$ stationed in $K, K', K'', \ldots$. In particular, any special properties assigned to the z direction of K by virtue of the fact that $[\mathbf{I}^2, I_z] = 0$ are also true for the directions $z', z'', \ldots$ of $K', K'', \ldots$. In other words, all rays emanating from the common origin of the several coordinate systems have the same properties—space is isotropic.

The equivalence of all spatial directions stems from the tacit assumption that the particle whose spin angular momentum is under consideration does not interact with its surroundings. When interactions are introduced, certain directions in space may be singled out as having special properties, so that the isotropy of space is destroyed. However, observers in different coordinate systems measuring properties of the same system in a given direction must obtain equivalent results; that is, all coordinate systems must be physically equivalent.

2. Analysis of the Eigenvalue Problem

A. Introduction of $I_x \pm iI_y$

The commutation relations satisfied by the operators I_x, I_y, I_z, and $\mathbf{I}^2$ imply that a set of vectors exists whose elements are simultaneous eigenvectors [4] of $\mathbf{I}^2$ and one of the components of $\mathbf{I}$. The choice of the commuting component is arbitrary, since the three component operators enter the problem in a symmetrical way and nothing has as yet been injected into the theory which indicates a preference for any spatial direction. One can maintain complete generality by denoting the

[4] The properties of vectors, vector spaces, Dirac's bra and ket notation, and the theorem on the eigenvectors of commuting operators are discussed in Appendix I.

commuting component I_j, without specification of j as x, y, or z. It has become customary, however, to set $j = z$, and this convention will be followed here.

A generic eigenvector of $\mathbf{I}^2$ and I_z will be denoted by a ket vector $|\lambda, \mu\rangle$, where λ and μ are the respective eigenvalues of $\mathbf{I}^2$ and I_z. The set of all linearly independent eigenvectors will be denoted[5] $\{|\lambda, \mu\rangle\}$, and the associated set of all bra or dual vectors will be denoted $\{\langle\lambda, \mu|\}$. In this notation, the eigenvalue equations are

$$\mathbf{I}^2 \,|\, \lambda, \mu\rangle = \lambda \,|\, \lambda, \mu\rangle, \tag{2.1}$$

$$I_z \,|\, \lambda, \mu\rangle = \mu \,|\, \lambda, \mu\rangle. \tag{2.2}$$

The analysis of the eigenvalue problem posed by (2.1) and (2.2) must be carried out by symbolic methods that make no reference to classical variables. What emerges from the analysis are the properties of the eigenvalues and their relation to the dimensionality of the vector space spanned by the eigenvectors $\{|\lambda, \mu\rangle\}$. The deduction of these properties is facilitated by the operators I_+ and I_-, defined by the equations

$$I_\pm = I_x \pm iI_y. \tag{2.3}$$

These operators[6] are not hermitian, since $I_\pm{}^\dagger = I_\mp$.

The commutation relations satisfied by $I_\pm$ follow immediately from those of the spin operators:

$$[\mathbf{I}^2, I_\pm] = 0, \tag{2.4}$$

$$[I_z, I_\pm] = \pm I_\pm, \tag{2.5}$$

$$[I_+, I_-] = 2I_z. \tag{2.6}$$

From (2.4) and (2.5) one may derive the important relations

$$\mathbf{I}^2 I_\pm{}^r = I_\pm{}^r \mathbf{I}^2, \tag{2.7}$$

$$I_z I_\pm{}^r = I_\pm{}^r (I_z \pm rI), \tag{2.8}$$

$$I_z{}^s I_\pm{}^r = I_\pm{}^r (I_z \pm rI)^s, \tag{2.9}$$

---

[5] The mere assertion that $\{|\lambda, \mu\rangle\}$ is the set of all eigenvectors does not prove the existence of this set. That such a set exists for some particles is demonstrated by experimental evidence, for example, the hyperfine structure in optical spectra. If the particle under consideration does not possess a spin angular momentum, the set $\{|\lambda, \mu\rangle\}$ is empty; that is, it contains no elements.

[6] The operators I_+ and I_- are often called the "raising" and "lowering" operators.

where $r, s = 1, 2, \ldots$. The validity of (2.7) is obvious in view of the fact that I_+ and I_- commute with $\mathbf{I}^2$. Equation (2.8) may be obtained by successive operator multiplications commencing with (2.5), but it is simpler to use mathematical induction. For $r = 1$, (2.8) reduces to (2.5). Suppose now that (2.8) is true for $r = k$. Multiplying on the right by $I_\pm$ one finds, with the help of (2.5),

$$I_z I_\pm^{k+1} = I_\pm^k(I_z I_\pm \pm kI_\pm) = I_\pm^k[I_\pm I_z \pm (k+1)I_\pm]$$
$$= I_\pm^{k+1}[I_z \pm (k+1)I],$$

which completes the proof. Equation (2.9) may be proved by mathematical induction on s, upon noting that it reduces to (2.8) when $s = 1$.

B. The Generating Process

Equations (2.7) and (2.8) permit the analysis of the eigenvalue problem by an elegant generating process which discloses characteristic and complementary properties of I_+ and I_- . Let $|\lambda_0, \mu_0\rangle$ be some arbitrarily chosen member of $\{|\lambda, \mu\rangle\}$, and operate on this eigenvector with (2.7) and (2.8) to obtain

$$\mathbf{I}^2[I_\pm^r|\lambda_0, \mu_0\rangle] = \lambda_0[I_\pm^r|\lambda_0, \mu_0\rangle], \qquad (2.10)$$

$$I_z[I_\pm^r|\lambda_0, \mu_0\rangle] = (\mu_0 \pm r)[I_\pm^r|\lambda_0, \mu_0\rangle]. \qquad (2.11)$$

It follows that by successive applications of the operators I_+ and I_- to $|\lambda_0, \mu_0\rangle$, one can generate a sequence of eigenvectors $\{I_\pm^r|\lambda_0, \mu_0\rangle\}$, $r = 0, 1, 2, \ldots$, that have the common eigenvalue λ_0 , but whose eigenvalues of I_z differ by integers. The last remark implies that the generated eigenvectors are orthogonal. Indeed, consider the scalar product $\langle s|I_z|r\rangle$, where the abbreviations $|r\rangle \equiv I_\pm^r|\lambda_0, \mu_0\rangle$ and $\langle s| \equiv \langle\lambda_0, \mu_0|I_\mp^s$ have been introduced to simplify the notation. Now $I_z|r\rangle = (\mu_0 \pm r)|r\rangle$ and, since I_z is hermitian, $\langle s|I_z = (\mu_0 \pm s)\langle s|$; hence

$$\langle s|I_z|r\rangle = (\mu_0 \pm s)\langle s|r\rangle = (\mu_0 \pm r)\langle s|r\rangle,$$

from which it follows that $\langle s|r\rangle = 0$ for $r \neq s$. Henceforth it will be assumed that the set of all eigenvectors is also a normalized set, so that $\langle s|r\rangle = \delta_{sr}$.

The unrestricted application of the generating process leads to the conclusion that from a given eigenvector one can generate a twofold infinity of independent eigenvectors. There is, however, a condition on the eigenvalues of I_z which imposes upper and lower bounds on the sequence: $\ldots\mu_0 - 2, \mu_0 - 1, \mu_0, \mu_0 + 1, \mu_0 + 2, \ldots$. This condition may be deduced from the equation obtained by taking the scalar product of (2.1) with $\langle\lambda, \mu\,|$, using (2.2) to eliminate $\langle\lambda, \mu\,|I_z^2|\,\lambda, \mu\rangle$. One finds that

$$\langle\lambda, \mu \mid I_x^2 + I_y^2 \mid \lambda, \mu\rangle = (\lambda - \mu^2)\,\langle\lambda, \mu \mid \lambda, \mu\rangle.$$

The left side of this equation represents the diagonal matrix element of a sum of squares of hermitian operators and is necessarily nonnegative. For if $H = (H_{ij})$ is hermitian, a diagonal element of H^2 is given by

$$\sum_k H_{ik}H_{ki} = \sum_k H_{ik}H_{ik}^* = \sum_k \mid H_{ik} \mid^2 \geqslant 0,$$

from which it follows that a sum of such elements is also nonnegative; hence

$$\lambda - \mu^2 \geqslant 0. \tag{2.12}$$

It is apparent that if r were to increase indefinitely, the squares of $\mu_0 \pm r$ would eventually become large enough to violate (2.12). The only way out of this difficulty is to admit the existence of least positive integers p and q such that

$$I_+^{\,p} \mid \lambda_0, \mu_0\rangle = 0, \tag{2.13}$$

$$I_-^{\,q} \mid \lambda_0, \mu_0\rangle = 0, \tag{2.14}$$

with $p, q \geqslant 1$. Operating on (2.13) with I_-, and on (2.14) with I_+, one obtains

$$\begin{aligned} I_-I_+^{\,p} \mid \lambda_0, \mu_0\rangle &= (I_-I_+)I_+^{p-1} \mid \lambda_0, \mu_0\rangle = 0, \\ I_+I_-^{\,q} \mid \lambda_0, \mu_0\rangle &= (I_+I_-)I_-^{q-1} \mid \lambda_0, \mu_0\rangle = 0. \end{aligned} \tag{2.15}$$

Now $I_+^{p-1}|\,\lambda_0, \mu_0\rangle$ and $I_-^{q-1}|\,\lambda_0, \mu_0\rangle$ are eigenvectors of I_z with the eigenvalues $\mu_0 + p - 1$ and $\mu_0 - q + 1$, and since

$$I_\pm I_\mp = \mathbf{I}^2 - I_z(I_z \mp 1), \tag{2.16}$$

it follows from (2.15) and (2.16) that

$$\begin{aligned} \lambda_0 - (\mu_0 + p - 1)(\mu_0 + p) &= 0, \\ \lambda_0 - (\mu_0 - q + 1)(\mu_0 - q) &= 0. \end{aligned} \tag{2.17}$$

Eliminating λ_0 from the preceding equations yields

$$(2\mu_0 + p - q)(p + q - 1) = 0.$$

The solution $p + q = 1$ is extraneous since $p, q \geqslant 1$; hence

$$\mu_0 = \tfrac{1}{2}(q - p). \tag{2.18}$$

Evidently μ_0 is positive or negative, accordingly as $q - p$ is positive or negative, and integral or half-integral, accordingly as $q - p$ is even or odd. Since the eigenvalues of I_z differ by integers, the integral or half-integral character persists for the entire sequence of eigenvalues from $\mu_0(\text{min})$ to $\mu_0(\text{max})$, where

$$\mu_0(\text{min}) = \mu_0 - q + 1, \qquad \mu_0(\text{max}) = \mu_0 + p - 1. \tag{2.19}$$

It is customary to express the preceding results in terms of a number I, called the *spin quantum number*, by the equation

$$2I = \mu_0(\text{max}) - \mu_0(\text{min}) = p + q - 2. \tag{2.20}$$

Since $p \geqslant 1, q \geqslant 1, I$ is nonnegative and equal to some fixed member of the sequence $0, \frac{1}{2}, 1, \frac{3}{2}, 2, \ldots$. From (2.17) through (2.20), it is now easy to show that

$$\mu_0(\text{max}) = +I, \qquad \mu_0(\text{min}) = -I, \qquad \lambda_0 = I(I + 1).$$

The (restricted) generating process yields $2I + 1$ eigenvectors whose eigenvalues of $\mathbf{I}^2$ are degenerate with the common value $I(I + 1)$, and whose eigenvalues of I_z range from $-I$ to $+I$ in integral steps. It is convenient to introduce the discrete spin variable m, whose domain consists of the eigenvalues of I_z, and to label the eigenvectors with the spin quantum number and the spin variable: $\{I_\pm{}^r | \lambda_0, \mu_0\rangle\} \equiv \{| I, m\rangle\}$, where r now ranges over all integers in the open interval determined by $I - m$ and $I + m$.

The preceding analysis shows only that the set of $2I + 1$ eigenvectors $\{| I, m\rangle\}$ is a subset of the set of all eigenvectors $\{| \lambda, \mu\rangle\}$. For the special case where the eigenvalues of I_z are nondegenerate and $\lambda = I(I + 1)$ for all $| \lambda, \mu\rangle$, the set $\{| I, m\rangle\}$ includes every eigenvector in the set $\{| \lambda, \mu\rangle\}$. For suppose there is an eigenvector $| \lambda_1, \mu_1\rangle$ not contained in $\{| \lambda, \mu\rangle\}$. Then, by assumption, $\lambda_1 = I(I + 1)$ and $\mu_1 \neq -I, -I + 1, \ldots, I - 1, I$. It follows that an application of the generating process to $| \lambda_1, \mu_1\rangle$ would lead to eigenvalues of I_z different from those in the set $\{| I, m\rangle\}$. But this would lead to a spin quantum number different from I, contrary to assumption. The possible values of μ_1 must therefore be identical with those of m. Since the eigenvalues of I_z are assumed to be nondegenerate, the eigenvectors generated from $| \lambda_1, \mu_1\rangle$

must be identical with $\{| I, m\rangle\}$ or, at most, differ from the latter by multiplicative scalars. From this result it follows that $I_{\pm}{}^{r}| I, m\rangle$ is a scalar multiple of $| I, m \pm r\rangle$. In particular, for $r = 1$,

$$I_{\pm} | I, m\rangle = C_{m\pm 1,m} | I, m \pm 1\rangle. \tag{2.21}$$

To evaluate the scalar in (2.21), note that since $I_{\mp} = I_{\pm}^{\dagger}$, the dual of (2.21) is

$$\langle I, m | I_{\mp} = C^{*}_{m\pm 1,m}\langle I, m \pm 1 |.$$

Taking the scalar product of (2.21) with $\langle I, m | I_{\mp}$ yields

$$\langle I, m | I_{\mp}I_{\pm} | I, m\rangle = | C_{m\pm 1,m} |^2 \langle I, m \pm 1 | I, m \pm 1\rangle = | C_{m\pm 1,m} |^2.$$

On the other hand,

$$\langle I, m | I_{\mp}I_{\pm} | I, m\rangle = (I \mp m)(I \pm m + 1),$$

by (2.16). Thus $C_{m\pm 1,m}$ is determined up to an arbitrary phase factor $\exp(i\theta_{m\pm 1,m})$. The standard convention sets $\theta_{m\pm 1,m} = 0$, so that

$$C_{m\pm 1,m} = [(I \mp m)(I \pm m + 1)]^{1/2}. \tag{2.22}$$

The results for the special case just considered are summarized by the following equations:

$$\begin{aligned} \mathbf{I}^2 | I, m\rangle &= I(I + 1)| I, m\rangle, \\ I_z | I, m\rangle &= m | I, m\rangle, \\ m &= -I, \quad -I + 1, \ldots, I - 1, \quad I, \\ \langle I, m' | I, m\rangle &= \delta_{m'm}, \\ I_{\pm} | I, m\rangle &= [(I \mp m)(I \pm m + 1)]^{1/2} | I, m \pm 1\rangle, \end{aligned} \tag{2.23}$$

where I is some fixed member of the sequence $0, \frac{1}{2}, 1, \frac{3}{2}, \ldots$. The effect of I_x or I_y on $| I, m\rangle$ may be obtained from the last of equations (2.23) and the equations

$$I_x = \frac{1}{2}(I_+ + I_-), \qquad I_y = \frac{i}{2}(I_- - I_+). \tag{2.24}$$

C. Matrix Representation of the Spin Operators

Equations (2.23) define a matrix representation for the spin operators relative to the basis of eigenvectors. Since the spin variable is nondegenerate, each spin operator is represented by a square matrix of dimension $2I + 1$. The matrix elements of any spin operator X may be denoted $\langle I, m' | X | I, m\rangle$, but as the spin quantum number is the same for all eigenvectors, it need not enter explicitly in the labeling.

The matrices for $\mathbf{I}^2$ and I_z are diagonal by choice of the basis. The matrix for $\mathbf{I}^2$ is quite simple; it is $I(I + 1)$ times an identity matrix of $2I + 1$ rows and columns:

$$\mathbf{I}^2 = I(I+1)\begin{pmatrix} 1 & 0 & 0 & \cdots & 0 \\ 0 & 1 & 0 & \cdots & 0 \\ \cdot & \cdot & \cdot & \cdots & \cdot \\ 0 & 0 & 0 & \cdots & 1 \end{pmatrix}.$$

The diagonal matrix elements of I_z are just the $2I + 1$ values of the spin variable, so that

$$I_z = \begin{pmatrix} I & 0 & 0 & \cdots & 0 \\ 0 & I-1 & 0 & \cdots & 0 \\ \cdot & \cdot & \cdot & \cdots & \cdot \\ 0 & 0 & 0 & \cdots & -I \end{pmatrix}.$$

The matrices for I_+ and I_- are easily constructed from the relation

$$\langle I, m' | I_\pm | I, m\rangle = [(I \mp m)(I \pm m + 1)]^{1/2}\delta_{m',m\pm 1}\,.$$

Thus

$$I_+ = \begin{pmatrix} 0 & [1\cdot(2I)]^{1/2} & 0 & 0 & \cdots & 0 \\ 0 & 0 & [2\cdot(2I-1)]^{1/2} & 0 & \cdots & 0 \\ 0 & 0 & 0 & [3\cdot(2I-2)]^{1/2} & \cdots & 0 \\ \cdot & \cdot & \cdot & \cdot & \cdots & \cdot \\ 0 & 0 & 0 & 0 & \cdots & [(2I)\cdot 1]^{1/2} \\ 0 & 0 & 0 & 0 & \cdots & 0 \end{pmatrix}.$$

The matrix for I_- is obtained by taking the adjoint of the matrix for I_+. One may then obtain the matrices representing I_x and I_y from (2.24).

When the spin operators are represented by $(2I + 1)$-dimensional matrices, the eigenvectors $\{| I, m\rangle\}$ are represented by $(2I + 1)$-rowed column vectors:

$$| I, I\rangle = \begin{pmatrix} 1 \\ 0 \\ 0 \\ \vdots \\ 0 \end{pmatrix}, \qquad | I, I-1\rangle = \begin{pmatrix} 0 \\ 1 \\ 0 \\ \vdots \\ 0 \end{pmatrix}, \ldots, | I, -I\rangle = \begin{pmatrix} 0 \\ 0 \\ 0 \\ \vdots \\ 1 \end{pmatrix}.$$

The corresponding bra or dual vectors are represented by row vectors with $2I + 1$ columns:

$$\langle I, I \mid = (1 \;\; 0 \;\; 0 \;\; \cdots \;\; 0),$$
$$\langle I, I-1 \mid = (0 \;\; 1 \;\; 0 \;\; \cdots \;\; 0),$$
$$\cdot \quad \cdot \quad \cdot \quad \cdot \quad \cdot \quad \cdot \quad \cdot \quad \cdot \quad \cdot \quad \cdot \quad \cdot \quad \cdot$$
$$\langle I, -I \mid = (0 \;\; 0 \;\; 0 \;\; \cdots \;\; 1).$$

The preceding calculations are illustrated by the following explicit results for $I = \frac{1}{2}$ and $I = 1$.

$I = \frac{1}{2}$:

$$I_x = \frac{1}{2}\begin{pmatrix} 0 & 1 \\ 1 & 0 \end{pmatrix}, \quad I_y = \frac{1}{2}\begin{pmatrix} 0 & -i \\ i & 0 \end{pmatrix}, \quad I_z = \frac{1}{2}\begin{pmatrix} 1 & 0 \\ 0 & -1 \end{pmatrix}.$$

$$\mathbf{I}^2 = \frac{3}{4}\begin{pmatrix} 1 & 0 \\ 0 & 1 \end{pmatrix}, \quad I_+ = \begin{pmatrix} 0 & 1 \\ 0 & 0 \end{pmatrix}, \quad I_- = \begin{pmatrix} 0 & 0 \\ 1 & 0 \end{pmatrix}.$$

$$\mid \tfrac{1}{2}, \tfrac{1}{2}\rangle = \begin{pmatrix} 1 \\ 0 \end{pmatrix}, \quad \mid \tfrac{1}{2}, -\tfrac{1}{2}\rangle = \begin{pmatrix} 0 \\ 1 \end{pmatrix}.$$

$I = 1$:

$$I_x = \frac{1}{\sqrt{2}}\begin{pmatrix} 0 & 1 & 0 \\ 1 & 0 & 1 \\ 0 & 1 & 0 \end{pmatrix}, \qquad I_y = \frac{1}{\sqrt{2}}\begin{pmatrix} 0 & -i & 0 \\ i & 0 & -i \\ 0 & i & 0 \end{pmatrix},$$

$$I_z = \begin{pmatrix} 1 & 0 & 0 \\ 0 & 0 & 0 \\ 0 & 0 & -1 \end{pmatrix}, \qquad \mathbf{I}^2 = 2\begin{pmatrix} 1 & 0 & 0 \\ 0 & 1 & 0 \\ 0 & 0 & 1 \end{pmatrix},$$

$$I_+ = \sqrt{2}\begin{pmatrix} 0 & 1 & 0 \\ 0 & 0 & 1 \\ 0 & 0 & 0 \end{pmatrix}, \qquad I_- = \sqrt{2}\begin{pmatrix} 0 & 0 & 0 \\ 1 & 0 & 0 \\ 0 & 1 & 0 \end{pmatrix}.$$

$$\mid 1, 1\rangle = \begin{pmatrix} 1 \\ 0 \\ 0 \end{pmatrix}, \quad \mid 1, 0\rangle = \begin{pmatrix} 0 \\ 1 \\ 0 \end{pmatrix}, \quad \mid 1, -1\rangle = \begin{pmatrix} 0 \\ 0 \\ 1 \end{pmatrix}.$$

The case $I = \frac{1}{2}$ is often described in terms of the vector operator $\boldsymbol{\sigma}$, defined by

$$\mathbf{I} = \tfrac{1}{2}\boldsymbol{\sigma}.$$

The components of $\boldsymbol{\sigma}$ are called the *Pauli spin operators*. Their matrix representatives, relative to the basis $\{\mid \frac{1}{2}, \pm \frac{1}{2}\rangle\}$, are

$$\sigma_x = \begin{pmatrix} 0 & 1 \\ 1 & 0 \end{pmatrix}, \quad \sigma_y = \begin{pmatrix} 0 & -i \\ i & 0 \end{pmatrix}, \quad \sigma_z = \begin{pmatrix} 1 & 0 \\ 0 & -1 \end{pmatrix}.$$

These operators satisfy the relations

$$[\sigma_j, \sigma_k] = 2i \sum_l e_{jkl}\sigma_l, \qquad \sigma_j^2 = 1, \qquad \sigma_j\sigma_k + \sigma_k\sigma_j = 0. \qquad (2.25)$$

Thus the square of each Pauli spin operator equals the (two-dimensional) identity operator, and any two distinct components of $\boldsymbol{\sigma}$ anticommute.

The eigenvectors of $\mathbf{I}^2$ and I_z for $I = \frac{1}{2}$ are often denoted

$$\alpha = |+\rangle = |\tfrac{1}{2}, \tfrac{1}{2}\rangle, \qquad \beta = |-\rangle = |\tfrac{1}{2}, -\tfrac{1}{2}\rangle.$$

D. The General Set of Eigenvectors

The simplest generalization of the preceding results is the removal of the nondegeneracy restriction on the eigenvalues of I_z. Suppose that besides $|I, m\rangle$, there is exactly one linearly independent eigenvector $|I, m)$ with the eigenvalue m. Applying the generating process to $|I, m)$, a second set, $\{|I, m)\}$, of $2I + 1$ eigenvectors is obtained whose members are orthogonal and therefore independent. The independence of $|I, m\rangle$ and $|I, m)$ implies that the $2(2I + 1)$ vectors, $\{|I, -I\rangle$, $|I, -I + 1\rangle, \ldots, |I, I\rangle; |I, -I), |I, -I + 1), \ldots, |I, I)\} \equiv \{|I, m\rangle; |I, m)\}$, are also independent. For if it is assumed that these vectors are dependent, then one or more of these vectors must be a linear combination of the preceding vectors. Now the vectors $\{|I, m\rangle\}$ are linearly independent, so that if the set $\{|I, m\rangle; |I, m)\}$ is a dependent set, one or more of the $|I, m)$ must be a linear combination of the preceding vectors. Suppose that $|I, m + 1)$ is one such vector. Then, since it is an eigenvector of I_z with the eigenvalue $m + 1$, it must be a linear combination of all those preceding eigenvectors with the common eigenvalue $m + 1$. But there is only one such eigenvector, namely, $|I, m + 1\rangle$; hence

$$|I, m + 1\rangle = c\,|I, m + 1).$$

Operating on this equation with I_-, and recalling that there are two independent eigenvectors with the eigenvalue m, one obtains a relation of the form

$$a\,|I, m\rangle + b\,|I, m) = 0,$$

where a and b are, in general, nonzero constants. But this equation contradicts the assumed independence of $|I, m\rangle$ and $|I, m)$, so that $|I, m + 1)$ and $|I, m + 1\rangle$ are linearly independent. By continuing this line of argument, one can show that the $2(2I + 1)$ eigenvectors $\{|I, m\rangle; |I, m)\}$ are linearly independent. Thus if any one of the eigenvectors in $\{| I, m\rangle\}$ is twofold-degenerate, the whole set is twofold-degenerate. By induction it follows that if $| I, m\rangle$ is g-fold degenerate, then every vector in the set $\{| I, m\rangle\}$ is g-fold degenerate. In this case, the set of all eigenvectors contains exactly $g(2I + 1)$ elements.

The most general set of eigenvectors of $\mathbf{I}^2$ and I_z is now easily described; it consists entirely of classes $G = A, B, \ldots$ such that all eigenvectors in a given class G have the spin quantum number I_G, and all spin variables in class G are g_G-fold degenerate. The total number of eigenvectors is, therefore,

$$\sum_G g_G(2I_G + 1).$$

The number g_G, which specifies the degree of degeneracy of the spin variables associated with a given value of the spin quantum number I_G, can also be regarded as specifying the number of independent sets, each with $2I_G + 1$ members, characterized by the spin quantum number I_G. From the latter point of view, g_G may be described as the *spin multiplicity*[7] of I_G.

The elements in the most general set of eigenvectors may be assumed to be normalized and orthogonal,[8] and will be distinguished by inserting additional indices into the corresponding ket vector; thus

$$| I_G, m_G; s_G\rangle.$$

The subscript G denotes the class, I_G the total spin quantum number for class G, and $s_G = 1, 2, \ldots, g_G$ the *spin multiplicity index*. In this notation, the orthonormality of the eigenvectors is expressed by the equation

$$\langle I_K, m_K'; s_K' | I_G, m_G; s_G\rangle = \delta_{KG}\, \delta_{m_K' m_G}\, \delta_{s_K' s_G}. \tag{2.26}$$

Thus eigenvectors belonging to different classes are orthogonal ($I_K \neq I_G$); eigenvectors in the same class ($K = G$) are orthogonal unless their I_z eigenvalues are identical ($m_G' = m_G$); eigenvectors in the same class with the same eigenvalues of I_z are orthogonal unless their spin multiplicity indices are the same ($s_G' = s_G$).

The results just obtained are associated with the theory of spin angular momentum for a system of particles. The special case of one class

[7] The number g_G is sometimes called the *statistical weight* of I_G, but *spin multiplicity* seems more appropriate.

[8] The proof of orthogonality given in Section 2.B applies only to nondegenerate eigenvectors. However, the theorem on the diagonalization of hermitian operators guarantees that the simultaneous eigenvectors of $\mathbf{I}^2$ and I_z are always orthogonal.

refers to the spin angular momentum of a single particle. The remainder of the chapter will be restricted to this case. The angular momentum of multispin systems will be considered at length in Chapter 4.

E. Spin States and Spin Space

The $2I + 1$ values of the spin variable represent, according to a fundamental postulate of quantum mechanics, the possible results of an experiment designed to measure the z component of the spin angular momentum. The maximum z component of angular momentum is equal to the spin quantum number I, and this maximum component is defined as the spin of the particle. But the equivalence of the theory of spin angular momentum for all spatial directions shows that the $2I + 1$ values of the spin variable are the possible results of an experiment designed to measure the component of spin angular momentum in any direction. Hence the spin of a particle may be invariantly defined as the maximum observable component of the spin angular momentum in any direction.

The most general spin state is, by the quantum mechanical principle of superposition, a linear combination of the $\{| I, m\rangle\}$:

$$| I, -\rangle = \sum_m C_m | I, m\rangle. \tag{2.27}$$

Such a state is not an eigenvector of I_z, and measurements of the z component of $\mathbf{I}$ in some given direction yields the eigenvalues of I_z with probabilities

$$P_m = |\langle I, m | I, -\rangle|^2 = | C_m |^2. \tag{2.28}$$

Since the several values of the spin variable are now determined according to a probability distribution, the ket on the left side of (2.27) is not labeled with a specific eigenvalue of I_z. However, since all kets in the expansion refer to spin states of a particle with spin I, $| I, -\rangle$ is still an eigenvector of $\mathbf{I}^2$.

From (2.27) it would appear that the complete specification of a general spin state requires $2I + 1$ complex numbers or $4I + 2$ real parameters, but this is not the case. Suppose that $| I, -\rangle$ is multiplied by an arbitrary complex number c giving a state

$$| I, -) = c | I, -\rangle.$$

The mean values of an operator X for the states $| I, -)$ and $| I, -\rangle$ differ only by a scale factor cc^*:

$$(I, - | X | I, -) = cc^* \langle I, - | X | I, -\rangle.$$

In particular, if c is a pure phase factor, $e^{i\varphi}$, the mean values are identical. The state $c| I, -\rangle$ is not really a new state, but merely the state $| I, -\rangle$ on a different scale. It follows that only the ratios of the C_m are physically significant. Thus the complete specification of an arbitrary spin state requires $2I$ complex numbers or $4I$ real parameters. The $2I$ complex numbers may be taken as the $2I$ ratios obtained by dividing each C_m by some arbitrarily chosen C_m, say C_I. There exists, therefore, a $4I$-fold infinity of spin states—but only $2I + 1$ *independent* spin states.[9]

Given a set of $2I + 1$ complex numbers for the specification of a spin state, two conditions may be imposed on these numbers. One of these conditions has been tacitly assumed in (2.28). For if the P_m are interpreted as probabilities, then

$$\sum_m | C_m |^2 = 1.$$

The second condition is available in the form of an arbitrary assignment of one of the phase factors of the C_m. If the C_m are expressed in polar form,

$$C_m = \rho_m e^{i\varphi_m},$$

then

$$| I, -\rangle = e^{i\varphi_I} \sum_m \rho_m e^{i(\varphi_m - \varphi_I)} | I, m\rangle,$$

with

$$\sum_m \rho_m^2 = 1.$$

Since a multiplicative phase factor does not alter mean values, φ_I may be arbitrarily chosen as a reference for the remaining φ_m.

The superposition principle for the construction of spin states leads to the conclusion that the spin states of a single particle form a vector space of dimension $2I + 1$. The states $\{| I, m\rangle\}$ are a particular orthonormal basis for this space, which will be called *spin space*. The same terminology will also be employed for the space defined by the spin

[9] This statement is frequently abused in the case $I = \frac{1}{2}$; one frequently encounters statements to the effect that there are only two states for a particle with $I = \frac{1}{2}$.

states of several particles with spin, but it will be unambiguously clear from context whether the term spin space refers to a single particle or a composite system.

If the spin states of a particle are to constitute a vector space, it is necessary that the zero vector be included among the elements of this space. Physically, one may interpret the zero vector as the "spin state" of a particle with no spin angular momentum. It is to be emphasized that this interpretation is not equivalent to the assertion that the spin quantum number is zero. The zero vector represents a particle with no spin quantum number at all. When this is the case, there is no spin variable, which means that the set of basis vectors is empty. The dimension of the spin space of a particle with no spin angular momentum is zero. By way of contrast, it will be noted that in the study of multispin systems, one often encounters situations in which the spin quantum number exists but is equal to zero. In such a case, there exists a $2I + 1 = 2 \cdot 0 + 1 =$ one-dimensional vector space spanned by a *nonzero* spin vector.

3. Transformation Theory

A. Transformation of the Spin Operators

The spin operators operate on vectors in the spin space. On the other hand, the components of the spin vector have been associated with the axes of a cartesian-coordinate system. The three-dimensional cartesian space and the spin space are conceptually and structurally distinct. The former space is the real three-dimensional vector space in which physical processes occur, whereas the latter is the complex multidimensional vector space required for the mathematical description of physical phenomena involving spin angular momentum. The two spaces are connected by the physical interpretation of quantum mechanics, and it is important to understand the relation between these spaces.

To sharpen the distinction between cartesian space and spin space, let (xyz) denote a fixed cartesian-coordinate system K which is associated with the basis $\{| I, m\rangle\}$. Physically, the association between these spaces is such that if a system is in a quantum state specified by one of the basis vectors, say $| I, m\rangle$, a measurement of the component of spin angular momentum in the z direction will yield the quantum number m with certainty.[10] This association sets up a correspondence between

[10] The preparation of a system in a given spin state and the analysis of spin states may be carried out, in principle at least, by (idealized) Stern-Gerlach experiments.

a given direction in physical space and the vectors of a particular basis in spin space. Consider now a second coordinate system K', related to K by the orthogonal transformation defined in Section 1.B. The new coordinate system can be associated with a basis $\{| I, m')\}$ in spin space by the same definition used for the original (xyz) system. But the spin operators in the coordinate system K' are, by the vector character of angular momentum, given by equations (1.5). From these equations it is clear that the basis in spin space associated with K is not the basis associated with K', since the elements of the latter basis must be eigenvectors of $I_{z'}$. Now any vector in spin space can be expressed as a linear combination of the vectors in any basis, so that the eigenvectors of $I_{z'}$ can be expressed in terms of the eigenvectors of I_z. The two bases (assumed to be orthonormal) are related by a unitary transformation U:

$$| I, m') = \sum_m U_{mm'} \, | I, m\rangle, \tag{3.1}$$

where

$$\sum_{m'} U_{mm'} U^*_{m''m'} = \delta_{mm''} . \tag{3.2}$$

When the basis of a vector space is transformed by a unitary transformation U, the operators defined on that space undergo a similarity transformation with U: $X \to X' = UXU^{-1}$. It follows that

$$\begin{aligned} I_{x'} &= UI_xU^\dagger = R_{11}I_x + R_{12}I_y + R_{13}I_z , \\ I_{y'} &= UI_yU^\dagger = R_{21}I_x + R_{22}I_y + R_{23}I_z , \\ I_{z'} &= UI_zU^\dagger = R_{31}I_x + R_{32}I_y + R_{33}I_z . \end{aligned} \tag{3.3}$$

It must be emphasized that the unitary transformation is applied to vectors and operators defined with respect to the spin space, and is represented by a square matrix whose dimension is equal to that of the spin space. Equations (3.3) show how this unitary transformation is related to the components of the orthogonal transformation R which sends K into K', and may be summarized by saying that an orthogonal transformation of the three-dimensional physical space *induces* a unitary transformation on the $(2I + 1)$-dimensional spin space.

B. The Exponential Form of the Rotation Operator

The form of the unitary transformation U is most simply derived by first considering the special case where the orthogonal transformation corresponds to a positive rotation through an angle φ about the z axis. In this case, equations (3.3) reduce to

$$\begin{aligned} UI_xU^\dagger &= I_x \cos\varphi + I_y \sin\varphi, \\ UI_yU^\dagger &= -I_x \sin\varphi + I_y \cos\varphi, \\ UI_zU^\dagger &= I_z\,. \end{aligned} \tag{3.4}$$

Multiplying the second transformation by $\pm i$ and adding the result to the first yields

$$UI_\pm U^\dagger = e^{\mp i\varphi} I_\pm\,. \tag{3.5}$$

Equation (2.9) will now be used to construct an operator function equivalent to U. The operator function is the exponential function of I_z, and may be obtained by multiplying (2.9) with $(-i\varphi)^s/s!$, and then summing the result from $s = 0$ to $s = \infty$. One finds that

$$\exp(-i\varphi I_z) I_\pm{}^r = I_\pm{}^r \exp[-i\varphi(I_z \pm r1)].$$

Since I_z and 1 commute, the last equation can be rewritten

$$e^{-i\varphi I_z} I_\pm{}^r\, e^{i\varphi I_z} = e^{\mp ir\varphi} I_\pm{}^r.$$

Putting $r = 1$ and comparing with (3.5), one concludes that[11]

$$U = e^{-i\varphi I_z}, \qquad U^\dagger = U^{-1} = e^{i\varphi I_z}. \tag{3.6}$$

Substituting these results in (3.4) one obtains the transformation formulas:

$$\begin{aligned} e^{-i\varphi I_z} I_x e^{i\varphi I_z} &= I_x \cos\varphi + I_y \sin\varphi, \\ e^{-i\varphi I_z} I_y e^{i\varphi I_z} &= -I_x \sin\varphi + I_y \cos\varphi, \\ e^{-i\varphi I_z} I_z e^{i\varphi I_z} &= I_z\,. \end{aligned} \tag{3.7}$$

The derivation of the preceding results used only (1.5) and the commutation rules. It follows, from the discussion of Section 1.D, that the operator for a rotation through an angle φ about the z' axis of the coordinate system K' is

$$U = e^{-i\varphi I_{z'}}.$$

This transformation may also be considered as the induced unitary transformation generated by a rotation through an angle φ about the unit vector $\mathbf{n} = (R_{31}, R_{32}, R_{33}) = (\cos\alpha, \cos\beta, \cos\gamma)$, so that

$$U = e^{-i\varphi \mathbf{n}\cdot\mathbf{I}}. \tag{3.8}$$

[11] The operator U is actually determined only up to a phase factor of unit modulus which has here been set equal to unity.

The transformation of I_x, I_y, and I_z when U is given by (3.8) may be obtained by operator manipulations of the sort used above, but it is very much simpler to note that the transforms of these operators can be obtained by formally applying the appropriate orthogonal matrix to the "column vector" formed from I_x, I_y, and I_z. This procedure is suggested by the form of equations (1.5), which can be written

$$\begin{pmatrix} I_{x'} \\ I_{y'} \\ I_{z'} \end{pmatrix} = \begin{pmatrix} UI_xU^\dagger \\ UI_yU^\dagger \\ UI_zU^\dagger \end{pmatrix} = \begin{pmatrix} R_{11} & R_{12} & R_{13} \\ R_{21} & R_{22} & R_{23} \\ R_{31} & R_{32} & R_{33} \end{pmatrix} \begin{pmatrix} I_x \\ I_y \\ I_z \end{pmatrix}.$$

Thus the desired transformations require only a knowledge[12] of the R_{ij}. In particular, the transformations corresponding to rotations through χ and θ about the x and y axes are

$$\begin{aligned} e^{-i\chi I_x} I_x e^{i\chi I_x} &= I_x, \\ e^{-i\chi I_x} I_y e^{i\chi I_x} &= I_y \cos\chi + I_z \sin\chi, \\ e^{-i\chi I_x} I_z e^{i\chi I_x} &= -I_y \sin\chi + I_z \cos\chi, \end{aligned} \tag{3.9}$$

$$\begin{aligned} e^{-i\theta I_y} I_x e^{i\theta I_y} &= I_x \cos\theta - I_z \sin\theta \\ e^{-i\theta I_y} I_y e^{i\theta I_y} &= I_y, \\ e^{-i\theta I_y} I_z e^{i\theta I_y} &= I_x \sin\theta + I_z \cos\theta. \end{aligned} \tag{3.10}$$

C. The Euler Decomposition of the Rotation Operator

In the theory of angular momentum, the expressions for the R_{ij} in terms of the angle of rotation and the direction cosines of the axis of rotation are seldom used. Instead, a general rotation is usually expressed in terms of the Eulerian angles φ, θ, and ψ. These angles are defined by the following rotations:

(1) A rotation about the z axis through an angle φ sending $(xyz) \rightarrow (x_1y_1z)$.

(2) A rotation about the y_1 axis through an angle θ sending $(x_1y_1z) \rightarrow (x_2y_1z')$.

(3) A rotation about the z' axis through an angle ψ sending $(x_2y_1z') \rightarrow (x'y'z')$.

---

[12] The three-dimensional rotation matrices in terms of direction cosines and Euler's angles are given in Appendix II.

The transformation from K to K' is accomplished by the product of these transformations:

$$R = R_{z'}(\psi)R_{y_1}(\theta)R_z(\varphi).$$

The unitary transformations corresponding to (1), (2), and (3) are

$$(1)\ \exp(-i\varphi I_z); \qquad (2)\ \exp(-i\theta I_{y_1}); \qquad (3)\ \exp(-i\psi I_{z'}).$$

Hence the unitary transformation corresponding to R is

$$U = \exp(-i\psi I_{z'}) \exp(-i\theta I_{y_1}) \exp(-i\varphi I_z), \tag{3.11}$$

which expresses U in terms of three rotations about axes referred to three different coordinate systems. It is possible, however, to express U in terms of rotations about the y and z axes of the coordinate system K by noting that $\exp(-i\theta I_{y_1})$ is the image of $\exp(-i\theta I_y)$ under the transformation $\exp(-i\varphi I_z)$, and that $\exp(-i\psi I_{z'})$ is the image of $\exp(-i\psi I_z)$ under $\exp(-i\theta I_{y_1})$:

$$\exp(-i\varphi I_z) \exp(-i\theta I_y) \exp(i\varphi I_z) = \exp(-i\theta I_{y_1}),$$

$$\exp(-i\theta I_{y_1}) \exp(-i\psi I_z) \exp(i\theta I_{y_1}) = \exp(-i\psi I_{z'}).$$

Substituting these equations in (3.11) one obtains

$$\begin{aligned} U(\varphi, \theta, \psi) &= e^{-i\varphi I_z} e^{-i\theta I_y} e^{-i\psi I_z}, \\ U^{-1}(\varphi, \theta, \psi) &= e^{i\psi I_z} e^{i\theta I_y} e^{i\varphi I_z}. \end{aligned} \tag{3.12}$$

When U is given in the form (3.12), one can express all operators associated with K' in terms of the operators associated with K. For example, since I_z commutes with $\exp(\pm i\psi I_z)$,

$$I_{z'} = UI_zU^{-1} = e^{-i\varphi I_z} e^{-i\theta I_y} I_z e^{i\theta I_y} e^{i\varphi I_z}.$$

The last expression can be evaluated explicitly with the help of (3.7) and (3.10). The final result is

$$I_{z'} = I_x \sin\theta \cos\varphi + I_y \sin\theta \sin\varphi + I_z \cos\theta. \tag{3.13}$$

D. The Eigenvectors of $\mathbf{I}' \cdot \mathbf{I}'$ and $I_{z'}$

The results obtained above permit the derivation of an exact operator expression for the eigenvectors of $\mathbf{I}' \cdot \mathbf{I}'$ and $I_{z'}$ in terms of those of I_z and $\mathbf{I}^2$. These eigenvectors are given by

$$| I, m') = e^{-i\varphi I_z} e^{-i\theta I_y} e^{-i\psi I_z} | I, m'\rangle. \tag{3.14}$$

That this is the formal solution follows at once from the equations

$$I_{z'} \mid I, m') = UI_zU^{-1}[U \mid I, m'\rangle] = UI_z \mid I, m'\rangle = m' \mid I, m'),$$
$$\mathbf{I}' \cdot \mathbf{I}' \mid I, m') = \mathbf{I}^2U \mid I, m'\rangle = U\mathbf{I}^2 \mid I, m'\rangle = I(I+1) \mid I, m').$$

In the last equation use has been made of the fact that $\mathbf{I}^2$ commutes with each exponential factor of U.

The explicit expression of the $\mid I, m')$ in the form (3.1) requires the matrix elements

$$U_{mm'}(\varphi, \theta, \psi) = e^{-im\varphi}\langle I, m \mid e^{-i\theta I_y} \mid I, m'\rangle e^{-im'\psi} = e^{-im\varphi}D_{mm'}(\theta)e^{-im'\psi}. \qquad (3.15)$$

A more precise notation would indicate the spin quantum number in the matrices for U and $D = \exp(-i\theta I_y)$; for example, $U^{(I)}(\varphi, \theta, \psi)$, $D^{(I)}(\theta)$. To simplify the notation, the spin quantum number will be omitted in all general formulas, but will be explicitly indicated whenever a specific value of I is contemplated.

The complete solution of the transformation problem is thus reduced to the calculation of the matrix elements of $\exp(-i\theta I_y)$ relative to the basis which diagonalizes I_z and $\mathbf{I}^2$. For a spin-$\frac{1}{2}$ particle, it is easily shown that

$$(\mathbf{n} \cdot \boldsymbol{\sigma})^{2k} = 1, \qquad (\mathbf{n} \cdot \boldsymbol{\sigma})^{2k-1} = \mathbf{n} \cdot \boldsymbol{\sigma}, \qquad (3.16)$$

for any positive integer k. Hence a direct expansion of the exponential function gives

$$\exp(i\Phi\mathbf{n} \cdot \mathbf{I}) = \exp(\tfrac{1}{2}i\Phi\mathbf{n} \cdot \boldsymbol{\sigma}) = 1 \cos\frac{\Phi}{2} + i\mathbf{n} \cdot \boldsymbol{\sigma} \sin\frac{\Phi}{2}. \qquad (3.17)$$

Putting $\mathbf{n} = \mathbf{e}_y$, $\Phi = -\theta$, and using the matrix for σ_y, one finds that

$$D^{(1/2)}(\theta) = \begin{pmatrix} \cos\frac{\theta}{2} & -\sin\frac{\theta}{2} \\ \sin\frac{\theta}{2} & \cos\frac{\theta}{2} \end{pmatrix}, \qquad (3.18)$$

and that

$$U^{(1/2)}(\varphi, \theta, \psi) = \begin{pmatrix} \exp[-\tfrac{1}{2}i(\varphi+\psi)]\cos\frac{\theta}{2} & -\exp[-\tfrac{1}{2}i(\varphi-\psi)]\sin\frac{\theta}{2} \\ \exp[\tfrac{1}{2}i(\varphi-\psi)]\sin\frac{\theta}{2} & \exp[\tfrac{1}{2}i(\varphi+\psi)]\cos\frac{\theta}{2} \end{pmatrix}. \qquad (3.19)$$

The eigenvectors $|\frac{1}{2}, \frac{1}{2})$ and $|\frac{1}{2}, -\frac{1}{2})$ are obtained by applying $U^{(1/2)}$ to the column-vector representations of $|\frac{1}{2}, \frac{1}{2}\rangle, |\frac{1}{2}, -\frac{1}{2}\rangle$:

$$|\tfrac{1}{2}, \tfrac{1}{2}) = e^{-i\psi/2} \begin{pmatrix} \exp(-\frac{1}{2}i\varphi)\cos\dfrac{\theta}{2} \\ \exp(\frac{1}{2}i\varphi)\sin\dfrac{\theta}{2} \end{pmatrix},$$

$$|\tfrac{1}{2}, -\tfrac{1}{2}) = e^{i\psi/2} \begin{pmatrix} -\exp(-\frac{1}{2}i\varphi)\sin\dfrac{\theta}{2} \\ \exp(\frac{1}{2}i\varphi)\cos\dfrac{\theta}{2} \end{pmatrix}. \tag{3.20}$$

It is easily verified that these are eigenvectors of

$$I_{z'} = \frac{1}{2}\begin{pmatrix} \cos\theta & e^{-i\varphi}\sin\theta \\ e^{i\varphi}\sin\theta & -\cos\theta \end{pmatrix}. \tag{3.21}$$

E. Determination of the Transformation Coefficients

The direct expansion of the exponential operator may be carried out for $I = 1$, but for higher values of I this procedure is not practical.[13] The matrix elements of U for arbitrary values of I may be obtained by group theoretical techniques (*4*) or by compounding $2I$ particles of spin $\frac{1}{2}$ into a single particle of spin I (*5*). In this section the transformation coefficients will be determined by a method (*6*) which makes no appeal to group theoretical arguments or to composite spin systems.

The solution to the problem requires a determination of the matrix which diagonalizes

$$I_{z'} = \tfrac{1}{2}\sin\theta\,(e^{-i\varphi}I_+ + e^{i\varphi}I_-) + \cos\theta\, I_z\,. \tag{3.22}$$

where the operators I_x and I_y have been replaced by their equivalent expressions in terms of $I_\pm$. This equation is independent of ψ, so that this angle does not appear explicitly in the expressions for the eigenvectors of $I_{z'}$. Thus the solution of the eigenvalue problem for $I_{z'}$ does not yield $U_{mm'}(\varphi, \theta, \psi)$, but rather $U_{mm'}(\varphi, \theta, 0)$, with

$$U_{mm'}(\varphi, \theta, \psi) = e^{-im'\psi}U_{mm'}(\varphi, \theta, 0), \tag{3.23}$$

[13] In principle, the desired expansion can be carried out for any given value of I with the help of the Cayley-Hamilton theorem.

as shown by (3.15). The same equation also shows that

$$U_{mm'}(\varphi, \theta, 0) = e^{-im\varphi} D_{mm'}(\theta), \tag{3.24}$$

so that the eigenvectors of $I_{z'}$ may be written

$$| I, m') = \sum_{m''} e^{-im''\varphi} D_{m''m'}(\theta) | I, m''\rangle. \tag{3.25}$$

Operating on the left of (3.25) with $I_{z'}$, and on the right with the expression for $I_{z'}$ given by (3.22), one finds, after taking the scalar product with $\langle I, m |$, that

$$(m' - m \cos \theta) D_{mm'} = \tfrac{1}{2} \sin \theta \{[(I + m)(I - m + 1)]^{1/2} D_{m-1,m'} + [(I - m)(I + m + 1)]^{1/2} D_{m+1,m'}\}. \tag{3.26}$$

In this equation, m' is fixed, while φ and θ appear only as parameters, so that (3.26) is a second-order linear difference equation for the $2I + 1$ elements in the m'th column of $D_{mm'}(\theta)$. Let

$$D_{mm'}(\theta) = N_{m'}[(I + m)!\,(I - m)!]^{1/2} F_{mm'}(\theta), \tag{3.27}$$

where $F_{mm'}$ is a function of the discrete variable m and depends parametrically on I, m', and θ. The factor $N_{m'}$ is assumed to be independent of m, but it may depend upon I, m', and θ. Substituting (3.27) in (3.26), and writing $m + 1$ for m in the resulting equation, one finds that $F_{mm'}(\theta)$ satisfies the difference equation of Laplace[14]:

$$(I + m + 2) F_{m+2,m'} + 2\{(m + 1) \cot \theta - m' \csc \theta\} F_{m+1,m'} + (I - m) F_{mm'} = 0. \tag{3.28}$$

The solution of (3.28) admits an integral representation of the form

$$F_{mm'} = \frac{1}{2\pi i} \int_c s^{m-1} v(s, m', I, \theta)\, ds. \tag{3.29}$$

Substituting (3.29) in (3.28), one finds that the integral will be a solution provided that[14]

$$v = s^{-I}(s - a_+)^{I-m'}(s - a_-)^{I+m'}, \tag{3.30}$$

where

$$a_+ = \tan \frac{\theta}{2}, \qquad a_- = -\cot \frac{\theta}{2}. \tag{3.31}$$

[14] See Appendix IV.

Furthermore, the contour of integration must be chosen so that the function

$$s^{m-I}(s - a_+)^{I-m'+1}(s - a_-)^{I+m'+1} \tag{3.32}$$

vanishes at both limits of integration if the contour is open, or returns to its initial value if the contour is closed. In either case, the integral (3.29), which now has the form

$$F_{mm'} = \frac{1}{2\pi i} \int_c \frac{(s - a_+)^{I-m'}(s - a_-)^{I+m'}}{s^{I-m+1}} \, ds \tag{3.33}$$

must not vanish identically on c.

Now the quantum numbers m and m' may be positive or negative, integral or half-integral. However, the combinations $I \pm m'$, $I - m$ are always integers greater than or equal to zero. It follows that if the contour of integration is taken as a closed path around the origin, the function (3.32) will return to its initial value and $F_{mm'}$ will be given by the residue of the integrand in (3.33) at the origin. The integrand has a pole of order $I - m + 1$ at $s = 0$, so that

$$F_{mm'} = \frac{1}{p!} \lim_{s \to 0} \frac{d^p}{ds^p} (s - a_+)^q (s - a_-)^r, \tag{3.34}$$

where

$$p = I - m, \qquad q = I - m', \qquad r = I + m'. \tag{3.35}$$

By Leibnitz's rule for the differentiation of a product, $F_{mm'}$ may be expressed in the following equivalent (real) forms:

$$F_{mm'} = \sum_k \binom{q}{p-k}\binom{r}{k}\left(-\tan\frac{\theta}{2}\right)^{q-p+k}\left(\cot\frac{\theta}{2}\right)^{r-k}, \tag{3.36}$$

$$F_{mm'} = \sum_k \binom{r}{p-k}\binom{q}{k}\left(\cot\frac{\theta}{2}\right)^{r-p+k}\left(-\tan\frac{\theta}{2}\right)^{q-k}, \tag{3.37}$$

where

$$\binom{x}{y} = \frac{x!}{(x-y)!\,y!}.$$

In either form, the summation is to be extended over those values of k for which no factorial argument is negative.

F. Generating Function and Orthonormality

The analysis of the preceding section determines the matrix D except for the orthonormality demanded by the unitary requirement. According to (3.27) this requirement demands that

$$[(I+m)!\,(I-m)!\,(I+m'')!\,(I-m'')!]^{1/2}\sum_{m'}|N_{m'}|^2F_{mm'}F_{m''m'}=\delta_{mm''}\,. \quad (3.38)$$

The orthonormality of the $D_{mm'}$ is most conveniently discussed by the method of generating functions. Equation (3.34) shows that $F_{mm'}$ is the coefficient of s^p in

$$G(s,m',I,\theta)\equiv G(s,m')=(s-a_+)^q(s-a_-)^r, \quad (3.39)$$

which is, therefore, the generating function of the $F_{mm'}$:

$$G(s,m')=\sum_m F_{mm'}s^p. \quad (3.40)$$

From the definition of $G(s, m')$, it is easily verified that

$$\sum_{m'}\binom{2I}{q}\left(\sin^2\frac{\theta}{2}\right)^r\left(\cos^2\frac{\theta}{2}\right)^q G(t,m')G(s,m')=(1+st)^{2I}. \quad (3.41)$$

Replacing $G(s, m')$ and $G(t, m')$ by their equivalent forms, as given by (3.40), and equating the coefficients of st on both sides of the resulting equation, one finds that

$$(I-m)!\,(I+m)!\sum_{m'}\frac{[\sin^2(\theta/2)]^r[\cos^2(\theta/2)]^q}{(I-m')!\,(I+m')!}F_{mm'}F_{m''m'}=\delta_{mm''}\,. \quad (3.42)$$

It follows that the functions

$$\left[\frac{(I-m)!\,(I+m)!}{(I-m')!\,(I+m')!}\right]^{1/2}\left(\sin\frac{\theta}{2}\right)^r\left(\cos\frac{\theta}{2}\right)^q F_{mm'} \quad (3.43)$$

are orthogonal with respect to summation over the points $m'=-I$, $-I+1, \ldots, +I$. Comparing (3.42) and (3.43) with (3.38), it is clear that, except for an arbitrary phase factor,

$$N_{m'}(\theta)=\frac{1}{[(I-m')!\,(I+m')!]^{1/2}}\left(\sin\frac{\theta}{2}\right)^{I+m'}\left(\cos\frac{\theta}{2}\right)^{I-m'}. \quad (3.44)$$

Combining (3.27), (3.36), and (3.44), one obtains the explicit formula

$$D_{mm'}(\theta)=[(I+m)!\,(I-m)!\,(I+m')!\,(I-m')!]^{1/2}\left(\cos\frac{\theta}{2}\right)^{2I}$$
$$\times\sum_k\frac{(-1)^{m-m'+k}[\tan(\theta/2)]^{m-m'+2k}}{(I-m-k)!\,(m-m'+k)!\,(I+m'-k)!\,k!}\,. \quad (3.45)$$

Equations (3.15) and (3.45) may now be combined to give the general solution of the transformation problem. One may check these equations by putting $I = \frac{1}{2}$, $m, m' = \pm \frac{1}{2}$, and comparing the results with the solution obtained previously.

A more symmetric expression for $D_{mm'}(\theta)$ may be derived by combining (3.27), (3.37), and (3.44) to obtain

$$D_{mm'}(\theta) = [(I+m)!\,(I-m)!\,(I+m')!\,(I-m')!]^{1/2}\left(\sin\frac{\theta}{2}\right)^{2I}$$

$$\times \sum_k \frac{(-1)^{I-m'-k}[\cot(\theta/2)]^{m+m'+2k}}{(I-m-k)!\,(m+m'-k)!\,(I-m'-k)!\,k!}. \tag{3.46}$$

The following symmetry properties of $D_{mm'}(\theta)$ are immediate consequences of (3.45) and (3.46):

$$\begin{aligned} D_{mm'}(\theta) &= (-1)^{m-m'} D_{m'm}(\theta) \\ &= D_{-m',\,-m}(\theta). \end{aligned} \tag{3.47}$$

Since $D_{mm'}(\theta)$ is real, it follows that

$$\begin{aligned} D^\dagger_{mm'}(\theta) = (-1)^{m-m'} D_{mm'}(\theta) &= (-1)^{m-m'} D_{-m',-m}(\theta) \\ &= \langle I, m' \mid \exp(i\theta I_y) \mid I, m \rangle, \end{aligned} \tag{3.48}$$

and that

$$\begin{aligned} U^\dagger_{mm'}(\varphi, \theta, \psi) &= \langle I, m' \mid e^{i\psi I_z} e^{i\theta I_y} e^{i\varphi I_z} \mid I, m \rangle \\ &= (-1)^{m-m'} e^{im\varphi} e^{im'\psi} D_{-m',-m}(\theta). \end{aligned} \tag{3.49}$$

REFERENCES

1. (a) P. A. M. Dirac, "The Principles of Quantum Mechanics," 4th ed., Chaps. II and VI. Oxford Univ. Press, London and New York, 1958. (b) L. I. Schiff, "Quantum Mechanics," 2nd ed., Chap. VI. McGraw-Hill, New York, 1955.
2. M. E. Rose, "Elementary Theory of Angular Momentum." Wiley, New York, 1957.
3. A. R. Edmonds, "Angular Momentum in Quantum Mechanics." Princeton Univ. Press, Princeton, New Jersey, 1957.
4. (a) E. P. Wigner, "Group Theory," Chap. 15. Academic Press, New York, 1959. (b) P. Güttinger. *Z. Physik* **73**, 169 (1932).
5. (a) E. Majorana, *Nuovo Cimento* **9**, 43 (1932). (b) F. Bloch and I. I. Rabi, *Rev. Mod. Phys.* **17**, 237 (1945).
6. P. L. Corio, Mobil Technical Report (unpublished).

CHAPTER 3

Quantum Mechanics of Magnetic Moments in External Fields

1. The Equation of Motion

A. The Schrödinger Equation

In the Schrödinger representation of quantum mechanics, the time development of a quantum mechanical system is governed by the equation

$$i\frac{\partial \Psi}{\partial t} = \mathscr{H}\Psi, \tag{1.1}$$

where Ψ is the state vector and $\mathscr{H}$ the hamiltonian operator.[1] Relative to a complete orthonormal basis $\{u_j\}$, the state vector may be expressed as

$$\Psi(t) = \sum_j c_j(t)u_j\,, \tag{1.2}$$

and the hamiltonian operator may be represented by an hermitian matrix:

$$\mathscr{H}_{jk} = (u_j\,, \mathscr{H}u_k); \qquad \mathscr{H}_{jk} = \mathscr{H}^*_{kj}\,. \tag{1.3}$$

The u_j are assumed to be independent of time, so that the time dependence of Ψ is entirely reflected by the time variation of the expansion coefficients c_j.

The general theory of quantum mechanics deals with infinite-dimensional vector spaces, but the quantum mechanical analysis of magnetic

[1] Here, and subsequently, $\mathscr{H}$ denotes the energy operator divided by $\hbar$.

moments interacting with magnetic fields requires only finite-dimensional vector spaces. It will be assumed, therefore, that the basis $\{u_j\}$ contains n elements (n finite). The hamiltonian operator will be represented by an $n \times n$ hermitian matrix and the state vector by an n-dimensional column vector. In specific problems, the u_j will be identified with the elements of a basis for an appropriate n-dimensional spin space. However, to ensure complete generality in the formulas to be developed in this section, the notation $\{u_j\}$ will be used to denote a basis whose elements will not be assumed to be eigenvectors of any operator unless an explicit statement is made to the contrary.

The time dependence of the expansion coefficients may be deduced from (1.1) upon noting that the effect of $\mathscr{H}$ on any element of the basis can always be expressed as a linear combination of the u_j :

$$\mathscr{H} u_j = \sum_{l=1}^{n} \mathscr{H}_{lj} u_l \qquad (j = 1, 2, ..., n), \tag{1.4}$$

with the $\mathscr{H}_{lj}$ given by (1.3). Substituting (1.2) and (1.4) in (1.1), and taking the scalar product of the resulting equation with u_k , one obtains

$$i\dot{c}_k = \sum_{j=1}^{n} \mathscr{H}_{kj} c_j \qquad (k = 1, 2, ..., n). \tag{1.5}$$

This set of equations can be written as the matrix equation

$$i \frac{\partial}{\partial t} \begin{pmatrix} c_1 \\ c_2 \\ \vdots \\ c_n \end{pmatrix} = \begin{pmatrix} \mathscr{H}_{11} & \mathscr{H}_{12} & \cdots & \mathscr{H}_{1n} \\ \mathscr{H}_{21} & \mathscr{H}_{22} & \cdots & \mathscr{H}_{2n} \\ \vdots & \vdots & & \vdots \\ \mathscr{H}_{n1} & \mathscr{H}_{n2} & \cdots & \mathscr{H}_{nn} \end{pmatrix} \begin{pmatrix} c_1 \\ c_2 \\ \vdots \\ c_n \end{pmatrix}, \tag{1.6}$$

which is the matrix representation of (1.1) relative to the basis $\{u_j\}$. It must be emphasized that (1.1) is a symbolic form for the equation of motion and is valid in all coordinate systems (bases); the matrix representation of the Schrödinger equation will be different relative to different bases.

For a given hamiltonian operator and a given basis, the time dependence of Ψ is obtained by solving n simultaneous first-order linear differential equations. The arbitrary constants of integration are given by the values of the components $c_k(t)$ at some initial moment, say $t = 0$.

The system (1.5) always has one integral which can be easily deduced by introducing the dual of Ψ:

$$\Psi^\dagger = (c_1{}^* \quad c_2{}^* \quad \cdots \quad c_n{}^*). \tag{1.7}$$

From (1.3) and (1.5) it is easy to show that $\Psi^\dagger$ satisfies

$$i\frac{\partial \Psi^\dagger}{\partial t} = -\Psi^\dagger \mathscr{H}. \tag{1.8}$$

Multiplying (1.1) from the left with $\Psi^\dagger$, and adding the result to the equation obtained by multiplying (1.8) from the right with Ψ, one finds that

$$\frac{\partial}{\partial t}(\Psi^\dagger \Psi) = 0,$$

or

$$\Psi^\dagger \Psi = \sum_j |\, c_j(t)|^2 = \text{constant}. \tag{1.9}$$

If the state vector is normalized, so that

$$\sum_j |\, c_j(t)|^2 = 1, \tag{1.10}$$

the $|\, c_j(t)|^2$ may be interpreted as the fractional contribution of u_j to the state Ψ at time t. Geometrically speaking, (1.10) requires the terminus of the state vector to lie on the surface of the unit hypersphere about the origin of an n-dimensional complex vector space.

B. Integration of the Schrödinger Equation

The integration of equations (1.5) is a relatively simple problem when $\mathscr{H}$ is not an explicit function of time. Moreover, if the basis is such that each u_k is an eigenvector of $\mathscr{H}$, the integration is trivial. For if

$$\mathscr{H} u_k = \Omega_k u_k\,, \tag{1.11}$$

then the matrix for $\mathscr{H}$ is diagonal,

$$(\mathscr{H}_{kj}) = (\Omega_k\, \delta_{kj}) = \begin{pmatrix} \Omega_1 & 0 & \cdots & 0 \\ 0 & \Omega_2 & \cdots & 0 \\ \vdots & \vdots & & \vdots \\ 0 & 0 & \cdots & \Omega_n \end{pmatrix}, \tag{1.12}$$

and equations (1.5) reduce to

$$i\dot{c}_k = \Omega_k c_k\,. \tag{1.13}$$

The condition $\partial\mathscr{H}/\partial t = 0$ requires the energy eigenvalues to be independent of time, so that equations (1.13) may be integrated to

$$c_k(t) = e^{-i\Omega_k t} c_k(0). \tag{1.14}$$

It follows that

$$\Psi(t) = \sum_k c_k(0) e^{-i\Omega_k t} u_k , \tag{1.15}$$

or, in matrix form,

$$\begin{pmatrix} c_1(t) \\ c_2(t) \\ \vdots \\ c_n(t) \end{pmatrix} = \begin{pmatrix} e^{-i\Omega_1 t} & 0 & \cdots & 0 \\ 0 & e^{-i\Omega_2 t} & \cdots & 0 \\ \vdots & \vdots & & \vdots \\ 0 & 0 & \cdots & e^{-i\Omega_n t} \end{pmatrix} \begin{pmatrix} c_1(0) \\ c_2(0) \\ \vdots \\ c_n(0) \end{pmatrix} . \tag{1.16}$$

The solution (1.15) expresses the state vector as a linear superposition of the eigenvectors of $\mathscr{H}$, but $\Psi(t)$ is not itself an eigenvector of $\mathscr{H}$ unless all $c_k(0) = 0$ except one, say $c_j(0)$. In this circumstance,

$$\Psi(t) = c_j(0) e^{-\Omega_j t} u_j .$$

Physically, this means that an energy measurement would yield the value Ω_j with certainty, since the normalization condition requires $| c_j(t)|^2 = 1$. On the other hand, if all c_k are nonzero, an energy measurement will yield the values $\Omega_1 , \Omega_2 , ...,$ with probabilities $| c_1(t)|^2$, $| c_2(t)|^2$, ... In any case, the probability distribution does not change with time, since $| c_k(t)|^2 = | c_k(0)|^2$ for all k.

The basis which reduces the matrix representative of a time-independent hamiltonian operator to diagonal form is called the *energy representation* or the *Heisenberg coordinate system.* This basis is seldom obvious in any given problem, whereas some other basis may be suggested by the specific nature of the problem. The integration of equations (1.5) can be reduced to the case just considered by transforming the initial basis into a basis for the Heisenberg coordinate system. Let $C(t)$ and $C'(t)$ denote the column-vector representations of $\Psi(t)$ relative to the initial basis and the Heisenberg coordinate system, respectively. Let T denote the matrix of the transformation relating these bases. $C(t)$ satisfies (1.6), and the substitution

$$C(t) = TC'(t) \tag{1.17}$$

transforms (1.6) to

$$i \frac{\partial C'}{\partial t} = (T^{-1} \mathscr{H} T) C'. \tag{1.18}$$

When the hamiltonian matrix is subjected to a similarity transformation with T, the latter reduces the former to diagonal form:

$$T^{\dagger} \mathscr{H} T = T^{-1} \mathscr{H} T = (\Omega_k \, \delta_{kj}), \tag{1.19}$$

and (1.5) is reduced to the form (1.13).

C. Operational Solution of the Schrödinger Equation

The square matrix in (1.16) satisfies all the requirements of a unitary matrix. In fact, this matrix is the representative of the unitary operator $e^{-i\mathscr{H}t}$ in the energy representation (cf. Appendix III). This can be verified by expanding the exponential operator and computing its matrix elements in the energy representation. The same result can also be derived by formal integration of (1.1) assuming that $\partial\mathscr{H}/\partial t = 0$. Alternatively, one can compute the successive derivatives of Ψ and expand the solution in a Taylor series. The latter computation proceeds as follows:

$$\frac{\partial\Psi}{\partial t} = -i\mathscr{H}\Psi, \qquad \frac{\partial^2\Psi}{\partial t^2} = -i\mathscr{H}\frac{\partial\Psi}{\partial t} = (-i\mathscr{H})^2\Psi, \cdots, \frac{\partial^k\Psi}{\partial t^k} = (-i\mathscr{H})^k\Psi;$$

hence

$$\Psi(t) = \sum_{k=0}^{\infty}\frac{t^k}{k!}\left(\frac{\partial^k\Psi}{\partial t^k}\right)_{t=0} = \sum_{k=0}^{\infty}\frac{(-it\mathscr{H})^k}{k!}\Psi(0),$$

or

$$\Psi(t) = e^{-i\mathscr{H}t}\Psi(0). \tag{1.20}$$

This equation provides an operational solution of the Schrödinger equation which is valid in any basis, subject to the condition $\partial\mathscr{H}/\partial t = 0$.

D. Constants of the Motion

The dynamical variables of a quantum mechanical system are represented by linear operators. If X denotes an arbitrary dynamical variable, its mean value at time t is defined (*1*) by the scalar product

$$\langle X\rangle_t = (\Psi, X\Psi) \equiv \Psi^\dagger X\Psi. \tag{1.21}$$

In matrix notation, this equation is equivalent to

$$\langle X\rangle_t = \sum_j\sum_k c_k{}^*c_jX_{kj}, \tag{1.22}$$

where $X_{kj} = (u_k, Xu_j)$. If the operator X is hermitian, it is easy to show that $\langle X\rangle_t$ is real.

To illustrate the use of this definition, consider the computation of $\langle\mathscr{H}\rangle_t$ for the state (1.15). From (1.15) and (1.21),

$$\langle\mathscr{H}\rangle_t = \Psi^\dagger\mathscr{H}\Psi = i\Psi^\dagger\frac{\partial\Psi}{\partial t} = \sum_k |c_k(0)|^2\Omega_k, \tag{1.23}$$

where the last form follows from the orthonormality of the u_k. Thus the mean value of the hamiltonian operator at time t is independent of the time and equal to the probable mean of the energy eigenvalues.

The mean value of an arbitrary operator will be a function of the time by virtue of the time dependence of the state vector Ψ. It is possible, however, to express the time dependence of an operator X in a purely operational form by defining the total time derivative of a quantum mechanical operator as

$$\Psi^\dagger \frac{dX}{dt} \Psi = \frac{d}{dt}\{\Psi^\dagger X \Psi\}. \tag{1.24}$$

Evidently this definition requires the mean value of $\dot{X}$ at time t to be equal to the time derivative of the mean value of X at time t. In particular, the mean value of X is a constant independent of the time if $\dot{X} = 0$. When this is the case, X is said to be a *constant of the motion.*

If the differentiation on the right side of (1.24) is carried out, one obtains, since Ψ and $\Psi^\dagger$ are nonzero,

$$\frac{dX}{dt} = \frac{\partial X}{\partial t} + i[\mathscr{H}, X]. \tag{1.25}$$

The first term on the right gives the contribution to the total time derivative from the explicit time dependence of X, and the second term refers to an implicit time dependence resulting from the lack of commutivity of X with $\mathscr{H}$. It follows that an operator X is a constant of the motion if it commutes with $\mathscr{H}$ and is not an explicit function of the time. In particular, if X is taken to be the hamiltonian operator, the energy of the system will be a constant of the motion, provided $\partial\mathscr{H}/\partial t = 0$. This condition was explicitly used in the derivation of (1.23).

The integration of (1.25) is easily carried out in the energy representation for an operator that is not an explicit function of the time. Upon resolving both sides of the equation into matrix elements, one obtains

$$\dot{X}_{kj}(t) = i(\Omega_k - \Omega_j)X_{kj}(t), \tag{1.26}$$

which integrates to

$$X_{kj}(t) = X_{kj}(0)e^{i(\Omega_k - \Omega_j)t}, \tag{1.27}$$

where $X_{kj}(0) = X_{kj}$. Equation (1.27) shows that the diagonal elements of X are constants, while the off-diagonal elements of X oscillate with the difference frequency $(\Omega_k - \Omega_j)$.

In the energy representation, the matrices of $e^{\pm i\mathscr{H}t}$ are diagonal with matrix elements

$$(e^{\pm i\mathscr{H}t})_{jk} = e^{\pm i\Omega_j t}\,\delta_{jk}.$$

Thus (1.27) can be written

$$X_{kj}(t) = \sum_l \sum_s (e^{i\mathscr{H}t})_{kl} X_{ls} (e^{-i\mathscr{H}t})_{sj},$$

or

$$X(t) = e^{i\mathscr{H}t} X(0) e^{-i\mathscr{H}t}. \tag{1.28}$$

This equation can be obtained without reference to any basis by a direct integration of (1.25) with $\partial X/\partial t = 0$. For this purpose, rewrite (1.25) in the form

$$\dot{X} - i\mathscr{H}X = e^{i\mathscr{H}t} \frac{d}{dt}(e^{-i\mathscr{H}t}X) = -iX\mathscr{H},$$

and multiply from the left with $e^{-i\mathscr{H}t}$ to obtain

$$\frac{dS}{dt} = -iS\mathscr{H},$$

where $S(t) = e^{-i\mathscr{H}t}X(t)$. This equation integrates to $S(t) = S(0)e^{-i\mathscr{H}t} = X(0)e^{-i\mathscr{H}t}$. The definition of S now yields (1.28).

2. Magnetic Moments in Stationary Fields

A. The Hamiltonian Operator

The hamiltonian operator for a nuclear magnetic moment in a magnetic field $\mathbf{H}$ is obtained by equating $\hbar\mathscr{H}$ to the classical energy $-\boldsymbol{\mu} \cdot \mathbf{H}$ and replacing $\boldsymbol{\mu}$ with the quantum mechanical vector operator $\gamma\hbar\mathbf{I}$. Thus $\hbar\mathscr{H} = -\gamma\hbar\mathbf{H} \cdot \mathbf{I}$, or

$$\mathscr{H} = -\gamma\mathbf{H} \cdot \mathbf{I}. \tag{2.1}$$

It will be assumed that $\mathbf{H}$ does not depend upon time, so that $\partial\mathscr{H}/\partial t = 0$. No restriction will be imposed upon the direction of $\mathbf{H}$, but it will be convenient to express the magnetic field in terms of its polar angles:

$$\mathbf{H} = H\mathbf{n} = H(\sin\theta\cos\varphi, \sin\theta\sin\varphi, \cos\theta), \tag{2.2}$$

where $\mathbf{n}$ is a unit vector in the direction of $\mathbf{H}$, and $H = |\mathbf{H}|$. In this notation, the hamiltonian operator becomes

$$\mathscr{H} = -\gamma H\mathbf{n} \cdot \mathbf{I} = -\gamma H(I_x \sin\theta\cos\varphi + I_y \sin\theta\sin\varphi + I_z\cos\theta). \tag{2.3}$$

B. The Spin-I Particle

Since $\partial\mathcal{H}/\partial t = 0$, the hamiltonian operator is a constant of the motion. Moreover, $\mathbf{I}^2$ commutes with each term in $\mathcal{H}$, so that the square of the spin angular momentum is also a constant of the motion. Thus the determination of the eigenvalues and eigenvectors of $\mathcal{H}$ is equivalent to the determination of the simultaneous eigenvectors of $\mathbf{I}^2$ and $\mathbf{n}\cdot\mathbf{I}$. The eigenvalues of $\mathbf{n}\cdot\mathbf{I}$ are $m = -I, -I+1, ..., I$, and the corresponding eigenvectors are

$$| I, m) = \sum_{m'} e^{-im'\varphi} D_{m'm}(\theta) | I, m'\rangle, \tag{2.4}$$

where the expansion on the right is in terms of the basis which diagonalizes I_z, and where the $D_{m'm}(\theta)$ are given by (3.45) or (3.46) of Chapter 2. The eigenvalues of $\mathcal{H}$ are

$$\Omega_m = -\gamma H m, \tag{2.5}$$

so that

$$\Psi(t) = \sum_m c_m(0) e^{im\gamma Ht} | I, m). \tag{2.6}$$

Equations (2.4) and (2.6) can now be used to compute the mean value of any spin operator. However, the expressions for $D_{m'm}(\theta)$ for arbitrary I are so complicated that they are not suitable for use in an illustrative example, whereas $I = \frac{1}{2}$ contains all the essential features of the general problem, and provides a convenient illustration of the results established in Section 1.

C. The Spin-$\frac{1}{2}$ Particle

The hamiltonian matrix, relative to the basis which diagonalizes I_z, may be obtained at once by writing $\mathbf{I} = \frac{1}{2}\boldsymbol{\sigma}$, and inserting the Pauli spin matrices in (2.3):

$$\mathcal{H} = -\frac{\gamma H}{2}\begin{pmatrix} \cos\theta & e^{-i\varphi}\sin\theta \\ e^{i\varphi}\sin\theta & -\cos\theta \end{pmatrix}. \tag{2.7}$$

The eigenvalues of $\mathcal{H}$ are given by the roots of $\det(\mathcal{H} - \lambda I) = 0$, namely $\lambda = \pm\frac{1}{2}\gamma H = \Omega_\pm$, in agreement with (2.5).

The eigenvectors of $\mathcal{H}$ satisfy the matrix equation

$$-\frac{\gamma H}{2}\begin{pmatrix} \cos\theta & e^{-i\varphi}\sin\theta \\ e^{i\varphi}\sin\theta & -\cos\theta \end{pmatrix}\begin{pmatrix} c_1 \\ c_2 \end{pmatrix} = \Omega_\pm \begin{pmatrix} c_1 \\ c_2 \end{pmatrix},$$

or, in expanded form,

$$\begin{aligned} -\frac{\gamma H}{2}(c_1 \cos\theta + c_2 e^{-i\varphi}\sin\theta) &= \Omega_\pm c_1 , \\ -\frac{\gamma H}{2}(c_1 e^{i\varphi}\sin\theta - c_2\cos\theta) &= \Omega_\pm c_2 . \end{aligned} \tag{2.8}$$

These equations are not independent, but either one can be used to determine the ratio c_2/c_1. The values of c_1 and c_2 are then determined, except for an arbitrary phase factor, by the normalization condition

$$|c_1|^2 + |c_2|^2 = 1.$$

For $\Omega_- = -\frac{1}{2}\gamma H$, the first of equations (2.8) gives

$$\frac{c_2}{c_1} = \frac{1-\cos\theta}{\sin\theta}e^{i\varphi} = e^{i\varphi}\tan\frac{\theta}{2}.$$

Combining this result with the normalization condition, one obtains

$$|c_1|^2 = \frac{1}{1+\tan^2(\theta/2)} = \cos^2\frac{\theta}{2},$$

so that

$$\left.\begin{aligned} c_1 &= e^{i\eta}\cos\frac{\theta}{2} \\ c_2 &= e^{i(\varphi+\eta)}\sin\frac{\theta}{2} \end{aligned}\right\} \qquad (\Omega_- = -\tfrac{1}{2}\gamma H),$$

where η is an arbitrary (real) phase angle.

An analogous calculation with Ω_+ yields

$$\left.\begin{aligned} c_1 &= e^{i\eta'}\sin\frac{\theta}{2} \\ c_2 &= -e^{i(\varphi+\eta')}\cos\frac{\theta}{2} \end{aligned}\right\} \qquad (\Omega_+ = \tfrac{1}{2}\gamma H).$$

The phases, for reasons to be indicated subsequently, are chosen as follows:

$$\eta = \frac{-\varphi}{2}, \qquad \eta' = \frac{-\varphi}{2} + \pi.$$

The eigenvectors of $\mathscr{H}$ can now be expressed as:

$$|+) = \exp(-\tfrac{1}{2}i\varphi)\cos\frac{\theta}{2}|+\rangle + \exp(\tfrac{1}{2}i\varphi)\sin\frac{\theta}{2}|-\rangle = \begin{pmatrix} \exp(-\tfrac{1}{2}i\varphi)\cos\frac{\theta}{2} \\ \exp(\tfrac{1}{2}i\varphi)\sin\frac{\theta}{2} \end{pmatrix}, \tag{2.9}$$

$$|-) = -\exp(-\tfrac{1}{2}i\varphi)\sin\frac{\theta}{2}|+\rangle + \exp(\tfrac{1}{2}i\varphi)\cos\frac{\theta}{2}|-\rangle = \begin{pmatrix} -\exp(-\tfrac{1}{2}i\varphi)\sin\frac{\theta}{2} \\ \exp(\tfrac{1}{2}i\varphi)\cos\frac{\theta}{2} \end{pmatrix}, \tag{2.10}$$

where $|\pm) \equiv |\tfrac{1}{2}, \pm\tfrac{1}{2})$ and $|\pm\rangle \equiv |\tfrac{1}{2}, \pm\tfrac{1}{2}\rangle$. [Note that $\mathscr{H}|\pm) = \Omega_{\mp}|\pm)$.] Compounding these eigenvectors into a 2×2 matrix, one obtains the unitary matrix which diagonalizes $\mathscr{H}$:

$$T = U^{(1/2)}(\varphi, \theta, 0) = \begin{pmatrix} \exp(-\tfrac{1}{2}i\varphi)\cos\frac{\theta}{2} & -\exp(-\tfrac{1}{2}i\varphi)\sin\frac{\theta}{2} \\ \exp(\tfrac{1}{2}i\varphi)\sin\frac{\theta}{2} & \exp(\tfrac{1}{2}i\varphi)\cos\frac{\theta}{2} \end{pmatrix}. \tag{2.11}$$

Equations (2.9) through (2.11) should be compared with the analysis in Section 3.D of Chapter 2, where identical results were obtained by expanding the operator $e^{i\theta\mathbf{n}\cdot\boldsymbol{\sigma}/2}$. The choice of the phase angles η and η' was in fact motivated by the desire to secure agreement with the previous calculation. One could also obtain $|\pm)$ and T from the general transformation formula derived in Chapter 2.

The state vector and its dual are given by

$$\begin{aligned} \Psi(t) &= c_+(0)e^{-i\Omega_- t}\,|+) + c_-(0)e^{-i\Omega_+ t}\,|-), \\ \Psi^\dagger(t) &= c_+{}^*(0)e^{i\Omega_- t}(+| + c_-{}^*(0)e^{i\Omega_+ t}(-|. \end{aligned} \tag{2.12}$$

From these equations, it follows that the mean value of a generic spin operator X is

$$\begin{aligned} \Psi^\dagger X \Psi = {} & |c_+(0)|^2 (+|X|+) + |c_-(0)|^2(-|X|-) \\ & + c_+{}^*(0)c_-(0)e^{-i\gamma Ht}(+|X|-) + c_+(0)c_-{}^*(0)e^{i\gamma Ht}(-|X|+). \end{aligned} \tag{2.13}$$

If the system is initially in the state $| +)$, $c_-(0) = 0$, and the mean value of I_z is

$$(+ \mid I_z \mid +) = \frac{1}{2}\cos^2\frac{\theta}{2} - \frac{1}{2}\sin^2\frac{\theta}{2}$$
$$= \frac{1}{2}\cos\theta.$$

The first line may be interpreted as stating that if one measures I_z for a system in the state $| +)$, one observes the values $m = +\frac{1}{2}$ and $m = -\frac{1}{2}$ with the probabilities $\cos^2(\theta/2)$ and $\sin^2(\theta/2)$, respectively; the second line shows that the mean value of I_z may be obtained by projecting the eigenvalue $\frac{1}{2}$ along the z direction. Similar remarks apply if the system is initially in the state $| -)$, so that $c_+(0) = 0$. The mean value of I_z is then

$$(- \mid I_z \mid -) = \frac{1}{2}\sin^2\frac{\theta}{2} - \frac{1}{2}\cos^2\frac{\theta}{2} = -\frac{1}{2}\cos\theta.$$

The results should be compared with the elementary discussion of the Stern-Gerlach experiment in Chapter 1.

When $c_+(0)$ and $c_-(0)$ are both nonzero, the mean values of I_+, I_-, and I_z are

$$\langle I_+\rangle_t = e^{i\varphi}\Big\{\tfrac{1}{2}(| c_+(0)|^2 - | c_-(0)|^2)\sin\theta$$
$$+ c_+{}^*(0)c_-(0)e^{-i\gamma Ht}\cos^2\frac{\theta}{2} - c_+(0)c_-{}^*(0)e^{i\gamma Ht}\sin^2\frac{\theta}{2}\Big\},$$
$$\langle I_-\rangle_t = e^{-i\varphi}\Big\{\tfrac{1}{2}(| c_+(0)|^2 - | c_-(0)|^2)\sin\theta$$
$$-c_+{}^*(0)c_-(0)e^{-i\gamma Ht}\sin^2\frac{\theta}{2} + c_+(0)c_-{}^*(0)e^{i\gamma Ht}\cos^2\frac{\theta}{2}\Big\},$$
$$\langle I_z\rangle_t = \tfrac{1}{2}\{(| c_+(0)|^2 - | c_-(0)|^2)\cos\theta$$
$$-(c_+{}^*(0)c_-(0)e^{-i\gamma Ht} + c_+(0)c_-{}^*(0)e^{i\gamma Ht})\sin\theta\}.$$

These equations show that $\langle I_x\rangle_t$, $\langle I_y\rangle_t$, and $\langle I_z\rangle_t$ are sinusoidal functions of time, and that the evaluation of the mean value of a component of the spin in any direction other than that of **H** requires a knowledge of $| c_+(0)|^2$, $| c_-(0)|^2$, and $c_+(0)c_-{}^*(0)$.

When the applied field is along the z axis ($\theta = 0$), I_z is a constant of the motion, and the preceding equations yield, taking $\varphi = 0$,

$$\langle I_x\rangle_t = \tfrac{1}{2}\{c_+{}^*(0)c_-(0)e^{-i\gamma Ht} + c_+(0)c_-{}^*(0)e^{i\gamma Ht}\},$$
$$\langle I_y\rangle_t = \frac{i}{2}\Big\{-c_+{}^*(0)c_-(0)e^{-i\gamma Ht} + c_+(0)c_-{}^*(0)e^{i\gamma Ht}\Big\}, \tag{2.14}$$
$$\langle I_z\rangle_t = \tfrac{1}{2}\{| c_+(0) |^2 - | c_-(0) |^2\}.$$

These equations show that the mean values of I_x and I_y generate a rotating component of angular momentum in the xy plane. Since $\boldsymbol{\mu} = \gamma\hbar\mathbf{I}$, similar remarks hold for the mean values of the components of $\boldsymbol{\mu}$. This appears to contradict the calculation of Section 4.A in Chapter 1, where the only nonvanishing component of the nuclear magnetization was $M_z = M_0$. One must recognize, however, that the mean values computed above refer to a single particle, whereas the calculation of Chapter 1 was based on statistical considerations. The components of the macroscopic magnetization are actually the statistical averages of the components of $\langle\boldsymbol{\mu}\rangle_t$ taken over the magnetic moments in a sufficiently large volume. If it is assumed that

$$\frac{1}{N_0}\sum_{j=1}^{N_0} c_{+j}(0)c_{-j}^{*}(0) = 0,$$

where N_0 is the number of nuclear magnetic moments per unit volume, then the statistical averages of $\langle I_x\rangle_t$ and $\langle I_y\rangle_t$ are zero. This could come about, for example, if the relative phases $\eta_{+j} - \eta_{-j}$ of the products $c_{+j}c_{-j}^{*} = r_{+j}r_{-j}\exp[i(\eta_{+j} - \eta_{-j})]$ are distributed at random (*2, 3*).

D. The Heisenberg Equations of Motion

The results derived in the preceding section may be regarded from a different point of view by using (1.25) to obtain the equations of motion for the components of the magnetic moment operator $\boldsymbol{\mu} = \gamma\hbar\mathbf{I}$. Upon evaluating the required commutators, one finds that

$$\begin{aligned}\dot{\mu}_x &= \gamma(H_z\mu_y - H_y\mu_z),\\ \dot{\mu}_y &= \gamma(H_x\mu_z - H_z\mu_x),\\ \dot{\mu}_z &= \gamma(H_y\mu_x - H_x\mu_y).\end{aligned} \tag{2.15}$$

These operator equations, which are valid for arbitrary fields, are called the *Heisenberg equations of motion* for the components of $\boldsymbol{\mu}$. An examination of the right-hand members of (2.15) shows that the Heisenberg equations can be condensed to

$$\frac{d\boldsymbol{\mu}}{dt} = -\gamma\mathbf{H}\times\boldsymbol{\mu}. \tag{2.16}$$

Since the components of $\mathbf{H}$ are scalar quantities, there is no problem with commutivity in the cross product $\mathbf{H}\times\boldsymbol{\mu}$.

The equation of motion satisfied by the expectation value of $\boldsymbol{\mu}$ follows at once from (1.24) and (2.16):

$$\frac{d}{dt}\langle\boldsymbol{\mu}\rangle_t = -\gamma\mathbf{H} \times \langle\boldsymbol{\mu}\rangle_t . \tag{2.17}$$

Thus the expectation value of the quantum mechanical operator for $\boldsymbol{\mu}$ satisfies the same equation of motion as a classical magnetic moment in a magnetic field $\mathbf{H}$. In particular, if $\mathbf{H}$ is independent of time, $\langle\boldsymbol{\mu}\rangle_t$ precesses about $\mathbf{H}$ with angular velocity $-\gamma\mathbf{H}$.

Equation (2.17) provides the quantum mechanical justification for the classical description of the resonance phenomenon presented in Chapter 1. Indeed, all the classical calculations carried out in Chapter 1 can be transcribed into the language of quantum mechanics by interpreting the classical variables as quantum mechanical expectation values.

The relation between the classical and quantum mechanical descriptions of the motion of a magnetic moment in an applied field admits an interesting geometric interpretation in the case of a particle with spin $\frac{1}{2}$. This interpretation is based on a simple geometric representation of the quantization of a particle with spin $\frac{1}{2}$.

The most general state of a spin-$\frac{1}{2}$ particle is of the form

$$\Psi = c_1 \mid \tfrac{1}{2}, \tfrac{1}{2}\rangle + c_2 \mid \tfrac{1}{2}, -\tfrac{1}{2}\rangle,$$

and is essentially determined by the ratio $\zeta = c_2/c_1$. When ζ is given, c_1 and c_2 are determined, except for an arbitrary phase factor, by the normalization condition.

Now the ratio c_2/c_1 can be represented by a point $\zeta = \xi + i\eta$ in the complex plane, and the latter can be stereographically projected onto the unit sphere about the origin, as described in Chapter 1. This projection sets up a one-to-one correspondence between the spin states of a spin-$\frac{1}{2}$ particle (points in the complex ζ plane) and the points on the unit sphere about the origin of a cartesian-coordinate system.

Let the point $P(\varphi, \theta)$ on the unit sphere be the image of ζ, and let ζ denote the spin state corresponding to $m = +\frac{1}{2}$ for the direction (φ, θ). From (2.14) of Chapter 1, it follows that

$$P(\varphi, \theta) \leftrightarrow \zeta = \frac{c_2}{c_1} = e^{i\varphi} \tan\frac{\theta}{2}, \qquad m = +\tfrac{1}{2}.$$

The point on the unit sphere corresponding to $m = -\frac{1}{2}$ is the point diametrically opposite to $P(\varphi, \theta)$:

$$P(\varphi + \pi, \pi - \theta) \leftrightarrow \zeta' = -\frac{1}{\zeta^*} = \frac{c_2}{c_1} = -e^{i\varphi} \cot\frac{\theta}{2}, \qquad m = -\tfrac{1}{2}.$$

These conclusions are verified by the ratios of the components of the eigenvectors $| \pm)$ given in (2.9) and (2.10).

The stereographic projection thus provides a geometric representation of the quantization of a spin-$\frac{1}{2}$ particle. The axis of quantization is represented by a line L passing through the center of the unit sphere S. The direction of L is defined by the polar angles φ and θ, and the spin states corresponding to $m = \pm \frac{1}{2}$ are represented by the two diametrically opposite points determined by the intersection of L with S. The generalization of this representation leads to the description of a particle with spin I as a composite system of $2I$ spin-$\frac{1}{2}$ particles (*4*).

Consider now the classical and quantum mechanical equations of motion:

$$i \frac{\partial \Psi}{\partial t} = -\frac{1}{2}\gamma \boldsymbol{\sigma} \cdot \mathbf{H}\Psi, \qquad \frac{d\boldsymbol{\mu}}{dt} = -\gamma \mathbf{H} \times \boldsymbol{\mu}.$$

The Schrödinger equation is equivalent to the matrix equation

$$\frac{\partial}{\partial t}\begin{pmatrix} c_1 \\ c_2 \end{pmatrix} = \frac{i\gamma}{2}\begin{pmatrix} H_z & H_- \\ H_+ & -H_z \end{pmatrix}\begin{pmatrix} c_1 \\ c_2 \end{pmatrix},$$

where $H_{\pm} = H_x \pm iH_y$, and thus to the system of linear differential equations

$$\dot{c}_1 = \frac{i\gamma}{2}(H_z c_1 + H_- c_2), \qquad \dot{c}_2 = \frac{i\gamma}{2}(H_+ c_1 - H_z c_2).$$

Upon introducing the parameter $\zeta = c_2/c_1$, one finds that ζ is a solution of

$$\dot{\zeta} = \frac{i\gamma}{2}(H_+ - 2H_z\zeta - H_-\zeta^2),$$

which is identical with (2.11) of Chapter 1. Hence the solutions of the classical and quantum mechanical equations of motion may be obtained from the solution of the Riccati equation common to both problems.

Geometrically speaking, the point ζ traces out a path in the complex plane whose time rate of change is governed by the equation $\dot{\Psi} = \frac{1}{2}i\gamma\mathbf{H} \cdot \boldsymbol{\sigma}\Psi$. Except for normalization, this path describes the change of c_2/c_1 with time. Each point of the path in the complex plane can be stereographically projected onto the unit sphere S; the projected path on S is identical to that generated by the motion of $\boldsymbol{\mu}/\mu$, which satisfies the equation of motion $\dot{\boldsymbol{\mu}}/\mu = -\gamma\mathbf{H} \times (\boldsymbol{\mu}/\mu)$.

3. Magnetic Moments in Rotating Fields

A. Transformation of the Hamiltonian Operator

When the magnetic field is an explicit function of the time, $\partial\mathscr{H}/\partial t \neq 0$, and the Schrödinger equation for a particle with spin I is equivalent to a set of $2I + 1$ simultaneous first order linear differential equations with variable coefficients. The integration of these equations is often a difficult problem, but the special case of a rotating magnetic field can be treated by a procedure that is analogous to the rotating coordinate transformation used in the corresponding classical problem.

For $\gamma > 0$, the rotating field is given by

$$H_x = H_1 \cos \omega t, \qquad H_y = -H_1 \sin \omega t, \qquad H_z = H_0 ,$$

and the hamiltonian operator by

$$\mathscr{H}(t) = -\gamma \mathbf{H} \cdot \mathbf{I} = -\{\omega_1(I_x \cos \omega t - I_y \sin \omega t) + \omega_0 I_z\}, \tag{3.1}$$

where $\omega_1 = \gamma H_1$ and $\omega_0 = \gamma H_0$.

The analogous classical problem was shown to be equivalent to that of a magnetic moment in a stationary field when observed from a coordinate system rotating about the z axis with frequency ω and a sense corresponding to the sign of $-\gamma$. It follows, from the transformation theory of Chapter 2, that the time dependence of the hamiltonian operator can be removed by introducing the transformation:

$$\Psi(t) = e^{i\omega t I_z} \Phi(t). \tag{3.2}$$

Differentiating and substituting the resulting expression for Ψ in (1.1) yields

$$i \frac{\partial \Phi}{\partial t} = \{e^{-i\omega t I_z} \mathscr{H}(t)\, e^{i\omega t I_z} + \omega I_z\}\Phi. \tag{3.3}$$

The indicated transformation of $\mathscr{H}(t)$ is easily carried out with the help of equations (3.7) of Chapter 2. The final result is

$$i \frac{\partial \Phi}{\partial t} = -\{\omega_1 I_x + \Delta I_z\}\Phi = -\Omega \mathbf{n} \cdot \mathbf{I}\Phi, \tag{3.4}$$

where the notational abbreviations are identical with those introduced in Chapter 1 [equations (3.8)].

The effective hamiltonian operator in (3.4) is $-\Omega \mathbf{n} \cdot \mathbf{I}$, and, since this operator does not depend explicitly upon the time, the operational solution of (3.4) is

$$\Phi(t) = e^{i\Omega t\mathbf{n}\cdot\mathbf{I}}\Phi(0). \tag{3.5}$$

From (3.2), $\Phi(0) = \Psi(0)$, and

$$\Psi(t) = e^{i\omega t I_z} e^{i\Omega t\mathbf{n}\cdot\mathbf{I}}\Psi(0). \tag{3.6}$$

B. The Transition Probability

The state vector can be expressed as a linear combination of the eigenvectors of I_z :

$$\Psi(t) = \sum_m C_m(t) | I, m\rangle. \tag{3.7}$$

The probability amplitudes $C_m(t)$ are no longer complex exponential functions of the time, so that the $| C_m(t)|^2$ change with time. These changes can be given a more precise physical interpretation by assuming that the rf-field amplitude is zero for $t < 0$, but equal to H_1 for $t \geqslant 0$. It will be assumed that when $t = 0$ the state vector is defined by $| C_m(0)|^2 = 1$, $C_{m'}(0) = 0$, for $m' \neq m$. At some time $t > 0$, the state vector is given by (3.7), and the absolute square of $C_{m'}(t)$ represents the probability that the spin is in the state $| I, m'\rangle$ at time t. This probability[2] will be denoted $P_{m\to m'}(t)$:

$$P_{m\to m'}(t) = | C_{m'}(t)|^2 = |\langle I, m' | \Psi(t)\rangle|^2. \tag{3.8}$$

From (3.6), (3.8), and the initial condition $\Psi(0) = C_m(0)| I, m\rangle$, it follows that

$$P_{m\to m'}(t) = |\langle I, m' | e^{i\omega t I_z} e^{i\Omega t\mathbf{I}\cdot\mathbf{n}} | I, m\rangle|^2.$$

Now $\langle I, m'| e^{i\omega t I_z} = e^{-im'\omega t}\langle I, m' |$, so that

$$P_{m\to m'}(t) = |\langle I, m' | e^{i\Omega t\mathbf{n}\cdot\mathbf{I}} | I, m\rangle|^2. \tag{3.9}$$

C. The Spin-$\frac{1}{2}$ Particle

Equation (3.9) can be applied at once to the case $I = \frac{1}{2}$ (*4, 5*), for the exponential operator expands to

$$e^{i\Omega t\mathbf{n}\cdot\mathbf{I}} = 1 \cos\frac{\Omega t}{2} + i\mathbf{n}\cdot\boldsymbol{\sigma} \sin\frac{\Omega t}{2},$$

[2] The probability defined by (3.8) is a *conditional probability*; $P_{m\to m'}(t)$ gives the probability that the spin is in the state $| I, m'\rangle$ at time t on the condition that it was in the state $| I, m\rangle$ at $t = 0$.

so that

$$\langle \tfrac{1}{2}, -\tfrac{1}{2} \mid e^{i\Omega t\mathbf{n}\cdot\mathbf{I}} \mid \tfrac{1}{2}, \tfrac{1}{2} \rangle = i \sin \frac{\Omega t}{2} \langle \tfrac{1}{2}, -\tfrac{1}{2} \mid \mathbf{n} \cdot \boldsymbol{\sigma} \mid \tfrac{1}{2}, \tfrac{1}{2} \rangle$$

$$= \frac{i\omega_1}{\Omega} \sin \frac{\Omega t}{2} .$$

Thus

$$P_{1/2\to-1/2}(t) = \sin^2\theta \sin^2 \frac{\Omega t}{2} = \frac{\omega_1{}^2}{(\omega_0 - \omega)^2 + \omega_1{}^2} \sin^2 \tfrac{1}{2}\Omega t. \qquad (3.10)$$

Equation (3.10) shows that $P_{1/2\to-1/2}(t)$ is an oscillatory function of the time with amplitude $\sin^2\theta = \omega_1{}^2/\Omega^2$ and angular oscillation frequency $\frac{1}{2}\Omega$. The maximum amplitude of $P_{1/2\to-1/2}(t)$ is unity, which is achieved at resonance ($\Delta = 0$) or when $|\omega_1| \gg |\Delta|$; in either case, the oscillation frequency is $\omega_1/2$. These properties are shown in Fig. 3.1, where $P_{1/2\to-1/2}(t)$ is plotted for several values of the parameter $x = \omega_1/\Omega$.

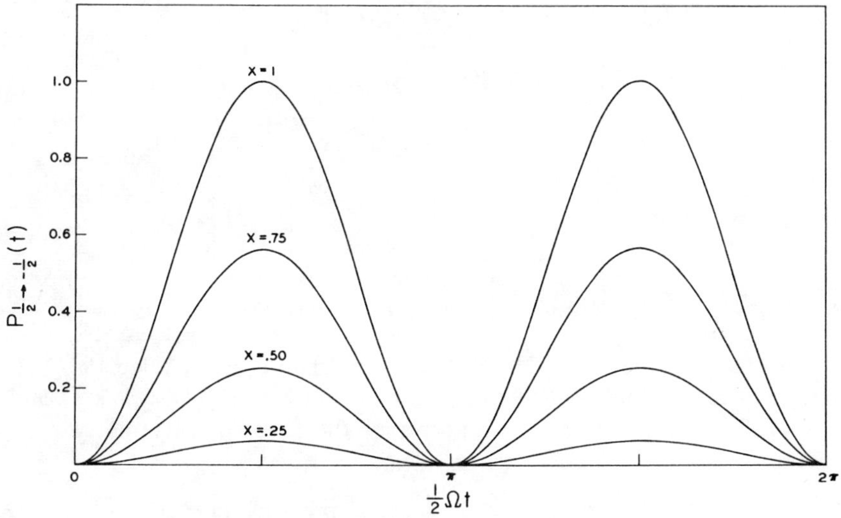

FIG. 3.1. The transition probability $P_{1/2\to-1/2}(t)$ for several values of the parameter $x = \omega_1/\Omega$.

D. Majorana's Formula for Spin I

The determination of $P_{m\to m'}(t)$ for a particle with spin I can be carried out by using the Euler decomposition

$$e^{i\Omega t\mathbf{n}\cdot\mathbf{I}} = e^{i\psi I_z} e^{i\chi I_y} e^{i\varphi I_z}, \qquad (3.11)$$

where Ωt and $\mathbf{n}$ are given parameters and the Euler angles ψ, χ, φ are to be determined. These quantities[3] satisfy the following relations:

$$\cos\alpha \sin\tfrac{1}{2}\Omega t = \sin\tfrac{1}{2}\chi \sin\tfrac{1}{2}(\psi - \varphi),$$
$$\cos\beta \sin\tfrac{1}{2}\Omega t = \sin\tfrac{1}{2}\chi \cos\tfrac{1}{2}(\psi - \varphi).$$
$$\cos\gamma \sin\tfrac{1}{2}\Omega t = \cos\tfrac{1}{2}\chi \sin\tfrac{1}{2}(\psi + \varphi),$$
$$\cos\tfrac{1}{2}\Omega t = \cos\tfrac{1}{2}\chi \cos\tfrac{1}{2}(\psi + \varphi),$$
$$\mathbf{n} = (\cos\alpha, \cos\beta, \cos\gamma) = (\omega_1/\Omega, 0, \Delta/\Omega).$$

Since $P_{m\to m'}(t)$ is the absolute square of a matrix element taken with respect to the eigenvectors of I_z, the decomposition (3.11) gives

$$P_{m\to m'}(t) = |\langle I, m' \mid e^{i\chi I_y} \mid I, m\rangle|^2 = D^2_{mm'}(\chi), \tag{3.12}$$

where the last equality follows from (3.48) of Chapter 2. Thus $P_{m\to m'}(t)$ is determined when χ is expressed in terms of known parameters. From $\cos\beta = 0$, it follows that $\psi - \varphi = \pi$, so that

$$\sin\tfrac{1}{2}\chi = \frac{\omega_1}{\Omega} \sin\tfrac{1}{2}\Omega t = \sin\theta \sin\tfrac{1}{2}\Omega t. \tag{3.13}$$

Therefore,

$$P_{m\to m'}(t) = (I+m)!\,(I-m)!\,(I+m')!\,(I-m')!\left(\cos\frac{\chi}{2}\right)^{4I} \times \left\{ \sum_k \frac{(-1)^k[\tan(\chi/2)]^{m'-m+2k}}{(I-m'-k)!\,(m'-m+k)!\,(I+m-k)!\,k!} \right\}^2. \tag{3.14}$$

Equation (3.14), which, by virtue of (3.10) and (3.13), relates $P_{m\to m'}(t)$ for arbitrary values of I to $P_{1/2\to -1/2}(t)$, is known as *Majorana's formula* (*3–4*). The Majorana formula possesses the following symmetry properties:

$$P_{m\to m'}(t) = P_{m'\to m}(t) = P_{-m\to -m'}(t), \tag{3.15}$$

which are direct consequences of the symmetry properties of the $D_{mm'}(\theta)$ established in Chapter 2.

The Majorana formula shows that if a spin is initially in the state $|\, I, m\rangle$, transitions to all other states $|\, I, m'\rangle$ are possible. To illustrate this point and the application of (3.14) in a specific instance, suppose that the spin is in the state $|\, I, -I\rangle$ at $t = 0$. For the assumed value

[3] See Appendix II.

of m, the only value of k allowed by the condition that no factorial argument be negative is $k = 0$, for all values of m'. Thus the Majorana formula reduces to

$$P_{-I\to m'}(t) = \binom{2I}{I - m'}\left(\cos^2\frac{\chi}{2}\right)^{2I}\left(\tan^2\frac{\chi}{2}\right)^{I+m'}. \tag{3.16}$$

This equation reduces to (3.10) for $I = m' = \frac{1}{2}$. It is easily verified that the $P_{-I\to m'}(t)$ satisfy the normalization condition

$$\sum_{m'} P_{-I\to m'}(t) = 1.$$

For upon changing the summation index from m' to $r = I - m' = 0, 1, ..., 2I$, and using the binomial expansion for $(1 + s)^{2I}$, one finds that

$$\sum_{m'} P_{-I\to m'}(t) = \left(\cos^2\frac{\chi}{2}\right)^{2I} \sum_{r=0}^{2I} \binom{2I}{r}\left(\tan^2\frac{\chi}{2}\right)^{2I-r}$$

$$= \left(\cos^2\frac{\chi}{2}\right)^{2I}\left(1 + \tan^2\frac{\chi}{2}\right)^{2I} = 1.$$

The probabilities of the transitions, $|I, -I\rangle \to |I, m'\rangle$, $m' = -I, -I + 1, ..., I$ are easily determined. For example, the probability that the spin is still in the state $|I, -I\rangle$ at time t is

$$P_{-I\to -I}(t) = \left(\cos^2\frac{\chi}{2}\right)^{2I},$$

while the probability that the single quantum transition $|I, -I\rangle \to |I, -I + 1\rangle$ has occurred in the time interval t is

$$P_{-I\to -I+1}(t) = 2I\left(\cos^2\frac{\chi}{2}\right)^{2I}\tan^2\frac{\chi}{2}.$$

The probability of the $2I$-tuple quantum transition $|I, -I\rangle \to |I, +I\rangle$ is

$$P_{-I\to +I}(t) = \left(\sin^2\frac{\chi}{2}\right)^{2I}.$$

The transition probabilities $P_{-1\to -1}(t)$, $P_{-1\to 0}(t)$, and $P_{-1\to 1}(t)$ are sketched in Fig. 3.2 for $I = 1$ and $x = \omega_1/\Omega = 1$ ($\Delta = 0$, or $|\omega_1| \gg |\Delta|$). From the figure it is clear that the probability of the single quantum transition $|1, -1\rangle \to |1, 0\rangle$ never exceeds $\frac{1}{2}$, whereas the probability

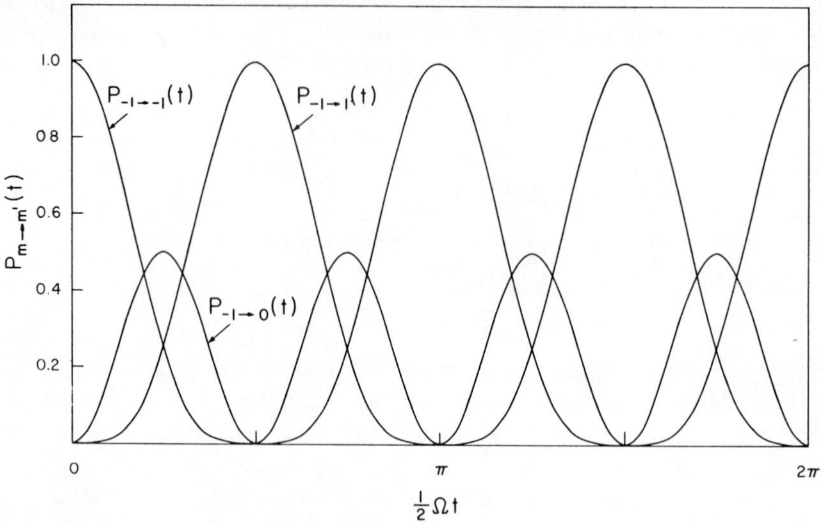

FIG. 3.2. The transition probabilities $P_{-1\to-1}(t)$, $P_{-1\to0}(t)$, and $P_{-1\to1}(t)$ for $I = 1$ and $x = \omega_1/\Omega = 1$.

of the double quantum transition $|1, -1\rangle \to |1, 1\rangle$ is unity for $\Omega t = \pi, 3\pi, \ldots$. It should be noted, however, that the rate of increase of $P_{-1\to1}(t)$ is not comparable to that of $P_{-1\to0}(t)$ until $t \approx \pi/5$.

REFERENCES

1. L. I. Schiff, "Quantum Mechanics," 2nd ed., Chap. VI. McGraw-Hill, New York 1955.
2. A. Abragam, "The Principles of Nuclear Magnetism," Chap. II. Oxford Univ. Press, London and New York, 1961.
3. R. C. Tolman, "The Principles of Statistical Mechanics," Chap. IX. Oxford Univ. Press, London and New York, 1938.
4. E. Majorana, *Nuovo Cimento* **9**, 43 (1932).
5. (a) J. Schwinger, *Phys. Rev.* **51**, 648 (1937). (b) I. I. Rabi, *ibid.* **51**, 652 (1937).

CHAPTER 4

Angular Momentum of Multispin Systems

1. Products of Vector Spaces

A. Introduction

The greater part of the theory of angular momentum developed in Chapter 2 was restricted to the case for which the eigenvalues of I_z were nondegenerate, and thereby limited to systems consisting of a single particle with spin quantum number I. This limitation is much too severe for later problems, which will be almost exclusively concerned with systems consisting of several spinning particles, occasionally even with systems composed of an arbitrary number of such particles. It is necessary, therefore, to generalize the single-particle theory of spin angular momentum to include multispin systems.

To fix ideas, let $\mathbf{I}_1$ and $\mathbf{I}_2$ denote two noninteracting spin angular momenta with $I_1 = \frac{1}{2}$ and $I_2 = 1$. An arbitrary state of the first particle can be represented by a normalized vector in a two-dimensional spin space:

$$| 1\rangle = a_{1/2} \,|\, \tfrac{1}{2}, \tfrac{1}{2}\rangle + a_{-1/2} \,|\, \tfrac{1}{2}, -\tfrac{1}{2}\rangle.$$

An arbitrary state of the second particle is represented by a normalized vector in a three-dimensional spin space:

$$| 2\rangle = b_1 \,|\, 1, 1\rangle + b_0 \,|\, 1, 0\rangle + b_{-1} \,|\, 1, -1\rangle.$$

Since the particles do not interact, a state of the composite spin system is defined whenever the states of its component systems are specified. Hence a generic state of the joint system is described by a vector pair such as $[| 1\rangle, | 2\rangle]$. Specifically, if both particles are quantized in the z direction, the combined system will be defined by one of the six vector couples: $[|\frac{1}{2}, \frac{1}{2}\rangle, |1, 1\rangle]$, $[|\frac{1}{2}, \frac{1}{2}\rangle, |1, 0\rangle]$, ..., which correspond to total z components of angular momentum $m = m_1 + m_2 = \frac{3}{2}, \frac{1}{2}, -\frac{1}{2}, \frac{1}{2}, -\frac{1}{2}, -\frac{3}{2}$.

For a single particle with spin I, the total number of m values (i.e., $2I + 1$) is equal to the dimension of the spin space, and the associated eigenvectors form a basis for this space. If it is assumed that these properties also hold for a composite spin system, it follows that the composite spin space is six-dimensional, and that the vector pairs which generate the six possible values of $m = m_1 + m_2$ constitute a basis for this space. On this assumption, a generic state $[|1\rangle, |2\rangle]$ may be expressed

$$[|1\rangle, |2\rangle] = \sum_{m_1} \sum_{m_2} c_{m_1 m_2} [|I_1, m_1\rangle, |I_2, m_2\rangle],$$

where, in terms of the notation introduced above,

$$c_{m_1 m_2} = a_{m_1} b_{m_2}.$$

This equality must hold if the expansion is to include the six vector pairs $\{[|I_1, m_1\rangle, |I_2, m_2\rangle]\}$ as special cases. For example, the pair $[|\frac{1}{2}, -\frac{1}{2}\rangle, |1, 0\rangle]$ is specified by the relations $a_{-1/2} = e^{i\alpha}$, $b_0 = e^{-i\alpha}$, $a_{1/2} = b_1 = b_{-1} = 0$, so that all $c_{m_1 m_2}$ are zero except $c_{-1/2,0} = a_{-1/2} b_0$, whose value is unity.

The preceding example does not provide a rigorous definition of the vector space required for the description of a composite spin system, but it does reveal some characteristic properties of this space. In particular, it shows that vectors in the composite spin space are constructed from vectors of the component spaces, and that the dimension of the composite space is equal to the product of the dimensions of the component spaces. These properties are characteristic of a *product space*, which will now be formally defined.

B. Definition of Product Spaces

Let S_1 and S_2 be finite-dimensional unitary vector spaces with $\dim S_1 = m$ and $\dim S_2 = n$. With every vector x in S_1 and every vector y in S_2, one can associate an ordered vector pair[1] $x \otimes y$ called the *product* of x and y. The vector $x \otimes y$ is an element in a new vector space, called the *product space* of S_1 and S_2, defined as the

[1] Henceforth, the ordered vector pair $[x, y]$ will be denoted $x \otimes y$.

set of all linear combinations of all ordered pairs $x \otimes y$ with the properties

$$(x_1 + x_2) \otimes y = x_1 \otimes y + x_2 \otimes y, \tag{1.1}$$

$$x \otimes (y_1 + y_2) = x \otimes y_1 + x \otimes y_2, \tag{1.2}$$

$$c(x \otimes y) = (cx) \otimes y = x \otimes (cy), \tag{1.3}$$

$$(x_1 \otimes y_1, x_2 \otimes y_2) = (x_1, x_2)(y_1, y_2). \tag{1.4}$$

The product of S_1 and S_2 will be denoted $S = S_1 \otimes S_2$.

Equations (1.1) through (1.4) provide the fundamental rules for the manipulation of ordered pairs $x \otimes y$. With these rules of operation, one can show that the set S satisfies all the axioms in the definition of a vector space (*1*, *2*).

Let $\{e_1, ..., e_m\}$ and $\{f_1, ..., f_n\}$ be orthonormal bases for S_1 and S_2. If x and y are vectors in S_1 and S_2, then

$$x = \sum_i \xi_i e_i, \qquad y = \sum_r \eta_r f_r,$$

and, by (1.1) through (1.3),

$$x \otimes y = \sum_i \sum_r \xi_i \eta_r e_i \otimes f_r. \tag{1.5}$$

Thus any ordered pair $x \otimes y$ may be expressed as a linear combination of the mn pairs $e_i \otimes f_r$, so that these elements span S. Moreover, these vectors are independent, for if

$$\sum_{i,r} c_{ir} e_i \otimes f_r = 0,$$

then the scalar product of this equation with $e_j \otimes f_s$ gives

$$\sum_{i,r} c_{ir}(e_j \otimes f_s, e_i \otimes f_r) = \sum_{i,r} c_{ir}\, \delta_{ji}\, \delta_{sr} \equiv c_{js} = 0,$$

by (1.4) and the assumed orthonormality of the e's and f's. Thus the set $\{e_i \otimes f_r\}$ is a basis for S, so that

$$\dim S = \dim S_1 \dim S_2.$$

The basis $\{e_i \otimes f_r\}$ will be referred to as the *product basis*.

The product space of a finite number of finite-dimensional vector spaces $S_1, S_2, ..., S_N$ is defined as follows. One first forms $S_1 \otimes S_2$, then $(S_1 \otimes S_2) \otimes S_3 \cdots$, and, finally, $\{(S_1 \otimes S_2) \otimes \cdots\} \otimes S_N$, which is abbreviated[2]

$$S = S_1 \otimes S_2 \otimes S_3 \cdots \otimes S_N .$$

S is spanned by the set of all linear combinations of all ordered vector N-tuples $x_1 \otimes x_2 \cdots \otimes x_N$, where each x_i is a vector in S_i. These N-tuples satisfy relations analogous to (1.1) through (1.4), and one can show that if $\{e_i\}$, $\{f_i\}$, $\{g_i\}$, ... are bases for $S_1, S_2, \ldots$, then $\{e_i \otimes f_j \otimes g_h \otimes \cdots\}$ is a basis for S; hence

$$\dim S = \dim S_1 \dim S_2 \cdots \dim S_N . \tag{1.6}$$

If the vector spaces $S_1, S_2, \ldots$ are spin spaces for particles with spin quantum numbers $I_1, I_2, \ldots$, then, since $\dim S_i = 2I_i + 1$, the dimension of the product spin space is

$$\dim S = \prod_{i=1}^{N} (2I_i + 1). \tag{1.7}$$

2. Kronecker Products of Linear Transformations

A. Definition of Kronecker Products

The completion of the mathematical basis for the theory of multispin systems requires only the concept of a *Kronecker product* of linear transformations. This concept provides the means for converting linear transformations defined on the component spaces into linear transformations on their product space.

The necessity for introducing the Kronecker product of linear transformations can be easily appreciated by considering the example discussed in the preceding section. If both spins are quantized in the z direction, the components of the total angular momentum along the z axis are given by $\frac{3}{2}, \frac{1}{2}, \frac{1}{2}, -\frac{1}{2}, -\frac{1}{2}, -\frac{3}{2}$. The question which immediately arises is: What operator is associated with these eigenvalues? Since the values of the total spin variable are obtained by summing the component spin variables, it seems natural to assume that the operator for the z component of the total angular momentum is

$$I_z = I_{z1} + I_{z2} .$$

[2] The order in which the vector spaces S_i are compounded to form their product space S is arbitrary, but once a definite order has been settled upon, it must be maintained. Two product spaces which differ only in the order in which their component spaces have been multiplied are related by a permutation transformation.

This assumption is not correct; for if I_{z1} and I_{z2} are represented by matrices, the right side of this equation will be represented by

$$\frac{1}{2}\begin{pmatrix} 1 & 0 \\ 0 & -1 \end{pmatrix} + \begin{pmatrix} 1 & 0 & 0 \\ 0 & 0 & 0 \\ 0 & 0 & -1 \end{pmatrix}.$$

This result is absurd. Not only is the sum of these matrices undefined, neither matrix is the representative of an operator defined on a six-dimensional space. These difficulties are removed by the Kronecker product of linear transformations.

Let A and A' denote arbitrary linear transformations of S_1 into itself, and I_1 the identity transformation on S_1. Similarly, let B and B' denote arbitrary linear transformations of S_2 into itself, and I_2 the identity transformation on S_2. If x and y denote arbitrary vectors in S_1 and S_2, respectively, then $x' = Ax$ and $y' = By$ are also vectors in these spaces. Thus when S_1 and S_2 are subjected to the transformations A and B, the product $x \otimes y$ is transformed into $Ax \otimes By = x' \otimes y'$. It follows that the linear transformations A and B together define a linear transformation on $S = S_1 \otimes S_2$. This transformation, called the *Kronecker product* of A and B, is denoted $A \otimes B$ and is defined by the equation

$$(A \otimes B)x \otimes y = Ax \otimes By. \tag{2.1}$$

From this definition, one can deduce a number of important properties of the transformation $A \otimes B$.

Consider first the case where $A = I_1$ and $B = I_2$. Since $I_1 x = x$ and $I_2 y = y$, it follows that $I_1 \otimes I_2$ is the identity operator for S. On the other hand, if $B = I_2$, but $A \neq I_1$, then

$$(A \otimes I_2)x \otimes y = Ax \otimes I_2 y = Ax \otimes y. \tag{2.2}$$

This equation shows that the operator $A \otimes I_2$ transforms the S_1 components of a vector in S but has no effect on the S_2 components. A similar remark applies to the operator $I_1 \otimes B$, since

$$(I_1 \otimes B)x \otimes y = I_1 x \otimes By = x \otimes By. \tag{2.3}$$

Equations (2.2) and (2.3) provide the rules for converting operators defined on the component spaces into operators on the product space. The prescription is simple: $A \to A \otimes I_2$, $B \to I_1 \otimes B$. Thus the answer to the question previously posed is $I_z = I_{z1} \otimes I_2 + I_1 \otimes I_{z2}$, and it will be shown below that this formula removes all the dimensionality problems encountered with the incorrect expression $I_{z1} + I_{z2}$.

Consider now the Kronecker product $A' \otimes B'$ and apply this operator to both sides of (2.1). Since x and y are arbitrary, one obtains

$$(A' \otimes B')(A \otimes B) = A'A \otimes B'B. \tag{2.4}$$

This equation states that the (ordinary) operator product of two Kronecker products is equal to the Kronecker product of the (ordinary) operator products. The order of the factors on both sides of (2.4) is important, since the operators A, A' or B, B' may not commute. Indeed, if the primed and unprimed quantities in (2.4) are interchanged, one concludes that $[A' \otimes B', A \otimes B] = 0$ if and only if $[A, A'] = [B, B'] = 0$. Since I_1 commutes with every A, and I_2 commutes with every B, it follows that

$$(A \otimes I_2)(I_1 \otimes B) = (I_1 \otimes B)(A \otimes I_2) = A \otimes B. \tag{2.5}$$

Hence operators defined with respect to distinct component spaces commute when interpreted as operators on the product spaces. Equation (2.5) is thus the mathematical expression of the quantum mechanical statement that operators referring to independent particles commute.

If A and B have inverses, then (2.4) with $A' = A^{-1}$ and $B' = B^{-1}$ shows that

$$(A \otimes B)^{-1} = A^{-1} \otimes B^{-1}. \tag{2.6}$$

In particular, if A and B are unitary, so that $A^{-1} = A^{\dagger}$ and $B^{-1} = B^{\dagger}$, then (2.6) can be written in the form

$$(A \otimes B)^{\dagger} = A^{\dagger} \otimes B^{\dagger}. \tag{2.7}$$

It will be shown in Section 2.B that (2.7) gives the general rule for determining the adjoint of $A \otimes B$. Hence $A \otimes B$ is unitary or hermitian if and only if A and B are both unitary or hermitian.

The generalization of the preceding results presents no difficulties. If C, D, ... denote linear transformations on S_3, S_4, ..., the Kronecker product $A \otimes B \otimes C \otimes \cdots$ is defined by

$$(A \otimes B \otimes C \otimes \cdots)(x_1 \otimes x_2 \otimes x_3 \otimes \cdots) = Ax_1 \otimes Bx_2 \otimes Cx_3 \otimes \cdots,$$

where x_i is a vector in S_i. The component operators A, B, C, ... are converted into operators on the product space $S_1 \otimes S_2 \otimes S_3 \otimes \cdots$ through the prescriptions

$$A \to A \otimes I_2 \otimes I_3 \cdots \otimes I_N, \qquad B \to I_1 \otimes B \otimes I_2 \cdots \otimes I_N,$$
$$C \to I_1 \otimes I_2 \otimes C \cdots \otimes I_N, \ldots,$$

and it is easily verified that these operators commute.

Finally, (2.4), (2.6), and (2.7) generalize to

$$(A' \otimes B' \otimes C' \otimes \cdots)(A \otimes B \otimes C \otimes \cdots) = A'A \otimes B'B \otimes C'C \otimes \cdots,$$
$$(A \otimes B \otimes C \otimes \cdots)^{\dagger} = A^{\dagger} \otimes B^{\dagger} \otimes C^{\dagger} \otimes \cdots,$$
$$(A \otimes B \otimes C \otimes \cdots)^{-1} = A^{-1} \otimes B^{-1} \otimes C^{-1} \otimes \cdots.$$

The last equation is valid only if the inverses on the right side exist.

B. Matrix Representations of Kronecker Products

The Kronecker product $A \otimes B$ can be represented by a matrix constructed from the matrices representing the operators A and B. The matrices of A and B are defined by their effect on the bases $\{e_i\}$, $\{f_j\}$ of the component spaces:

$$Ae_r = \sum_l A_{lr} e_l, \qquad Bf_s = \sum_q B_{qs} f_q,$$

where $l, r = 1, 2, ..., m$; $q, s = 1, 2, ..., n$. It is necessary, however, to introduce an ordering convention for the elements of the product basis $\{e_i \otimes f_j\}$. The customary procedure is the so-called *lexicographical ordering*, defined by the prescription

$$\{e_i \otimes f_j\} = \{e_1 \otimes f_1, e_1 \otimes f_2, ..., e_1 \otimes f_n, e_2 \otimes f_1,$$
$$e_2 \otimes f_2, ..., e_2 \otimes f_n, ..., e_m \otimes f_1, e_m \otimes f_2, ..., e_m \otimes f_n\}.$$

Operating with $A \otimes B$ on the r, s element of this basis gives

$$(A \otimes B)e_r \otimes f_s = Ae_r \otimes Bf_s = \sum_l \sum_q A_{lr} B_{qs} e_l \otimes f_q.$$

Taking the scalar product of this equation with $e_i \otimes f_j$ gives, by virtue of (1.4) and the orthonormality of the component bases,

$$(e_i \otimes f_j, A \otimes Be_r \otimes f_s) = \sum_l \sum_q A_{lr} B_{qs} (e_i, e_l)(f_j, f_q)$$
$$= \sum_l \sum_q A_{lr} B_{qs} \delta_{il} \delta_{jq} = A_{ir} B_{js}.$$

The scalar product $(e_i \otimes f_j, A \otimes Be_r \otimes f_s)$ will be denoted $(A \otimes B)_{ij;rs}$, so that the matrix elements of $A \otimes B$ are given by

$$(A \otimes B)_{ij;rs} = A_{ir} B_{js}. \tag{2.8}$$

Equation (2.8) shows that the rows of $A \otimes B$ are labeled with row indices of A and B. One speaks of the "11 row" (read "one-one row"), the "12 row," etc. To compute the 12 row, one sets $i = 1, j = 2$, and then allows r and s to take on all values in their respective ranges, taking care to order these indices lexicographically, as previously noted for the product basis. Similar remarks hold for the columns of $A \otimes B$, so that the full matrix has the form

$$\begin{pmatrix} A_{11}B_{11} & A_{11}B_{12} & \cdots & A_{11}B_{1n} & A_{12}B_{11} & A_{12}B_{12} & \cdots & A_{12}B_{1n} & \cdots & A_{1m}B_{1n} \\ \vdots & \vdots & & \vdots & \vdots & \vdots & & \vdots & & \vdots \\ A_{11}B_{n1} & A_{11}B_{n2} & \cdots & A_{11}B_{nn} & A_{12}B_{n1} & A_{12}B_{n2} & \cdots & A_{12}B_{nn} & \cdots & A_{1m}B_{nn} \\ A_{21}B_{11} & A_{21}B_{12} & \cdots & A_{21}B_{1n} & A_{22}B_{11} & A_{22}B_{12} & \cdots & A_{22}B_{1n} & \cdots & A_{2m}B_{1n} \\ \vdots & \vdots & & \vdots & \vdots & \vdots & & \vdots & & \vdots \\ A_{21}B_{n1} & A_{21}B_{n2} & \cdots & A_{21}B_{nn} & A_{22}B_{n1} & A_{22}B_{n2} & \cdots & A_{22}B_{nn} & \cdots & A_{2m}B_{nn} \\ \cdot & \cdot & \cdot & \cdot & \cdot & \cdot & \cdot & \cdot & \cdot & \cdot \\ A_{m1}B_{11} & A_{m1}B_{12} & \cdots & A_{m1}B_{1n} & A_{m2}B_{11} & A_{m2}B_{12} & \cdots & A_{m2}B_{1n} & \cdots & A_{mm}B_{1n} \\ \vdots & \vdots & & \vdots & \vdots & \vdots & & \vdots & & \vdots \\ A_{m1}B_{n1} & A_{m1}B_{n2} & \cdots & A_{m1}B_{nn} & A_{m2}B_{n1} & A_{m2}B_{n2} & \cdots & A_{m2}B_{nn} & \cdots & A_{mm}B_{nn} \end{pmatrix}.$$

This matrix is called the *Kronecker product* of A and B; its form suggests the following simple procedure for writing down the matrix of $A \otimes B$ from the matrices for A and B. Form the m^2 matrices $A_{ij}B$ and write

$$A \otimes B = \begin{pmatrix} A_{11}B & A_{12}B & \cdots & A_{1m}B \\ A_{21}B & A_{22}B & \cdots & A_{2m}B \\ \vdots & \vdots & & \vdots \\ A_{m1}B & A_{m2}B & \cdots & A_{mm}B \end{pmatrix}. \tag{2.9}$$

An examination of either form of $A \otimes B$ shows that $A \otimes B$ is an $mn \times mn$ square matrix and that (2.7) is a generally valid expression for $(A \otimes B)^\dagger$.

The computation of Kronecker products will be illustrated by evaluating $I_{z1} \otimes 1_2$ and $1_1 \otimes I_{z2}$ for two spin angular momenta with $I_1 = \frac{1}{2}$ and $I_2 = 1$. The identity operator 1_2 is represented by a three-dimensional identity matrix, so that

$$I_{z1} \to I_{z1} \otimes 1_2 = \frac{1}{2}\begin{pmatrix} 1 & 0 \\ 0 & -1 \end{pmatrix} \otimes \begin{pmatrix} 1 & 0 & 0 \\ 0 & 1 & 0 \\ 0 & 0 & 1 \end{pmatrix} = \frac{1}{2}\begin{pmatrix} 1 & 0 & 0 & 0 & 0 & 0 \\ 0 & 1 & 0 & 0 & 0 & 0 \\ 0 & 0 & 1 & 0 & 0 & 0 \\ 0 & 0 & 0 & -1 & 0 & 0 \\ 0 & 0 & 0 & 0 & -1 & 0 \\ 0 & 0 & 0 & 0 & 0 & -1 \end{pmatrix}.$$

Similarly,

$$I_{z2} \to 1_1 \otimes I_{z2} = \begin{pmatrix} 1 & 0 \\ 0 & 1 \end{pmatrix} \otimes \begin{pmatrix} 1 & 0 & 0 \\ 0 & 0 & 0 \\ 0 & 0 & -1 \end{pmatrix} = \begin{pmatrix} 1 & 0 & 0 & 0 & 0 & 0 \\ 0 & 0 & 0 & 0 & 0 & 0 \\ 0 & 0 & -1 & 0 & 0 & 0 \\ 0 & 0 & 0 & 1 & 0 & 0 \\ 0 & 0 & 0 & 0 & 0 & 0 \\ 0 & 0 & 0 & 0 & 0 & -1 \end{pmatrix}.$$

The sum of $I_{z1} \otimes 1_2$ and $1_2 \otimes I_{z2}$ is

$$I_z = \begin{pmatrix} \frac{3}{2} & 0 & 0 & 0 & 0 & 0 \\ 0 & \frac{1}{2} & 0 & 0 & 0 & 0 \\ 0 & 0 & -\frac{1}{2} & 0 & 0 & 0 \\ 0 & 0 & 0 & \frac{1}{2} & 0 & 0 \\ 0 & 0 & 0 & 0 & -\frac{1}{2} & 0 \\ 0 & 0 & 0 & 0 & 0 & -\frac{3}{2} \end{pmatrix}.$$

These matrices have all the properties demanded by the dimensionality of the product space and the formula $m = m_1 + m_2$.

Further examples of Kronecker products are given in Table 4.1, which lists the 16 possible Kronecker products for two spin-$\frac{1}{2}$ nuclei relative to the bases which diagonalize I_{z1} and I_{z2}. In this tabulation, 1 denotes the 2×2 identity matrix, 0 the 2×2 zero matrix, and σ_x, σ_y, and σ_z the 2×2 Pauli spin matrices.

TABLE 4.1

KRONECKER PRODUCTS

$\otimes$	1_2	I_{x2}	I_{y2}	I_{z2}
1_1	$\begin{pmatrix} 1 & 0 \\ 0 & 1 \end{pmatrix}$	$\frac{1}{2}\begin{pmatrix} \sigma_x & 0 \\ 0 & \sigma_x \end{pmatrix}$	$\frac{1}{2}\begin{pmatrix} \sigma_y & 0 \\ 0 & \sigma_y \end{pmatrix}$	$\frac{1}{2}\begin{pmatrix} \sigma_z & 0 \\ 0 & \sigma_z \end{pmatrix}$
I_{x1}	$\frac{1}{2}\begin{pmatrix} 0 & 1 \\ 1 & 0 \end{pmatrix}$	$\frac{1}{4}\begin{pmatrix} 0 & \sigma_x \\ \sigma_x & 0 \end{pmatrix}$	$\frac{1}{4}\begin{pmatrix} 0 & \sigma_y \\ \sigma_y & 0 \end{pmatrix}$	$\frac{1}{4}\begin{pmatrix} 0 & \sigma_z \\ \sigma_z & 0 \end{pmatrix}$
I_{y1}	$\frac{i}{2}\begin{pmatrix} 0 & -1 \\ 1 & 0 \end{pmatrix}$	$\frac{i}{4}\begin{pmatrix} 0 & -\sigma_x \\ \sigma_x & 0 \end{pmatrix}$	$\frac{i}{4}\begin{pmatrix} 0 & -\sigma_y \\ \sigma_y & 0 \end{pmatrix}$	$\frac{i}{4}\begin{pmatrix} 0 & -\sigma_z \\ \sigma_z & 0 \end{pmatrix}$
I_{z1}	$\frac{1}{2}\begin{pmatrix} 1 & 0 \\ 0 & -1 \end{pmatrix}$	$\frac{1}{4}\begin{pmatrix} \sigma_x & 0 \\ 0 & -\sigma_x \end{pmatrix}$	$\frac{1}{4}\begin{pmatrix} \sigma_y & 0 \\ 0 & -\sigma_y \end{pmatrix}$	$\frac{1}{4}\begin{pmatrix} \sigma_z & 0 \\ 0 & -\sigma_z \end{pmatrix}$

The formula for computing the Kronecker product of two matrices also holds for the vectors $e_i \otimes f_j$ of the product basis. Consider, for example, two spin-$\frac{1}{2}$ particles. The product basis is $\{|+\rangle \otimes |+\rangle, |+\rangle \otimes |-\rangle, |-\rangle \otimes |+\rangle, |-\rangle \otimes |-\rangle\}$, where $|\pm\rangle \equiv |\frac{1}{2}, \pm\frac{1}{2}\rangle$, and where the first ket in each product refers to particle 1, the second ket to particle 2. Upon introducing the column vectors for $|+\rangle$ and $|-\rangle$, one obtains

$$|+\rangle \otimes |+\rangle = \begin{pmatrix}1\\0\end{pmatrix} \otimes \begin{pmatrix}1\\0\end{pmatrix} = \begin{pmatrix}1\\0\\0\\0\end{pmatrix}, \qquad |+\rangle \otimes |-\rangle = \begin{pmatrix}1\\0\end{pmatrix} \otimes \begin{pmatrix}0\\1\end{pmatrix} = \begin{pmatrix}0\\1\\0\\0\end{pmatrix},$$

$$|-\rangle \otimes |+\rangle = \begin{pmatrix}0\\1\end{pmatrix} \otimes \begin{pmatrix}1\\0\end{pmatrix} = \begin{pmatrix}0\\0\\1\\0\end{pmatrix}, \qquad |-\rangle \otimes |-\rangle = \begin{pmatrix}0\\1\end{pmatrix} \otimes \begin{pmatrix}0\\1\end{pmatrix} = \begin{pmatrix}0\\0\\0\\1\end{pmatrix}.$$

C. Diagonalization of Kronecker Products

The matrix representative of a Kronecker product $A \otimes B$ depends upon the matrix representatives of A and B. In fact, an examination of the matrix for $A \otimes B$ reveals that it is diagonal if and only if A and B are diagonal. This result is a direct consequence of equations (2.5) and the theorem on commuting operators (cf. Appendix I).

The matrix which diagonalizes $A \otimes B$ is given by the Kronecker product of the matrices which diagonalize A and B. For if $R^{-1}AR = (A_i \, \delta_{ir})$ and $S^{-1}BS = (B_j \, \delta_{js})$, then

$$(R \otimes S)^{-1}(A \otimes B)(R \otimes S) = R^{-1} \otimes S^{-1}(A \otimes B)R \otimes S = R^{-1}AR \otimes S^{-1}BS,$$

so that

$$[(R \otimes S)^{-1}(A \otimes B)(R \otimes S)]_{ij;rs} = A_i B_j \, \delta_{ir} \, \delta_{js} \,. \tag{2.10}$$

From this equation it follows that the determinant and trace of $A \otimes B$ are given by

$$\det A \otimes B = (\det A)^n (\det B)^m, \tag{2.11}$$

$$\operatorname{tr} A \otimes B = \operatorname{tr} A \operatorname{tr} B. \tag{2.12}$$

Equations (2.11) and (2.12) are generally valid, since they can be easily deduced from the weaker assumption that A and B can be simultaneously brought into triangular form.

The preceding results may be readily generalized. If $A, B, C, \ldots$

denote square matrices of dimensions $n_A, n_B, n_C, \ldots$ which are diagonalized by R, S, T, ..., respectively, then

$$(A \otimes B \otimes C \otimes \cdots)_{ijk\cdots;rst\cdots} = A_{ir}B_{js}C_{kt}\cdots,$$

$$[(R^{-1} \otimes S^{-1} \otimes T^{-1} \otimes \cdots)(A \otimes B \otimes C \otimes \cdots)(R \otimes S \otimes T \otimes \cdots)]_{ijk\cdots;rst\cdots} = A_iB_jC_k \cdots \delta_{ir}\,\delta_{js}\,\delta_{kt}\cdots,$$

$$\operatorname{tr} A \otimes B \otimes C \otimes \cdots = \operatorname{tr} A \operatorname{tr} B \operatorname{tr} C \cdots.$$

3. General Theory of Spin Angular Momentum

A. The Angular Momentum Operators

The mathematical ideas developed in the preceding sections provide the basis for the theoretical treatment of a system of particles with nonvanishing spin angular momenta. The general problem can be treated by a straightforward solution of an eigenvalue problem, but considerable expedition can be achieved with the aid of other techniques (*3*). In this section the general problem will be outlined and derivations of some important results required for subsequent developments will be given.

Let N denote the total number of particles, $\mathbf{I}_j = (I_{xj}, I_{yj}, I_{zj})$ the vector spin operator for the jth particle, and $\mathbf{I}_j{}^2 = I_{xj}^2 + I_{yj}^2 + I_{zj}^2$ its square. The operators I_{xj}, I_{yj}, I_{zj}, and $\mathbf{I}_j{}^2$ satisfy the commutation rules

$$[\mathbf{I}_j{}^2, I_{\lambda j}] = 0, \qquad [I_{\lambda j}, I_{\mu j}] = i\sum_{\nu} e_{\lambda\mu\nu} I_{\nu j}, \tag{3.1}$$

where $j = 1, 2, \ldots, N$; $\lambda, \mu, \nu = x, y, z$; $i = \sqrt{-1}$; and $e_{\lambda\mu\nu}$ is the Levi-Civita tensor density defined in Chapter 2.

The spin operators for the jth particle operate on the vectors of a $(2I_j + 1)$-dimensional spin space S_j, and the eigenvectors of $\mathbf{I}_j{}^2$ and I_{zj} constitute a particular basis for S_j. This basis is denoted $\{|\, I_j, m_j\rangle\}$, $m_j = -I_j, -I_j + 1, \ldots, I_j$, and its elements are such that

$$\mathbf{I}_j{}^2 \,|\, I_j, m_j\rangle = I_j(I_j + 1)|\, I_j, m_j\rangle, \tag{3.2}$$

$$I_{zj} \,|\, I_j, m_j\rangle = m_j \,|\, I_j, m_j\rangle, \tag{3.3}$$

$$I_j{}^{\pm} \,|\, I_j, m_j\rangle = [(I_j \mp m_j)(I_j \pm m_j + 1)]^{1/2} \,|\, I_j, m_j \pm 1\rangle, \tag{3.4}$$

$$\langle I_j, m_j' \,|\, I_j, m_j\rangle = \delta_{m_j' m_j}, \tag{3.5}$$

where[3]

$$I_j^{\pm} = I_{xj} \pm iI_{yj} \,. \tag{3.6}$$

The vector space S of the composite spin system is the Kronecker product of the N spaces S_i, and its dimension is given by (1.7).

The product basis for S is given by the set of all products of the form $|I_1, m_1\rangle \otimes |I_2, m_2\rangle \cdots \otimes |I_N, m_N\rangle$, but it will simplify matters if the symbol $\otimes$ is omitted. Thus a typical element of the product basis will be denoted

$$|I_1, m_1\rangle\, |I_2, m_2\rangle \cdots |I_N, m_N\rangle \equiv |I_1, m_1; I_2, m_2; \cdots ; I_N, m_N\rangle,$$

with the understanding that the first ket refers to the first particle, the second ket to the second particle, and so forth. If all particles have spin $\frac{1}{2}$, the notation will often be simplified by writing $|+\rangle$ for $|\frac{1}{2}, \frac{1}{2}\rangle$, and $|-\rangle$ for $|\frac{1}{2}, -\frac{1}{2}\rangle$. For example, if $N = 5$, $|++--+\rangle$ will mean $|+\rangle \otimes |+\rangle \otimes |-\rangle \otimes |-\rangle \otimes |+\rangle$. This product ket may also be denoted $\alpha\alpha\beta\beta\alpha$.[4]

The spin operators associated with any one of the component spaces become operators on the product space by forming the Kronecker product of these operators and identity operators taken from the other component spaces. For example if X_j denotes any spin operator defined on S_j, then X_j becomes an operator on S through the prescription

$$X_j \rightarrow 1_1 \otimes 1_2 \cdots \otimes 1_{j-1} \otimes X_j \otimes 1_{j+1} \cdots \otimes 1_N \,. \tag{3.7}$$

According to the theory of Kronecker products, the operators constructed from X_j and X_k' commute if $j \neq k$. On the other hand, if $j = k$, then the operators constructed from X_j and X_j' satisfy commutation relations of the same form as those satisfied by X_j and X_j'. For example, if $X_j = I_{xj}$ and $X_k' = I_{yk}$, then

$$I_{xj} \rightarrow 1_1 \otimes 1_2 \cdots \otimes 1_{j-1} \otimes I_{xj} \otimes 1_{j+1} \cdots \otimes 1_N \,,$$

$$I_{yk} \rightarrow 1_1 \otimes 1_2 \cdots \otimes 1_{k-1} \otimes I_{yk} \otimes 1_{k+1} \cdots \otimes 1_N \,.$$

If $j \neq k$, then the Kronecker products on the right commute, whereas the commutator of these Kronecker products is i times

$$1_1 \otimes 1_2 \cdots \otimes 1_{k-1} \otimes I_{zk} \otimes 1_{k+1} \cdots \otimes 1_N,$$

---

[3] The "raising" and "lowering" operators are here denoted $I^{\pm}$, to facilitate the use of subscripts.

[4] Although the symbols α, β are no less concise than $|+\rangle$, $|-\rangle$, there are no standard symbols for the eigenvectors when $I > \frac{1}{2}$. However, the Dirac notation concisely describes the spin states of particles with arbitrary spin quantum numbers and will be used throughout.

when $j = k$. Hence all commutation relations satisfied by the operators X_i preserve their form when the X_i are interpreted as operators on the product space S.

The notation for the Kronecker products of operators is extremely awkward, and its continued use would considerably inhibit the writing and manipulation of operators referred to the product space S. Henceforth the symbol $\otimes$ and the identity factors will be omitted in all operator expressions. Thus the operator on the right of (3.7) will be denoted X_j. It must be emphasized that the various symbols are omitted only for notational convenience, and that the remaining symbols would be meaningless unless the omitted notation is understood to be present without being explicitly written down. For example, the operator product $I_{\lambda j} I_{\mu k}$ $(j \neq k)$ without the above convention is meaningless, but according to convention, this symbol signifies the operator product of two Kronecker products,

$$(1_1 \otimes \cdots 1_{j-1} \otimes I_{\lambda j} \otimes 1_{j+1} \cdots \otimes 1_N)(1_1 \otimes \cdots 1_{k-1} \otimes I_{\mu k} \otimes 1_{k+1} \cdots \otimes 1_N)$$
$$= 1_1 \otimes \cdots 1_{j-1} \otimes I_{\lambda j} \otimes 1_{j+1} \cdots 1_{k-1} \otimes I_{\mu k} \otimes 1_{k+1} \cdots \otimes 1_N \equiv I_{\lambda j} I_{\mu k} .$$

With this understanding, all sums and products of operators will be meaningful in their abbreviated form. For example, all the commutation relations satisfied by the spin operators can now be written quite concisely as

$$[\mathbf{I}_j^2, I_{\lambda k}] = 0, \tag{3.8}$$

$$[I_{\lambda j}, I_{\mu k}] = i\delta_{jk} \sum_{\nu} e_{\lambda\mu\nu} I_{\nu j} . \tag{3.9}$$

B. The Total Angular Momentum Operators

The total spin vector for a system of N particles is defined as

$$\mathbf{I} = (I_x, I_y, I_z) = \sum_{j=1}^{N} \mathbf{I}_j ,$$

where, in the conventional notation,

$$I_\lambda = \sum_{j=1}^{N} I_{\lambda j} \qquad (\lambda = x, y, z), \tag{3.10}$$

and $\mathbf{I}_j = (I_{xj}, I_{yj}, I_{zj})$. The square of the total spin angular momentum is defined as

$$\mathbf{I}^2 = I_x^2 + I_y^2 + I_z^2, \tag{3.11}$$

which is equivalent to

$$\mathbf{I}^2 = \sum_j \mathbf{I}_j^2 + 2 \sum\sum_{j<k} \mathbf{I}_j \cdot \mathbf{I}_k . \tag{3.12}$$

These definitions are generalizations of the corresponding definitions for a single angular momentum operator. Their significance is that whatever the value of N, the operators $\mathbf{I}^2$, I_x, I_y, and I_z satisfy the same commutation relations:

$$[\mathbf{I}^2, I_\lambda] = 0, \tag{3.13}$$

$$[I_\lambda , I_\mu] = i \sum_\nu e_{\lambda\mu\nu} I_\nu . \tag{3.14}$$

Equation (3.14) follows directly from (3.9), since

$$[I_\lambda , I_\mu] = \sum_j \sum_k [I_{\lambda j} , I_{\mu k}] = i \sum_j \sum_k \sum_\nu \delta_{jk} e_{\lambda\mu\nu} I_{\nu k} = i \sum_\nu e_{\lambda\mu\nu} I_\nu .$$

To prove (3.13), suppose first that $\lambda = z$. Since I_z commutes with $\mathbf{I}_j^2$ and $I_{zj} I_{zk}$ for all j and k, the commutator of I_z and $\mathbf{I}^2$ simplifies to

$$[\mathbf{I}^2, I_z] = \sum\sum_{j \neq k} [I_{xj} I_{xk} + I_{yj} I_{yk} , \sum_l I_{zl}].$$

Now every term in $\sum_l I_{zl}$ with $l \neq j$ or k commutes with $I_{xj} I_{xk} + I_{yj} I_{yk}$, so that it is necessary to consider only those terms for which $l = k$ and $l = j$. But

$$[I_{xj} I_{xk} + I_{yj} I_{yk} , I_{zj} + I_{zk}] = 0,$$

so that $[\mathbf{I}^2, I_z] = 0$, as asserted. Similar arguments can be used to establish the commutation of I_x and I_y with $\mathbf{I}^2$.

The identity of the commutation properties of I_x, I_y, I_z, and $\mathbf{I}^2$ with those of the corresponding operators for a single particle permits the formal adaptation of all properties deduced from these relations in Chapter 2 to the general multispin system. In particular, one can introduce the operators

$$I^\pm = \sum_j I_j^\pm = \sum_j I_{xj} \pm i \sum_j I_{yj} \tag{3.15}$$

and show that a proper rotation of the cartesian axes through an angle φ about the unit vector $\mathbf{n}$ induces a unitary transformation[5]

$$e^{-i\varphi \mathbf{n} \cdot \mathbf{I}} = \prod_{j=1}^{N} e^{-i\varphi \mathbf{n} \cdot \mathbf{I}_j} \tag{3.16}$$

[5] The factorization on the right side of (3.16) is permissible since $[\mathbf{n} \cdot \mathbf{I}_j , \mathbf{n} \cdot \mathbf{I}_k] = 0$.

of the vectors of the spin space S. Moreover, the set of all eigenvectors of the square and z component of the total spin angular momentum must have the properties of the most general set of eigenvectors established in Chapter 2. Thus the eigenvectors of $\mathbf{I}^2$ and I_z may be partitioned into classes $G = A, B, \ldots$ such that each class is characterized by the spin quantum number I_G with spin multiplicity g_{I_G}. The total number of eigenvectors is

$$\sum_G g_{I_G}(2I_G + 1),$$

and, since this is the maximum number of linearly independent eigenvectors, it must be equal to the dimension of S:

$$\sum_G g_{I_G}(2I_G + 1) = \prod_{j=1}^{N} (2I_j + 1). \tag{3.17}$$

The right-hand member of (3.17) is the dimension of S as determined by the number of elements in the product basis, whereas the left-hand member expresses the dimension of S as determined by an enumeration of the elements in the basis of eigenvectors of $\mathbf{I}^2$ and I_z. The equality of these numbers expresses the invariance of the dimension of S.

Although the values of I_G and g_{I_G} are not determined by the counting procedures just described, enough information is available to describe the general form of the matrices for $\mathbf{I}^2$ and I_z relative to the basis of eigenvectors. Consider first the submatrix of $\mathbf{I}^2$ generated by a generic class G. This submatrix has the form indicated in Fig. 4.1. All matrix elements not enclosed by the square blocks vanish, and each block consists of a $(2I_G + 1)$-dimensional square matrix of the form

$$I_G(I_G + 1)\begin{pmatrix} 1 & 0 & 0 & \cdots & 0 \\ 0 & 1 & 0 & \cdots & 0 \\ \vdots & \vdots & \vdots & & \vdots \\ 0 & 0 & 0 & \cdots & 1 \end{pmatrix}. \tag{3.18}$$

Since there are g_{I_G} identical blocks, the complete submatrix consists of $I_G(I_G + 1)$ times a $[g_{I_G}(2I_G + 1)]$-dimensional unit matrix. The full matrix for $\mathbf{I}^2$ is obtained by forming the submatrices for all classes and assembling them into a diagonal matrix. In other words, the matrix for $\mathbf{I}^2$ is the direct sum[6] of all submatrices of the form described. It must be noted, however, that the spin quantum numbers $I_A, I_B, \ldots,$ are distinct, so that $\mathbf{I}^2$ is not a scalar matrix.

[6] See Appendix I.

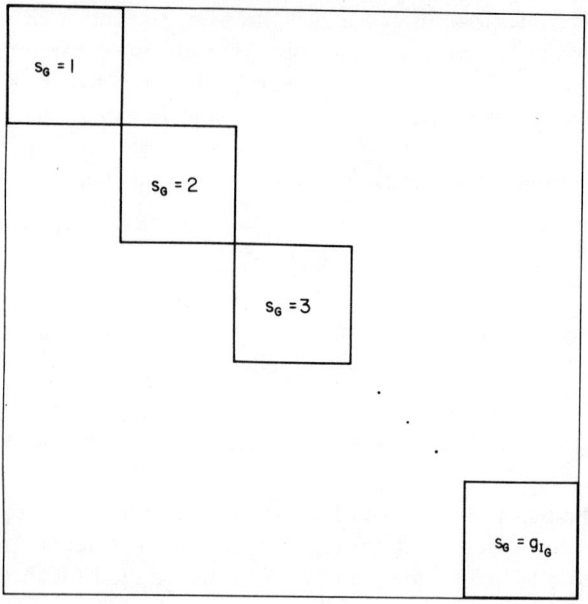

FIG. 4.1. The form of the submatrices of $\mathbf{I}^2$ and I_z generated by a generic class G of eigenvectors. Each square block is a diagonal matrix of dimension $2I_G + 1$; all other matrix elements vanish.

The submatrix of I_z for class G also has the form shown in Fig. 4.1, except that each subblock has the form

$$\begin{pmatrix} I_G & 0 & 0 & \cdots & 0 \\ 0 & I_G - 1 & 0 & \cdots & 0 \\ \vdots & \vdots & \vdots & & \vdots \\ 0 & 0 & 0 & \cdots & -I_G \end{pmatrix}. \tag{3.19}$$

The matrix for I_z is obtained by direct summation over all classes.

The eigenvectors of $\mathbf{I}^2$ and I_z will be denoted $| I_G, m_G; s_G\rangle$, where $s_G = 1, 2, ..., g_{I_G}$ is the spin multiplicity index,[7] and $G = A, B, ...$. These eigenvectors satisfy the orthogonality conditions

$$\langle I_K, m_{K'}; s_{K'} | I_G, m_G; s_G\rangle = \delta_{KG}\, \delta_{m_{K'} m_G} \delta_{s_{K'} s_G}. \tag{3.20}$$

The spin quantum numbers I_G, their spin multiplicities g_{I_G}, and the eigenvectors of $\mathbf{I}^2$ and I_z may be determined by an analysis of the eigen-

[7] The spin-multiplicity index will be omitted whenever $g_{I_G} = 1$.

value problem as formulated in the product basis. The matrix for I_z is diagonal, and its diagonal elements are all taken from the sequence

$$I_{\max}, \quad I_{\max} - 1, \ldots, -I_{\max} + 1, \quad -I_{\max}, \tag{3.21}$$

where

$$I_{\max} = \sum_{j=1}^{N} I_j .$$

This sequence contains $2I_{\max} + 1$ terms, and is generated by the distinct values of the total spin variable

$$m = m_1 + m_2 + \cdots + m_N, \tag{3.22}$$

$$-I_j \leqslant m_j \leqslant I_j \qquad (j = 1, 2, \ldots, N). \tag{3.23}$$

Since

$$2I_{\max} + 1 < \prod_{j=1}^{N} (2I_j + 1) = \dim I_z ,$$

whenever N is greater than unity,[8] all values of m except $m = \pm I_{\max}$ are degenerate. The degree of degeneracy of a given value of m, which will be denoted $\nu(m)$, is equal to the number of ways in which the m_j can be chosen so as to satisfy (3.22), subject to the restrictions imposed by (3.23). Evidently, $\nu(m)$ has the following properties:

$$\begin{gathered} \nu(m) = \nu(-m), \\ \nu(I_{\max}) = \nu(-I_{\max}) = 1, \\ \sum_{-I_{\max}}^{+I_{\max}} \nu(m) = \prod_{j=1}^{N} (2I_j + 1). \end{gathered} \tag{3.24}$$

For small values of N, the values of $\nu(m)$ may be determined by explicit construction of the product basis. For example, if $N = 2$, and $I_1 = I_2 = 1$, $\dim S = (2I_1 + 1)(2I_2 + 1) = 9$, and there are $2I_{\max} + 1 = 2(1 + 1) + 1 = 5$ values of m with $\nu(\pm 2) = 1$, $\nu(\pm 1) = 2$, $\nu(0) = 3$ (Table 4.2). If $N = 2$, and $I_1 = \frac{3}{2}$, $I_2 = 1$, then $\dim S = 12$, and there are $2(\frac{3}{2} + 1) + 1 = 6$ values of m with $\nu(\pm\frac{5}{2}) = 1$, $\nu(\pm\frac{3}{2}) = 2$, $\nu(\pm\frac{1}{2}) = 3$ (Table 4.3). The values of $\nu(m)$ for arbitrary values of I_1 and I_2 will be determined in Section 4.E.

[8] This statement can be proved by mathematical induction on N.

TABLE 4.2

PRODUCT KETS FOR TWO SPINS WITH $I_1 = I_2 = 1$

Product ket	m_1	m_2	m	$\nu(m)$
$\|1, 1; 1, 1\rangle$	1	1	2	1
$\|1, 1; 1, 0\rangle$	1	0	1	2
$\|1, 0; 1, 1\rangle$	0	1	1	
$\|1, 1; 1, -1\rangle$	1	-1	0	3
$\|1, 0; 1, 0\rangle$	0	0	0	
$\|1, -1; 1, 1\rangle$	-1	1	0	
$\|1, -1; 1, 0\rangle$	-1	0	-1	2
$\|1, 0; 1, -1\rangle$	0	-1	-1	
$\|1, -1; 1, -1\rangle$	-1	-1	-2	1

TABLE 4.3

PRODUCT KETS FOR TWO SPINS WITH $I_1 = \frac{3}{2}, I_2 = 1$

Product ket	m_1	m_2	m	$\nu(m)$
$\|\frac{3}{2}, \frac{3}{2}; 1, 1\rangle$	$\frac{3}{2}$	1	$\frac{5}{2}$	1
$\|\frac{3}{2}, \frac{3}{2}; 1, 0\rangle$	$\frac{3}{2}$	0	$\frac{3}{2}$	2
$\|\frac{3}{2}, \frac{1}{2}; 1, 1\rangle$	$\frac{1}{2}$	1	$\frac{3}{2}$	
$\|\frac{3}{2}, \frac{3}{2}; 1, -1\rangle$	$\frac{3}{2}$	-1	$\frac{1}{2}$	3
$\|\frac{3}{2}, \frac{1}{2}; 1, 0\rangle$	$\frac{1}{2}$	0	$\frac{1}{2}$	
$\|\frac{3}{2}, -\frac{1}{2}; 1, 1\rangle$	$-\frac{1}{2}$	1	$\frac{1}{2}$	
$\|\frac{3}{2}, -\frac{3}{2}; 1, 1\rangle$	$-\frac{3}{2}$	1	$-\frac{1}{2}$	3
$\|\frac{3}{2}, -\frac{1}{2}; 1, 0\rangle$	$-\frac{1}{2}$	0	$-\frac{1}{2}$	
$\|\frac{3}{2}, \frac{1}{2}; 1, -1\rangle$	$\frac{1}{2}$	-1	$-\frac{1}{2}$	
$\|\frac{3}{2}, -\frac{3}{2}; 1, 0\rangle$	$-\frac{3}{2}$	0	$-\frac{3}{2}$	2
$\|\frac{3}{2}, -\frac{1}{2}; 1, -1\rangle$	$-\frac{1}{2}$	-1	$-\frac{3}{2}$	
$\|\frac{3}{2}, -\frac{3}{2}; 1, -1\rangle$	$-\frac{3}{2}$	-1	$-\frac{5}{2}$	1

In the important special case of a spin system consisting entirely of spin-$\frac{1}{2}$ particles, a simple combinatorial argument leads to the formula

$$\nu(m) = \frac{N!}{\left(\frac{N}{2} - m\right)! \left(\frac{N}{2} + m\right)!} \tag{3.25}$$

The sum of $\nu(m)$ from $m = -N/2$ to $m = +N/2$ is 2^N, so that (3.25) has all the properties required by (3.24).

The preceding results can be used to described the general structure of the matrix for $\mathbf{I}^2$ in the product basis. Since $\mathbf{I}^2$ commutes with I_z,

$$\langle m' \mid \mathbf{I}^2 I_z - I_z \mathbf{I}^2 \mid m \rangle = (m - m')\langle m' \mid \mathbf{I}^2 \mid m \rangle = 0,$$

where $\mid m\rangle$ and $\mid m'\rangle$ are abbreviations for two product kets with the indicated eigenvalues of I_z. It follows that the matrix elements of $\mathbf{I}^2$ vanish unless $m' = m$. Thus the matrix for $\mathbf{I}^2$ is the direct sum of $2I_{\max} + 1$ submatrices whose dimensions are given by the $\nu(m)$. The form of the matrix for $\mathbf{I}^2$ is shown in Fig. 4.2. All matrix elements not enclosed by the diagonal blocks vanish. The label in each block specifies the eigenvalue of I_z; that is, the submatrices enclosed by these blocks

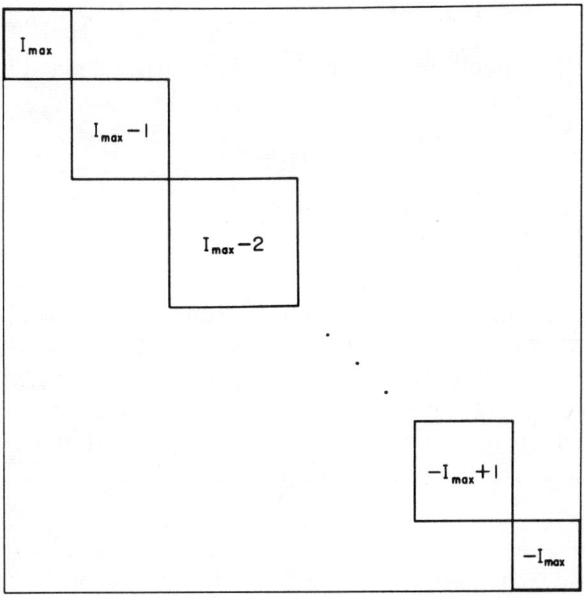

FIG. 4.2. The form of the matrix for $\mathbf{I}^2$ in the product basis. The square blocks are labeled with the eigenvalues of I_z and contain all nonvanishing matrix elements of $\mathbf{I}^2$.

are generated by elements in the product basis with the indicated value of m. Since $\nu(\pm I_{\max}) = 1$, it follows that the two products kets $|I_1, \pm I_1; I_2, \pm I_2; ...; I_N, \pm I_N\rangle$ are eigenvectors of $\mathbf{I}^2$ with the eigenvalue $I_{\max}(I_{\max} + 1)$. This may be directly verified by introducing the operator identity

$$\mathbf{I}_j \cdot \mathbf{I}_k = I_{zj}I_{zk} + \tfrac{1}{2}(I_j^+I_k^- + I_j^-I_k^+) \tag{3.26}$$

into the expression for $\mathbf{I}^2$, obtaining

$$\mathbf{I}^2 = \sum_j \mathbf{I}_j^2 + 2\sum_{j<k}\sum I_{zj}I_{zk} + \sum_{j<k}\sum (I_j^+I_k^- + I_j^-I_k^+), \tag{3.27}$$

and operating with $\mathbf{I}^2$ on $|I_1, \pm I_1; ...; I_N, \pm I_N\rangle$. These kets are but two of the $2I_{\max} + 1$ spin states associated with a spin quantum number $I = I_{\max}$. The remaining $2I_{\max} - 1$ states with $I = I_{\max}$, and all other spin quantum numbers, are obtained by diagonalizing[9] the sub-matrices of $\mathbf{I}^2$ whose dimensions exceed unity.

It is clear that no spin quantum number can exceed $I_{\max}$, and, since $\nu(I_{\max}) = 1$, $g_{I_{\max}} = 1$. The spin quantum numbers will be of the form (cf. Section 3.E)

$$I = I_{\max},\quad I_{\max} - 1,\quad I_{\max} - 2, ..., I_{\min} \geqslant 0, \tag{3.28}$$

where the spin quantum number $I_{\min}$ is implicitly defined by the condition

$$\sum_{I=I_{\min}}^{I_{\max}} g_I(2I + 1) = \prod_{j=1}^{N} (2I_j + 1). \tag{3.29}$$

C. Systems with Spin $\frac{1}{2}$

When the spin quantum numbers have been determined, sets of linear equations can be formed whose solutions can be used to express the eigenvectors of $\mathbf{I}^2$ and I_z as linear combinations of elements in the product basis (*3*). However, the results required most frequently in the analysis of high-resolution spectra are the values of the spin quantum numbers and their multiplicities for systems composed of identical

[9] The matrices for $\mathbf{I}^2$ and I_z, relative to the product basis, have been labeled by the values of the total spin variable m. Upon reduction to diagonal form, these matrices will not, in general, have the diagonal form described previously, but the desired form can be achieved by some trivial interchanges of rows and columns in the matrices for $\mathbf{I}^2$, I_z, and the diagonalizing unitary matrix.

particles with all $I_j = \frac{1}{2}$. These results can be deduced without solving the eigenvalue problem, but before carrying out the analysis, the explicit solution of the eigenvalue problem will be illustrated for some relevant special cases.

1. $N = 2$. The product basis is $\{|++\rangle, |+-\rangle, |-+\rangle, |--\rangle\}$, whose elements are represented by the column vectors determined in Section 2.B. Operating on the product kets with $I_z = I_{z1} + I_{z2}$, one obtains

$$I_z|++\rangle = 1 \cdot |++\rangle, \qquad I_z|+-\rangle = 0 \cdot |+-\rangle,$$
$$I_z|-+\rangle = 0 \cdot |-+\rangle, \qquad I_z|--\rangle = -1 \cdot |--\rangle.$$

These equations show that the matrix for I_z is

$$I_z = \begin{pmatrix} 1 & 0 & 0 & 0 \\ 0 & 0 & 0 & 0 \\ 0 & 0 & 0 & 0 \\ 0 & 0 & 0 & -1 \end{pmatrix},$$

a result which could have been written down immediately by adding the Kronecker products for $I_{z1} \otimes 1_2$ and $1_1 \otimes I_{z2}$ given in Table 4.1.

The product kets $|++\rangle$ and $|--\rangle$ are eigenvectors of

$$\mathbf{I}^2 = \mathbf{I}_1{}^2 + \mathbf{I}_2{}^2 + 2I_{z1}I_{z2} + I_1{}^+I_2{}^- + I_1{}^-I_2{}^+,$$

both eigenvectors corresponding to a total spin of $I_{\max} = I_1 + I_2 = \frac{1}{2} + \frac{1}{2} = 1$. The only other possible value of I allowed by (3.28) is $I = I_{\max} - 1 = 0$. Since $\dim S = 2^2 = 4$, $2I_{\max} + 1 = 3$, and $2(I_{\max} - 1) + 1 = 1$, it follows that $g_1 = g_0 = 1$, in agreement with (3.17), here specialized to

$$g_1(2 \cdot 1 + 1) + g_0(2 \cdot 0 + 1) = 2^2.$$

The matrix for $\mathbf{I}^2$ may be obtained from the following calculations:

$$\mathbf{I}^2|+-\rangle = (\tfrac{3}{4} + \tfrac{3}{4} - \tfrac{1}{2})\{|+-\rangle + |-+\rangle\} = |+-\rangle + |-+\rangle,$$
$$\mathbf{I}^2|-+\rangle = (\tfrac{3}{4} + \tfrac{3}{4} - \tfrac{1}{2})\{|-+\rangle + |+-\rangle\} = |+-\rangle + |-+\rangle,$$
$$\langle +-|\mathbf{I}^2|+-\rangle = \langle -+|\mathbf{I}^2|+-\rangle = \langle +-|\mathbf{I}^2|-+\rangle = 1;$$

hence

$$\mathbf{I}^2 = \begin{pmatrix} 2 & 0 & 0 & 0 \\ 0 & 1 & 1 & 0 \\ 0 & 1 & 1 & 0 \\ 0 & 0 & 0 & 2 \end{pmatrix}.$$

The matrix for $\mathbf{I}^2$ may also be obtained from Table 4.1.

The eigenvalues of $\mathbf{I}^2$ are obtained by solving

$$\det(\mathbf{I}^2 - \lambda I) = \lambda(2 - \lambda)^3 = 0.$$

Evidently $\lambda = 2, 2, 2, 0$. These eigenvalues can be written in the form $I(I + 1)$, so that $I = 1, 1, 1, 0$, in agreement with the results obtained previously.

The eigenvectors of $\mathbf{I}^2$ that are linear combinations of $|+-\rangle$ and $|-+\rangle$ have the column-vector form:

$$c_1 \,|+-\rangle + c_2 \,|-+\rangle = \begin{pmatrix} 0 \\ c_1 \\ c_2 \\ 0 \end{pmatrix},$$

and satisfy the matrix equation

$$\begin{pmatrix} 2 & 0 & 0 & 0 \\ 0 & 1 & 1 & 0 \\ 0 & 1 & 1 & 0 \\ 0 & 0 & 0 & 2 \end{pmatrix} \begin{pmatrix} 0 \\ c_1 \\ c_2 \\ 0 \end{pmatrix} = \lambda \begin{pmatrix} 0 \\ c_1 \\ c_2 \\ 0 \end{pmatrix},$$

where $\lambda = 0$ for $I = 0$ and $\lambda = 2$ for $I = 1$. From this matrix equation one obtains

$$c_1 + c_2 = \lambda c_1 , \qquad c_1 + c_2 = \lambda c_2 .$$

For $\lambda = 0$, $c_1 = -c_2$, and for $\lambda = 2$, $c_1 = c_2$. Combining these results with the normalization condition $|c_1|^2 + |c_2|^2 = 1$, and choosing the phase factors so that the coefficients are real, one obtains

$$\frac{1}{\sqrt{2}}\{|+-\rangle + |-+\rangle\} \quad \text{for } I = 1, \qquad \frac{1}{\sqrt{2}}\{|+-\rangle - |-+\rangle\} \quad \text{for } I = 0.$$

The results of this analysis are collected in Table 4.4.

TABLE 4.4

EIGENVECTORS OF $\mathbf{I}^2$ AND I_z FOR TWO SPIN-$\frac{1}{2}$ PARTICLES

Eigenvector	Notation
$\|++\rangle$	$\|1, 1\rangle$
$\frac{1}{\sqrt{2}}\{\|+-\rangle + \|-+\rangle\}$	$\|1, 0\rangle$
$\|--\rangle$	$\|1, -1\rangle$
$\frac{1}{\sqrt{2}}\{\|+-\rangle - \|-+\rangle\}$	$\|0, 0\rangle$

The three eigenvectors with $I = 1$ are often called a *triplet* (of spin states); the eigenvector with $I = 0$ is called a *singlet* (spin state). The triplet-state spin eigenvectors are symmetric with respect to an interchange of particles 1 and 2; the singlet-state eigenvector is antisymmetric with respect to this operation.

2. $N = 3$. The product basis is given in Table 4.5, from which it is at once evident that the 8×8 matrix for $\mathbf{I}^2$ is the direct sum of four submatrices of dimensions 1, 3, 3, 1. The two 1×1 submatrices are generated by the states $|+++\rangle$ and $|---\rangle$, for which the spin variable has its maximum $(+\frac{3}{2})$ and minimum $(-\frac{3}{2})$ value for a total spin $I = I_{max} = \frac{3}{2}$. The only other value of I allowed by (3.17) is $I_{max} - 1 = \frac{1}{2}$, and, since $g_{3/2} = 1$, it follows that

$$1 \cdot (2 \cdot \tfrac{3}{2} + 1) + g_{1/2}(2 \cdot \tfrac{1}{2} + 1) = 2^3,$$

or $g_{1/2} = 2$. Thus one of the three eigenvectors formed from $|++-\rangle$, $|+-+\rangle$, and $|-++\rangle$ will have $I = \frac{3}{2}$, $m = \frac{1}{2}$; the remaining pair will have $I = \frac{1}{2}$, $m = \frac{1}{2}$. Similarly, three linear combinations of $|--+\rangle$, $|-+-\rangle$, and $|+--\rangle$ will provide one eigenvector with $I = \frac{3}{2}$, $m = -\frac{1}{2}$, and two eigenvectors with $I = \frac{1}{2}$ and $m = -\frac{1}{2}$.

TABLE 4.5

PRODUCT BASIS FOR THREE SPIN-$\frac{1}{2}$ PARTICLES

Product ket	m
$\|+++\rangle$	$\frac{3}{2}$
$\|++-\rangle, \|+-+\rangle, \|-++\rangle$	$\frac{1}{2}$
$\|+--\rangle, \|-+-\rangle, \|--+\rangle$	$-\frac{1}{2}$
$\|---\rangle$	$-\frac{3}{2}$

The 3×3 submatrices of $\mathbf{I}^2$ corresponding to $m = \pm \frac{1}{2}$ are easily computed. In fact, both matrices have the same structure,

$$\begin{pmatrix} \frac{7}{4} & 1 & 1 \\ 1 & \frac{7}{4} & 1 \\ 1 & 1 & \frac{7}{4} \end{pmatrix}.$$

Thus the linear equations for the $m = \pm \frac{1}{2}$ states are

$$\tfrac{7}{4}c_1 + c_2 + c_3 = \lambda c_1 ,$$
$$c_1 + \tfrac{7}{4}c_2 + c_3 = \lambda c_2 ,$$
$$c_1 + c_2 + \tfrac{7}{4}c_3 = \lambda c_3 ,$$

where c_1, c_2, and c_3 are the coefficients of $| ++- \rangle, | +-+ \rangle, | -++ \rangle$, or $| --+ \rangle, | -+- \rangle, | +-- \rangle$, respectively. For $\lambda = \frac{3}{2}(\frac{3}{2} + 1) = \frac{15}{4}$, these equations reduce to

$$-2c_1 + c_2 + c_3 = 0,$$
$$c_1 - 2c_2 + c_3 = 0,$$
$$c_1 + c_2 - 2c_3 = 0.$$

From the first two equations it follows that $c_1 = c_2 = c_3$. Hence the normalized eigenvectors with $I = \frac{3}{2}$, $m = \pm \frac{1}{2}$, are

$$\frac{1}{\sqrt{3}}\{| ++- \rangle + | +-+ \rangle + | -++ \rangle\},$$
$$\frac{1}{\sqrt{3}}\{| --+ \rangle + | -+- \rangle + | +-- \rangle\}.$$

TABLE 4.6

EIGENVECTORS OF $\mathbf{I}^2$ AND I_z FOR THREE SPIN-$\frac{1}{2}$ PARTICLES

Eigenvector	Notation
$\| +++ \rangle$	$\| \frac{3}{2}, \frac{3}{2} \rangle$
$\frac{1}{\sqrt{3}}\{\| ++- \rangle + \| +-+ \rangle + \| -++ \rangle\}$	$\| \frac{3}{2}, \frac{1}{2} \rangle$
$\frac{1}{\sqrt{3}}\{\| --+ \rangle + \| -+- \rangle + \| +-- \rangle\}$	$\| \frac{3}{2}, -\frac{1}{2} \rangle$
$\| --- \rangle$	$\| \frac{3}{2}, -\frac{3}{2} \rangle$
$\frac{1}{\sqrt{6}}\{\| ++- \rangle + \| +-+ \rangle -2 \| -++ \rangle\}$	$\| \frac{1}{2}, \frac{1}{2}; 1 \rangle$
$\frac{1}{\sqrt{6}}\{2 \| +-- \rangle - \| -+- \rangle - \| --+ \rangle\}$	$\| \frac{1}{2}, -\frac{1}{2}; 1 \rangle$
$\frac{1}{\sqrt{2}}\{\| ++- \rangle - \| +-+ \rangle\}$	$\| \frac{1}{2}, \frac{1}{2}; 2 \rangle$
$\frac{1}{\sqrt{2}}\{\| -+- \rangle - \| --+ \rangle\}$	$\| \frac{1}{2}, -\frac{1}{2}; 2 \rangle$

TABLE 4.7

EIGENVECTORS OF $\mathbf{I}^2$ AND I_z FOR FOUR SPIN-$\frac{1}{2}$ NUCLEI

Eigenvector	Notation
$\|++++\rangle$	$\|2, 2\rangle$
$\frac{1}{2}\{\|+++-\rangle + \|++-+\rangle + \|+-++\rangle + \|-+++\rangle\}$	$\|2, 1\rangle$
$\frac{1}{\sqrt{6}}\{\|++--\rangle + \|-++-\rangle + \|+--+\rangle + \|--++\rangle + \|+-+-\rangle + \|-+-+\rangle\}$	$\|2, 0\rangle$
$\frac{1}{2}\{\|---+\rangle + \|--+-\rangle + \|-+--\rangle + \|+---\rangle\}$	$\|2, -1\rangle$
$\|----\rangle$	$\|2, -2\rangle$
$\frac{1}{2}\{\|+++-\rangle - \|++-+\rangle + \|+-++\rangle - \|-+++\rangle\}$	$\|1, 1; 1\rangle$
$\frac{1}{\sqrt{2}}\{\|+-+-\rangle - \|-+-+\rangle\}$	$\|1, 0; 1\rangle$
$\frac{1}{2}\{\|+---\rangle - \|-+--\rangle + \|--+-\rangle - \|---+\rangle\}$	$\|1, -1; 1\rangle$
$\frac{1}{2}\{\|+++-\rangle + \|++-+\rangle - \|+-++\rangle - \|-+++\rangle\}$	$\|1, 1; 2\rangle$
$\frac{1}{\sqrt{2}}\{\|++--\rangle - \|--++\rangle\}$	$\|1, 0; 2\rangle$
$\frac{1}{2}\{\|+---\rangle + \|-+--\rangle - \|--+-\rangle - \|---+\rangle\}$	$\|1, -1; 2\rangle$
$\frac{1}{2}\{\|+++-\rangle + \|-+++\rangle - \|++-+\rangle - \|+-++\rangle\}$	$\|1, 1; 3\rangle$
$\frac{1}{\sqrt{2}}\{\|-++-\rangle - \|+--+\rangle\}$	$\|1, 0; 3\rangle$
$\frac{1}{2}\{\|--+-\rangle + \|-+--\rangle - \|---+\rangle - \|+---\rangle\}$	$\|1, -1; 3\rangle$
$\frac{1}{\sqrt{12}}\{\|++--\rangle + \|-++-\rangle + \|+--+\rangle + \|--++\rangle - 2\|+-+-\rangle - 2\|-+-+\rangle\}$	$\|0, 0; 1\rangle$
$\frac{1}{2}\{\|++--\rangle - \|-++-\rangle - \|+--+\rangle + \|--++\rangle\}$	$\|0, 0; 2\rangle$

For $\lambda = \frac{1}{2}(\frac{1}{2} + 1) = \frac{3}{4}$, there is only one independent equation for the determination of the eigenvectors corresponding to $I = \frac{1}{2}$ and $m = \pm \frac{1}{2}$,

$$c_1 + c_2 + c_3 = 0.$$

This equation together with the normalization equation and any condition on c_1, c_2, and c_3 consistent with these equations may be used to determine the c_j. The conditions (1) $c_3 = 0$ and (2) $c_1 = c_2$ lead to the eigenvectors given in Table 4.6.

3. $N = 4$. The results are given in Table 4.7. The explicit calculations will not be given, but are left as an exercise for the interested reader. It should be noted that $g_2 = 1$, $g_1 = 3$, and $g_0 = 2$, in agreement with the relation

$$5g_2 + 3g_1 + g_0 = 16,$$

obtained from (3.17). The validity of the general orthogonality relations [equations (3.20)] should be noted for all three cases.

D. Spin Quantum Numbers and Spin Multiplicities for N Spin-$\frac{1}{2}$ Particles

The spin quantum numbers and their spin multiplicities for N spin-$\frac{1}{2}$ particles can be deduced by the following simple argument. The product of N $|+\rangle$'s, that is, $|+++ \cdots +\rangle$, has $m = N/2$, and corresponds to $I = I_{\max} = N/2$, $g_{N/2} = 1$. If one of the $|+\rangle$'s is replaced by $|-\rangle$, a product ket with $m = (N/2) - 1$ results. Now one can form exactly N such product kets ($|-++ \cdots +\rangle, |+-+ \cdots +\rangle, \ldots$), and, in the diagonal scheme, one linear combination must have $I = N/2$ and $m = (N/2) - 1$. The remaining $N - 1$ eigenvectors correspond to a new total spin quantum number $I = (N/2) - 1$, with spin multiplicity $g_I = N - 1$.

Suppose, now, that two $|+\rangle$'s in $|+++ \cdots +\rangle$ are replaced with two $|-\rangle$'s to form $N(N-1)/2!$ product kets with $m = \frac{1}{2}(N-2) - 2 \cdot \frac{1}{2} = \frac{1}{2}N - 2$. In the diagonal scheme, one linear combination of these product kets must correspond to $I = N/2$, $m = N - 2$, and $N - 1$ linear combinations to $I = (N/2) - 1$. Since there are no other values of I to be accommodated, the remaining

$$\frac{N(N-1)}{2!} - \frac{(N-1)}{1!} - \frac{1}{0!}$$

linear combinations must generate a new total spin quantum number $I = \frac{1}{2}N - 2$.

In general, $k \mid +\rangle$'s can be replaced with $k \mid -\rangle$'s in

$$\frac{N(N-1)(N-2)\cdots(N-k+1)}{k!} = \binom{N}{k}$$

distinct ways, and these product kets generate a new total spin quantum number $I = \frac{1}{2}N - k$, with spin multiplicity

$$g_I = g_{(N/2)-k} \equiv g_k = \binom{N}{k} - \sum_{j=0}^{k-1} g_j \,. \tag{3.30}$$

This functional relation can be solved by replacing k with $k - 1$, and subtracting the resulting equation from (3.30) to obtain

$$g_k = \binom{N}{k} - \binom{N}{k-1}.$$

The process of replacing $\mid +\rangle$'s with $\mid -\rangle$'s can be continued until its repeated application would lead to values of $I < 0$, and/or values of $\mid m \mid$ exceeding $N/2$. These conditions require k to be less than or equal

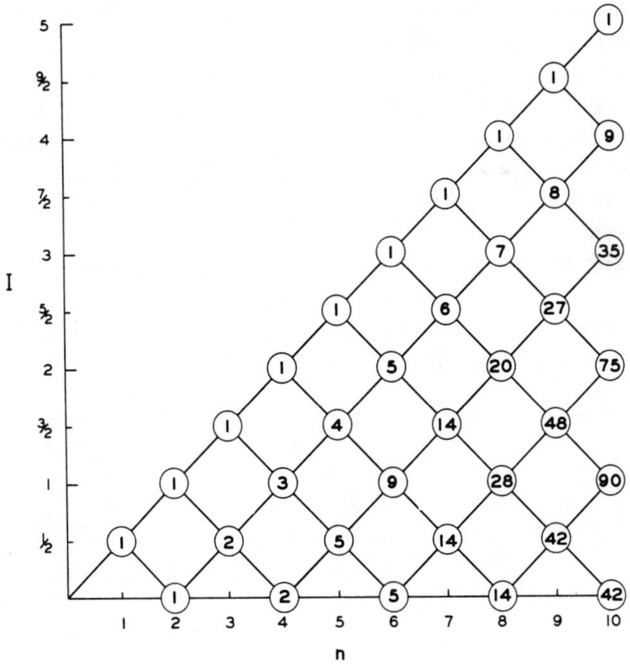

FIG. 4.3. Total spin quantum numbers and their multiplicities for N spin-$\frac{1}{2}$ particles.

to $N/2$ or $(N-1)/2$, accordingly as N is even or odd. Thus for N spin-$\frac{1}{2}$ particles,

$$I = \tfrac{1}{2}N - k, \tag{3.31}$$

$$g_I = (N - 2k + 1)\frac{N!}{(N-k+1)!\,k!}, \tag{3.32}$$

$$k = 0, 1, 2, \ldots, \begin{cases} \tfrac{1}{2}N, & \text{if } N \text{ is even,} \\ \tfrac{1}{2}(N-1), & \text{if } N \text{ is odd.} \end{cases} \tag{3.33}$$

Equation (3.17) is now equivalent to

$$\sum_k (N - 2k + 1)^2 \frac{N!}{(N-k+1)!\,k!} = 2^N, \tag{3.34}$$

which is in fact an identity.

The values of I and g_I computed with (3.31) and (3.32) are given in the branching diagram shown in Fig. 4.3 for several values of N.

E. Two Angular Momenta with $I_1 \geqslant I_2$

The possible values of the total spin quantum numbers for a system of two particles with spins I_1 and I_2 may also be deduced by the procedure described above. The maximum value of the spin variable occurs for the state $|I_1, I_1\rangle\,|I_2, I_2\rangle$, for which $m = I_{\max} = I_1 + I_2$. The next largest value of m, $I_{\max} - 1$, is generated by the states $|I_1, I_1 - 1\rangle\,|I_2, I_2\rangle$ and $|I_1, I_1\rangle\,|I_2, I_2 - 1\rangle$. In the diagonal scheme, one of the two linear combinations of these states must have $I = I_1 + I_2$ and $m = I_1 + I_2 - 1$, and the second linear combination must correspond to a new total spin $I_1 + I_2 - 1$, for which the spin variable has its maximum value.

Continuing this process, onc can generate the product kets shown in the accompanying tabulation.

$I_{\max}$	$I_{\max} - 1$	$I_{\max} - 2$	$I_{\max} - k$
$\|I_1, I_1\rangle\,\|I_2, I_2\rangle$	$\|I_1, I_1 - 1\rangle\,\|I_2, I_2\rangle$	$\|I_1, I_1 - 2\rangle\,\|I_2, I_2\rangle$	$\cdots\,\|I_1, I_1 - k\rangle\,\|I_2, I_2\rangle$
	$\|I_1, I_1\rangle\,\|I_2, I_2 - 1\rangle$	$\|I_1, I_1 - 1\rangle\,\|I_2, I_2 - 1\rangle$	$\cdots\,\|I_1, I_1 - k + 1\rangle\,\|I_2, I_2 - 1\rangle$
		$\|I_1, I_1\rangle\,\|I_2, I_2 - 2\rangle$	$\cdots\,\|I_1, I_1 - k + 2\rangle\,\|I_2, I_2 - 2\rangle$
			$\vdots$
			$\cdots\,\|I_1, I_1 - 1\rangle\,\|I_2, I_2 - k + 1\rangle$
			$\cdots\,\|I_1, I_1\rangle\,\|I_2, I_2 - k\rangle$

At the kth step, one obtains $k + 1$ product kets with $m = I_{max} - k$. In the diagonal scheme, k linear combinations of these product kets will be associated with spin quantum numbers already obtained; the remaining linear combination introduces a new spin quantum number $I = I_{max} - k$. Since only one new value of I is introduced at each step, it follows that $g_I = 1$ for all I, and that

$$\sum_{I_{min}}^{I_{max}} (2I + 1) = (2I_1 + 1)(2I_2 + 1). \tag{3.35}$$

The above process cannot be continued indefinitely, since the spin variables m_1 and m_2 must satisfy

$$-I_1 \leqslant m_1 \leqslant I_1, \qquad -I_2 \leqslant m_2 \leqslant I_2.$$

The value of k is in fact delimited by I_1 or I_2, whichever is smaller. It will be assumed that $I_2 \leqslant I_1$. Thus if $I_2 = \frac{1}{2}$, k cannot exceed 1, since $| m_2 |$ cannot exceed $\frac{1}{2}$.

The upper limit on k can be obtained by carrying out the summation in (3.35). For this purpose one requires the summation formulas:

$$\sum_{x_1}^{x_2} x = \sum_{x_0}^{x_2} x - \sum_{x_0}^{x_1-1} x, \qquad \sum_{x_0}^{n} x = \frac{n(n+1)}{2},$$

where the values of x are integrally spaced, but may be integral or half-integral, and $x_0 = \frac{1}{2}$ or 1. It follows that

$$\sum_{I_{min}}^{I_{max}} (2I + 1) = \{I_{max}(I_{max} + 1) - I_{min}(I_{min} - 1)\} + I_{max} - I_{min} + 1,$$

and, since $I_{max} = I_1 + I_2$, that $I_{min}^2 = (I_1 - I_2)^2$. By assumption, $I_2 \leqslant I_1$; hence

$$I_{min} = I_1 - I_2. \tag{3.36}$$

These results are summarized in the following equations:

$$\begin{aligned} I = I_1 + I_2 - k; \qquad & k = 0, 1, ..., 2I_2; \\ g_I = 1; \qquad & I_2 \leqslant I_1. \end{aligned} \tag{3.37}$$

It is now easy to enumerate the degeneracy of each m value in (3.21). The results are given in Table 4.8, whose columns give the $2I + 1$ eigenvectors of $\mathbf{I}^2$ and I_z for the specified value of I. The last column gives the degeneracy function $\nu(m)$, that is, the number of eigenvectors in each row of the table.

TABLE 4.8

QUANTUM NUMBERS FOR TWO SPIN ANGULAR MOMENTA

I_{max}	$I_{max} - 1$	$I_{max} - 2$		I_{min}	$\nu(m)$
I_{max}					1
$I_{max} - 1$	$I_{max} - 1$				2
$I_{max} - 2$	$I_{max} - 2$	$I_{max} - 2$			3
.	.	.	...		.
I_{min}	I_{min}	I_{min}	...	I_{min}	$2(I_{max} - I_{min}) + 1$
$I_{min} - 1$	$I_{min} - 1$	$I_{min} - 1$	...	$I_{min} - 1$	$2(I_{max} - I_{min}) + 1$
.	.	.	...	.	.
$-I_{min} + 1$	$-I_{min} + 1$	$-I_{min} + 1$	...	$-I_{min} + 1$	$2(I_{max} - I_{min}) + 1$
$-I_{min}$	$-I_{min}$	$-I_{min}$	...	$-I_{min}$	$2(I_{max} - I_{min}) + 1$
.	.	.	...		.
$-I_{max} + 2$	$-I_{max} + 2$	$-I_{max} + 2$			3
$-I_{max} + 1$	$-I_{max} + 1$				2
$-I_{max}$					1

Equations (3.37) can be used to construct tables of the spin quantum numbers and their multiplicities for $N > 2$. Consider, for example, two particles with $I_1 = I_2 = 1$. According to (3.37), the values of I are 2, 1, 0, with $g_2 = g_1 = g_0 = 1$. The values of I and g_I for three particles with spin 1 are obtained by applying (3.37) to the results for $N = 2$. In this way one obtains scheme (a). The first two columns give I and g_I for $N = 2$.

2	1	3,	2,	1
1	1		2,	1, 0
0	1			1

(a) $I_1 = I_2 = I_3 = 1$; $N = 3$.

3	1	4,	3,	2		
2	2		3,	2,	1	
1	3			2,	1,	0
0	1				1	

(b) $I_1 = I_2 = I_3 = I_4 = 1$; $N = 4$.

The numbers after the heavy vertical rule in any horizontal row are the spin quantum numbers obtained by adding the third spin quantum number to the value of I entered at the left. Each new spin quantum number has the multiplicity entered to the left of the heavy rule. Thus three particles with spin 1 yield $I = 3, 2, 1, 0$, with $g_3 = 1$, $g_2 = 2$,

$g_1 = 3$, $g_0 = 1$. With four spin-1 particles, one has scheme (b), so that $I = 4, 3, 2, 1, 0$, with $g_4 = 1$, $g_3 = 3$, $g_2 = 6$, $g_1 = 6$, $g_0 = 1$.

Table 4.9 gives some additional results for spin-1 particles, Table 4.10 some results for particles with spin $\frac{3}{2}$. In each table, the first column tabulates the values of I, the last row the values of N.

TABLE 4.9

SPIN QUANTUM NUMBERS AND SPIN MULTIPLICITIES FOR N PARTICLES WITH SPIN 1

8								1
7							1	7
6						1	6	28
5					1	5	21	76
4				1	4	15	49	151
3			1	3	10	29	81	223
2		1	2	6	15	37	93	259
1	1	1	3	6	12	27	85	205
0		1	1	3	9	21	27	85
	N: 1	2	3	4	5	6	7	8

TABLE 4.10

SPIN QUANTUM NUMBERS AND SPIN MULTIPLICITIES FOR N PARTICLES WITH SPIN $\frac{3}{2}$

9						1
17/2						
8						5
15/2					1	
7						15
13/2					4	
6				1		35
11/2					10	
5				3		64
9/2			1		20	
4				6		96
7/2			2		30	
3		1		10		120
5/2			3		36	
2		1		11		120
3/2	1		4		34	
1		1		9		90
1/2			2		20	
0		1		4		34
	N: 1	2	3	4	5	6

REFERENCES

1. P.R. Halmos, "Finite-Dimensional Vector Spaces," 2nd ed., Chaps. I and II. Van Nostrand, Princeton, New Jersey, 1958.
2. (a) H. Weyl, "The Theory of Groups and Quantum Mechanics," pp. 89–93. Dover, New York, 1949. (b) E. P. Wigner, "Group Theory," Chap. 2. Academic Press, New York, 1959.
3. (a) Reference 2(b), Chaps. 21 and 24. (b) M. E. Rose, "Elementary Theory of Angular Momentum," Chap. III. Wiley, New York, 1957. (c) A. R. Edmonds, "Angular Momentum in Quantum Mechanics," Chap. 3. Princeton Univ. Press, Princeton, New Jersey, 1957. (d) E. U. Condon and G. H. Shortley, "Theory of Atomic Spectra," Chap. III. Cambridge Univ. Press, London and New York, 1935.

CHAPTER 5

General Theory of Steady-State Spectra

1. Characteristics of High-Resolution Spectra

A. Atomic Shifts

When an isolated nucleus is subjected to a stationary z-field $\mathbf{H}$, the nuclear magnetic moment, considered as a classical vector, precesses about $\mathbf{H}$ with angular Larmor frequency $|\gamma|H$. If the nucleus also experiences a circularly polarized rf field,

$$\mathbf{H}_{\mathrm{rf}} = H_1\left(\mathbf{e}_x \cos \omega t - \mathbf{e}_y \frac{\gamma}{|\gamma|} \sin \omega t\right) \qquad (\dot{\omega} = 0),$$

the nuclear magnetic moment will execute the classical motion described in Chapter 1. However, the nucleus will not undergo the rather dramatic changes in orientation characteristic of the resonance phenomenon if

$$|\gamma| H \neq \omega.$$

To establish the resonance condition, the magnitude of the z field must be adjusted to

$$H_0 = \frac{\omega}{|\gamma|}. \tag{1.1}$$

The situation is somewhat different when the nucleus is contained in an atom or molecule, for it is then necessary to include the contributions of secondary magnetic fields set up at the nucleus by the field-induced motions of the atomic or molecular electrons. For atoms in S states, the atomic electrons precess about $\mathbf{H}$ with angular velocity $\boldsymbol{\omega} = -e\mathbf{H}/2m_e c$.

This precession is equivalent to a diamagnetic current, and a simple classical analysis (*1*) can be used to obtain the relation

$$\mathbf{H}_{\text{ind}} = \frac{eV(0)}{3m_e c^2}\mathbf{H} = -\sigma\mathbf{H}, \tag{1.2}$$

where $V(0)$ is the electrostatic potential of the electronic charge distribution at the nucleus. Since $V(0)$ is negative, the induced field opposes the applied field, so that the net field at the nucleus is

$$\mathbf{H}_{\text{nuc}} = (1 - \sigma)\mathbf{H}. \tag{1.3}$$

The positive constant $\sigma = -eV(0)/3m_e c^2$ is called the *nuclear shielding constant*; its value reflects the extent to which the enveloping electrons shield the nucleus from the field **H**.

For a hydrogen atom in a $1S$ state, $V(0)$ is equal to the average value of $-e/r$. Thus

$$\sigma_{1S}^{(H)} = \frac{e^2}{3m_e c^2 a_0} = 1.78 \times 10^{-5},$$

where a_0 is the Bohr radius. For atoms with large Z, the Fermi-Thomas approximation (*1*) for $V(0)$ yields

$$\sigma = 3.19 \times 10^{-5} Z^{4/3},$$

from which one may easily estimate atomic shielding constants. For example, the shielding constants of fluorine ($Z = 9$) and phosphorus ($Z = 15$) atoms are about 30 and 70 times greater than $\sigma_{1S}^{(H)}$ (*2*).

From (1.3) it follows that if $\mathbf{H}_0$ is the field required for resonance with the unshielded nucleus, the resonance condition for the shielded atomic nucleus will be established when the applied field is increased to a value $\mathbf{H}_R$ such that

$$\mathbf{H}_0 = (1 - \sigma)\mathbf{H}_R\,. \tag{1.4}$$

Thus the magnitude of the applied field at resonance is

$$H_R = \frac{H_0}{1-\sigma} = H_0(1 + \sigma + \sigma^2 + \cdots).$$

Since σ is usually small compared with unity, powers of σ higher than the first may be neglected, so that

$$\sigma = \frac{H_R - H_0}{H_0} \qquad (\sigma \ll 1). \tag{1.5}$$

In this approximation, σ may be described as the fractional increase required in H_0 to establish the resonance condition in a shielded atom.

B. Molecular Shifts

The shielding corrections described above are known as *Lamb corrections*; they are characterized by their diamagnetic, isotropic nature—direct consequences of the assumed spherical symmetry of the electronic charge distribution. In a molecule the charge distribution about a given nucleus is seldom spherically symmetric, so that the induced field at the nucleus need not be purely diamagnetic with respect to the applied field or even collinear with it. The anisotropy of molecular shielding must be described by a shielding tensor. The shielding tensor is a function of the orientation of the molecule and is usually denoted $\boldsymbol{\sigma}_\lambda$, where the subscript λ denotes all parameters required to specify the orientation of the molecule with respect to an (xyz) coordinate system fixed in the laboratory. For a specified orientation λ, the resultant field at the nucleus is given by

$$\mathbf{H}_\lambda = (I - \boldsymbol{\sigma}_\lambda)\mathbf{H},$$

where I is the (second-rank) unit tensor.

The general form of the magnetic shielding tensor is not required in liquid systems, where the collision frequency is much larger than the nuclear Larmor frequency. For such systems, to which the remainder of this book is restricted, it is permissible to assume that all orientations λ occur with equal probability. For the Larmor frequency of a nucleus in a molecule should not be very different from that in an atom, which is about 10^7 sec^{-1} for fields of the order of 10,000 G, and a collision frequency of 10^{12} sec^{-1} is not uncommon in liquids at room temperature. During a single Larmor period a particular molecule will experience some 10^5 collisions, so the assumption that all molecular orientations are equally probable will normally be a good one.

The random average of $\boldsymbol{\sigma}_\lambda$ may be conveniently described in terms of the principal axes of the shielding tensor. The principal axes are orthogonal $(x'y'z')$ axes fixed in the molecule with the origin of coordinates at the nucleus in question. Each principal axis is associated with a scalar σ_k $(k = x', y', z')$, called a *principal component* of $\boldsymbol{\sigma}_\lambda$, such that if a field $\mathbf{H}$ is directed along a principal axis, the field at the nucleus is $(1 - \sigma_k)\mathbf{H}$. When the molecule, and with it the principal axes, undergo rapid, random reorientations with respect to the space-fixed coordinate system, each of the principal axes enters with probability $\frac{1}{3}$, so that

$$\langle\boldsymbol{\sigma}\rangle_{\mathrm{av}\lambda} = \tfrac{1}{3}(\sigma_{x'} + \sigma_{y'} + \sigma_{z'})I = \tfrac{1}{3}(\mathrm{tr}\,\boldsymbol{\sigma}_\lambda)I.$$

Defining σ to be $\frac{1}{3}$ of the trace of $\boldsymbol{\sigma}_\lambda$, it follows that

$$\langle \mathbf{H}_\lambda \rangle_{\text{av}\lambda} = \langle I - \boldsymbol{\sigma}_\lambda \rangle_{\text{av}} \mathbf{H} = (1 - \sigma)\mathbf{H}.$$

Random averaging thus leads to an effectively isotropic shielding of the nucleus.

A theoretical expression for the molecular shielding constant can be derived by a straightforward application of perturbation theory (*3*, *4*). The (averaged) shielding constant is obtained as a sum of two terms: (1) a diamagnetic term analogous to (1.2), with $V(0)$ interpreted as the electrostatic potential set up at the nucleus by the molecular electrons; (2) a paramagnetic correction, which may cancel all or some part of the diamagnetic term. The paramagnetic term is the major obstacle to the calculation of molecular shielding constants. Its evaluation requires a knowledge of the wave functions and energy levels of the unperturbed system—quantities that are not presently available. The magnitude of the paramagnetic terms in molecules can be illustrated by molecular hydrogen, for which $\sigma(H_2) = 2.62 \times 10^{-5}$. The diamagnetic and paramagnetic contributions are 3.21×10^{-5} and -0.59×10^{-5}, respectively (*3*).

One significant result of the theory is that it accounts for the fact that a given nucleus exhibits different resonant fields (or frequencies) when contained in different molecules. For, since the wave functions and energies vary from molecule to molecule, the shielding constant of a given nucleus should be different in molecules of different chemical composition.

The difference of the resonant fields for the shielded and unshielded nucleus is called the *chemical shift* (*5*). The difference of the chemical shifts for a given nucleus, as observed in two different molecules, is called the *intermolecular chemical shift*. For example, the observed intermolecular shift between the protons of hydrogen and those of water is 6 mG at 10,000 G. The intermolecular shifts (*6*) of some common nuclei are indicated in Fig. 5.1.

The lack of input data required for exact theoretical determinations of molecular shielding constants has compelled the use of approximate calculations (*6*). Although the results of these calculations are in reasonable agreement with observed chemical shifts and provide firm support for the general theory, accurate chemical shifts must be determined experimentally.[1]

[1] Experimentally the shift of the resonance of a given nucleus in a particular compound is usually measured with respect to the resonance of the same nucleus in a suitable reference compound.

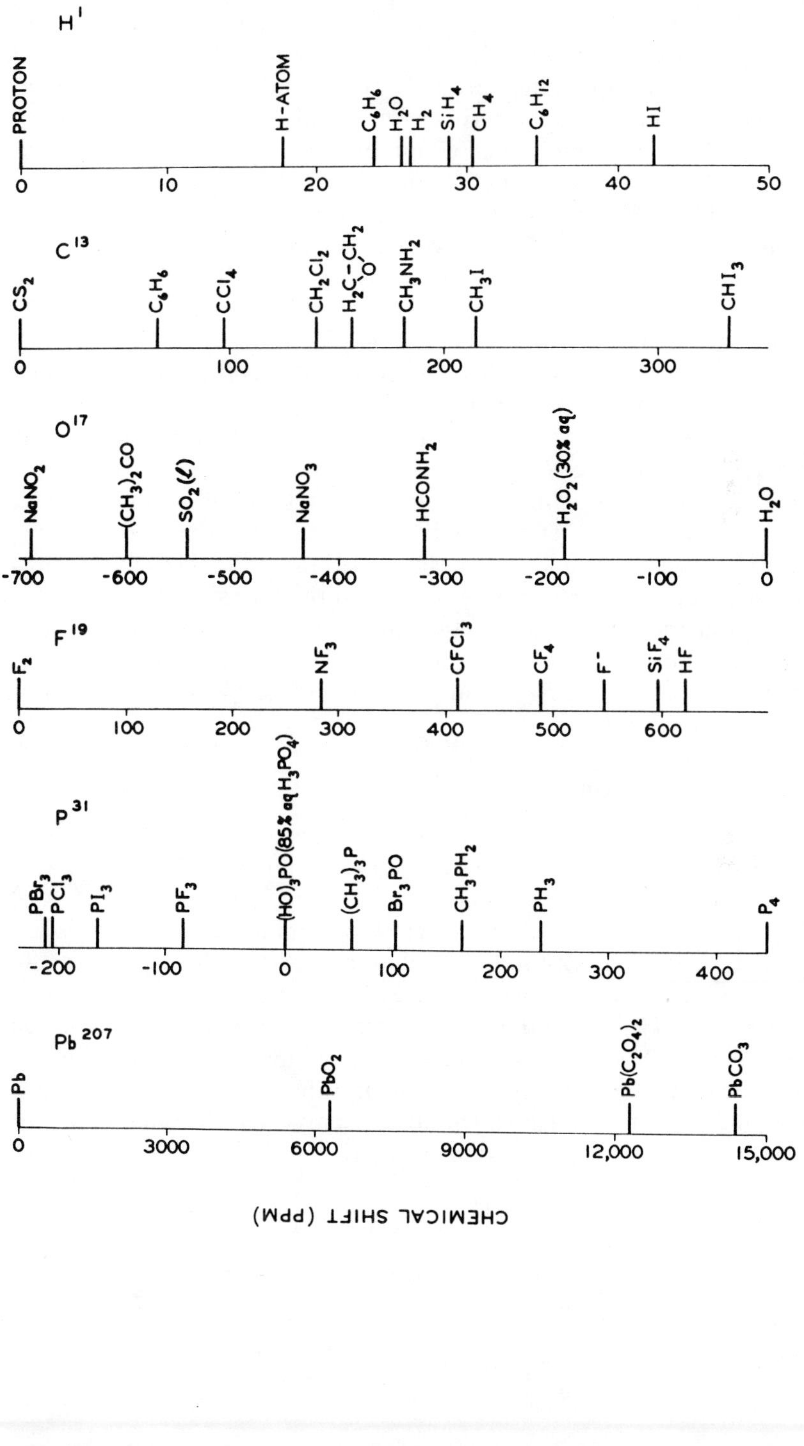

FIG. 5.1. Representative intermolecular chemical shifts (uncorrected for bulk susceptibility) for some common nuclei.

It should be recognized that calculated shielding constants refer to the isolated molecule, while experimental observations are referred to macroscopic samples. The shielding constant of a nucleus in an isolated molecule depends upon the molecular electronic structure, which in turn depends upon the internuclear distances. Since internuclear distances vary during molecular vibrations and rotations, the shielding constant will depend upon the rotational and vibrational states of the molecule. The frequencies of molecular rotations are comparable to the collision frequency in liquid systems, so that the lifetimes of rotational states in liquids are of the order of 10^{-12} sec. Thus the shielding constant is effectively averaged over any accessible rotational states.[2] On the other hand, the high-frequency vibrational states are not collision-averaged; their characteristic frequencies (10^{12} to 10^{14} cps) are much larger than nuclear Larmor frequencies, so that the shielding constants associated with such states are averaged over the vibrational motions to the values associated with the corresponding equilibrium configurations. The observed shielding constant of a molecule in a liquid system thus includes a weighted average of the shielding constants for the various vibrational states, the most important contribution at the temperatures of high-resolution experiments coming from the lowest vibrational state.

Inter- and intramolecular interactions (e.g., hydrogen bonding) can also make important contributions to observed shielding constants, and appropriate referencing techniques must be used whenever chemical shifts are compared (*6*).

C. Intramolecular Chemical Shifts

In the preceding section it was tacitly assumed that only one of the nuclei in the molecule possessed a magnetic moment. Consider now a molecule containing two magnetic nuclei with gyromagnetic ratios γ_j and γ_k. If $\gamma_j \neq \gamma_k$, an intramolecular shift certainly exists, but it is too large to be included within the small range of field sweeps normally used in high-resolution experiments. For example, if $j = H^1$, $k = F^{19}$, and $H_R = 10{,}000$ G for the proton, the fluorine resonance will be shifted some 630 G ($\gamma_H/\gamma_F = 1.063$) toward high field. A more interesting situation occurs when the nuclei are identical ($\gamma_i = \gamma_j \equiv \gamma$) but possess different molecular shielding constants (*6a, 7*). The values of the applied field required for resonance are

$$H_i = \frac{H_0}{1 - \sigma_i}, \qquad H_j = \frac{H_0}{1 - \sigma_j} \qquad \left(H_0 = \frac{\omega}{|\gamma|}\right),$$

[2] The lifetimes of rotational states in liquids are so short that it is almost meaningless to talk about discrete rotational states.

and the internal or intramolecular chemical shift is defined as

$$H_{ij} \equiv H_i - H_j \approx H_0(\sigma_j - \sigma_i) = |\gamma|^{-1}\omega_{ij}.$$

When internal chemical shifts are reported in magnetic field units, the value of the fixed frequency ω or the equivalent value of H_0 must be given, since H_{ij} is proportional to ω. The value of ω need not be specified if the internal shift is reported in dimensionless units, such as the intramolecular shift in parts per million (ppm):

$$\frac{H_i - H_j}{H_0} \times 10^6 = \frac{|\gamma|(H_i - H_j)}{\omega} \times 10^6 \approx (\sigma_j - \sigma_i) \times 10^6.$$

In a fixed-frequency experiment, the applied field is increased from an initial value less than H_i and H_j to a final value greater than H_i and H_j. If $\sigma_i < \sigma_j$, the resonances appear in the order (i, j). On the other hand, if the applied field has the fixed value H_0, and the frequency of the rf field is increased from an initial value less than either resonance frequency to a final value greater than either resonance frequency, the resonances appear in reversed order. Although most experiments are performed at a fixed rf frequency, chemical shifts are often reported in frequency units, and this practice will be followed here. Furthermore, all spectral calculations will be carried out in terms of experiments performed at a fixed field.

An example of an internal chemical shift is provided by the proton resonances of dichloroacetic acid (Fig. 5.2). The observed internal

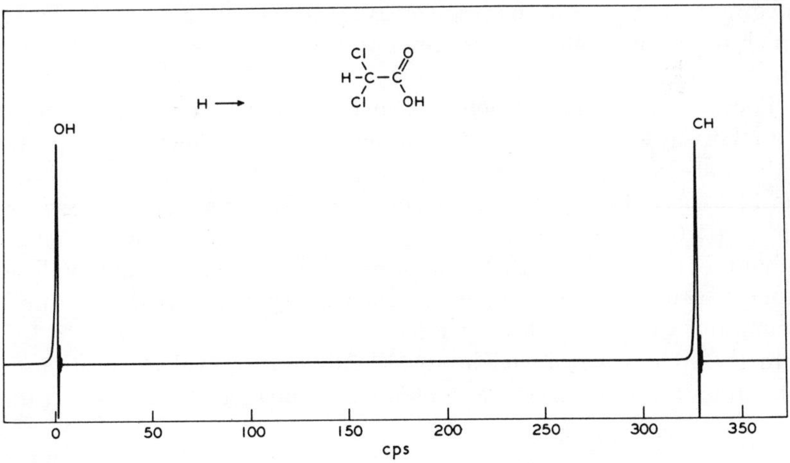

FIG. 5.2. Proton magnetic resonance spectrum of pure dichloracetic acid at 60 Mcps.

shift at 60 Mcps is 325.2 cps or 5.42 ppm. Since the intensities of both resonances are equal, the magnetic resonance spectrum alone does not provide enough information to decide which proton gives rise to a particular resonance. To settle questions of this nature, it is frequently necessary to refer to accumulated data (*6*). In the present instance, these data indicate that the carboxyl group proton is responsible for the low field resonance.[3]

When two, or more, identical nuclei occupy structurally equivalent positions in the molecule, then $\omega_{jk} = 0$ for all structurally equivalent pairs (j, k). For example, the internal proton shifts vanish in benzene because the symmetry of the molecule demands that $\omega_j = \omega_k = \cdots$ for all protons. There are also many instances where the internal shifts of a set of nuclei vanish through an effective symmetry brought about by a rapid internal rotation. Internal rotation simply introduces another averaging process for the molecular shielding constants. If the mean rate of the internal rotation is large compared to the range of variation of the nuclear Larmor frequencies, the shielding constants of the nuclei may be replaced by a single averaged shielding constant. This condition is satisfied by the methyl and methylene protons in many molecules, for example, CH_3OH, CH_3CH_2Cl, CH_3CH_2OH. An example is provided by the proton magnetic resonance spectrum of 1,1-di-neopentyl-2-*t*-butylethylene (Fig. 5.3). If there is rapid rotation about all carbon-carbon single bonds, one anticipates three *t*-butyl group resonances, two methylene resonances, and a single olefinic proton resonance. The observed spectrum confirms these expectations. Furthermore, the integrated intensities of the resonances are in the ratios 1 : 2 : 2 : 9 : 9 : 9, which permit immediate discrimination between the olefinic, methylene, and *t*-butyl group protons.

The analysis of a high-resolution nuclear magnetic resonance spectrum is a relatively simple problem when only shielding effects are important. If the nuclei are distributed among n distinct environments, the spectrum can be expected to consist of n resonances. Each resonance is associated with a particular environment and its intensity will be proportional to the number of nuclei in that environment. These remarks are applicable in most instances, but there are occasional departures from the implicit assumptions upon which they are based.

In the first place, nuclei in structurally nonequivalent positions are sometimes found to have nearly identical resonance frequencies. If these

[3] Unless otherwise noted, all spectra reported in this book were obtained with standard Varian high-resolution spectrometers and recorded at a constant (but unmonitored) temperature, usually in the range 25 to 40°C.

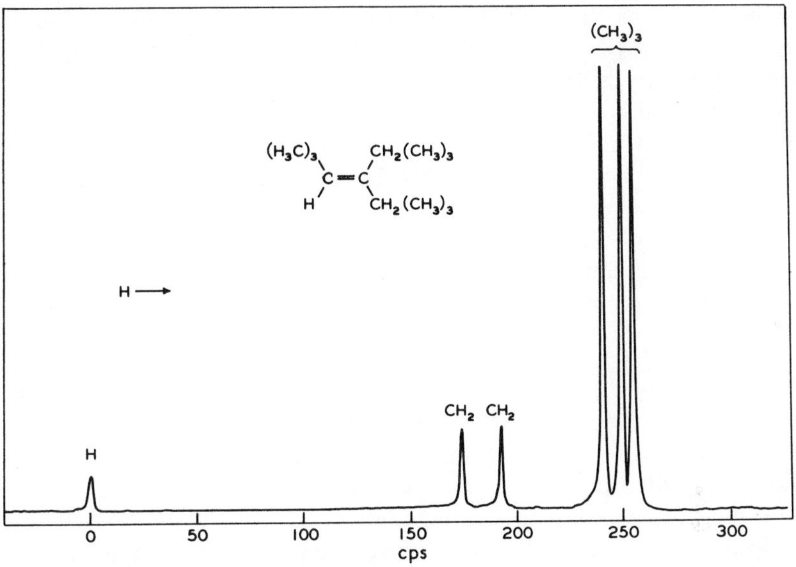

FIG. 5.3. Proton magnetic resonance spectrum of pure 1,1-di-neopentyl-2-*t*-butylethylene at 60 Mcps.

nuclei happen to be such that a chemical shift difference cannot be resolved, the shielding constants are said to be *accidentally degenerate.*

Second, intermolecular interactions can change the shielding constants appreciably from their values in the isolated molecule and may result in accidental degeneracies.[4]

Finally, rapid internal rotation does not always require that the shielding constants of the nuclei in motion be averaged to a common value (*6c, 6d*). For example, if the carbon atom in XCH_2- ($X \neq H$) or XCF_2- ($X \neq F$) is bonded to an asymmetrically substituted carbon atom ($-CPQR$), an internal chemical shift may be observed between the hydrogen or fluorine nuclei, even though there is rapid rotation about the carbon-carbon single bond.

D. Spin-Spin Interactions

Internal chemical shifts generate a set of resonances with the property that the separation of any pair of chemical-shift components is directly proportional to the applied field. It was not long after the discovery of the internal chemical shift that a fine structure of the chemical-shift

[4] An example is given in Chapter 6.

components was detected in both transient (*7a, 8, 9*) and steady-state experiments (*10, 11, 12*). This fine structure could not be attributed to shielding effects, since the separations of the fine-structure components were not linear functions of the applied field. In fact, these separations were frequently independent of the applied field. Moreover, the multiplet structure could not be the result of a direct dipolar coupling of the nuclei, which leads to a fine structure in solids, because the coupling persists in liquid systems, where the average value of the dipolar interaction is expected to be vanishingly small.

The interaction responsible for the multiplet structure will be denoted $-\hbar V$. The properties and consequences of this interaction, as revealed by experimental observations, may be summarized as follows:

(1) $-\hbar V$ is a rotationally invariant interaction.

(2) The magnetic nuclei in numerous molecules can be grouped into sets of identical nuclei such that all nuclei in a given set possess the same Larmor frequency (e.g., the methyl, methylene, and hydroxyl group protons in ethyl alcohol are three such sets). In many (*but not all*) molecules of this type, the interactions between nuclei in chemically shifted sets lead to an observable fine structure, but no multiplet structure can be attributed to the interactions of nuclei within a given set.

(3) Multiplet structure is conspicuously absent in the spectra of all systems whose nuclei have identical Larmor frequencies, examples being the protons in water, benzene, or methane.[5]

(4) For two sets A and X, of spin-$\frac{1}{2}$ nuclei of the type described in (2), with $|\omega_{AX}|$ much larger than the separation of the fine-structure components, one observes an "A multiplet" and an "X multiplet", such that successive components of the A multiplet have the common field separation ΔH_A, and successive components of the X multiplet have the common field separation ΔH_X. The characteristic splittings, ΔH_A and ΔH_X, have the same value when expressed in frequency units,

$$|J_{AX}| = |\gamma_A \Delta H_A| = |\gamma_X \Delta H_X|.$$

The resonance frequencies and their relative intensities are given in Table 5.1, where n_A and n_X are the numbers of nuclei in sets A and X, and $m_G = \frac{1}{2}n_G, \frac{1}{2}n_G - 1, \ldots, -\frac{1}{2}n_G + 1, -\frac{1}{2}n_G$ (G = A, X). The A

[5] Here, and subsequently, locutions such as "the protons in water" always refer to molecules composed of the most abundant nuclei. The same reservation will be made concerning chemical formulas. Thus "H_2O" and "the protons in water" refer to the protons in H_2O^{16}. Similarly, $CH_4 \equiv C^{12}H_4$, $C_6H_6 \equiv C_6^{12}H_6$. References to other isotopes will be explicitly indicated by the appropriate chemical formulas: $C^{13}H_4$, $N^{15}H_3$, etc.

TABLE 5.1

RESONANCE FREQUENCIES AND RELATIVE INTENSITIES

	Frequency	Relative intensity
A multiplet	$\omega_A + J_{AX}m_X$	$\binom{n_X}{\frac{1}{2}n_X + m_X}$
X multiplet	$\omega_X + J_{AX}m_A$	$\binom{n_A}{\frac{1}{2}n_A + m_A}$

multiplet consists of $n_X + 1$ resonances, and the X multiplet consists of $n_A + 1$ resonances. In a given multiplet there is one resonance for each distinct value of the z component of angular momentum for the second set; the intensity of the resonance associated with a given value of m_A or m_X is equal to the degree of degeneracy of m_A or m_X (cf. Section 3.B, Chapter 4).[6]

If A and X refer to a pair of nuclei with different gyromagnetic ratios, the frequencies of the A and X multiplets are still given by Table 5.1, but, since each value of m_A or m_X is nondegenerate, the intensity ratios of successive resonances in either multiplet are $1 : 1 : 1 : \cdots$.

(5) The constant J_{AX}, called the *spin-spin coupling constant*, is independent of the applied field.

Property (1) is demanded by the fact that the multiplet structure persists in liquid systems, where the molecules undergo frequent changes in orientation. Property (2) focuses attention on certain sets of nuclei, called *groups of magnetically equivalent nuclei*; their precise definition and a rigorous proof of (2) will be given in Section 4. Property (3) is a special case of property (2), and (4) is a limiting special case of (2).

The proton magnetic resonance spectrum of acetaldehyde, CH_3CHO (Fig. 5.4), illustrates property (4). The eigenvalues of the z component of angular momentum for the three methyl-group protons are $\frac{3}{2}$, $\frac{1}{2}$, $-\frac{1}{2}$, $-\frac{3}{2}$, with $\nu(\pm\frac{3}{2}) = 1$, $\nu(\pm\frac{1}{2}) = 3$. Thus the aldehyde proton resonance is split into a $1 : 3 : 3 : 1$ quartet with characteristic spacing $|J_{AX}| = 2.85$ cps. The eigenvalues of the z component of angular momentum for the single aldehyde proton are $\pm\frac{1}{2}$, with $\nu(\pm\frac{1}{2}) = 1$. Thus the resonance of the methyl group protons is split into a $1 : 1$ doublet, with the characteristic spacing 2.85 cps. A second example is

[6] The derivation of these rules and a more precise statement of the conditions for their validity will be given in Chapter 7.

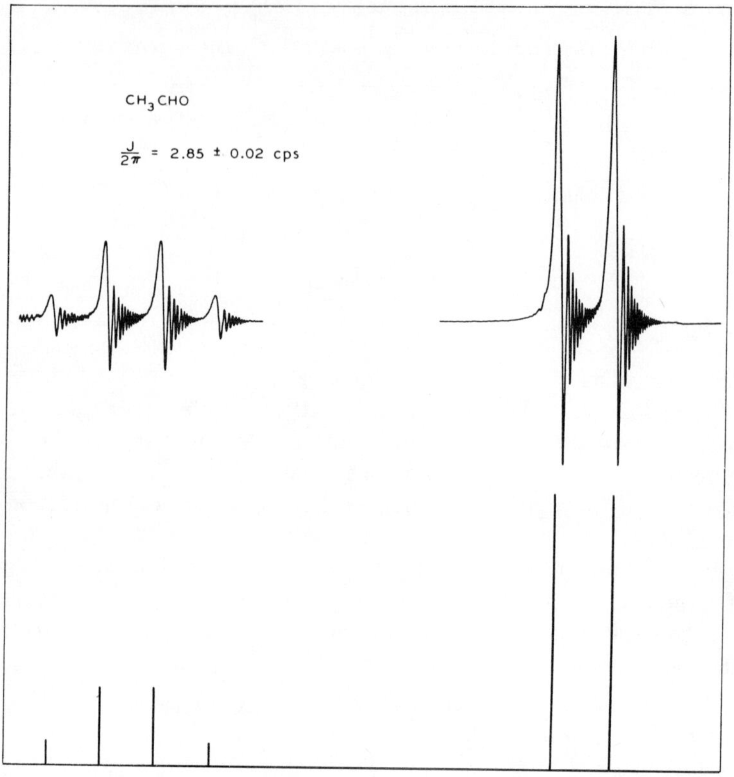

FIG. 5.4. Proton magnetic resonance spectrum of pure acetaldehyde at 60 Mcps.

provided by the P^{31} resonances of trimethylphosphite, Fig. 5.5. The coupling of the phosphorus atom to the protons should yield 10 distinct lines ($n_A + 1 = 10$), but the intensities of the two outermost resonances are hidden in the background noise. The H^1 spectrum of $P(OCH_3)_3$ (not shown) consists of a 1 : 1 doublet whose components are 10.5 cps apart.

Properties (1) through (5) led to the conclusion (*8–12*) that the interaction between a pair of nuclear moments could be represented as a scalar product

$$-\hbar V_{ij} = K_{ij}\boldsymbol{\mu}_i \cdot \boldsymbol{\mu}_j \,, \tag{1.6}$$

where K_{ij} is a scalar quantity, symmetric in i and j, and, according to (5), independent of the applied field. The proportionality constant has the dimensions G^2 erg^{-1}, but it is customary to write the interaction in terms of spin vectors,

$$K_{ij}\boldsymbol{\mu}_i \cdot \boldsymbol{\mu}_j = \gamma_i\gamma_j\hbar^2 K_{ij}\mathbf{I}_i \cdot \mathbf{I}_j,$$

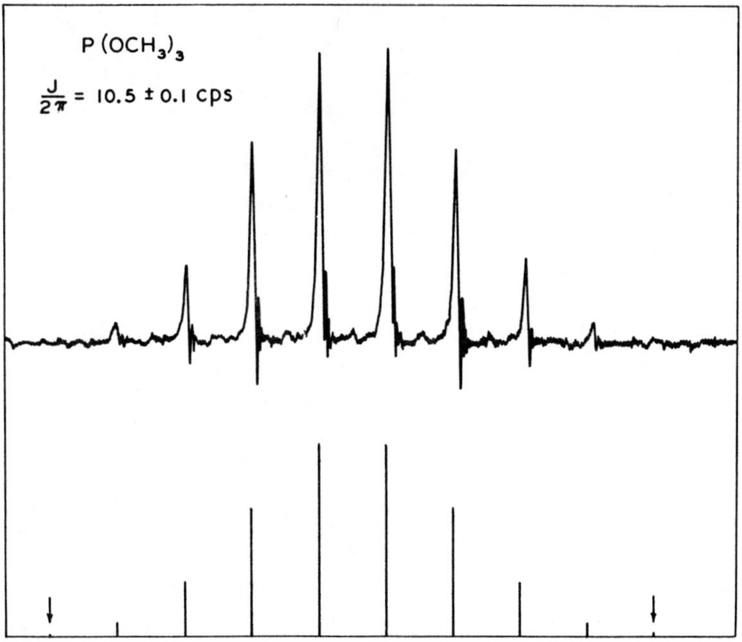

FIG. 5.5. Phosphorus magnetic resonance spectrum of pure trimethylphosphite at 24.3 Mcps.

and to define the spin-spin coupling constant (in angular frequency units) as

$$J_{ij} = \gamma_i \gamma_j \hbar K_{ij} = J_{ji} \,. \tag{1.7}$$

Combining the last three equations, one obtains

$$V_{ij} = -J_{ij} \mathbf{I}_i \cdot \mathbf{I}_j \,. \tag{1.8}$$

The interaction (1.8) is linear with respect to the spin operators of both nuclei, so that V_{ij} is called a *bilinear interaction*, and J_{ij} the *bilinear spin-spin coupling constant*. For an assembly of nuclear moments, the total coupling energy is obtained by summing over all pairs:

$$-\hbar V = -\hbar \sum_{i<j}\sum J_{ij} \mathbf{I}_i \cdot \mathbf{I}_j \equiv -\tfrac{1}{2}\hbar \sum_{i \neq j}\sum J_{ij} \mathbf{I}_i \cdot \mathbf{I}_j \,.$$

If the spin operators are considered as classical vectors, (1.8) shows that the bilinear interaction may be interpreted as the interaction of nucleus i with an intramolecular magnetic field proportional to $J_{ij}\mathbf{I}_j$.

These intramolecular fields are transmitted from nucleus to nucleus by the molecular electrons. Indeed, the bilinear interaction can be deduced from a general molecular hamiltonian that includes the Fermi contact interaction (*13*, *14*). The Fermi interaction provides a coupling mechanism between the nuclear moments and the spin magnetic moments of the electrons and, in the second order of perturbation, leads to dot-product coupling.[7] Thus the spin-spin coupling constant is a function of the molecular electronic structure, and therefore normally independent of the applied field and temperature.

A second mechanism is provided by the interaction of the nuclear moments with the orbital magnetic moments of the electrons (*12*). However, the orbital contribution to the spin-spin coupling constant is about an order of magnitude smaller than that obtained with the Fermi interaction.

The theoretical expression for the coupling constant is applied with some difficulty to the direct computation of coupling constants. As in the case of molecular shielding constants, the difficulty stems from the lack of knowledge of the wave functions and energies for excited states of molecules. However, approximate calculations (*6*) confirm the coupling mechanisms and have been somewhat more successful than shielding constant calculations.

The observed values of spin-spin coupling constants range from a few tenths of a cycle per second to 1 or more kilocycles per second. Some representative values are given in Table 5.2. The coupling constants tabulated for the interaction between chemically shifted protons in CH_3CH_2X, CH_3SH, and CH_3OH represent averages over the internal rotation.

According to property (3), the interactions of the protons in CH_4 and H_2 are not observable. The recorded values of the coupling constants were deduced from the observable interaction between the hydrogen and deuterium nuclei in HD and CH_3D. For example, the proton spectrum of HD consists of a 1 : 1 : 1 triplet [$m_D = 1, 0, -1; \nu(\pm 1) = \nu(0) = 1$], and the deuterium spectrum consists of a 1 : 1 doublet [$m_H = +\frac{1}{2}, -\frac{1}{2}; \nu(\pm\frac{1}{2}) = 1$]. The observed coupling constant is $|J_{HD}| = 43.5$ cps (*15*). Now the bilinear coupling is proportional to the product of the gyromagnetic ratios, so that the coupling constants for HD and H_2 are of the form

$$J_{HD} = \gamma_H \gamma_D \hbar K_{HD}, \qquad J_{HH} = \gamma_H{}^2 \hbar K_{HH}.$$

[7] The interaction is actually obtained as a sum of the scalar and a tensor interaction, but the random average of the tensor interaction vanishes.

TABLE 5.2

REPRESENTATIVE VALUES OF SPIN-SPIN COUPLING CONSTANTS

Compound	Coupled nuclei	Coupling configuration	| J | (cps)
H_2	(H, H)	H−H	277[a]
HD	(H, D)	H−D	43.5
CH_4	(H, H)	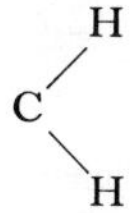	12.4[a]
CH_3D	(H, D)	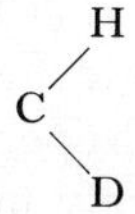	1.9
CH_3OH	(H, H)	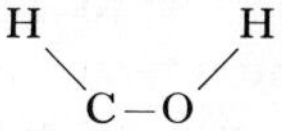	4.8
CH_3SH	(H, H)	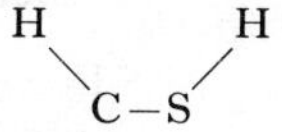	7.4
CH_3CH_2X	(H, H)	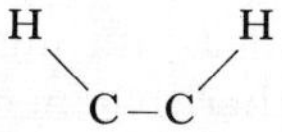	6–8
$CH_2{=}CHX$	(H, H)	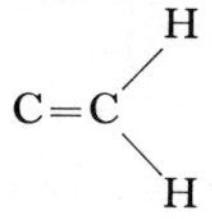	1–2
$CH_2{=}CHX$	(H, H)	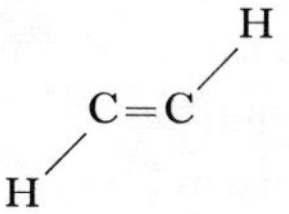	15–18
$CH_2{=}CHX$	(H, H)	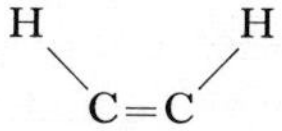	6–10
$C^{13}H_4$	(C^{13}, H)	C^{13}−H	125
PH_3	(P, H)	P−H	179
PF_3	(P, F)	P−F	1410

[a] Calculated from the corresponding deuterium coupling; see the text.

If it is assumed that the substitution of D for H has negligible effect on the molecular electronic structure, and that changes in the zero-point vibrational amplitude can be neglected, then $K_{HD} = K_{HH}$, and

$$\frac{J_{HH}}{2\pi} = \frac{\gamma_H}{\gamma_D}\left(\frac{J_{HD}}{2\pi}\right) = 6.51\left(\frac{J_{HD}}{2\pi}\right).$$

Thus $| J_{HH} |/2\pi = (6.51)(43.5) = 277$ cps. Similarly, the proton spectrum of CH_3D consists of a 1 : 1 : 1 triplet with $| J_{HD} |/2\pi = 1.9$ cps (*16*), so that $| J_{HH} |/2\pi = (6.51)(1.9) = 12.4$ cps.

E. Multilinear Interactions

The conclusion that the observed properties of the indirect coupling of nuclear magnetic moments demand a bilinear interaction is by no means obvious. Property (5) reveals nothing about the form of the interaction; it merely provides a condition—valid for a certain range of experience—that is to be imposed upon the numerical coefficients appearing in the interaction. Property (4) specifically refers to a limiting case, so that no general conclusions can be drawn about the form of the interaction. Properties (2) and (3) are general consequences of the interaction, but provide no information concerning its form.

The crucial property is the rotational invariance of V. It is not a statement about a limiting case or a theorem following from the interaction, but rather a general condition which must be satisfied by the interaction. Mathematically speaking, the rotational invariance of V means that if the laboratory coordinate system is rotated through an arbitrary angle φ about an axis defined by the unit vector $\mathbf{n}$, the form of the (hermitian) operator V in the new coordinate system is identical with its form in the original coordinate system. Since V is a quantum mechanical operator defined with respect to a spin space, the three-dimensional rotation of the physical space induces a unitary transformation of all vectors in the spin space and a similarity transformation of all spin operators. The induced unitary transformation is $e^{-i\varphi\mathbf{n}\cdot\mathbf{I}}$, where $\mathbf{I}$ is the total spin vector, so that the rotational invariance of V is expressed by the equation

$$e^{-i\varphi\mathbf{n}\cdot\mathbf{I}} V e^{i\varphi\mathbf{n}\cdot\mathbf{I}} = V. \tag{1.9}$$

The bilinear interaction $J_{jk}\mathbf{I}_j \cdot \mathbf{I}_k$ is rotationally invariant, but in this respect it is not unique. For example, the scalar operator $c1$, where c is a constant, is also rotationally invariant. Insofar as the energy is concerned, the operator $c1$ merely adds a constant term to the total energy which is cancelled upon taking a difference of energies. It can be shown that, for two spin-$\frac{1}{2}$ particles, the three scalar products $\mathbf{I}_1^2$, $\mathbf{I}_2^2$, and $\mathbf{I}_1 \cdot \mathbf{I}_2$ are the only rotationally invariant operators, other than $c\mathit{1}$. The operators $\mathbf{I}_1^2$ and $\mathbf{I}_2^2$ do not represent interactions between the spins, so that the only possibility is the bilinear interaction $J_{12}\mathbf{I}_1 \cdot \mathbf{I}_2$.

If there are three or more spins, other rotationally invariant interactions can also be constructed; e.g., $\mathbf{I}_1 \times \mathbf{I}_2 \cdot \mathbf{I}_3$, $\mathbf{I}_1 \times (\mathbf{I}_2 \times \mathbf{I}_3) \cdot \mathbf{I}_4$, etc. The invariance of these *multilinear interactions* follows from the fact that under any rotation of the coordinate system, the transform of a cross product of two vectors is equal to the cross product of the transformed vectors: $(\mathbf{A} \times \mathbf{B})' = \mathbf{A}' \times \mathbf{B}'$.

It must be noted, however, that the bilinear interaction—clearly the simplest nontrivial rotationally invariant interaction—has been eminently successful in accounting for the fine structure observed in high-resolution spectra. For this reason, the bilinear interaction will be used in all subsequent calculations. The discussion of multilinear interactions will be deferred to another occasion (*17*).

2. The Hamiltonian Operator and Its Properties

A. The Mathematical Model

The discussion in the preceding section leads to a simple mathematical model for the study of complex high-resolution nuclear magnetic resonance spectra. Specifically, consider a liquid system containing a collection of identical molecules, each molecule in the collection containing N nuclear magnetic moments $\boldsymbol{\mu}_i = \gamma_i \hbar \mathbf{I}_i$, $i = 1, 2, ..., N$. It will be assumed that the system is maintained at a fixed temperature, that random averaging over molecular orientations is permissible, and, for the moment, that the system is subjected only to a stationary external field $\mathbf{H}$. Under these conditions, the hamiltonian operator for the nuclear spin system in a representative molecule will include two types of interactions: (1) the Zeeman energy of the nuclear spins in the applied field $\mathbf{H}$, and (2) the rotationally invariant spin-spin interactions of the nuclei with each other.

The nuclear Zeeman energy is

$$-\hbar Z = -\hbar \sum_i \gamma_i(1 - \sigma_i)\mathbf{I}_i \cdot \mathbf{H},$$

where σ_i is the effective isotropic shielding constant for the ith nucleus, including the contributions from intermolecular interactions. The operator $-\hbar Z$ is the hamiltonian operator for the spin system in the absence of spin-spin interactions; its form reveals an important simplification which stems from the assumption of isotropic nuclear shielding —that, although the uncoupled nuclear Larmor frequencies

$$\omega_i = \gamma_i(1 - \sigma_i)|\,\mathbf{H}\,|$$

will usually be different for different nuclei, the direction of the shielded field at each nucleus is parallel to the direction of the applied field.

The energy operator for the spin-spin interactions is

$$-\hbar V = -\hbar \sum_{j<k}\sum J_{jk}\mathbf{I}_j \cdot \mathbf{I}_k \qquad (J_{jk} = J_{kj}),$$

so that the complete energy operator is $\hbar\mathscr{H} = -\hbar(Z + V)$, or

$$\mathscr{H} = -(Z + V) = -\left\{\sum_j \omega_j \mathbf{n} \cdot \mathbf{I}_j + \sum_{j<k}\sum J_{jk}\mathbf{I}_j \cdot \mathbf{I}_k\right\}, \tag{2.1}$$

where $\mathbf{n}$ is a unit vector in the direction of $\mathbf{H}$.

Equation (2.1) holds for arbitrary nuclear spin systems, but it should be noted that a nucleus with spin greater than $\frac{1}{2}$ possesses an electric quadrupole moment that interacts with the electric field gradient in its neighborhood. This interaction can induce rapid transitions between the various spin states of the quadrupolar nucleus, with the result that spin states of other nuclei are not correlated with definite states of the quadrupolar nucleus. In this circumstance, spin-$\frac{1}{2}$ nuclei are effectively decoupled from nuclei with spins greater than $\frac{1}{2}$, and the corresponding coupling terms can be omitted from the stationary hamiltonian operator. Chlorine ($I = \frac{3}{2}$), bromine ($I = \frac{3}{2}$), and iodine ($I = \frac{5}{2}$) nuclei are well-known examples.

If the quadrupole moment is small and/or the electrostatic field at the nucleus does not markedly deviate from spherical symmetry, the lifetimes of the spin states of nuclei with $I > \frac{1}{2}$ may be long enough to permit the observation of their spin-spin interactions with other nuclei. For example, deuterium-proton couplings are frequently observed.[8]

For the most part, all subsequent discussions will be concerned with spin systems with all $I_j = \frac{1}{2}$. However, it is necessary to maintain complete generality with respect to the spin quantum numbers, since sets of spin-$\frac{1}{2}$ nuclei often occur that are described by spin quantum

[8] Roughly speaking, the coupling of a nucleus A to a second nucleus B will begin to be observable when the lifetime of a spin state of A is of the order of $1/|\,J_{\mathrm{AB}}\,|$.

numbers greater than $\frac{1}{2}$. It must be emphasized that these quantum numbers have nothing to do with quadrupolar nuclei—they arise only by virtue of the laws of composition of spin angular momenta.

The remarkable simplicity of the hamiltonian operator (2.1) requires further comment. In particular, (2.1) is not the hamiltonian operator for a nuclear spin system contained in an isolated molecule—it is the hamiltonian operator for the nuclear spin system contained in a representative molecule of the liquid system. Insofar as the structure of its magnetic resonance spectrum is concerned, the properties of this "average," or representative, molecule are summarily described by the N shielding constants σ_j and the $N(N-1)/2$ spin-spin coupling constants J_{jk}. Equation (2.1) is thus the hamiltonian operator for an idealized model of the real spin system. The model refers only to the magnetic nuclei in the representative molecule and includes only those interactions that generate a fine structure in its high-resolution nuclear magnetic resonance spectrum.

In a specific case, there may be auxiliary conditions imposed upon some of the Larmor frequencies and the spin-spin coupling constants by a symmetry of the parent molecule or an effective symmetry brought about by rapid internal rotation.[9] Consider, for example, the protons in thiophene:

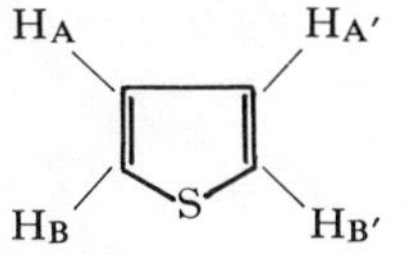

The symmetry of the molecule requires that

$$\omega_A = \omega_{A'}, \qquad \omega_B = \omega_{B'}, \qquad J_{AB} = J_{A'B'}, \qquad J_{A'B} = J_{AB'},$$

so that the hamiltonian operator for the model nuclear spin system is

$$\mathscr{H} = -\{[\omega_A(\mathbf{I}_A + \mathbf{I}_{A'}) + \omega_B(\mathbf{I}_B + \mathbf{I}_{B'})] \cdot \mathbf{n} + J_{AA'}\mathbf{I}_A \cdot \mathbf{I}_{A'} + J_{BB'}\mathbf{I}_B \cdot \mathbf{I}_{B'}$$
$$+ J_{AB}(\mathbf{I}_A \cdot \mathbf{I}_B + \mathbf{I}_{A'} \cdot \mathbf{I}_{B'}) + J_{AB'}(\mathbf{I}_A \cdot \mathbf{I}_{B'} + \mathbf{I}_{A'} \cdot \mathbf{I}_B)\}.$$

For an example of effective symmetry, consider the protons in methyl alcohol. Rapid internal rotation about the C-O bond leads to the following conditions on the uncoupled Larmor frequencies and the spin-spin coupling constants:

$$\omega_{A_1} = \omega_{A_2} = \omega_{A_3} \equiv \omega_A,$$

$$J_{A_1B} = J_{A_2B} = J_{A_3B} \equiv J_{AB},$$

[9] The theory of symmetrical spin systems will be discussed in Chapter 8.

where A_i ($i = 1, 2, 3$) denotes the ith proton of the methyl group, and B denotes the hydroxyl-group proton. The hamiltonian operator for the spin system is

$$\mathscr{H} = -\{[\omega_A(\mathbf{I}_{A_1} + \mathbf{I}_{A_2} + \mathbf{I}_{A_3}) + \omega_B\mathbf{I}_B] \cdot \mathbf{n} + J_{AB}(\mathbf{I}_{A_1} + \mathbf{I}_{A_2} + \mathbf{I}_{A_3}) \cdot \mathbf{I}_B$$
$$+ J_{A_1A_2}\mathbf{I}_{A_1} \cdot \mathbf{I}_{A_2} + J_{A_1A_3}\mathbf{I}_{A_1} \cdot \mathbf{I}_{A_3} + J_{A_2A_3}\mathbf{I}_{A_2} \cdot \mathbf{I}_{A_3}\}.$$

It will be shown in Section 4 that the last three terms can be omitted from the hamiltonian operator.

Since most details of the molecular structure are not explicitly indicated in the hamiltonian operator, the hamiltonian operators for the model spin systems of two distinct molecules may have the same mathematical form. For example, the hamiltonian operator for the protons in furan has the same mathematical form as that of the protons in thiophene. Presumably differences in the parent molecules will be reflected by differences in the chemical shifts and coupling constants.

B. Constants of the Motion

The structure of the hamiltonian (2.1) reveals that the square of each spin vector is a constant of the motion. For $\mathbf{I}_j^2$ is not an explicit function of t and commutes with $I_{\lambda k}$ ($\lambda = x, y, z$), for all k, so that

$$[\mathscr{H}, \mathbf{I}_j^2] = 0 \qquad (j = 1, 2, ..., N).$$

These constants of the motion, which imply the conservation of the spin quantum numbers I_j, are valid for any time variation of the applied field.

When the applied field does not change with time, two additional constants of the motion can be deduced—the hamiltonian operator itself and the operator for the component of the total spin angular momentum in the direction of $\mathbf{H}$. That $\mathscr{H}$ is a constant of the motion is evident from the general formula

$$\frac{dX}{dt} = \frac{\partial X}{\partial t} + i[\mathscr{H}, X], \tag{2.2}$$

upon putting $X = \mathscr{H}$, and noting that $\partial\mathscr{H}/\partial t = 0$ if $\dot{\mathbf{H}} = 0$.

To prove that $\mathbf{n} \cdot \mathbf{I}$ is a constant of the motion when $\dot{\mathbf{H}} = 0$ it is necessary to show that $\mathbf{n} \cdot \mathbf{I}$ commutes with $\mathscr{H}$. This can be demonstrated by direct calculation, but it is much simpler to appeal to the rotational invariance of $-\hbar V$.

If (1.9) is multiplied from the left with $e^{i\varphi \mathbf{n}\cdot\mathbf{I}}$, one obtains

$$Ve^{i\varphi \mathbf{n}\cdot\mathbf{I}} = e^{i\varphi \mathbf{n}\cdot\mathbf{I}}V.$$

Since the angle of rotation is arbitrary, the exponential operators may be expanded and like powers of φ equated to obtain

$$[(\mathbf{n}\cdot\mathbf{I})^k, V] = 0 \qquad (k = 0, 1, 2, \ldots). \tag{2.3}$$

Thus V commutes with every integral power of the component of the total spin angular momentum in the direction $\mathbf{n}$. If $\mathbf{n}$ is successively taken as $\mathbf{e}_x$, $\mathbf{e}_y$, and $\mathbf{e}_z$, (2.3) with $k = 1$ yields

$$[V, I_x] = [V, I_y] = [V, I_z] = 0. \tag{2.4}$$

For $k = 2$, the same choices for $\mathbf{n}$ lead to the conclusion that V commutes with $I_x{}^2$, $I_y{}^2$, and $I_z{}^2$, and, therefore, also with the square of the total spin angular momentum[10]:

$$[V, \mathbf{I}^2] = 0. \tag{2.5}$$

If the unit vector in (1.9) is now identified with the direction of the applied field, it follows that

$$\mathbf{n}\cdot\mathbf{I} = \sum_j \mathbf{n}\cdot\mathbf{I}_j$$

commutes with $\mathscr{H}$. Thus $\mathbf{n}\cdot\mathbf{I}$ is a constant of motion if $\partial\mathbf{n}/\partial t = 0$. If the direction of the applied field changes with the time, neither $\mathscr{H}$ nor $\mathbf{n}\cdot\mathbf{I}$ will be constants of the motion. For the particular case of an applied field independent of the time and directed along the positive z axis, the quantum mechanical analysis of a coupled spin system proceeds from the equations

$$\mathscr{H} = -\Big\{\sum_j \omega_j I_{zj} + \sum_{j<k}\sum J_{jk}\mathbf{I}_j\cdot\mathbf{I}_k\Big\},$$

$$\frac{d\mathscr{H}}{dt} = 0, \qquad \frac{dI_z}{dt} = [\mathscr{H}, I_z] = 0, \tag{2.6}$$

$$\frac{d\mathbf{I}_j{}^2}{dt} = [\mathscr{H}, \mathbf{I}_j{}^2] = 0 \qquad (j = 1, 2, \ldots, N).$$

---

[10] It should be noted that (2.3) through (2.5) are valid for any rotationally invariant interaction.

C. The Heisenberg Equations of Motion

The constants of the motion can be deduced in a somewhat different manner by examining the equations of motion for each component of every spin vector.

The required equations of motion may be obtained from (2.1) and (2.2) by straightforward evaluations of the requisite commutators. One finds that the time derivatives of the components of $\mathbf{I}_j$ are given by

$$\begin{aligned} \dot{I}_{xj} &= I_{yj}\omega_{zj} - I_{zj}\omega_{yj} + \sum_{k\neq j} J_{jk}(I_{yj}I_{zk} - I_{zj}I_{yk}), \\ \dot{I}_{yj} &= I_{zj}\omega_{xj} - I_{xj}\omega_{zj} + \sum_{k\neq j} J_{jk}(I_{zj}I_{xk} - I_{xj}I_{zk}), \\ \dot{I}_{zj} &= I_{xj}\omega_{yj} - I_{yj}\omega_{xj} + \sum_{k\neq j} J_{jk}(I_{xj}I_{yk} - I_{yj}I_{xk}), \end{aligned} \tag{2.7}$$

where $\boldsymbol{\omega}_j = \omega_j\mathbf{n}$. Upon examining the form of these equations, it is easy to see that they may be compressed into the single equation

$$\frac{d\mathbf{I}_j}{dt} = \omega_j\mathbf{I}_j \times \mathbf{n} + \sum_{k\neq j} J_{jk}\mathbf{I}_j \times \mathbf{I}_k\,. \tag{2.8}$$

The N equations obtained from this expression by putting $j = 1, 2, ..., N$ are the Heisenberg equations of motion for the spin vectors $\mathbf{I}_1, \mathbf{I}_2, ..., \mathbf{I}_N$.

If the spin vectors are considered to be vectors in the classical sense, then (2.8) has a very simple physical interpretation. The term $\omega_j\mathbf{I}_j \times \mathbf{n}$ represents the torque exerted by the external field on the magnetic moment of nucleus j; the second term represents the sum of the torques exerted on nucleus j by the remaining magnetic nuclei *via* intramolecular fields. The magnitudes of the coupling torques are directly proportional to the spin-spin coupling constants. If all J_{jk} vanish, and if the applied field is constant, the motion of $\mathbf{I}_j$ consists of a precession of $\mathbf{I}_j$ about the direction $\mathbf{n}$ with uniform frequency ω_j. On the other hand, if the coupling constants are nonzero, then, whether the applied field is stationary or time-dependent, the motion of $\mathbf{I}_j$ may be described in terms of infinitesimal rotations about instantaneous axes whose directions are parallel to

$$\omega_j\mathbf{n}(t) + \sum_{k\neq j} J_{jk}\mathbf{I}_k(t).$$

A complete geometric description of the motion requires an integration of the equations of motion, but this analysis will not be necessary.

Instead, a simple property of equations (2.8) will be used to deduce constants of the motion by ordinary vector operations.

An examination of equations (2.7) shows that all quantities in the right-hand members—including the spin vectors—commute. The implication is that the spin vectors in (2.7) or (2.8) can be manipulated like ordinary vectors without obtaining an incorrect result, provided that the manipulations are carried out according to the usual rules concerning vector cross products, scalar triple products, etc. For example, upon computing the (ordinary) scalar product on both sides of (2.8) with $\mathbf{I}_j$, one obtains

$$\mathbf{I}_j \cdot \frac{d\mathbf{I}_j}{dt} = 0,$$

since a scalar triple product vanishes if two of its factors are equal. This equation is equivalent to $d(\mathbf{I}_j^2)/dt = 0$, which implies that $\mathbf{I}_j^2$ is a constant of the motion.

A second condition upon the spin operators may be obtained by taking the scalar product of (2.8) with $\mathbf{n}$ and then summing over j to obtain

$$\sum_j \mathbf{n} \cdot \frac{d\mathbf{I}_j}{dt} = 0.$$

The double sum over $\mathbf{n} \cdot \mathbf{I}_j \times \mathbf{I}_k$ vanishes by virtue of relations of the form $\mathbf{A} \cdot \mathbf{B} \times \mathbf{C} = -\mathbf{A} \cdot \mathbf{C} \times \mathbf{B}$. If the field does not change with time, $\dot{\mathbf{n}} = 0$, and the preceding equation is equivalent to

$$\sum_j \frac{d}{dt}(\mathbf{n} \cdot \mathbf{I}_j) = \frac{d}{dt}(\mathbf{n} \cdot \mathbf{I}) = 0,$$

which implies that the component of the total angular momentum along the direction of $\mathbf{H}$ is conserved.

D. Structure of the Hamiltonian Matrix

According to equations (2.6), the stationary states of a spin system subjected to a steady magnetic field along the z axis may be chosen to be simultaneous eigenvectors of $\mathscr{H}$, I_z, and all $\mathbf{I}_j^2$. The basis that reduces the matrix representatives of all constants of the motion to diagonal form will seldom be obvious, but the determination of this basis is facilitated by choosing an initial basis that diagonalizes as many constants of the motion as possible.

The product basis

$$\{|I_1, m_1\rangle | I_2, m_2\rangle \cdots | I_N, m_N\rangle\} \equiv \{| I_1, m_1; I_2, m_2; ...; I_N, m_N\rangle\}$$

diagonalizes the matrix representatives of I_z and all $\mathbf{I}_j^2$, and is thus a suitable initial basis. The diagonal elements of $\mathbf{I}_j^2$ are all equal to $I_j(I_j + 1)$, whereas those of I_z are given by

$$m = m_1 + m_2 + \cdots + m_N, \tag{2.9}$$

where

$$-I_j \leqslant m_j \leqslant I_j \qquad (j = 1, 2, ..., N). \tag{2.10}$$

The values of m range from $I_{\max} = \sum I_j$ to $-I_{\max}$ in integral steps, and all values of m, except $m = \pm I_{\max}$, are degenerate. The degree of degeneracy of a given value of m is given by the functions $\nu(m)$, whose properties are described in Section 3.B of Chapter 4. In the important special case of a system with all $I_j = \frac{1}{2}$, $I_{\max} = \frac{1}{2}N$, and

$$\nu(m) = \frac{N!}{\left(\frac{N}{2} - m\right)! \left(\frac{N}{2} + m\right)!} \qquad (\text{all} \quad I_j = \tfrac{1}{2}). \tag{2.11}$$

Since there are $\nu(m)$ linearly independent product kets for each value of m, an index $n = 1, 2, ..., \nu(m)$ will often be used to distinguish these kets. It will also be convenient to indicate the eigenvalue of I_z. However, the notation will occasionally be simplified by omitting any labels not relevant to the discussion. Thus the following notation will be used to denote a generic element of the product basis:

$$| I_1, m_1; ...; I_N, m_N\rangle, \quad | I_1, m_1; ...; I_N, m_N; m; n\rangle, \quad | m; n\rangle, \quad | m\rangle.$$

The matrix representative of the hamiltonian operator is not diagonal with respect to the product basis, but its form is considerably simplified by this basis. In fact, the hamiltonian matrix is the direct sum of $2I_{\max} + 1$ submatrices whose dimensions are just the $2I_{\max} + 1$ values of $\nu(m)$. This decomposition of $\mathscr{H}$ is a direct consequence of the commutation of I_z and $\mathscr{H}$. Indeed, $[\mathscr{H}, I_z] = 0$ implies that

$$\langle m'; n' | I_z\mathscr{H} | m; n\rangle - \langle m'; n' | \mathscr{H}I_z | m; n\rangle = (m' - m)\langle m'; n' | \mathscr{H} | m; n\rangle = 0;$$

hence

$$\langle m'; n' | \mathscr{H} | m; n\rangle = 0 \qquad (\text{for} \quad m' \neq m). \tag{2.12}$$

It may happen that some of the matrix elements of $\mathscr{H}$ with $m = m'$ also vanish, but (2.12) refers only to the vanishing of the matrix elements of $\mathscr{H}$ between states with distinct values of m.

As an example of the direct sum decomposition of the hamiltonian matrix, consider the case of two nuclei with spins $\frac{3}{2}$ and 1. According to Table 4.3, the hamiltonian matrix can be expressed as the direct sum of six submatrices whose dimensions are 1×1, 2×2, 3×3, 3×3, 2×2, and 1×1. The structure of the hamiltonian matrix is indicated in Fig. 5.6. All matrix elements not enclosed by the diagonal blocks vanish; the numbers enclosed by the blocks are the eigenvalues of I_z.

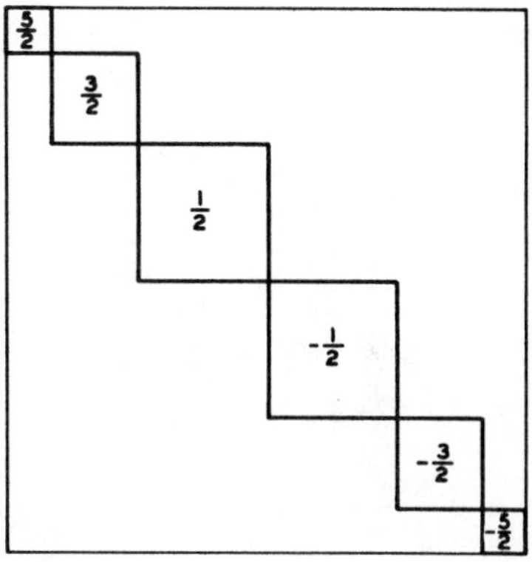

FIG. 5.6. Structure of the hamiltonian matrix for a two-spin system with $I_1 = \frac{3}{2}$, $I_2 = 1$.

In the particular case where all $I_j = \frac{1}{2}$, the hamiltonian matrix is of dimension $2^N \times 2^N$, but decomposes into a direct sum of $2I_{\text{max}} + 1 = N + 1$ submatrices whose dimensions are given by the binomial sequence [cf. (2.11)]

$$\binom{N}{0}, \binom{N}{1}, \ldots, \binom{N}{k}, \ldots, \binom{N}{N}.$$

For example, if $N = 3$, the hamiltonian matrix decomposes into four submatrices whose dimensions are 1×1, 3×3, 3×3, and 1×1.

The commutation of $\mathscr{H}$ with all $\mathbf{I}_j^2$ does not lead to any additional factorization of the hamiltonian matrix, since the spin quantum numbers do not range over a sequence of values. However, when the theory is applied to certain groups of nuclei (Section 4), the several values of the spin quantum numbers associated with these groups lead to additional direct-sum decompositions of the hamiltonian matrix. The existence of symmetry in a molecule can often be used to effect further decompositions of the hamiltonian matrix, but in this section only the decomposition with respect to the total spin variable will be considered.

The eigenvalues of $\mathscr{H}$ may be obtained by separately diagonalizing each of the $2I_{\text{max}} + 1$ submatrices of $\mathscr{H}$. The submatrix of $\mathscr{H}$ generated by the product functions with a given value of m will be denoted $\mathscr{H}(m)$; its diagonalization requires the solution of an algebraic equation of degree $\nu(m)$ whose roots are the eigenvalues of $\mathscr{H}(m)$. When these eigenvalues have been determined, one can set up linear equations for the corresponding $\nu(m)$ eigenvectors.

The eigenvalues of $\mathscr{H}(m)$ will be denoted Ω_{mn} or simply Ω_m, if the index n does not have any essential relevance to the discussion. An eigenvector of $\mathscr{H}(m)$ will be denoted $| \Omega, I_1, I_2, ..., I_N, m; n)$, where both subscripts on Ω are omitted, since these indices are explicitly displayed in the eigenket. It will be assumed that the expansion coefficients have been so chosen that the eigenvectors of $\mathscr{H}$ are an orthonormal set:

$$(\Omega', I_1, ..., I_N, m'; n' \mid \Omega, I_1, I_2, ..., I_N, m; n) = \delta_{\Omega'\Omega}\, \delta_{m'm}\, \delta_{n'n}\,. \tag{2.13}$$

The notation for the eigenvectors will often be simplified by omitting any quantum numbers or indices not bearing directly on the discussion. The following notation will be used to denote a simultaneous eigenvector of $\mathscr{H}, I_z, \mathbf{I}_1^2, ..., \mathbf{I}_N^2$:

$$| \Omega, I_1, ..., I_N, m; n), \quad | \Omega, m; n), \quad | \Omega_{mn}), \quad | \Omega_m), \quad | m; n), \quad | m).$$

E. The Matrix Elements of $\mathscr{H}$

The evaluation of the matrix elements of the stationary hamiltonian operator, relative to the product basis, is facilitated by introducing the operator identity

$$\mathbf{I}_j \cdot \mathbf{I}_k = I_{zj} I_{zk} + \tfrac{1}{2}(I_j^+ I_k^- + I_j^- I_k^+)$$

into the first of equations (2.6) to obtain

$$\mathscr{H} = -\Big\{\sum_j \omega_j I_{zj} + \sum_{j<k}\sum J_{jk} I_{zj} I_{zk} + \tfrac{1}{2}\sum_{j<k}\sum J_{jk}(I_j^+ I_k^- + I_j^- I_k^+)\Big\}. \tag{2.14}$$

Since the elements of the product basis are eigenvectors of I_z, I_{zj}, and $\mathbf{I}_j^2$, (2.14) shows that the diagonal elements of $\mathscr{H}$ are generated by the terms containing I_{zj} and $I_{zj} I_{zk}$, whereas the terms containing $I_j^{\pm} I_k^{\mp}$ generate off-diagonal elements. The diagonal matrix elements are given by

$$\langle I_1, m_1; I_2, m_2; ...; I_N, m_N \mid \mathscr{H} \mid I_1, m_1; I_2, m_2; ...; I_N, m_N\rangle$$

$$= -\Big\{\sum_j \omega_j m_j + \sum_{j<k}\sum J_{jk} m_j m_k\Big\}, \tag{2.15}$$

and the nonvanishing off-diagonal elements by

$$\langle \cdots I_j, m_j + 1; \ldots; I_k, m_k - 1; \ldots \mid \mathscr{H} \mid \ldots I_j, m_j; \ldots; I_k, m_k; \ldots \rangle$$
$$= -\tfrac{1}{2} J_{jk} \{(I_j - m_j)(I_k + m_k)(I_j + m_j + 1)(I_k - m_k + 1)\}^{1/2}. \qquad (2.16)$$

The use of (2.15) and (2.16) will be illustrated by applying them to the calculation of $\mathscr{H}(\frac{1}{2})$ for $N = 2$ and $I_1 = \frac{3}{2}, I_2 = 1$. The diagonal matrix elements are

$$\langle \tfrac{3}{2}, \tfrac{3}{2}; 1, -1 \mid \mathscr{H} \mid \tfrac{3}{2}, \tfrac{3}{2}; 1, -1 \rangle = -\{\tfrac{3}{2}\omega_1 - \omega_2 - \tfrac{3}{2}J\},$$
$$\langle \tfrac{3}{2}, \tfrac{1}{2}; 1, 0 \mid \mathscr{H} \mid \tfrac{3}{2}, \tfrac{1}{2}; 1, 0 \rangle = -\tfrac{1}{2}\omega_1,$$
$$\langle \tfrac{3}{2}, -\tfrac{1}{2}; 1, 1 \mid \mathscr{H} \mid \tfrac{3}{2}, -\tfrac{1}{2}; 1, 1 \rangle = -\{-\tfrac{1}{2}\omega_1 + \omega_2 - \tfrac{1}{2}J\},$$

where $J_{12} = J_{21} \equiv J$. The nonvanishing off-diagonal elements of $\mathscr{H}(\frac{1}{2})$ are, according to (2.16), generated by those bra and ket vectors for which the quantum numbers m_j, $m_j + 1$, m_k, $m_k - 1$ are consistent with the spin quantum numbers I_j and I_k. For example, with the ket $\mid \frac{3}{2}, \frac{3}{2}; 1, -1\rangle$ one cannot take $j = 1$ in (2.16), since $m_j + 1 = m_1 + 1 = \frac{5}{2}$, which exceeds $I_1 = \frac{3}{2}$. The only consistent choices for k and j are $k = 1$ and $j = 2$; that is, $m_k = \frac{3}{2}$, $m_j = -1$. For this case,

$$\langle \tfrac{3}{2}, \tfrac{1}{2}; 1, 0 \mid \mathscr{H} \mid \tfrac{3}{2}, \tfrac{3}{2}; 1, -1 \rangle = \langle \tfrac{3}{2}, \tfrac{3}{2}; 1, -1 \mid \mathscr{H} \mid \tfrac{3}{2}, \tfrac{1}{2}; 1, 0 \rangle = -\tfrac{1}{2}J\sqrt{6}$$

where the first equality is a consequence of the hermitian property of $\mathscr{H}$. On the other hand,

$$\langle \tfrac{3}{2}, -\tfrac{1}{2}; 1, 1 \mid \mathscr{H} \mid \tfrac{3}{2}, \tfrac{3}{2}; 1, -1 \rangle = \langle \tfrac{3}{2}, \tfrac{3}{2}; 1, -1 \mid \mathscr{H} \mid \tfrac{3}{2}, -\tfrac{1}{2}; 1, 1 \rangle = 0.$$

These matrix elements vanish because $|\Delta m_1|$ and $|\Delta m_2| = 2$, while (2.16) shows that the only nonvanishing off-diagonal matrix elements involve changes in m_1 and m_2 of ± 1. The other nonvanishing matrix elements of $\mathscr{H}(\frac{1}{2})$ are

$$\langle \tfrac{3}{2}, \tfrac{1}{2}; 1, 0 \mid \mathscr{H} \mid \tfrac{3}{2}, -\tfrac{1}{2}; 1, 1 \rangle = \langle \tfrac{3}{2}, -\tfrac{1}{2}; 1, 1 \mid \mathscr{H} \mid \tfrac{3}{2}, \tfrac{1}{2}; 1, 0 \rangle = -J\sqrt{2},$$

so that

$$\mathscr{H}(\tfrac{1}{2}) = \begin{pmatrix} -\tfrac{3}{2}\omega_1 + \omega_2 + \tfrac{3}{2}J & -\tfrac{1}{2}J\sqrt{6} & 0 \\ -\tfrac{1}{2}J\sqrt{6} & -\tfrac{1}{2}\omega_1 & -J\sqrt{2} \\ 0 & -J\sqrt{2} & \tfrac{1}{2}\omega_1 - \omega_2 + \tfrac{1}{2}J \end{pmatrix}$$

As an alternative to the above method of juggling the m_i, one may operate directly on the various product kets and obtain the matrix elements by taking scalar products. For example, operating on $|\frac{3}{2}, \frac{3}{2}; 1, -1\rangle$ with $\mathscr{H}$, one obtains

$$\mathscr{H}\,|\,\tfrac{3}{2}, \tfrac{3}{2}; 1, -1\rangle = -\{(\tfrac{3}{2}\omega_1 - \omega_2 - \tfrac{3}{2}J)|\,\tfrac{3}{2}, \tfrac{3}{2}; 1, -1\rangle + \tfrac{1}{2}J\sqrt{6}\,|\,\tfrac{3}{2}, \tfrac{1}{2}; 1, 0\rangle + 0 \cdot |\,\tfrac{3}{2}, -\tfrac{1}{2}; 1, 1\rangle\}.$$

Upon forming the scalar products of this equation with $\langle\frac{3}{2}, \frac{3}{2}; 1, -1|$, $\langle\frac{3}{2}, \frac{1}{2}; 1, 0|$, and $\langle\frac{3}{2}, -\frac{1}{2}; 1, 1|$, one obtains the first column of $\mathscr{H}(\frac{1}{2})$. The remaining two columns of $\mathscr{H}(\frac{1}{2})$ are obtained by operating with $\mathscr{H}$ on $|\frac{3}{2}, \frac{1}{2}; 1, 0\rangle$ and $|\frac{3}{2}, -\frac{1}{2}; 1, 1\rangle$.

When all $I_j = \frac{1}{2}$, (2.15) and (2.16) reduce to

$$\langle\tfrac{1}{2}, m_1; \tfrac{1}{2}, m_2; ...; \tfrac{1}{2}, m_N\,|\,\mathscr{H}\,|\,\tfrac{1}{2}, m_1; \tfrac{1}{2}, m_2; ...; \tfrac{1}{2}, m_N\rangle = -\tfrac{1}{2}\Big\{\sum \omega_j s_j + \tfrac{1}{2}\sum_{j<k}\sum J_{jk}s_j s_k\Big\}, \tag{2.17}$$

$$\langle...; \tfrac{1}{2}, m_j + 1; ...; \tfrac{1}{2}, m_k - 1; ...\,|\,\mathscr{H}\,|\,...; \tfrac{1}{2}, m_j; ...; \tfrac{1}{2}, m_k; ...\rangle = -\tfrac{1}{2}J_{jk}\,\delta_{s_j,-}\,\delta_{s_k,+} \tag{2.18}$$

where s_j and s_k denote the algebraic signs ($+$ or $-$) of m_j and m_k. Since the evaluation of the matrix elements ultimately depends upon the signs of the m_j, it is permissible to omit the spin quantum numbers in all product kets and to write, for example, $|+-+\rangle$, for $|\frac{1}{2}, \frac{1}{2}; \frac{1}{2}, -\frac{1}{2}; \frac{1}{2}, \frac{1}{2}\rangle$.

To illustrate the use of (2.17) and (2.18), consider the product ket $|++-\rangle$. Here, $s_1 = +$, $s_2 = +$, $s_3 = -$, and (2.17) yields

$$\langle++-\,|\,\mathscr{H}\,|\,++-\rangle = -\tfrac{1}{2}\{\omega_1 + \omega_2 - \omega_3 + \tfrac{1}{2}(J_{12} - J_{13} - J_{23})\}. \tag{2.19}$$

To apply (2.18) to $|++-\rangle$, one must put $j = 3$, but k may take the values 1 or 2, so that

$$\langle-++\,|\,\mathscr{H}\,|\,++-\rangle = -\tfrac{1}{2}J_{13}, \qquad \langle+-+\,|\,\mathscr{H}\,|\,++-\rangle = -\tfrac{1}{2}J_{23}. \tag{2.20}$$

The hamiltonian operator is hermitian, so that $\mathscr{H}_{ij} = \mathscr{H}_{ji}^*$, a relation that provides some relief in the calculation of matrix elements. The calculations can be further expedited by some useful rules whose derivation requires the introduction of a new spin operator, often called a *spin inversion operator*.

Let λ_i denote an operator for the ith spin with the defining property

$$\lambda_i\,|\,I_i, m_i\rangle = |\,I_i, -m_i\rangle. \tag{2.21}$$

From this definition, it is clear that λ_i is represented by a square matrix of the form

$$\begin{pmatrix} 0 & \cdots & 0 & 1 \\ 0 & \cdots & 1 & 0 \\ \cdot & \cdot & \cdot & \cdot \\ 0 & 0 & 1 & \cdots & 0 \\ 0 & 1 & 0 & \cdots & 0 \\ 1 & 0 & 0 & \cdots & 0 \end{pmatrix}.$$

Moreover, $\lambda_i^2 = I$, so that λ_i is hermitian and unitary:

$$\lambda_i = \lambda_i^\dagger = \lambda_i^{-1}. \tag{2.22}$$

Furthermore,

$$\lambda_i I_i^{\pm} \lambda_i = I_i^{\mp}, \tag{2.23}$$

$$\lambda_i I_{zi} \lambda_i = -I_{zi}, \tag{2.24}$$

$$\lambda_i \mathbf{I}_i^2 \lambda_i = \mathbf{I}_i^2, \tag{2.25}$$

as may be readily verified by applying the operators on the left to a generic ket $| I_i, m_i\rangle$. Equations (2.23) are equivalent to

$$\lambda_i I_{xi} \lambda_i = I_{xi}, \qquad \lambda_i I_{yi} \lambda_i = -I_{yi}.$$

For the entire spin system, one introduces the operator

$$\Lambda = \prod_{i=1}^{N} \lambda_i, \tag{2.26}$$

with $\Lambda = \Lambda^\dagger = \Lambda^{-1}$. When all $I_i = \frac{1}{2}$, Λ becomes a (Kronecker) product of the Pauli spin operators σ_{xi}.

The first term of the stationary hamiltonian operator is

$$-\sum \omega_j I_{zj} = -Z,$$

and, relative to the product basis, this operator contributes only to the diagonal matrix elements. The coupling term generates diagonal and off-diagonal elements, so that the matrix elements are of the form

$$\langle m \mid \mathscr{H} \mid m\rangle = -\langle m \mid Z \mid m\rangle - \langle m \mid V \mid m\rangle = -Z_{mm} - V_{mm}, \tag{2.27}$$

$$\langle m' \mid \mathscr{H} \mid m\rangle = -\langle m' \mid V \mid m\rangle = -V_{m'm}. \tag{2.28}$$

Now

$$\Lambda Z \Lambda = -Z, \qquad \Lambda V \Lambda = V, \tag{2.29}$$

so that

$$\Lambda \mathscr{H} \Lambda = Z - V. \tag{2.30}$$

Hence

$$\langle m \mid \Lambda \mathscr{H} \Lambda \mid m \rangle = \langle -m \mid \mathscr{H} \mid -m \rangle = Z_{mm} - V_{mm}, \tag{2.31}$$

$$\langle m' \mid \Lambda \mathscr{H} \Lambda \mid m \rangle = \langle -m' \mid V \mid -m \rangle = -V_{m'm}. \tag{2.32}$$

It follows that if the matrix elements of $\mathscr{H}$ are calculated for the states with $m', m > 0$, the last two equations give the matrix elements of $\mathscr{H}$ for the states with $m', m < 0$. For example, from (2.19) and (2.20) one can immediately write down the matrix elements

$$\langle --+ \mid \mathscr{H} \mid --+ \rangle = -\tfrac{1}{2}\{-\omega_1 - \omega_2 + \omega_3 + \tfrac{1}{2}(J_{12} - J_{13} - J_{23})\},$$

$$\langle +-- \mid \mathscr{H} \mid --+ \rangle = -\tfrac{1}{2}J_{13}, \quad \langle -+- \mid \mathscr{H} \mid --+ \rangle = -\tfrac{1}{2}J_{23}.$$

Similarly, the matrix $\mathscr{H}(\frac{1}{2})$ computed above yields

$$\mathscr{H}(-\tfrac{1}{2}) = \begin{pmatrix} \frac{3}{2}\omega_1 - \omega_2 + \frac{1}{2}J & -\frac{1}{2}J\sqrt{6} & 0 \\ -\frac{1}{2}J\sqrt{6} & \frac{1}{2}\omega_1 & -J\sqrt{2} \\ 0 & -J\sqrt{2} & -\frac{1}{2}\omega_1 + \omega_2 + \frac{1}{2}J \end{pmatrix}.$$

If $m = 0$ there are two extreme cases: (1) Λ permutes the several $\mid 0\rangle$, and the diagonal elements are related by (2.27) and (2.31); (2) Λ does not permute the $\mid 0\rangle$, so that (2.27) and (2.31) may be equated to give $Z_{00} = 0$. In general, $\{\mid 0\rangle\}$ has two subsets conforming to (1) and (2).

3. Transition Probabilities

A. The Hamiltonian Operator for Rotating Fields

Once the eigenvalues and eigenvectors of the stationary hamiltonian operator have been determined, there remains only the problem of calculating the probabilities of the transitions induced by the application of a radiofrequency field $2H_1 \cos \omega t$. Since the amplitude of the rf field is very much smaller than the steady z field ($H_1/H_0 \sim 10^{-7}$), the linearly polarized field can be decomposed into its circularly polarized components. There is no essential loss of generality in assuming all $\gamma_j > 0$ (cf. Section 2.B, Chapter 9), so that the applied field ($2H_1 \cos \omega t$, 0, H_0) may be replaced by the rotating field

$$\mathbf{H}(t) = (H_1 \cos \omega t, -H_1 \sin \omega t, H_0).$$

The interaction of the nuclei with $\mathbf{H}(t)$ is given by

$$-\hbar \sum_j \gamma_j(1-\sigma_j)\mathbf{I}_j \cdot \mathbf{H}(t) = -\hbar \sum_j [\gamma_j(1-\sigma_j)H_1(I_{xj}\cos\omega t - I_{yj}\sin\omega t) + \omega_j I_{zj}]$$

where

$$\omega_j = \gamma_j(1-\sigma_j)H_0 .$$

Since $H_1 \ll H_0$ and $\sigma_j \ll 1$, the shielding correction to H_1 will be omitted. Thus the hamiltonian operator for a system of coupled nuclei in a rotating field is

$$\mathscr{H}(t) = -\left\{\sum_j [\gamma_j H_1(I_{xj}\cos\omega t - I_{yj}\sin\omega t) + \omega_j I_{zj}] + V\right\}. \tag{3.1}$$

Since the hamiltonian is an explicit function of t, it is not a constant of the motion. Furthermore, the interaction of the nuclei with the rf field precludes the conservation of I_z. However, all $\mathbf{I}_j^2$ are still constants of the motion.

The quantum mechanical state vector may be written

$$\Psi(t) = \sum_m \sum_n C_{mn}(t) | m; n), \tag{3.2}$$

where the $| m; n)$ are eigenvectors of the stationary hamiltonian operator

$$\mathscr{H} = -\left\{\sum_i \omega_j I_{zj} + V\right\} \tag{3.3}$$

satisfying

$$\begin{aligned} \mathscr{H} \mid m; n) &= \Omega_{mn} \mid m; n), \\ I_z \mid m; n) &= m \mid m; n), \\ (m'; n' \mid m, n) &= \delta_{m'm}\, \delta_{n'n} . \end{aligned} \tag{3.4}$$

It will be assumed that the rf field is turned on at $t = 0$, and that the system is initially in the state $| m; n)$; that is, $| C_{mn}(0)|^2 = 1$ and $C_{m'n'}(0) = 0$ for $m \neq m'$, $n \neq n'$. The probability of the transition $| m; n) \rightarrow | m'; n')$ during a time interval t is

$$|(m'; n' \mid \Psi(t)|^2 \equiv P_{mn \rightarrow m'n'}(t) = | C_{m'n'}(t)|^2. \tag{3.5}$$

Thus the calculation of transition probabilities requires a knowledge of the probability amplitudes $C_{mn}(t)$, which can be obtained by solving the time-dependent Schrödinger equation

$$i \frac{\partial}{\partial t} \Psi(t) = \mathscr{H}(t)\Psi(t). \tag{3.6}$$

B. Probability Amplitudes

The time dependence of $\mathscr{H}(t)$ can be removed by introducing the transformation

$$\Psi(t) = e^{i\omega t I_z}\Phi(t). \tag{3.7}$$

Differentiating (3.7) and substituting the result in (3.6), one obtains

$$i\frac{\partial}{\partial t}\Phi(t) = \{e^{-i\omega t I_z}\mathscr{H}(t)e^{i\omega t I_z} + \omega I_z\}\Phi(t).$$

The indicated transformation of $\mathscr{H}(t)$ may be carried out by noting that V is a rotationally invariant interaction, and that

$$e^{-i\omega t I_z}I_{xj}e^{i\omega t I_z} = I_{xj}\cos\omega t + I_{yj}\sin\omega t,$$
$$e^{-i\omega t I_z}I_{yj}e^{i\omega t I_z} = -I_{xj}\sin\omega t + I_{yj}\cos\omega t.$$

Hence

$$i\frac{\partial}{\partial t}\Phi(t) = -\left\{\sum_j[(\omega_j - \omega)I_{zj} + \gamma_j H_1 I_{xj}] + V\right\}\Phi(t) = 0. \tag{3.8}$$

Equation (3.8) will be written in the abbreviated form

$$i\frac{\partial}{\partial t}\Phi(t) = -\{W + X\}\Phi(t), \tag{3.9}$$

where

$$W = \sum_j(\omega_j - \omega)I_{zj} + V = -(\mathscr{H} + \omega I_z), \tag{3.10}$$

$$X = H_1\sum_j\gamma_j I_{xj}\,. \tag{3.11}$$

From (3.10) and (3.4),

$$W\mid m; n) = -(\Omega_{mn} + m\omega)\mid m; n). \tag{3.12}$$

The operators W and X are not explicit functions of the time, so that the symbolic solution of (3.9) is

$$\Phi(t) = e^{i(W+X)t}\Phi(0). \tag{3.13}$$

From the definition of $\Phi(t)$,

$$\Psi(t) = e^{i\omega t I_z}e^{i(W+X)t}\Psi(0). \tag{3.14}$$

Equation (3.5) and the initial conditions now yield

$$P_{mn\to m'n'}(t) = |(m'; n' \mid e^{i\omega t I_z} e^{i(W+X)t} \mid m; n)|^2. \tag{3.15}$$

This expression can be simplified upon noting that

$$(m'; n' \mid e^{i\omega t I_z} = e^{im'\omega t}(m'; n' \mid,$$

so that

$$P_{mn\to m'n'}(t) = |(m'; n' \mid e^{i(W+X)t} \mid m; n)|^2. \tag{3.16}$$

The unitary nature of $e^{i(W+X)t}$ guarantees that

$$\sum_{m'}\sum_{n'} P_{mn\to m'n'}(t) = 1.$$

The exponential operator $e^{i(W+X)t}$ cannot be factored to $e^{iWt}e^{iXt}$, since W and X do not commute. However, one can develop an expansion[11] for $e^{i(W+X)t}$ in powers of X. Denoting the eigenvalues and eigenvectors of W by $W_m = -(\Omega_m + m\omega)$ and $\mid m) = \mid m; n)$, the expansion of $e^{i(W+X)t}$ to the second order in X yields

$$\begin{aligned}(m' \mid & e^{i(W+X)t} \mid m) \\ &= e^{iW_{m'}t}\,\delta_{m'm} + \frac{e^{iW_{m'}t} - e^{iW_m t}}{W_{m'} - W_m}(m' \mid X \mid m) \\ &+ \sum_{m''} \frac{(m' \mid X \mid m'')(m'' \mid X \mid m)}{W_m - W_{m''}} \left\{ \frac{e^{iW_{m'}t} - e^{iW_m t}}{W_{m'} - W_m} - \frac{e^{iW_{m''}t} - e^{iW_m t}}{W_{m''} - W_m} \right\}.\end{aligned} \tag{3.17}$$

This equation represents the probability amplitude for the state $\mid m')$ at time t as an expansion in powers of X.

The first term on the right side of (3.17) is the zero-order approximation to $C_{m'}$; it vanishes for $H_1 \to 0$ or $t \to 0$, and, for $m = m'$, its absolute square is unity, in agreement with the initial condition $\mid C_m(0)|^2 = 1$. It can be shown (cf. Section 1, Chapter 9) that only those terms in (3.17) of even order in X contribute to the probability that the system is still in the state $\mid m)$ at time t.

The second term in the expansion (3.17) represents a first-order contribution to probability amplitude of $\mid m')$, provided that $(m' \mid X \mid m) \neq 0$. It will be shown below that this matrix element is nonzero for $m' = m \pm 1$.

The third term on the right side yields contributions to the probability amplitude in which the initial state is connected to $\mid m')$ through inter-

[11] The expansion is derived in Appendix IV.

mediate states $| m'')$. It will be shown in Section 1, Chapter 9, that the second-order term includes contributions to the probability amplitudes for states $| m')$ with $m' = m$, $m' = m \pm 2$.

The first-order approximation to the probability amplitude $C_{m'n'}(t)$ retains only the second term in (3.17); hence the probability that a transition from $| m)$ to $| m')$ has occurred during the time interval t is

$$P_{mn\to m'n'}(t) = |(m'; n' \mid X \mid m; n)|^2 \frac{\sin^2 \frac{1}{2}\{[\Omega_{m'} - \Omega_m + (m' - m)\omega]t\}}{\{\frac{1}{2}[\Omega_{m'} - \Omega_m + (m' - m)\omega]\}^2}. \tag{3.18}$$

Since X is an hermitian operator,

$$P_{mn\to m'n'}(t) = P_{m'n'\to mn}(t). \tag{3.19}$$

C. Selection Rules

According to (3.18), the only allowed transitions in the first-order approximation are those for which the matrix elements $(m'| X |m)$ are nonzero. An important selection rule for first-order transitions can be obtained by noting that

$$[[X, I_z], I_z] = X, \tag{3.20}$$

which may be expanded to

$$XI_z^2 - 2I_zXI_z + (I_z^2 - 1)X = 0. \tag{3.21}$$

Resolving this relation into its matrix components relative to $\{| m; n)\}$, one obtains

$$(m^2 - 2mm' + m'^2 - 1)(m' \mid X \mid m) = 0, \tag{3.22}$$

so that

$$(m' \mid X \mid m) = 0, \qquad \text{unless} \quad m' = m \pm 1. \tag{3.23}$$

The selection rule $\Delta m = m' - m = -1$ corresponds to an absorption of a single quantum of radiation from the rf field; $\Delta m = +1$ corresponds to an emission of a single quantum of radiation. Higher-order corrections to the probability amplitude yield probabilities for the absorption or emission of several quanta, that is, multiple quantum transitions. Unless otherwise noted, the terms "probability amplitude," "transition probability," etc., will always refer to single quantum transitions. Multiple quantum transitions will be treated in Chapter 9.

The operator X does not discriminate between absorption and emission, but one can easily achieve such a distinction by introducing the operators

$$X^{\pm} = H_1 \sum \gamma_j I_j^{\pm}. \tag{3.24}$$

From this definition it follows that

$$X = \tfrac{1}{2}(X^+ + X^-). \tag{3.25}$$

By an argument similar to that used in the demonstration of (3.22), one can show that the operator X^+ corresponds to emission ($\Delta m = +1$), and that X^- corresponds to absorption ($\Delta m = -1$). It is permissible, therefore, to replace $|(m'|\, X\, |m)|^2$ with $\frac{1}{4}\,|(m'|\, X^{\pm}\, |m)|^2$, accordingly as $m' = m \pm 1$.

Additional selection rules on the allowed transitions result if there are operators Q_j that commute with $\mathscr{H}$, I_z, and X. When this is the case, the stationary eigenvectors will be eigenvectors of the Q_j with the eigenvalues q_j. The commutation of X with any Q_j and the selection rule on m require that

$$(m', q_j' \mid X \mid m, q_j) = 0\,, \qquad \text{unless } m' = m \pm 1 \quad \text{and} \quad q_j = q_j' \text{ for all } j\,.$$

Examples of the Q_j are the operators $\mathbf{I}_j^2$. The selection rules are $I_j'(I_j' + 1) = I_j(I_j + 1)$, which are equivalent to $\Delta I_j = 0$.

D. Transition Probabilities and Transition Rates

The first-order transition probability for absorption may be written

$$P_{m\to m-1}(t) = t^2\,|(m - 1 \mid X \mid m)|^2 \left(\frac{\sin \frac{1}{2}\Delta t}{\frac{1}{2}\Delta t}\right)^2, \tag{3.26}$$

where

$$\Delta = \omega - (\Omega_{m-1} - \Omega_m), \tag{3.27}$$

and where the indices n and n' have been omitted to simplify the notation. In (3.26) t is a fixed quantity denoting the time interval during which the rf field is applied to the system, and Ω_m and Ω_{m-1} are fixed energies presumed known from an analysis of the unperturbed problem. Equation (3.26) thus expresses the transition probability as a function of the frequency of the rf field. The functional relation between $P_{m\to m-1}(t)$ and ω can be inferred from Fig. 5.7, which shows that the transition probability is negligible for $|\,\Delta\,| \gg 4\pi/t$, and attains its maximum value $|(m - 1|\, X\, |m)|^2 t^2$ when $\Delta = 0$, that is, when

$$\omega = \Omega_{m-1} - \Omega_m\,.$$

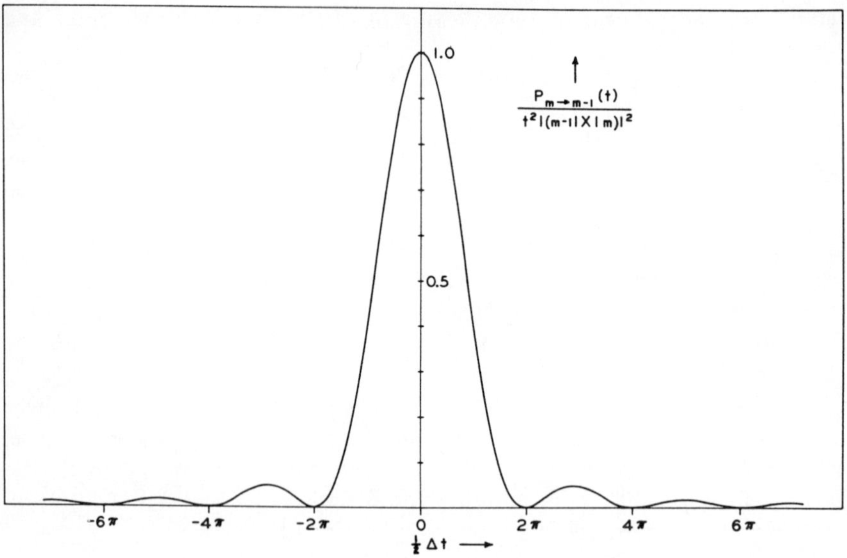

FIG. 5.7. The transition probability $P_{m\rightarrow m-1}(t)$.

This relation, which is just the Bohr frequency condition in angular units, is the resonance condition for the absorption of a single quantum of energy from the rf field.

At first sight it may appear somewhat paradoxical that the transition probability between the two "discrete" states $| m)$ and $| m - 1)$ takes on large values over a range of values of Δ. However, the contradiction is easily resolved with the aid of the uncertainty principle. For the rf field may be interpreted as a device which measures the energy difference $\Omega_{m-1} - \Omega_m$, but at the same time perturbs the system and introduces an uncertainty in the measurement. Since the measurement is carried out over a time interval t, the uncertainty principle demands an energy uncertainty of order $1/t$; the width of the principal arch of $4\Delta^{-2} \sin^2 \frac{1}{2} \Delta t$ is indeed of order $1/t$. It is interesting to note, however, that the transition probability attains its maximum value when the rf frequency equals the difference of the unperturbed energies.

For long times of observation, the transition probability takes on large values over a very narrow range of frequencies in the neighborhood of $\Delta = 0$. This range tends to zero in the limit as $t \rightarrow \infty$. In terms of the uncertainty principle, this means that the uncertainty in $\Omega_{m-1} - \Omega_m$ tends to zero, so that the transition may be interpreted as occurring between two spin states with sharply defined energies.

Although the transition probability $P_{m\rightarrow m-1}(t)$ clearly reveals the resonance absorption of radiation as $\omega \to \Omega_{m-1} - \Omega_m$, the transitions induced by the rf field are more appropriately described in terms of transition probabilities per unit time. The latter, which will be denoted $w_{m\to m-1}$, can be obtained from a study of the function

$$\frac{1}{t} P_{m\to m-1}(t)\, d\Delta,$$

which is the probability per unit time that the transition $|\, m) \to |\, m-1)$ terminates in the frequency range from Δ to $\Delta + d\Delta$. The function $P_{m\to m-1}(t)\, d\Delta/t$ depends upon the time interval t, but by considering the limiting case where the time of observation is very long, one can obtain a constant transition probability per unit time between two sharply defined states. This can be seen qualitatively by noting that for large values of t the width of the main arch of $P_{m\to m-1}(t)$ tends to zero; that is, for large t the uncertainty in the energy decreases as $1/t$. On the other hand, the height of the main arch of the curve increases in proportion to t^2. For large t, the area under the curve is proportional to $(t^2)(1/t) = t$; hence $(1/t)P_{m\to m-1}(t)$ is a constant independent of t. The differential of $w_{m\to m-1}$ is formally defined by passing to the limit $t \to \infty$:

$$dw_{m\to m-1} = \lim_{t\to\infty} \left\{ \frac{1}{t} P_{m\to m-1}(t) \right\} d\Delta. \tag{3.28}$$

The condition that t be infinitely large can be relaxed somewhat by requiring that t be large compared to the uncertainty $\Delta\Omega$ in the energy:

$$t \gg \frac{1}{\Delta\Omega}. \tag{3.29}$$

However, t must not be too long, because the probability of finding the system in the initial state $|\, m)$ at time t must not be very different from unity to ensure the validity of the first-order perturbation calculation for $P_{m\to m-1}(t)$. This requires that

$$tw_{mn\to m-1,n'} \ll 1. \tag{3.30}$$

The limit in (3.28) can be put into a more convenient form with the help of the Dirac delta function, $\delta(x)$, defined by the relations

$$\int_{-\infty}^{\infty} \delta(x)\, dx = 1, \qquad \delta(x) = 0 \quad (\text{for } x \neq 0). \tag{3.31}$$

The delta function can be represented as the limit of a number of continuous functions. In particular, one can show that

$$\delta(x) = \lim_{t\to\infty} \left\{ \frac{\sin^2 xt}{\pi x^2 t} \right\}, \tag{3.32}$$

where the variable x is assumed to range from $-\infty$ to ∞. The proof of (3.32) follows by direct appeal to the definition of $\delta(x)$. When $x = 0$,

$$\left(\frac{\sin^2 xt}{\pi x^2 t}\right)_{x=0} = \frac{t}{\pi}\left(\frac{\sin xt}{xt}\right)^2_{x=0} = \frac{t}{\pi},$$

which tends to $+\infty$ as $t \to +\infty$. If $x \neq 0$, the limit tends to zero as $t \to +\infty$. Finally, by changing the variable to $u = xt$, one can show that

$$\lim_{t\to\infty} \int_{-\infty}^{\infty} \frac{\sin^2 xt}{\pi x^2 t}\, dx = \frac{1}{\pi}\int_{-\infty}^{\infty} \frac{\sin^2 u}{u^2} = 1.$$

From (3.28) and (3.32) it now follows that for any t satisfying (3.29) and (3.30),

$$dw_{m\to m-1} = \pi\, |(m-1 \mid X \mid m)|^2\, \delta(\tfrac{1}{2}\Delta)\, d\Delta = 2\pi\, |(m-1 \mid X \mid m)|^2\, \delta(\Delta)\, d\Delta, \tag{3.33}$$

where the last form for $dw_{m\to m-1}$ follows from the fact that $\delta(ax) = a^{-1}\,\delta(x)$ for any $a > 0$. Integrating (3.33) from $-\infty$ to $+\infty$ yields

$$\begin{aligned} w_{m\to m-1} &= 2\pi\, |(m-1 \mid X \mid m)|^2 \\ &= \tfrac{1}{2}\pi\, |(m' \mid X^- \mid m)|^2 \end{aligned} \tag{3.34}$$

for the transition probability per unit time between two spin states with sharply defined energies.

E. Signal Intensities

The transition probabilities $w_{m\to m-1}$ will now be used to calculate the energy absorbed by a collection of identical spin systems. In a macroscopic sample at thermal equilibrium, all spin states are realized with occupation numbers given by the Boltzmann distribution

$$N_{mn} = \frac{N_0 e^{-\hbar\Omega_{mn}/kT}}{\sum_{m'}\sum_{n'} e^{-\hbar\Omega_{m'n'}/kT}} \tag{3.35}$$

where N_{mn} is the number of spin systems per unit volume in the quantum state $\mid m; n)$ with energy Ω_{mn}, and N_0 the number of spin systems per unit volume. Because of this distribution, which clearly satisfies the condition

$$\sum_m \sum_n N_{mn} = N_0,$$

all possible transitions $|\, m; n) \rightarrow |\, m - 1; n')$ are induced by the rf field and collectively generate the magnetic resonance spectrum of the spin system.[12]

The observed signal intensities can be related to the rate at which energy is absorbed from the rf field. To obtain the signal intensity for a particular transition, it is necessary to compute the net rate of energy absorption between two states with fixed values of n and n'. This rate is

$$\left(\frac{dE}{dt}\right)_{mn\to m-1,n'} = \hbar\{N_{mn}(\Omega_{m-1,n'} - \Omega_{mn})w_{mn\to m-1,n'} - N_{m-1,n'}(\Omega_{m-1,n'} - \Omega_{mn})w_{m-1,n'\to mn}\}.$$

The first term on the right gives the rate at which the energy $\hbar N_{mn}(\Omega_{m-1,n'} - \Omega_{mn})$ is absorbed by the system in transitions from $|\, m; n)$ to $|\, m - 1; n')$; the second term represents the rate at which the same amount of energy is emitted by stimulated emission.[13] Since $w_{mn\to m-1,n'} = w_{m-1,n'\to mn}$, by the hermitian character of X, one can write

$$\left(\frac{dE}{dt}\right)_{mn\to m-1,n'} = \hbar(\Omega_{m-1,n'} - \Omega_{mn})w_{mn\to m-1,n'}(N_{mn} - N_{m-1,n'}).$$

By virtue of (3.34), the last equation can be written in the symmetrical form

$$\left(\frac{dE}{dt}\right)_{mn\to m'n'} = \tfrac{1}{2}\pi H_1^2\hbar(\Omega_{m'n'} - \Omega_{mn})|(m'; n' \,|\, \sum_j \gamma_j I_j^- \,|\, m; n)|^2(N_{mn} - N_{m'n'}), \tag{3.36}$$

since the matrix element on the right vanishes unless $m' = m - 1$.

Equation (3.36) shows that the rate at which energy is absorbed is proportional to the square of the rf-field amplitude, the absolute square of the matrix element of $\sum \gamma_j I_j^-$ connecting the states involved in the resonance, the difference of the populations of these states, and the difference of their energies. However, observed signal intensities are proportional to H_1, rather than H_1^2, since one observes not $(dE/dt)_{mn\to m'n'}$ but an induced voltage generated by the time rate of change of the x and y components of nuclear magnetization (cf. Section 4.C, Chapter 1). Aside from numerical factors reflecting the geometry of the experimental

---

[12] The assumption that the populations of the various energy states can be described by a Boltzmann distribution in the presence of the rf field requires that the rf field does not significantly change the equilibrium values of the N_{mn}.

[13] The rate of spontaneous emission in magnetic resonance is negligible compared to the rates of stimulated absorption and emission.

arrangement, the intensity associated with the transition $|\, m; n) \to |\, m; n')$ is

$$(\mathrm{Int})_{mn\to m'n'} = \frac{1}{H_1}\left(\frac{dE}{dt}\right)_{mn\to m'n'}. \tag{3.37}$$

The formula for the signal intensity can be simplified by noting that the functions $\exp(-\hbar\Omega_{mn}/kT)$ are the diagonal matrix elements of $e^{-\hbar\mathscr{H}/kT}$, relative to the basis which diagonalizes $\mathscr{H}$:

$$(m'; n' \mid e^{-\hbar\mathscr{H}/kT} \mid m; n) = e^{-\hbar\Omega_{mn}/kT}\,\delta_{m'm}\,\delta_{n'n}\,.$$

The denominator of (3.35) is the sum of the eigenvalues of $e^{-\hbar\mathscr{H}/kT}$, so that

$$\sum_{m'}\sum_{n'} e^{-\hbar\Omega_{m'n'}/kT} = \mathrm{tr}\{e^{-\hbar\mathscr{H}/kT}\}.$$

Since the magnetic energies will be much smaller than the thermal energy, $\hbar|\,\Omega_{mn}\,| \ll kT$, for temperatures at which high-resolution experiments are performed, it is permissible to expand the exponentials to first order in $\hbar\Omega_{mn}/kT$. Thus the denominator of (3.35) becomes

$$\mathrm{tr}\left\{1 - \frac{\hbar\mathscr{H}}{kT}\right\} = \mathrm{tr}\, 1 - \frac{\hbar}{kT}\,\mathrm{tr}\,\mathscr{H} = \prod_{j=1}^{N}(2I_j + 1),$$

since the trace of $\mathscr{H}$ is zero.[14]
Thus (3.35) can be written

$$N_{mn} = \frac{N_0}{\prod_j(2I_j + 1)}\left\{1 - \frac{\hbar\Omega_{mn}}{kT}\right\}. \tag{3.38}$$

Combining (3.36) through (3.38), one obtains

$$(\mathrm{Int})_{mn\to m'n'} = \frac{1}{2}N_0\pi H_1\left(\frac{\hbar^2}{kT}\right)(\Omega_{m'n'} - \Omega_{mn})^2\,\frac{|(m'; n' \mid \sum\gamma_j I_j^- \mid m; n)|^2}{\prod_j(2I_j + 1)}. \tag{3.39}$$

Equation (3.39) shows that the relative intensities of a number of closely spaced resonances are measured by the matrix elements

$$|(m'; n' \mid \sum\gamma_j I_j^- \mid m; n)|^2 = 2\,|(m'; n' \mid \sum\gamma_j I_{xj} \mid m; n)|^2, \tag{3.40}$$

since the various factors $(\Omega_{m'n'} - \Omega_{mn})^2$ will be effectively constant for the several components of the multiplet. When the nuclei are identical the relative intensities will be proportional to

$$|(m'; n' \mid I^- \mid m; n)|^2 = 2\,|(m'; n' \mid I_x \mid m; n)|^2. \tag{3.41}$$

[14] The evaluation of traces is described in Appendix V.

Thus the steady-state spectrum is obtained by determining the eigenvalues and eigenvectors of the stationary hamiltonian, and then computing the spectrum according to the prescription

$$\begin{array}{ll} \text{Transition:} & |\, m; n) \rightarrow |\, m'; n'), \\ \text{Resonance frequency:} & \Omega_{m'n'} - \Omega_{mn}, \\ \text{Relative intensity:} & |(m'; n' \,|\, \sum_j \gamma_j I_j^- \,|\, m; n)|^2, \\ \text{Selection rules:} & m' = m - 1, \qquad \text{all } \Delta I_j = 0. \end{array} \tag{3.42}$$

From the results of such a calculation, a theoretical spectrum is obtained by plotting lines of zero width and height $|(m'; n' \,|\, \sum \gamma_j I_j^- \,|\, m; n)|^2$ at the frequencies $\Omega_{m'n'} - \Omega_{mn}$. One could also construct a "theoretical" spectrum by superposing Lorentzian lines of various widths, centered about the frequencies $\Omega_{m'n'} - \Omega_{mn}$, with integrated intensities equal to $|(m'; n' \,|\, \sum \gamma_j I_j^- \,|\, m; n)|^2$. This procedure would yield spectra that conform more closely to those observed experimentally and one may occasionally find this method useful. However, as the calculations leading to (3.42) provide no information concerning the widths of observed resonances, all theoretical calculations will be illustrated by the simpler representation described above. In the event that the widths of two adjacent resonance lines preclude their resolution into distinct components, these resonances will be represented in the calculated spectrum by a single resonance line whose intensity is equal to the sum of the calculated intensities for the separate components, and positioned at a frequency equal to the intensity-weighted mean of the resonance frequencies for the separate components.

Despite the elementary nature of the calculations leading to (3.39), the more general statistical theory—which includes the interaction of the spin system with its molecular surroundings—yields an identical formula for the integrated signal intensity of an unsaturated transition (*18*).

F. A Theorem on the Signs of Coupling Constants

The energy associated with the bilinear interaction of spins j and k is sensitive to the sign of J_{jk}. For N nuclei there will be $2^{N(N-1)/2}$ possible combinations of algebraic signs for the spin-spin coupling constants. For example, if $N = 3$, there will be $2^3 = 8$ possibilities: $(s_{12}, s_{13}, s_{23}) = (+++), (++-), (+-+), (-++), (+--), (-+-), (--+)$, and $(---)$, where s_{jk} denotes the algebraic sign of J_{jk}.

One might expect that the signs of the coupling constants could be determined by computing theoretical spectra for each possible combination of algebraic signs and comparing the results with the observed spectrum. It is not possible, however, to determine the absolute signs of the coupling constants from the analysis of an experimental spectrum—only the relative signs of the coupling constants can be determined. The reason is that a given spectrum is invariant under the transformation $J_{jk} \to -J_{jk}$, for all j and k.

The proof of this theorem is easily carried out with the help of the spin inversion operator Λ. Let

$$\mathscr{H} = -\Big\{\sum_j \omega_j I_{zj} + \sum_{j<k}\sum J_{jk}\mathbf{I}_j \cdot \mathbf{I}_k\Big\} = -(Z + V)$$

be the stationary hamiltonian operator for a given choice of signs for the J_{jk}, and let $\{\Omega_{mn}\}$ and $\{| m; n)\}$ denote the eigenvalues and eigenvectors of $\mathscr{H}$. The hamiltonian operator for the case when the signs of all coupling constants are reversed is

$$\mathscr{H}' = -\Big\{\sum_j \omega_j I_{zj} - \sum_{j<k}\sum J_{jk}\mathbf{I}_j \cdot \mathbf{I}_k\Big\} = -(Z - V).$$

According to (2.30),

$$\Lambda\mathscr{H}\Lambda = Z - V = -\mathscr{H}',$$

or, since $\Lambda = \Lambda^{-1}$,

$$\mathscr{H}'\Lambda = -\Lambda\mathscr{H}.$$

Furthermore,

$$-\Lambda\mathscr{H} \mid m; n) = -\Omega_{mn}[\Lambda \mid m; n)] = \mathscr{H}'[\Lambda \mid m; n)].$$

Thus the eigenvalues and eigenvectors of $\mathscr{H}'$ are $\{-\Omega_{mn}\}$ and $\{\Lambda| \ m; n)\}$.

Suppose now that $| m; n) \to | m'; n')$ is an allowed transition for the system defined by $\mathscr{H}$. One can then write

Transition	Intensity	Frequency
$\mid m; n) \to \mid m'; n')$	$(\Omega_{m'n'} - \Omega_{mn})^2 \lvert (m'; n' \mid \sum_j \gamma_j I_{xj} \mid m; n)\rvert^2$	$\Omega_{m'n'} - \Omega_{mn}$

For simplicity, all constant factors have been dropped from the expression for the signal intensity, and $\sum_j \gamma_j I_j^-$ has been replaced by $\sum_j \gamma_j I_{xj}$. Now the operator Λ merely replaces a given m value with its negative, so that if $| m; n) \to | m'; n')$ is a transition with $m' = m - 1$, then

$\Lambda| m'; n') \rightarrow \Lambda| m; n)$ is an allowed transition for the system defined by $\mathscr{H}'$. Moreover,

$$
\begin{aligned}
|(m'; n' \mid \sum_j \gamma_j I_{xj} \mid m; n)|^2 &= |(m; n \mid \sum_j \gamma_j I_{xj} \mid m'; n')|^2 \\
&= |(m; n \mid \sum_j \gamma_j I_{xj} \Lambda^2 \mid m'; n')|^2 \\
&= |\{(m; n \mid \Lambda\}| \sum_j \gamma_j I_{xj} |\{\Lambda \mid m'; n')\}|^2,
\end{aligned}
$$

since $\sum_j \gamma_j I_{xj}$ is hermitian, $\Lambda^2 = 1$, and Λ commutes with each I_{xj}. It follows that the spectrum calculated with the eigenvalues and eigenvectors of $\mathscr{H}'$ is

Transition	Intensity	Frequency
$\Lambda \mid m'; n') \rightarrow \Lambda \mid m; n)$	$[-\Omega_{mn} - (-\Omega_{m'n'})]^2 \times |(m'; n' \mid \sum_j \gamma_j I_{xj} \mid m; n)|^2$	$-\Omega_{mn} - (-\Omega_{m'n'})$

which is identical with the spectrum determined by the eigenvalues and eigenvectors of $\mathscr{H}$. It should be emphasized that the validity of this theorem rests upon the validity of the first-order expansion (3.38).

G. The Total Intensity Theorem

Equation (3.39) provides an expression for the determination of the intensity associated with those spin systems undergoing a particular transition $| m; n) \rightarrow | m'; n')$. The total intensity is obtained by summing over all values of m, n, m', and n':

$$
\text{Int} = \sum_m \sum_n \sum_{m'} \sum_{n'} (\text{Int})_{mn \rightarrow m'n'} . \tag{3.43}
$$

Evidently, the derivation of an explicit formula for the total intensity requires an evaluation of the fourfold sum

$$
\sum_m \sum_n \sum_{m'} \sum_{n'} (\Omega_{m'n'} - \Omega_{mn})^2 \, |(m'; n' \mid \sum \gamma_j I_j^- \mid m; n)|^2 .
$$

For this purpose it will be convenient to introduce single letters to denote index pairs such as (m', n') and (m, n). Thus if $r = (m', n')$ and $s = (m, n)$, then

$$
\text{Int} = \frac{1}{2} N_0 \pi H_1 \left(\frac{\hbar^2}{kT}\right) \left\{\prod_j (2I_j + 1)\right\}^{-1} \sum_r \sum_s (\Omega_r - \Omega_s)^2 \, |(r \mid \sum_j \gamma_j I_j^- \mid s)|^2 , \tag{3.44}
$$

where the summations are understood to be taken over all index pairs r, s.

The absolute square in (3.44) can be written

$$|(r \mid \sum_j \gamma_j I_j^- \mid s)|^2 = (r \mid \sum_j \gamma_j I_j^- \mid s) \left\{ (r \mid \sum_j \gamma_j I_j^- \mid s) \right\}^*$$

$$= (r \mid \sum_j \gamma_j I_j^- \mid s)(s \mid \sum_j \gamma_j I_j^+ \mid r),$$

since $\sum_j \gamma_j I_j^+$ is the adjoint of $\sum_j \gamma_j I_j^-$. Furthermore,

$$(\Omega_r - \Omega_s)^2 \, |(r \mid \sum_j \gamma_j I_j^- \mid s)|^2$$

$$= \left\{ (\Omega_r - \Omega_s)(r \mid \sum_j \gamma_j I_j^- \mid s) \right\} \left\{ (s \mid \sum_j \gamma_j I_j^+ \mid r)(\Omega_r - \Omega_s) \right\}$$

$$= \Big[\mathscr{H}, \sum_j \gamma_j I_j^- \Big]_{rs} \Big[\sum_j \gamma_j I_j^+, \mathscr{H} \Big]_{sr},$$

as one may readily verify by computing the matrix elements of the indicated commutators, making use of the fact that $\mathscr{H}_{\lambda\mu} = \Omega_\lambda \, \delta_{\lambda\mu}$. Summing the last equation over r and s and inserting the result in (3.44) yields

$$\text{Int} = \frac{1}{2} N_0 \pi H_1 \frac{\hbar^2}{kT} \left\{ \prod_j (2I_j + 1) \right\}^{-1} \text{tr} \left\{ \Big[\mathscr{H}, \sum_j \gamma_j I_j^- \Big] \Big[\sum_j \gamma_j I_j^+, \mathscr{H} \Big] \right\}. \quad (3.45)$$

The commutators in (3.45) may be obtained from the first and second equations of (2.7), whose right-hand members are equal to $i[\mathscr{H}, I_{xj}]$ and $i[\mathscr{H}, I_{yj}]$, respectively. Putting $\omega_{xj} = \omega_{yj} = 0$ and $\omega_{zj} = \omega_j$, one finds that

$$[\mathscr{H}, \gamma_j I_j^-] = \gamma_j \left\{ \omega_j I_j^- + \sum_{k \neq j} J_{jk} (I_j^- I_{zk} - I_{zj} I_k^-) \right\}.$$

Summing over j, one obtains

$$\Big[\mathscr{H}, \sum_j \gamma_j I_j^- \Big] = \sum_j \gamma_j \omega_j I_j^- + \sum_{j<k}\sum (\gamma_j - \gamma_k) J_{jk} (I_j^- I_{zk} - I_{zj} I_k^-).$$

The remaining commutator in (3.45) need not be explicitly calculated, since

$$\Big[\sum_j \gamma_j I_j^+, \mathscr{H} \Big] = \Big[\mathscr{H}, \sum_j \gamma_j I_j^- \Big]^\dagger.$$

A straightforward trace calculation now yields

$$\text{Int} = \frac{\pi N_0 H_1}{3}\left(\frac{\hbar^2}{kT}\right)\Big\{\sum_j \gamma_j^2 \omega_j^2 I_j(I_j+1)$$

$$+\frac{2}{3}\prod_{i=1}^{N}(2I_i+1)\sum_{j<k}\sum J_{jk}^2(\gamma_j-\gamma_k)^2 I_j^2(I_j+1)^2\Big\}. \qquad (3.46)$$

As a first application of (3.46), consider a system composed of identical nuclei, so that $\gamma_1 = \gamma_2 = \cdots \equiv \gamma$, $I_1 = I_2 = \cdots \equiv I$. In this case (3.46) reduces to

$$\text{Int} = \frac{\pi N_0 H_1}{3}\left(\frac{\hbar^2}{kT}\right)\gamma^4 H_0^2 I(I+1)\sum_{j=1}^{N}(1-\sigma_j)^2. \qquad (3.47)$$

Since σ_j^2 and $2\sigma_j$, $j = 1, 2, ..., N$, are expected to be very much less than unity for all but the heaviest nuclei, the summation on the right side of (3.46) will normally be well approximated by N. If all internal chemical shifts vanish, so that $\sigma_1 = \sigma_2 = \cdots \equiv \sigma$, the sum is exactly $(1-\sigma)^2 N$. In either case the total intensity is independent of the spin-spin coupling constants and proportional to the total number of nuclei in the spin system.

A similar result holds for mixed nuclear spin systems, that is, spin systems containing nuclei with different gyromagnetic ratios. For, since most gyromagnetic ratios are $\sim 10^3$ G sec^{-1}, the first summation in (3.46) will be of the order of $N \times 10^{18}$, for $\omega_i \sim 10^6$ cps. However, the double sum in (3.46) will be smaller by a factor of roughly 10^6, even for coupling constants in the kilocycle range, so that

$$\text{Int} = \frac{\pi N_0 H_1}{3}\frac{\hbar^2}{kT}H_0^2\sum_s \gamma_s n_s, \qquad (3.48)$$

where n_s is the number of nuclei with gyromagnetic ratio γ_s, and where the usual approximations $\sigma_i^2, 2\sigma_i \ll 1$, have been used. Thus the contribution of the resonances from a given nuclear species to the total spectral intensity is proportional to the number of nuclei of that species.

The preceding intensity theorems are of theoretical interest only, since the main interest in high-resolution experiments centers upon the relative intensities of closely spaced resonances rather than their absolute intensities. In particular, the intensities of the resonances of nuclei with different gyromagnetic ratios are observed in separate experiments and not, as implied in the derivation of (3.46), by a single sweep over the resonance frequencies of all nuclei. There is, in fact, a "separation theorem" for mixed nuclear spin systems which states that the allowed transitions and relative intensities for a given nuclear species s are determined by the nonvanishing matrix elements of

$$I_s^- = \gamma_s \sum_i I_{si}^- .$$

A detailed discussion of the separation theorem will be given in Chapter 7. The remainder of this chapter will be concerned with spin systems composed of identical nuclei, so that the relative intensity of a particular transition will be given by (3.41).

4. Theory of Magnetically Equivalent Nuclei

A. The A_N System

Let A_N denote a spin system composed of N identical nuclei such that

$$\sigma_1 = \sigma_2 = \cdots = \sigma_N \equiv \sigma. \tag{4.1}$$

These conditions, which demand the equality of the uncoupled nuclear Larmor frequencies in a steady magnetic field, are often realized for spin systems whose parent molecules are symmetrical or possess effective symmetries brought about by rapid internal rotation. A somewhat more remote possibility is the coincidental equality of all shielding constants, but for the purpose of the following discussion it will not be necessary to make any assumptions concerning the reasons for the validity of equations (4.1).

The theory of the A_N system is quite important, since it leads to the concept of a group of magnetically equivalent nuclei. The generalization of this concept provides a number of important theorems which facilitate the study of spin systems much more complicated than the A_N system.

B. The Spectra of A_N Systems

The hamiltonian operator for an A_N system in a rotating field is

$$\mathscr{H}_0(t) = -\{\omega_1(I_x \cos \omega t - I_y \sin \omega t) + \omega_0 I_z + V\}, \tag{4.2}$$

where

$$\omega_0 = \gamma(1 - \sigma)H_0 , \qquad \omega_1 = \gamma(1 - \sigma)H_1 , \tag{4.3}$$

and V denotes the spin-spin interactions. For the A_N system, only the rotational invariance of V will be assumed. This property alone is required in the demonstration that the transition probabilities and the resonance frequencies are independent of the spin-spin interactions.

The stationary hamiltonian operator for an A_N system is obtained from (4.2) by dropping the terms in I_x and I_y:

$$\mathscr{H}_0 = -\{\omega_0 I_z + V\}. \tag{4.4}$$

It follows that I_z is a constant of the motion in the field $H_0\mathbf{e}_z$. A second constant of the motion follows from the fact that V commutes with I_z and, therefore, with $\mathscr{H}_0$. Moreover, the square of the total angular momentum is also a constant of the motion, since $\mathbf{I}^2$ commutes with I_z and V. Thus the stationary states of an A_N system are simultaneous eigenvectors of $\mathscr{H}_0$, $\mathbf{I}^2$, I_z, and V.

The eigenvalues of $\mathscr{H}_0$, I_z, and V will be denoted Ω_m, m, and v, respectively. Distinct eigenvalues will be distinguished by primes. Thus the eigenvalues of $\mathscr{H}_0$ are $\Omega_m = -(m\omega_0 + v)$, so that the energy change associated with the transition $|\,\Omega_m, I, m, v) \to |\,\Omega_{m'}, I', m', v')$ is

$$\Omega_{m'} - \Omega_m = (m - m')\omega_0 + v - v'. \tag{4.5}$$

The allowed transitions and their probabilities are determined by the solution of the time-dependent Schrödinger equation with the hamiltonian operator (4.2). The analysis is exactly analogous to that used in Section 3.B. In the present case, (3.8) reduces to

$$\begin{aligned} i\frac{\partial}{\partial t}\Phi(t) &= -\{\Delta I_z + \omega_1 I_x + V\}\Phi(t) \\ &= -\{\Omega\mathbf{n}\cdot\mathbf{I} + V\}\Phi(t), \end{aligned} \tag{4.6}$$

where

$$\Delta = \omega_0 - \omega, \qquad \Omega = (\Delta^2 + \omega_1{}^2)^{1/2},$$

$$\mathbf{n} = (\omega_1/\Omega, 0, \Delta/\Omega).$$

The operator $-\{\Omega\mathbf{n}\cdot\mathbf{I} + V\}$ is the transform of $\mathscr{H}_0(t)$:

$$-\{\Omega\mathbf{n}\cdot\mathbf{I} + V\} = e^{-i\omega t I_z}\mathscr{H}_0(t)e^{i\omega t I_z},$$

and, since the transformed hamiltonian is not an explicit function of the time, the solution of (4.6) is

$$\Phi(t) = e^{it(\Omega\mathbf{n}\cdot\mathbf{I}+V)}\Phi(0) = e^{i\Omega t\mathbf{n}\cdot\mathbf{I}}e^{itV}\Phi(0),$$

where the last form follows from the fact that V commutes with $\mathbf{n} \cdot \mathbf{I}$. From (3.7) it follows that

$$\Psi(t) = e^{i\omega t I_z} e^{i\Omega t \mathbf{n}\cdot\mathbf{I}} e^{itV} \Psi(0).$$

If the system is initially in the state $|\, \Omega_m, I, m, v)$, the probability that the system is in the state $|\, \Omega_{m'}, I', m', v')$ at time t is equal to the absolute square of

$$(\Omega_{m'}, I', m', v' \,|\, e^{i\omega t I_z} e^{itV} e^{i\Omega t \mathbf{n}\cdot\mathbf{I}} \,|\, \Omega_m, I, m, v)$$
$$= e^{i\omega m' t} e^{iv' t} (\Omega_{m'}, I', m', v' \,|\, e^{i\Omega t \mathbf{n}\cdot\mathbf{I}} \,|\, \Omega_m, I, m, v). \tag{4.7}$$

The absolute square of the right-hand member depends only upon the matrix elements of $e^{i\Omega t \mathbf{n}\cdot\mathbf{I}}$, so that the transition probability is independent of V, as asserted.

The transition $|\, \Omega_m, I, m, v) \rightarrow |\, \Omega_{m'}, I', m', v')$ will occur with a nonvanishing probability provided that the matrix element on the right side of (4.7) is nonvanishing. Two selection rules for transitions may be obtained upon noting that since $\mathbf{I}^2$ and V commute with every power of $\mathbf{n} \cdot \mathbf{I}$,

$$\mathbf{I}^2 e^{i\Omega t \mathbf{n}\cdot\mathbf{I}} - e^{i\Omega t \mathbf{n}\cdot\mathbf{I}} \mathbf{I}^2 = 0,$$

$$V e^{i\Omega t \mathbf{n}\cdot\mathbf{I}} - e^{i\Omega t \mathbf{n}\cdot\mathbf{I}} V = 0.$$

Resolving these equations into their matrix components yields

$$\{I'(I'+1) - I(I+1)\}(\Omega_{m'}, I', m', v' \,|\, e^{i\Omega t \mathbf{n}\cdot\mathbf{I}} \,|\, \Omega_m, I, m, v) = 0,$$
$$(v' - v)(\Omega_{m'}, I', m', v' \,|\, e^{i\Omega t \mathbf{n}\cdot\mathbf{I}} \,|\, \Omega_m, I, m, v) = 0.$$

It follows that an allowed transition $|\, \Omega_m, I, m, v) \rightarrow |\, \Omega_{m'}, I', m', v')$ is characterized by the selection rules:

$$I = I', \qquad v = v'. \tag{4.8}$$

These conservation laws could have been obtained in a more direct manner upon noting that $\mathbf{I}^2$ and V are constants of the motion with respect to the time-dependent hamiltonian operator $\mathscr{H}_0(t)$. In fact, $\mathbf{I}^2$ and V are constants of the motion for any time variation of the applied field.

From (4.5) and (4.8) it follows that $\Omega_{m'} - \Omega_m = (m - m')\omega_0$. For absorption, the possible values of $m - m'$ are 1, 2, ..., $2I$. It will be shown in Chapter 9 that the frequency of an absorptive multiple quantum transition (i.e., a transition with $m - m' > 1$) is

$$\omega = \frac{1}{m - m'}(\Omega_{m'} - \Omega_m).$$

It follows that the spectrum of an A_N system consists of a single resonance at ω_0. The transition probabilities for arbitrary I, m, and m' are given by the Majorana formula [Chapter 3, equation (3.14)].

The preceding analysis applies only when the amplitude of the rf field is much smaller than the steady z field, so that the energy is approximately conserved. When H_1 is comparable to H_0 or, more generally, when the applied field is an arbitrary function of the time, the concept of a stationary state becomes meaningless. However, the theorem on the transition probabilities is still valid. For upon introducing the substitution $\Psi(t) = e^{iVt}\Phi(t)$ into the Schrödinger equation

$$i\frac{\partial \Psi}{\partial t} = -\{\gamma \mathbf{H}(t) \cdot \mathbf{I} + V\}\Psi,$$

one obtains

$$i\frac{\partial \Phi}{\partial t} = -\{\gamma \mathbf{H}(t) \cdot \mathbf{I}\}\Phi.$$

Thus the time development of the transformed state vector is independent of the spin-spin interactions. The observed signal voltage is proportional to the time derivative of

$$\langle I_y \rangle_t = \Psi^\dagger I_y \Psi = \Phi^\dagger e^{iVt} I_y e^{-iVt} \Phi = \Phi^\dagger I_y \Phi.$$

Hence the observed signal is independent of the spin-spin interactions.

The same result may also be deduced from the Heisenberg equation of motion for the total spin vector:

$$\frac{d\mathbf{I}}{dt} = -\gamma \mathbf{H}(t) \times \mathbf{I}.$$

This equation shows that the time development of the components of $\mathbf{I}$ is independent of the spin-spin interactions. The Heisenberg equation also shows that the square of the total spin angular momentum of an A_N system is a constant of the motion in arbitrary fields.

C. Groups of Magnetically Equivalent Nuclei

Equations (4.1) imply that the square of the total spin angular momentum is a constant of the motion. Conversely, the conservation of the square of the total spin angular momentum implies equations (4.1). Thus the necessary and sufficient condition that a nuclear spin system be an A_N system is that the square of its total spin angular momentum be a constant of the motion.

Consider now a nuclear spin system which can be decomposed into sets G = A, B, C, ..., such that the nuclei in each set have identical uncoupled Larmor frequencies

$$\omega_{Gj} = \omega_{Gk} = \cdots \equiv \omega_G \qquad (G = A, B, ...), \tag{4.9}$$

where Gj denotes nucleus j in set G. The number of nuclei in set G will be denoted n_G.

The hamiltonian operator for the system may be written

$$\mathscr{H} = -\Big\{\sum_G \omega_G \mathbf{n} \cdot \mathbf{I}_G + \sum_G V_G + \sum_{G<G'}\sum V_{GG'}\Big\}, \tag{4.10}$$

where $\mathbf{n}$ denotes the direction of the applied field, which may depend upon time;

$$\mathbf{I}_G = \sum_{j=1}^{n_G} \mathbf{I}_{Gj}, \tag{4.11}$$

is the total spin vector for set G;

$$V_G = \sum_{j<k}\sum J_{GjGk} \mathbf{I}_{Gj} \cdot \mathbf{I}_{Gk} \tag{4.12}$$

is the operator representing the coupling of the nuclei within set G; and

$$V_{GG'} = \sum_j \sum_k J_{GjG'k} \mathbf{I}_{Gj} \cdot \mathbf{I}_{G'k} \tag{4.13}$$

denotes the interactions between nuclei in distinct sets.[15] The possibility that some set Q consists of a single nucleus ($n_Q = 1$) is not excluded. However, if $n_Q = 1$, V_Q must be omitted from $\sum_G V_G$, and all sums over Q reduce to a single term. Similar remarks apply if more than one n_G is equal to unity. If all n_G are unity, all V_G are to be omitted from $\mathscr{H}$, which then reduces to (2.1). To avoid the special case $n_A = n_B = \cdots = 1$, it will be assumed that at least one n_G, say n_S, is greater than unity.

If the total spin angular momentum of the system is conserved, then $\omega_A = \omega_B = \cdots$, so that the system is equivalent to an A_N system with $N = n_A + n_B + \cdots$. A more general result is obtained if one demands only the conservation of the square of the total spin angular momentum of set S.

[15] The notation G < G′, introduced in the last term of (4.10), may be interpreted to mean that G precedes G′ alphabetically.

The conditions for the conservation of

$$\mathbf{I}_S^2 = \sum_j \mathbf{I}_{Sj}^2 + 2 \sum_{j<k}\sum \mathbf{I}_{Sj} \cdot \mathbf{I}_{Sk}$$

may be deduced by evaluating the commutator of $\mathscr{H}$ and $\mathbf{I}_S^2$. Since V_S is a rotationally invariant interaction, $[\mathbf{I}_S^2, V_S] = 0$. Furthermore, $[\mathbf{I}_S^2, \mathbf{n} \cdot \mathbf{I}_S] = 0$, and, since operators for distinct particles commute,

$$[\mathscr{H}, \mathbf{I}_S^2] = -\sum_{G<G'}\sum [V_{GG'}, \mathbf{I}_S^2] = 2i \sum_G \sum_l \sum_{j<k}\sum (J_{SjGl} - J_{SkGl})\mathbf{I}_{Sk} \cdot \mathbf{I}_{Sj} \times \mathbf{I}_{Gl} .$$

This result may also be obtained by ordinary vector operations on the Heisenberg equation of motion for $\mathbf{I}_S$. It follows that $\mathbf{I}_S^2$ will be a constant of the motion if

$$J_{SjGl} = J_{SkGl}, \qquad \text{for all} \quad Sj, Sk, Gl \qquad (G \neq S). \tag{4.14}$$

These equations show that the coupling constant for the bilinear interaction between any nucleus in set S and nucleus Gl is equal to the coupling constant for the bilinear interaction between any other nucleus in set S and nucleus Gl. Thus the conditions for the conservation of $\mathbf{I}_S^2$ are

$$\begin{aligned} \omega_{Sj} &= \omega_{Sk} = \cdots \equiv \omega_S, \\ J_{SjGl} &= J_{SkGl} = \cdots \equiv J_{SGl}, \\ l &= 1, 2, \ldots, n_G, \\ G &= A, B, \ldots, \neq S. \end{aligned} \tag{4.15}$$

Conversely, the conservation of $\mathbf{I}_S^2$ implies equations (4.15). Any set of nuclei conforming to conditions (4.15) is said to be a *group of magnetically equivalent* nuclei. Therefore a necessary and sufficient condition for a set of nuclei to be a group of magnetically equivalent nuclei is that the square of its total spin angular momentum be a constant of the motion.

When $\mathbf{I}_S^2$ is conserved, the interactions V_S can be omitted from the hamiltonian (4.10). For (4.13) and (4.15) show that the bilinear interactions coupling the nuclei in S to the remaining nuclei are given by

$$\begin{aligned} \sum_{G' \neq S} V_{SG'} &= \sum_{G' \neq S} \sum_j \sum_k J_{SjG'k} \mathbf{I}_{Sj} \cdot \mathbf{I}_{G'k} \\ &= \mathbf{I}_S \cdot \left\{ \sum_{G' \neq S} \sum_k J_{SG'k} \mathbf{I}_{G'k} \right\}. \end{aligned}$$

Since V_S commutes with all components of $\mathbf{I}_S$, $[\mathscr{H}, V_S] = 0$. Thus, by the same form of argument used in the discussion of the A_N system, V_S

makes no contribution to the frequencies of observable transitions or their transition probabilities.

If equations (4.15) hold for $S = \mathrm{A, B}, \ldots$, the spin system will be entirely decomposed into groups of magnetically equivalent nuclei. In this case, every V_{G} may be dropped from the hamiltonian operator, which then simplifies to

$$\mathscr{H} = -\left\{ \sum_{\mathrm{G}} \omega_{\mathrm{G}} \mathbf{n} \cdot \mathbf{I}_{\mathrm{G}} + \sum_{\mathrm{G}<\mathrm{G}'}\sum J_{\mathrm{GG}'} \mathbf{I}_{\mathrm{G}} \cdot \mathbf{I}_{\mathrm{G}'} \right\}, \tag{4.16}$$

where $J_{\mathrm{GG}'}$ denotes the coupling constant for the interaction of any nucleus in group G with any nucleus in group G′. Since the square of the total spin angular momentum for each magnetically equivalent group G is a constant of the motion,

$$[\mathscr{H}, \mathbf{I}_{\mathrm{G}}^2] = 0 \qquad (\mathrm{G} = \mathrm{A, B}, \ldots), \tag{4.17}$$

which implies that in any allowed transition the spin quantum numbers must be conserved:

$$\Delta I_{\mathrm{G}} = 0 \qquad (\mathrm{G} = \mathrm{A, B}, \ldots). \tag{4.18}$$

When the Larmor frequencies of all magnetically equivalent groups are equal, (4.16) reduces to the hamiltonian operator for an A_N system. Thus the N nuclei of an A_N system constitute a single group of magnetically equivalent nuclei. For an A_N system, equations (4.14) are meaningless, since there is only one set of nuclei. In this case, the conservation of the total angular momentum requires only the equality of the Larmor frequencies.

A group G of magnetically equivalent nuclei is said to be trivial or nontrivial, accordingly as $n_{\mathrm{G}} = 1$ or $n_{\mathrm{G}} > 1$. When all n_{G} are unity, (4.16) correctly reduces to the N-particle hamiltonian (2.1). Equations (4.18) then state that the angular momentum of each particle is conserved.

The preceding results can be generalized by considering the possibility that (4.9) and (4.14) hold for two or more groups of magnetically equivalent nuclei. By arguments analogous to those used above, it can be shown that the total spin angular momentum of the combined groups is conserved, so that these groups may be treated as a single group of magnetically equivalent nuclei. Consider, for example, the protons in propane ($CH_3CH_2CH_3$). Assuming rapid internal rotation, the methyl- and methylene-group protons are groups of magnetically equivalent nuclei. However, the six protons of the two methyl groups satisfy (4.9) and (4.14), so that the methyl-group protons may be considered as a single group of six magnetically equivalent nuclei. Other examples of molecules containing groups of magnetically equivalent nuclei are given in Table 5.3.

Systems composed of groups of magnetically equivalent nuclei are denoted $A_{n_A}B_{n_B}C_{n_C}\cdots$. For example, the spin system defined by the protons in propane is denoted A_6B_2. However, this notation is ambiguous, since the theory of magnetically equivalent nuclei applies to nuclei with arbitrary spin quantum numbers. Thus the spin system defined by the deuterons in $CD_3CD_2CD_3$, which consists of two magnetically equivalent groups with $n_A = 6$, $n_B = 2$, is also denoted A_6B_2. Most applications are to nuclei with spin $\frac{1}{2}$, so that the notation $A_{n_A}B_{n_B}\cdots$ usually refers to groups of magnetically equivalent nuclei with $I = \frac{1}{2}$. Further developments in notation will be discussed in Section 4.E and in Chapters 7 and 8.

TABLE 5.3

MOLECULES CONTAINING GROUPS OF MAGNETICALLY EQUIVALENT NUCLEI

Molecule	No. of groups	n_A	n_B	n_C
Benzene, C_6H_6	1	6		
Neopentane,[a] $(CH_3)_4C$	1	12		
Chlorotrifluoride, ClF_3	2	2	1	
Methyl mercaptan,[a] CH_3SH	2	3	1	
Ethyl iodide,[a] CH_3CH_2I	2	3	2	
Propane,[a] $CH_3CH_2CH_3$	2	6	2	
Isobutane,[a] $(CH_3)_3CH$	2	9	1	
Vinyl chloride, $H_2C{=}CHCl$	3	1	1	1

[a] Rapid internal rotation assumed.

D. Structure of the Hamiltonian Matrix

The conservation of the angular momentum of each magnetically equivalent group implies that the hamiltonian matrix is the direct sum of lower-dimensional submatrices, each submatrix in the direct-sum decomposition being characterized by a particular set of spin quantum numbers $(I_A, I_B, \ldots)$. For there can be no mixing between two product kets in which a given group G is assigned the quantum number I_G in the one and a different spin quantum number I_G' in the other, since the commutation of $\mathscr{H}$ and $\mathbf{I}_G^2$ leads to the conclusion that

$$(\cdots I_G' \cdots | \mathscr{H} | \cdots I_G \cdots) = 0,$$

if $I_G' \neq I_G$. Furthermore, there can be no mixing between two states with different spin multiplicity indices $s_G = 1, 2, \ldots, g_{I_G}$, since such states are independent and can be assumed to have been orthogonalized (e.g., by the Gram-Schmidt process). It follows that the submatrix characterized by the quantum numbers $(I_A, I_B, ...)$ will occur $g_{I_A} g_{I_B} \cdots$ times in the direct sum decomposition of $\mathscr{H}$.

The submatrix defined by the quantum numbers $I_A, I_B, ...$ is called an $(I_A, I_B, ...)$-block. The dimension of an $(I_A, I_B, ...)$-block will be denoted $\dim(I_A, I_B, ...)$. Evidently

$$\dim(I_A, I_B, ...) = \prod_{G=A,B,...} (2I_G + 1). \tag{4.19}$$

The spin quantum numbers and their spin multiplicities may be determined by the methods described in Section 3 of Chapter 4. In the important special case of a group of magnetically equivalent spin-$\frac{1}{2}$ nuclei, one has the explicit relations

$$I_G = \tfrac{1}{2}n_G - k, \qquad g_{I_G} = \frac{n_G!\,(n_G - 2k + 1)}{(n_G - k + 1)!\,k!},$$
$$k = \begin{cases} 0, 1, ..., \tfrac{1}{2}n_G & \text{for } n_G \text{ even}, \\ 0, 1, ..., \tfrac{1}{2}n_G - 1 & \text{for } n_G \text{ odd}. \end{cases} \tag{4.20}$$

For small values of n_G, I_G and g_{I_G} may be obtained from Fig. 4.3.

The factorization of the hamiltonian matrix into $(I_A, I_B, ...)$-blocks holds for arbitrary fields. In the particular case of a steady z field, there is a further decomposition of each $(I_A, I_B, ...)$-block according to the eigenvalues of I_z. Thus the determination of the eigenvalues and eigenvectors of the stationary hamiltonian may be obtained by separately diagonalizing each $(I_A, I_B, ...)$-block. Except for some trivial changes in notation, the matrix elements for these blocks are given by (2.15) and (2.16).

If a particular $(I_A, I_B, ...)$-block occurs more than once, only one diagonalization is required, since the matrices enclosed by these blocks are identical. Thus the eigenvalues of a given $(I_A, I_B, ...)$-block are $g_{I_A} g_{I_B} \cdots$-fold degenerate. The eigenvectors associated with identical $(I_A, I_B, ...)$-blocks will have the same form (i.e., the corresponding expansion coefficients will be equal), but their independence is guaranteed by the independence of the basis kets that span the corresponding subspaces.

E. Irreducible Components; Superposition

The conservation of the total spin quantum numbers $I_A, I_B, ...,$ and the orthogonality of the basis vectors generating identical $(I_A, I_B, ...)$-blocks implies that the probabilities for transitions between states "belonging to" distinct $(I_A, I_B, ...)$-blocks are identically zero. Transitions with nonvanishing probability amplitudes occur only between states belonging to the same $(I_A, I_B, ...)$-block. A particular $(I_A, I_B, ...)$-block may thus be considered to generate an independent component system in which the group A nuclei behave as a single particle with spin I_A, the group B nuclei behave as a single particle with spin I_B, and so on. Since the spin quantum numbers that describe groups A, B, ... in a given $(I_A, I_B, ...)$-block cannot be reduced to smaller values, the spin system defined by these quantum numbers is said to be *irreducible* and denoted $A_{I_A}B_{I_B} \cdots$. The decomposition of the hamiltonian matrix of an $A_{n_A}B_{n_B} \cdots$ system into $(I_A, I_B, ...)$-blocks may be described as a reduction of the spin system to its irreducible component spin systems. It must be emphasized, however, that although the spin quantum numbers may be different for different irreducible components, the chemical shifts and spin-spin coupling constants are the same for all irreducible components.

When the applied magnetic field takes the form

$$\mathbf{H}(t) = (H_1 \cos \omega t, -H_1 \sin \omega t, H_0)$$

with $H_1 \ll H_0$, it is permissible to speak of the spectrum generated by an irreducible component system. The spectrum is computed by solving the eigenvalue problem for the corresponding $(I_A, I_B, ...)$-block and computing frequencies and intensities by the rules given in Section 3. Each irreducible component system yields its own characteristic spectrum, since the matrix elements of I^- between states belonging to different $(I_A, I_B, ...)$-blocks vanish identically. If a given $(I_A, I_B, ...)$-block occurs $g_{I_A}g_{I_B} \cdots$ times, one obtains the same set of resonance frequencies and relative intensities $g_{I_A}g_{I_B} \cdots$ times. The contribution of all blocks is obtained by calculating the spectrum for one such block and multiplying the relative intensities by $g_{I_A}g_{I_B} \cdots$. Iterating this process for all $(I_A, I_B, ...)$-blocks and superposing the subspectra thus obtained, one obtains the spectrum of the $A_{n_A}B_{n_B} \cdots$ system. The decomposition may be symbolically expressed by the equation

$$A_{n_A}B_{n_B}C_{n_C} \cdots = \sum_{I_A}\sum_{I_B}\sum_{I_C} \cdots (g_{I_A}g_{I_B}g_{I_C} \cdots) A_{I_A}B_{I_B}C_{I_C} \cdots . \tag{4.21}$$

For integral values of $I_A, I_B, ...$, ambiguities may arise in the notation used for spin systems and irreducible component systems. For example, A_3B_2 could denote a spin system with $n_A = 3$ and $n_B = 2$, or an irreducible component of a higher two-group system with $I_A = 3$ and $I_B = 2$. The context will always indicate whether the notation refers to a spin system or an irreducible component.

Equation (4.21) shows that a spin system with all $n_G = 1$ is irreducible, and that any spin system with one or more $n_G > 1$ is always reducible.

The analysis of a reducible spin system can often be expedited if the spectra of its irreducible components can be detected in the experimental spectrum. In some instances the spectrum of a single irreducible component may permit a direct determination of the chemical shifts and coupling constants. However, it must not be concluded that all irreducible component systems provide enough information for a complete analysis. Consider, for example, the case where all n_G are even. One irreducible component is $A_0B_0C_0 \cdots$, but since particles with zero spin do not interact with external or internal magnetic fields, the $A_0B_0C_0 \cdots$ system generates no spectrum at all.

The reduction of spin systems into their irreducible components is illustrated in Table 5.4 for the A_6B_2 system (all $I_j = \frac{1}{2}$) and in Table 5.5

TABLE 5.4

IRREDUCIBLE COMPONENTS OF THE A_6B_2 SYSTEM WITH ALL $I_j = \frac{1}{2}$

$A_{I_A}B_{I_B}$	$g_{I_A}g_{I_B}$	$\dim(I_A, I_B)$	Int $A_{I_A}B_{I_B}$	$g_{I_A}g_{I_B}$ Int $A_{I_A}B_{I_B}$
A_3B_1	1	21	196	196
A_3B_0	1	7	56	56
A_2B_1	5	15	80	400
A_2B_0	5	5	20	100
A_1B_1	9	9	24	216
A_1B_0	9	3	4	36
A_0B_1	5	3	4	20
A_0B_0	5	1	0	0

TABLE 5.5

IRREDUCIBLE COMPONENTS OF THE $A_5B_3C_2$ SYSTEM WITH ALL $I_j = \frac{1}{2}$

$A_{I_A}B_{I_B}C_{I_C}$	$g_{I_A}g_{I_B}g_{I_C}$	$\dim(I_A, I_B, I_C)$	Int $A_{I_A}B_{I_B}C_{I_C}$	$g_{I_A}g_{I_B}g_{I_C}$ Int $A_{I_A}B_{I_B}C_{I_C}$
$A_{5/2}B_{3/2}C_1$	1	72	696	696
$A_{5/2}B_{3/2}C_0$	1	24	200	200
$A_{5/2}B_{1/2}C_1$	2	36	276	552
$A_{5/2}B_{1/2}C_0$	2	12	76	152
$A_{3/2}B_{3/2}C_1$	4	48	304	1216
$A_{3/2}B_{3/2}C_0$	4	16	80	320
$A_{3/2}B_{1/2}C_1$	8	24	104	832
$A_{3/2}B_{1/2}C_0$	8	8	24	192
$A_{1/2}B_{3/2}C_1$	5	24	104	520
$A_{1/2}B_{3/2}C_0$	5	8	24	120
$A_{1/2}B_{1/2}C_1$	10	12	28	280
$A_{1/2}B_{1/2}C_0$	10	4	4	40

for the $A_5B_3C_2$ system (all $I = \frac{1}{2}$). The first column in each table lists the irreducible components, the second column the number of times these components appear in the decomposition of the system, and the third column the dimension of the subspace spanned by the states of each irreducible component. The significance of the remaining columns will be indicated in the following section. Each $(I_A, I_B, ...)$-block is further decomposed according to the eigenvalues of I_z. For example, the spin states of the irreducible A_3B_1 component of the A_6B_2 system span a 21-dimensional space. According to Table 4.8, this space can be decomposed into nine subspaces of dimensions 1, 2, 3, 3, 3, 3, 3, 2, and 1. Thus the analysis of the eigenvalue problem requires the solution of determinantal equations of degrees 1, 2, and 3.

F. Intensities of Irreducible Components

The total intensity of an arbitrary irreducible component $A_{I_A}B_{I_B}C_{I_C}\cdots$ is obtained by summing the absolute squares of the matrix elements of I^- over the $(2I_A+1)(2I_B+1)(2I_C+1)\cdots$ states of the system. This sum is equal to the trace of I^+I^-, so that

$$\text{Int}\, A_{I_A} B_{I_B} C_{I_C} \cdots = \frac{2}{3}\left\{\sum_G I_G(I_G+1)\right\}\prod_G (2I_G+1). \tag{4.22}$$

Since the $A_{I_A}B_{I_B}C_{I_C}\cdots$ system appears $g_{I_A}g_{I_B}g_{I_C}\cdots$ times in the reduction of the spin system, the contribution of all $A_{I_A}B_{I_B}C_{I_C}\cdots$ systems to the total intensity of the spin system is

$$(g_{I_A}g_{I_B}g_{I_C}\cdots)\,\text{Int}\, A_{I_A} B_{I_B} C_{I_C}\cdots. \tag{4.23}$$

These results provide a check on the assignment of observed resonances to a particular irreducible component. Table 5.6 gives the values of (4.22) for the irreducible components of two-group systems.

The total intensity of spin systems composed of N particles with spins $I_1, I_2, ...$ is equal to the trace of I^+I^-, where $I^+ = I_1^+ + I_2^+ \cdots$:

$$\text{tr}\, I^+I^- = \frac{2}{3}\prod_{r=1}^{N}(2I_r+1)\left\{\sum_{r=1}^{N} I_r(I_r+1)\right\}. \tag{4.24}$$

For $I_1 = I_2 = \cdots = I$, this reduces to

$$\text{tr}\, I^+I^- = \tfrac{2}{3}NI(I+1)(2I+1)^N, \tag{4.25}$$

and for all $I_j = \frac{1}{2}$ to

$$\text{tr}\, I^+I^- = 2^{N-1}N. \tag{4.26}$$

TABLE 5.6

INTENSITIES OF IRREDUCIBLE COMPONENTS OF TWO-GROUP SYSTEMS

	0	1/2	1	3/2	2	5/2	3	7/2	4	9/2	5
0	0	1	4	10	20	35	56	84	120	165	220
1/2		4	11	24	45	76	119	176	249	340	451
1			24	46	80	129	196	284	396	535	704
3/2				80	130	200	294	416	570	760	990
2					200	295	420	580	780	1025	1320
5/2						420	581	784	1035	1340	1705
3							784	1036	1344	1715	2156
7/2								1344	1716	2160	2684
4									2160	2685	3300
9/2										3300	4015
5											4840

These equations, in conjunction with (4.22) and (4.23), can be used to compute the fractional contribution of a component system to the total intensity. For example, the eight identical $A_{3/2}B_{1/2}C_1$ components of the $A_5B_3C_2$ system make up 9/80 of the total intensity.

G. Further Remarks Concerning Irreducible Components

Tables 5.4 and 5.5 illustrate an important point concerning irreducible-component spin systems, which is that, although these tables were constructed for spin systems composed entirely of spin-$\frac{1}{2}$ nuclei, the reduction of these systems to their irreducible components requires the consideration of systems with spin quantum numbers greater than $\frac{1}{2}$. Thus there is no essential loss of generality in restricting all subsequent calculations to magnetically equivalent groups composed of spin-$\frac{1}{2}$ particles. For the results of these calculations may also be used in the study of spin systems composed of particles with spins greater than $\frac{1}{2}$. However, care must be taken to use the correct spin multiplicities. For example, the spectrum of the A_1B_1 component of an A_6B_2 system with all $I_j = \frac{1}{2}$ also provides the spectrum of two spin-1 particles (e.g., two coupled deuterons). On the other hand, the A_1B_1 intensities must be multiplied by a factor of 27 (cf. Table 4.9) when considered as an irreducible component of an A_6B_2 system with all $I_j = 1$.

A very important practical consideration is the occurrence of irreducible components in which one or more of the spin quantum numbers is zero. For, since particles with $I = 0$ do not interact with external or internal magnetic fields, groups with spin zero do not influence the spectrum generated by groups with nonzero spins. Thus an $A_{I_A}B_{I_B}C_0$ component of a three-group system generates an $A_{I_A}B_{I_B}$ component of a two-group system. If the spectrum of the $A_{I_A}B_{I_B}$ component can be identified, one can determine ω_{AB} and $|J_{AB}|$. As a second example, consider the irreducible components A_3B_0, A_2B_0, A_1B_0, and A_0B_1 of the A_6B_2 system (Table 5.4). The spectrum of each component with $I_B = 0$ consists of a single resonance at ω_A. The total intensity of the resonance at ω_A is $56 + 100 + 36 = 192$. Similarly, the A_0B_1 component yields a single resonance at ω_B of relative intensity 20. One may state, therefore, that in any A_6B_2 system with all $I_j = \frac{1}{2}$, there are two resonances whose frequency separation is ω_{AB}, and whose intensities are in the ratio 9.6:1.

REFERENCES

1. W. E. Lamb, *Phys. Rev.* **60**, 817 (1941).
2. For more accurate values of atomic shielding constants see W. C. Dickinson, *Phys. Rev.* **81**, 717 (1951).
3. N. F. Ramsey, *Phys. Rev.* **78**, 699 (1950).
4. N. F. Ramsey, "Molecular Beams," pp. 162–166, 206–208, 230–233. Oxford Univ. Press, London and New York, 1956.
5. W. D. Knight, *Phys. Rev.* **76**, 1259 (1949); W. G. Proctor and F. C. Yu, *ibid.* **77**, 717 (1950); W. C. Dickinson, *ibid.* **77**, 736 (1950).
6. The following references may be consulted for further information on the calculation of molecular shielding constants, spin-spin coupling constants, compilations of experimental data, and general questions related to the application of high-resolution nuclear magnetic resonance to chemical problems:
(a) H. S. Gutowsky and C. J. Hoffman, *J. Chem. Phys.* **19**, 1259 (1951). (b) L. H. Meyer, A. Saika, and H. S. Gutowsky, *J. Am. Chem. Soc.* **75**, 4567 (1953). (c) J. A. Pople, W. G. Schneider, and H. J. Bernstein, "High-Resolution Nuclear Magnetic Resonance." McGraw-Hill, New York, 1959. (d) H. S. Gutowsky, *in* "Physical Methods of Organic Chemistry" (A. Weissberger, ed.), 3rd ed., Vol. I, Pt. IV, Chap. XLI, pp. 2663–2799. Wiley (Interscience), New York, 1960. (e) J. G. Powles, *Rept. Progr. Phys.* **22**, 433 (1959). (f) W. D. Phillips, *in* "Determination of Organic Structures by Physical Methods" (F. C. Nachod and W. D. Phillips, eds.), Vol. 2, Chap. 6. Academic Press, New York, 1961. (g) P. C. Lauterbur, *ibid.*, Chap. 7. (h) J. D. Roberts, "Nuclear Magnetic Resonance." McGraw-Hill, New York, 1959. (i) L. M. Jackman, "Applications of Nuclear Magnetic Resonance Spectroscopy in Organic Chemistry." Pergamon Press, New York, 1959. (j) High Resolution NMR Spectra Catalog, Vols. I and II. Varian Associates, Palo Alto, California. (k) Nuclear Magnetic Resonance Spectral Data. American Petroleum Institute Research Project 44, College Station, Texas. (l) Nuclear Magnetic Resonance. *Ann. N. Y. Acad. Sci.* **70**, 763–930 (1958). (m) Review articles on magnetic resonance containing complete literature surveys may be found in the following volumes of *Ann. Rev. Phys. Chem.*, Annual Reviews, Inc., Palo Alto, California: H. S. Gutowsky, **5**, 333 (1954); J. N. Shoolery and H. E. Weaver, **6**, 433 (1955); C. A. Hutchison, Jr., **7**, 359 (1956);

H. M. McConnell, **8**, 105 (1957); J. E. Wertz, **9**, 93 (1958); G. K. Fraenkel and B. Segal, **10**, 435 (1959); R. Bersohn, **11**, 369 (1960); S. I. Weissman, **12**, 151 (1961); R. G. Shulman, **13**, 325 (1962); S. Meiboom, **14**, 335 (1963); D. M. Grant, **15**, 489 (1964).

7. (a) E. L. Hahn, *Phys. Rev.* **80**, 580 (1950). (b) J. T. Arnold, S. S. Dharmatti, and M. E. Packard, *J. Chem. Phys.* **19**, 507 (1951). (c) J. T. Arnold, *Phys. Rev.* **102**, 136 (1956).
8. E. L. Hahn and D. E. Maxwell, *Phys. Rev.* **84**, 1246 (1951); *ibid.* **88**, 243 (1952).
9. E. B. McNeil, C. P. Slichter, and H. S. Gutowsky, *Phys. Rev.* **84**, 1245 (1951).
10. H. S. Gutowsky and D. W. McCall, *Phys. Rev.* **82**, 748 (1951).
11. H. S. Gutowsky, D. W. McCall, and C. P. Slichter, *Phys. Rev.* **84**, 589 (1951).
12. H. S. Gutowsky, D. W. McCall, and C. P. Slichter, *J. Chem. Phys.* **21**, 279 (1953).
13. N. F. Ramsey and E. M. Purcell, *Phys. Rev.* **85**, 143 (1952).
14. N. F. Ramsey, *Phys. Rev.* **91**, 303 (1953).
15. H. Y. Carr and E. M. Purcell, *Phys. Rev.* **88**, 415 (1952).
16. M. Karplus, D. H. Anderson, T. C. Farrar, and H. S. Gutowsky, *J. Chem. Phys.* **27**, 597 (1957).
17. P. L. Corio, to be published.
18. F. Bloch, *Phys. Rev.* **102**, 104 (1956).

CHAPTER 6

Systems with Two Groups of Magnetically Equivalent Nuclei

The stationary hamiltonian operator for a spin system composed of two groups of magnetically equivalent spin-$\frac{1}{2}$ nuclei is given by (*1–6*)

$$\mathscr{H} = -\{\omega_A I_{Az} + \omega_B I_{Bz} + J\mathbf{I}_A \cdot \mathbf{I}_B\}$$

where $J \equiv J_{AB} = J_{BA}$, and where the spin-spin interactions within each group have been omitted (cf. Section 4, Chapter 5). This hamiltonian admits three constants of the motion: $\mathbf{I}_A{}^2$, $\mathbf{I}_B{}^2$, and $I_z = I_{Az} + I_{Bz}$. An initial basis for the analysis of the eigenvalue problem is provided by the set of all product kets $\{|I_A, m_A\rangle|I_B, m_B\rangle\}$.

Before proceeding with the study of particular systems, it will be convenient to adopt certain conventions concerning the relative magnitudes of ω_A and ω_B, the sign of J, and the classification of transitions.

(1) For systems with $n_A > n_B$, all theoretical spectra will be calculated on the assumption $\omega_A > \omega_B$, so that the internal chemical shift

$$\delta = \omega_A - \omega_B$$

is a positive quantity. Graphical representations of theoretical spectra with $n_A > n_B$ will be drawn with the frequency origin at ω_B. By reflecting these graphs in the line $\omega = \omega_B + \frac{1}{2}\delta = \frac{1}{2}(\omega_A + \omega_B)$, one obtains the graphs for the case where $\omega_A < \omega_B$. It will be shown in Section 4 that when $n_A = n_B$, the spectrum is symmetrical with respect to a frequency origin at $\frac{1}{2}(\omega_A + \omega_B)$.

(2) Since the steady-state spectrum of any two-group system does not depend upon the sign of J, it will be arbitrarily assumed that $J > 0$.

(3) All theoretical calculations will use angular frequency units for Larmor frequencies and coupling constants. The theoretical expressions

for the relative signal intensities depend only on the ratio of the parameters J and δ, so that these quantities do not depend upon the choice of units. The expressions for the resonance frequencies may be converted to linear frequency units by dividing by 2π, but inasmuch as there is an arbitrary scale factor in any experimental spectrum, all theoretical expressions for the resonance frequencies may be applied to practical computations as though they were computed in linear units. However, notational consistency will be maintained by writing $\delta/2\pi$ and $J/2\pi$ for the chemical shift and spin-spin coupling constant in linear frequency units.

(4) Transitions will be classified according to the limiting values of their resonance frequencies when $J \to 0$. The limiting resonance frequencies are of the form $-(\omega_A \Delta m_A + \omega_B \Delta m_B)$, where $\Delta m_A + \Delta m_B = \Delta m = -1$.

A transition whose resonance frequency approaches ω_G as $J \to 0$ is said to be a transition in group G. Evidently, a transition in group G is such that $\Delta m_G = -1$, while $\Delta m_{G'} = 0$, G, G$' =$ A, B (G $\neq$ G$'$).

A transition whose resonance frequency approaches a linear combination of Larmor frequencies is said to be a mixed transition. For a mixed transition, $\Delta m_A \neq 0, \Delta m_B \neq 0$, subject, of course, to the general restriction $\Delta m = \Delta m_A + \Delta m_B = -1$.

To illustrate these definitions, consider the irreducible $A_1B_{1/2}$ system. The A, B, and M transitions are determined by enumerating all possible changes $(m_A, m_B) \to (m_A', m_B')$, consistent with $I_A = 1, I_B = \frac{1}{2}$, and $\Delta m_A + \Delta m_B = -1$. A simple calculation shows that there are four transitions in group A, three in group B, and one mixed transition (see accompanying tabulation). The limiting frequencies of the A, B, and M transitions are ω_A, ω_B, and $2\omega_A - \omega_B$, respectively.

A Transitions	B Transitions	M Transition
$(1, \frac{1}{2}) \to (0, \frac{1}{2})$	$(1, \frac{1}{2}) \to (1, -\frac{1}{2})$	$(1, -\frac{1}{2}) \to (-1, \frac{1}{2})$
$(1, -\frac{1}{2}) \to (0, -\frac{1}{2})$	$(0, \frac{1}{2}) \to (0, -\frac{1}{2})$	
$(0, \frac{1}{2}) \to (-1, \frac{1}{2})$	$(-1, \frac{1}{2}) \to (-1, -\frac{1}{2})$	
$(0, -\frac{1}{2}) \to (-1, -\frac{1}{2})$		

This method of classifying transitions, which may also be used to describe the transitions of a system composed of an arbitrary number of magnetically equivalent groups, is merely a convenient bookkeeping method. When $J \neq 0$, an allowed transition involves two linear combinations of product kets. For convenience, one speaks of the transition in terms of the product kets to which these linear combinations reduce as $J \to 0$.

1. The AB System

A. Diagonalization of the Hamiltonian Matrix

The simplest two-group system is the irreducible AB system ($AB \equiv A_{1/2}B_{1/2}$). The only nontrivial constant of the motion in a steady z field is I_z, so that a suitable initial basis is provided by the product kets $|++\rangle, |+-\rangle, |-+\rangle, |--\rangle$, whose I_z eigenvalues are 1, 0, 0, −1, respectively. Operating on the elements of this basis with $\mathscr{H}$ yields

$$\mathscr{H}\,|++\rangle = -\tfrac{1}{2}(\omega_A + \omega_B + \tfrac{1}{2}J)|++\rangle, \tag{1.1}$$

$$\mathscr{H}\,|+-\rangle = -\tfrac{1}{2}(\delta - \tfrac{1}{2}J)|+-\rangle - \tfrac{1}{2}J\,|-+\rangle, \tag{1.2}$$

$$\mathscr{H}\,|-+\rangle = \tfrac{1}{2}(\delta + \tfrac{1}{2}J)|-+\rangle - \tfrac{1}{2}J\,|+-\rangle, \tag{1.3}$$

$$\mathscr{H}\,|--\rangle = \tfrac{1}{2}(\omega_A + \omega_B - \tfrac{1}{2}J)|--\rangle. \tag{1.4}$$

Equations (1.1) and (1.4) show that $|++\rangle$ and $|--\rangle$ are eigenvectors of $\mathscr{H}$; (1.2) and (1.3) show that the two eigenvectors of $\mathscr{H}$ with $m = 0$, to be denoted $|0;1\rangle$ and $|0;2\rangle$, are linear combinations of $|-+\rangle$ and $|+-\rangle$. Note that the hamiltonian matrix for the AB system could have been written down immediately by replacing all spin operators in the hamiltonian with the appropriate Kronecker products given in Table 4.1.

The eigenvalues and eigenvectors of $\mathscr{H}$ corresponding to $m = 0$ are obtained by diagonalizing the 2×2 submatrix of $\mathscr{H}$ defined by (1.2) and (1.3):

$$\mathscr{H}(0) = \frac{1}{2}\begin{pmatrix} \frac{1}{2}J - \delta & -J \\ -J & \frac{1}{2}J + \delta \end{pmatrix}, \tag{1.5}$$

The eigenvalues of this matrix, obtained by solving $\det[\mathscr{H}(0) - \Omega I] = 0$, are

$$\begin{aligned} \Omega_1(0) &= \tfrac{1}{2}(\tfrac{1}{2}J + R_{1/2,-1/2}), \\ \Omega_2(0) &= \tfrac{1}{2}(\tfrac{1}{2}J - R_{1/2,-1/2}), \end{aligned} \tag{1.6}$$

where[1]

$$R_{1/2,-1/2} = (\delta^2 + J^2)^{1/2}. \tag{1.7}$$

[1] The significance of the notational abbreviations introduced here and in the following section will be indicated in Section 3.

The eigenvectors of $\mathscr{H}(0)$ are of the form

$$|0;j\rangle = a_j\,|+-\rangle + b_j\,|-+\rangle \qquad (j = 1, 2), \tag{1.8}$$

where a_j and b_j satisfy

$$\frac{1}{2}\begin{pmatrix} \frac{1}{2}J - \delta & -J \\ -J & \frac{1}{2}J + \delta \end{pmatrix}\begin{pmatrix} a_j \\ b_j \end{pmatrix} = \Omega_j(0)\begin{pmatrix} a_j \\ b_j \end{pmatrix}. \tag{1.9}$$

From this matrix equation one obtains two linear equations for a_j and b_j. These equations are not independent, but either equation can be combined with the normalization condition to determine $|0;1\rangle$ and $|0;2\rangle$. The calculation is straightforward and yields

$$\begin{aligned} |0;1\rangle &= \frac{1}{(1+Q^2_{1/2,-1/2})^{1/2}}\{|-+\rangle - Q_{1/2,-1/2}\,|+-\rangle\}, \\ |0;2\rangle &= \frac{1}{(1+Q^2_{1/2,-1/2})^{1/2}}\{Q_{1/2,-1/2}\,|-+\rangle + |+-\rangle\}, \end{aligned} \tag{1.10}$$

where

$$Q_{1/2,-1/2} = \frac{J}{\delta + R_{1/2,-1/2}}, \tag{1.11}$$

and where the phases of a_j and b_j have been chosen so as to make these quantities real. The eigenvalues and eigenvectors of the AB system are collected in Table 6.1.

TABLE 6.1

EIGENVALUES AND EIGENVECTORS FOR THE AB SYSTEM

Eigenvector	Eigenvalue
$\|++\rangle$	$-\frac{1}{2}(\omega_A + \omega_B) - \frac{1}{4}J$
$\frac{1}{(1+Q^2_{1/2,-1/2})^{1/2}}\{\|-+\rangle - Q_{1/2,-1/2}\,\|+-\rangle\}$	$\frac{1}{2}(\frac{1}{2}J + R_{1/2,-1/2})$
$\frac{1}{(1+Q^2_{1/2,-1/2})^{1/2}}\{Q_{1/2,-1/2}\,\|-+\rangle + \|+-\rangle\}$	$\frac{1}{2}(\frac{1}{2}J - R_{1/2,-1/2})$
$\|--\rangle$	$\frac{1}{2}(\omega_A + \omega_B) - \frac{1}{4}J$

B. Spectra of AB Systems

The spectrum of an AB system is generated by transitions $| j\rangle \to | k\rangle$ satisfying $\Delta m = -1$. The resonance frequencies are computed by the Bohr frequency rule, and the corresponding relative intensities are proportional to the absolute squares of $\langle k| I^- |j\rangle = \langle k| I_A^- |j\rangle + \langle k| I_B^- |j\rangle$.

Operating on the stationary eigenvectors with I^-, one obtains, after some elementary algebra,

$$I^- | ++\rangle = | +-\rangle + | -+\rangle$$

$$= \left(1 - \frac{J}{R_{1/2,-1/2}}\right)^{1/2} | 0; 1\rangle + \left(1 + \frac{J}{R_{1/2,-1/2}}\right)^{1/2} | 0; 2\rangle,$$

$$I^- | 0; 1\rangle = \left(1 - \frac{J}{R_{1/2,-1/2}}\right)^{1/2} | --\rangle,$$

$$I^- | 0; 2\rangle = \left(1 + \frac{J}{R_{1/2,-1/2}}\right)^{1/2} | --\rangle,$$

$$I^- | --\rangle = 0.$$

It follows that there are exactly four transitions satisfying $\Delta m = -1$:

$$\text{A:} \quad \begin{cases} | ++\rangle \to | 0; 1\rangle, \\ | 0; 2\rangle \to | --\rangle, \end{cases} \qquad \text{B:} \quad \begin{cases} | ++\rangle \to | 0; 2\rangle, \\ | 0; 1\rangle \to | --\rangle. \end{cases}$$

The A transitions correspond, in the limit $J \to 0$, to transitions for which $\Delta m_A = -1$ and $\Delta m_B = 0$; the B transitions correspond to $\Delta m_A = 0$ and $\Delta m_B = -1$. The relative intensities of these transitions are given by

$$|\langle 0; 1 | I^- | ++\rangle|^2 = |\langle -- | I^- | 0; 1\rangle|^2 = 1 - \frac{J}{R_{1/2,-1/2}},$$

$$|\langle 0; 2 | I^- | ++\rangle|^2 = |\langle -- | I^- | 0; 2\rangle|^2 = 1 + \frac{J}{R_{1/2,-1/2}}.$$

The corresponding resonance frequencies are obtained by computing the differences of the appropriate energy eigenvalues given in Table 6.1. The complete spectrum is given in Table 6.2, where, according to the conventions adopted above, the resonance frequencies[2] are in the order $A_1 \geqslant A_2 \geqslant B_2 \geqslant B_1$.

---

[2] Here, and subsequently, the symbol G_i will be used to denote the ith transition in group G and the corresponding resonance frequency. The intensity of G_i will be denoted Int G_i. Similarly, M_i and Int M_i denote the frequency and intensity of the mixed transition M_i.

TABLE 6.2

RESONANCE FREQUENCIES AND RELATIVE INTENSITIES FOR THE AB SYSTEM

Transition[a]	Intensity	Frequency
$A_1: \; \|++\rangle \rightarrow \|-+\rangle$	$1 - \frac{J}{R_{1/2,-1/2}}$	$\frac{1}{2}(\omega_A + \omega_B + J + R_{1/2,-1/2})$
$A_2: \; \|+-\rangle \rightarrow \|--\rangle$	$1 + \frac{J}{R_{1/2,-1/2}}$	$\frac{1}{2}(\omega_A + \omega_B - J + R_{1/2,-1/2})$
$B_1: \; \|-+\rangle \rightarrow \|--\rangle$	$1 - \frac{J}{R_{1/2,-1/2}}$	$\frac{1}{2}(\omega_A + \omega_B - J - R_{1/2,-1/2})$
$B_2: \; \|++\rangle \rightarrow \|+-\rangle$	$1 + \frac{J}{R_{1/2,-1/2}}$	$\frac{1}{2}(\omega_A + \omega_B + J - R_{1/2,-1/2})$

[a] Transition in the limit $J \rightarrow 0$.

From Table 6.2 it is evident that the AB spectrum is symmetrical with respect to the mean resonance frequency $\frac{1}{2}(\omega_A + \omega_B)$, and that the following intensity relations hold:

$$\text{Int } A_1 = \text{Int } B_1, \qquad \text{Int } A_2 = \text{Int } B_2, \qquad \text{Int } A_1 \leqslant \text{Int } A_2,$$

$$\text{Int } A_1 + \text{Int } A_2 = 2,$$

$$\text{Int } A_1 + \text{Int } A_2 + \text{Int } B_1 + \text{Int } B_2 = 4.$$

The last equation also follows from the general formula for $n_A + n_B \cdots = N$ spin-$\frac{1}{2}$ nuclei,

$$\text{Int } A_{n_A} B_{n_B} C_{n_C} \cdots = 2^{N-1} N, \tag{1.12}$$

or the general formula for the intensity of an irreducible component system

$$\text{Int } A_{I_A} B_{I_B} C_{I_C} \cdots = \frac{2}{3} \prod_G (2I_G + 1) \Big\{ \sum_G I_G(I_G + 1) \Big\} \tag{1.13}$$

(cf. Section 4.F, Chapter 5). For the irreducible $A_{I_A}B_{I_B}$ system, (1.13) reduces to

$$\text{Int } A_{I_A} B_{I_B} = \tfrac{2}{3}(2I_A + 1)(2I_B + 1)\{I_A(I_A + 1) + I_B(I_B + 1)\}. \tag{1.14}$$

If $I_A = I_B = \frac{1}{2}$, (1.14) yields $\text{Int } A_{1/2}B_{1/2} = 4$.

The spectrum of an AB system for $J/\delta = 0.5$ is shown in Fig. 6.1. From the figure, or Table 6.2, it is evident that the spin-spin coupling constant is given by

$$J = B_2 - B_1 = A_1 - A_2 .$$

If one measures the frequency differences $A_1 - B_1$ and $A_2 - B_2$, J and δ are given by

$$J = \tfrac{1}{2}\{(A_1 - B_1) - (A_2 - B_2)\}, \qquad \delta = [(A_1 - B_1)(A_2 - B_2)]^{1/2}.$$

Theoretical spectra for the AB system are illustrated in Fig. 6.2 for several values of J/δ. When $J = 0$, $\delta \neq 0$, all transitions are of equal intensity, but since $B_1 = B_2$ and $A_1 = A_2$, only two resonances are observed. When $0 < J \ll \delta$, all four transitions are observed.[3]

As $J \to \infty$, Int A_2, Int $B_2 \to 2$, and both resonance frequencies converge to $\frac{1}{2}(\omega_A + \omega_B)$. In the same limit, the resonance frequencies of A_1 and B_1 diverge to $+\infty$ and $-\infty$, respectively, where their intensities are zero. For large values of J/δ, $R_{1/2,-1/2} \approx J + \delta^2/2J$, so that $A_2 - B_2 \approx \delta^2/2J$. Thus as $J \to \infty$, or $\delta \to 0$, one observes a single resonance at $\frac{1}{2}(\omega_A + \omega_B)$. These remarks are illustrated by the energy-level diagram shown in Fig. 6.3.

The reason only a single resonance is observed when $\delta \ll J$ is that the total angular momentum of the system [i.e., $(\mathbf{I}_A + \mathbf{I}_B)^2$] is approximately conserved. This may be verified by introducing the identities

$$\omega_A = \tfrac{1}{2}(\omega_A + \omega_B) + \tfrac{1}{2}\delta, \qquad \omega_B = \tfrac{1}{2}(\omega_A + \omega_B) - \tfrac{1}{2}\delta$$

into the hamiltonian operator, obtaining

$$\mathscr{H} = -\{\tfrac{1}{2}(\omega_A + \omega_B)I_z + \tfrac{1}{2}\delta(I_{Az} - I_{Bz}) + J\mathbf{I}_A \cdot \mathbf{I}_B\}.$$

For $J \gg \delta$, the term containing δ may be neglected, so that

$$\begin{aligned}\mathscr{H} &\approx -\{\tfrac{1}{2}(\omega_A + \omega_B)I_z + J\mathbf{I}_A \cdot \mathbf{I}_B\} \\ &= -\{\tfrac{1}{2}(\omega_A + \omega_B)I_z + \tfrac{1}{2}J(\mathbf{I}^2 - \mathbf{I}_A{}^2 - \mathbf{I}_B{}^2)\},\end{aligned}$$

[3] The assertion that a particular frequency separation is observable always carries with it the assumption that the separation of resonances exceeds the spectrometer resolution. In graphical representations, frequency separations presumed to be unobservable will be indicated by a single resonance at the intensity-weighted mean frequency of the unresolved components with an intensity equal to the sum of the component intensities.

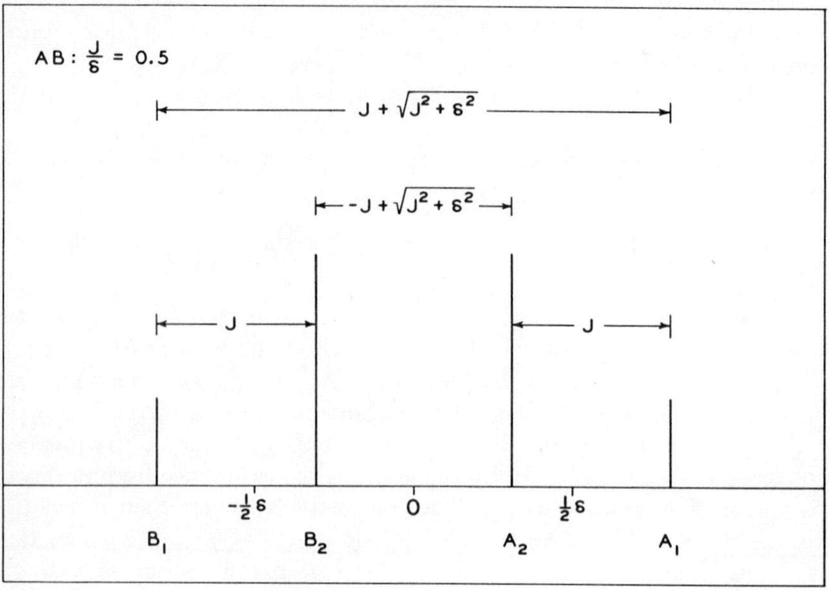

FIG. 6.1. Theoretical AB spectrum for $J/\delta = 0.5$. The frequency origin is at $\frac{1}{2}(\omega_A + \omega_B)$.

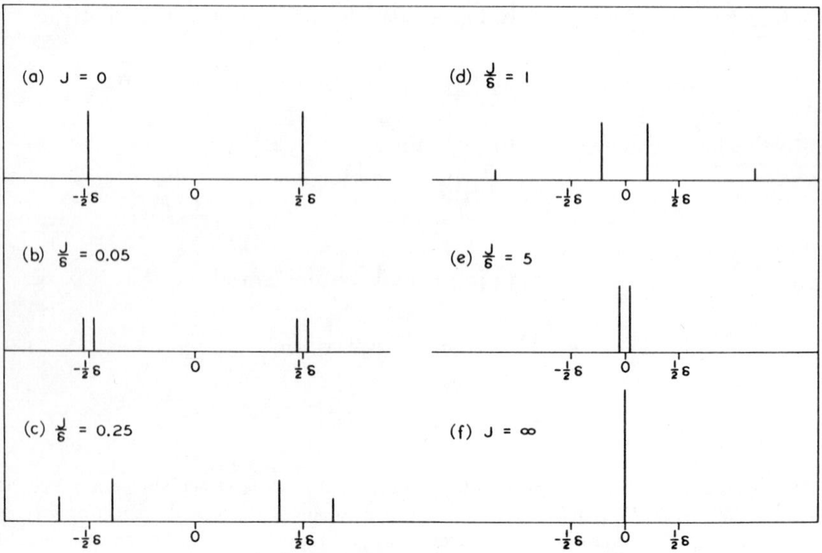

FIG. 6.2. Theoretical AB spectra.

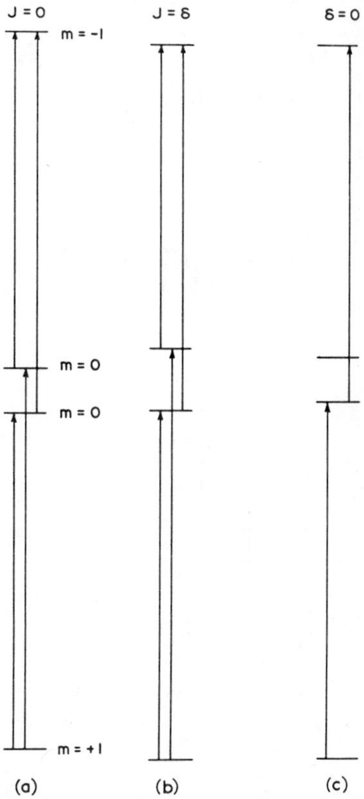

FIG. 6.3. Schematic energy-level diagram for the AB system.

where the last form for $\mathscr{H}$ is obtained by use of the identity

$$\mathbf{I}^2 = \mathbf{I}_A{}^2 + \mathbf{I}_B{}^2 + 2\mathbf{I}_A \cdot \mathbf{I}_B \, .$$

The eigenvalues and eigenvectors for this limiting case are given in the accompanying tabulation. Since $\mathbf{I}^2$ is conserved, transitions that do

Eigenvalue	Eigenvector	I	m
$-\frac{1}{2}\{(\omega_A + \omega_B) + \frac{1}{2}J\}$	$\|++\rangle$	1	1
$-\frac{1}{4}J$	$\frac{1}{\sqrt{2}}\{\|+-\rangle + \|-+\rangle\}$	1	0
$\frac{1}{2}\{(\omega_A + \omega_B) - \frac{1}{2}J\}$	$\|--\rangle$	1	-1
$\frac{3}{4}J$	$\frac{1}{\sqrt{2}}\{\|+-\rangle - \|-+\rangle\}$	0	0

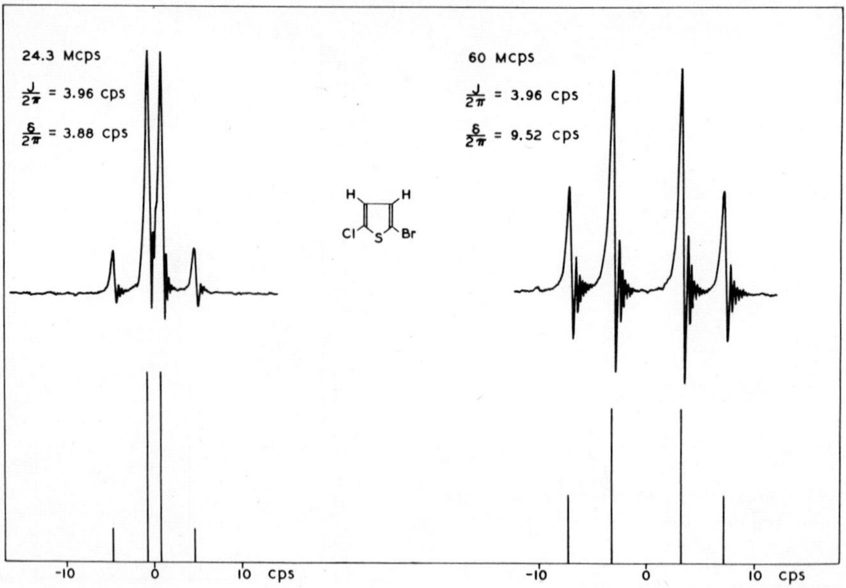

FIG. 6.4. Experimental and theoretical spectra for the protons in pure 2-bromo-5-chlorothiophene.

not conserve the total spin quantum number are strictly forbidden. The only transitions satisfying the selection rules $\Delta I = 0$, $\Delta m = -1$, are

$$|++\rangle \rightarrow \frac{1}{\sqrt{2}}\{|+-\rangle + |-+\rangle\}, \qquad \frac{1}{\sqrt{2}}\{|+-\rangle + |-+\rangle\} \rightarrow |--\rangle.$$

The energy corresponding to the eigenvector with $I = 1$, $m = 0$, is the arithmetic mean of the energies corresponding to the eigenvectors with $I = 1$, $m = \pm 1$, so that only a single resonance is observed, although two transitions are allowed.

The experimental spectra of the protons in 2-bromo-5-chlorothiophene, as observed at 24.3 and 60 Mcps, are shown in Fig. 6.4. The theoretical spectra for $J/\delta = 0.416$ and 1.02 are added for comparison with the experimental traces. The ratio of the observed internal chemical shifts is $3.88/9.52 = 0.408$, in good agreement with the ratio $24.3/60 = 0.405$.

2. The A_2B System

A. Diagonalization of the Hamiltonian Matrix

The A_2B system represents the next step in complexity beyond the simple AB system and provides an opportunity to apply the theory of magnetically equivalent nuclei to a nontrivial case.

The magnetic equivalence of the A nuclei demands the conservation of the total angular momentum of group A, which in turn implies the conservation of the total spin quantum numbers. Since group A contains two spin-$\frac{1}{2}$ nuclei, the values of I_A are 1 and 0, each with spin multiplicity equal to unity. The product kets for group A will be denoted $|1, 1\rangle$, $|1, 0\rangle$, $|1, -1\rangle$, $|0, 0\rangle$, those for group B, $|\frac{1}{2}, \frac{1}{2}\rangle$, $|\frac{1}{2}, -\frac{1}{2}\rangle$. The eight possible products of these kets, which provide a basis for the joint system, are given in Table 6.3.

TABLE 6.3

BASIS VECTORS FOR THE A_2B SYSTEM

$I_A = 1$	$I_A = 0$	m
$\|1, 1; \frac{1}{2}, \frac{1}{2}\rangle$		$\frac{3}{2}$
$\|1, 1; \frac{1}{2}, -\frac{1}{2}\rangle$, $\|1, 0; \frac{1}{2}, \frac{1}{2}\rangle$	$\|0, 0; \frac{1}{2}, \frac{1}{2}\rangle$	$\frac{1}{2}$
$\|1, -1; \frac{1}{2}, \frac{1}{2}\rangle$, $\|1, 0; \frac{1}{2}, -\frac{1}{2}\rangle$	$\|0, 0; \frac{1}{2}, -\frac{1}{2}\rangle$	$-\frac{1}{2}$
$\|1, -1; \frac{1}{2}, -\frac{1}{2}\rangle$		$-\frac{3}{2}$

Operating on the elements of the product basis with $\mathscr{H}$, one finds that the two product kets with $I_A = 1$, $m = \pm\frac{3}{2}$, and the two product kets with $I_A = 0$, $m = \pm\frac{1}{2}$, are eigenvectors of $\mathscr{H}$. The corresponding eigenvalues are given in Table 6.4.

The kets with $I_A = 1$, $m = \pm\frac{1}{2}$, generate a pair of 2×2 submatrices of $\mathscr{H}$, so that the hamiltonian matrix has the form indicated in Fig. 6.5(a). Thus the diagonalization of the hamiltonian matrix requires only the diagonalization of the submatrices

$$-\frac{1}{2}\begin{pmatrix} \pm\omega_B & J\sqrt{2} \\ J\sqrt{2} & \pm\omega_A \pm \delta - J \end{pmatrix}.$$

The results are given in Table 6.4, where the following notational abbreviations have been introduced:

$$R_{1,0} = (\delta^2 - J\delta + 9J^2/4)^{1/2}, \qquad R_{1,-1} = (\delta^2 + J\delta + 9J^2/4)^{1/2},$$

$$Q_{1,0} = \frac{J\sqrt{2}}{\delta - \frac{1}{2}J + R_{1,0}}, \qquad Q_{1,-1} = \frac{J\sqrt{2}}{\delta + \frac{1}{2}J + R_{1,-1}}.$$

The basis employed in the solution of the eigenvalue problem led to a particularly simple decomposition of the hamiltonian matrix, but it

TABLE 6.4

EIGENVALUES AND EIGENVECTORS FOR THE A_2B SYSTEM

Eigenvector	Eigenvalue
$\|1,1;\frac{1}{2},\frac{1}{2}\rangle$	$-\frac{1}{2}(2\omega_A+\omega_B+J)$
$\frac{1}{(1+Q_{1,0}^2)^{1/2}}\{\|1,0;\frac{1}{2},\frac{1}{2}\rangle - Q_{1,0}\|1,1;\frac{1}{2},-\frac{1}{2}\rangle\}$	$-\frac{1}{2}(\omega_A-\frac{1}{2}J-R_{1,0})$
$\frac{1}{(1+Q_{1,0}^2)^{1/2}}\{Q_{1,0}\|1,0;\frac{1}{2},\frac{1}{2}\rangle + \|1,1;\frac{1}{2},-\frac{1}{2}\rangle\}$	$-\frac{1}{2}(\omega_A-\frac{1}{2}J+R_{1,0})$
$\frac{1}{(1+Q_{1,-1}^2)^{1/2}}\{\|1,-1;\frac{1}{2},\frac{1}{2}\rangle - Q_{1,-1}\|1,0;\frac{1}{2},-\frac{1}{2}\rangle\}$	$\frac{1}{2}(\omega_A+\frac{1}{2}J+R_{1,-1})$
$\frac{1}{(1+Q_{1,-1}^2)^{1/2}}\{Q_{1,-1}\|1,-1;\frac{1}{2},\frac{1}{2}\rangle + \|1,0;\frac{1}{2},-\frac{1}{2}\rangle\}$	$\frac{1}{2}(\omega_A+\frac{1}{2}J-R_{1,-1})$
$\|1,-1;\frac{1}{2},-\frac{1}{2}\rangle$	$\frac{1}{2}(2\omega_A+\omega_B-J)$
$\|0,0;\frac{1}{2},\frac{1}{2}\rangle$	$-\frac{1}{2}\omega_B$
$\|0,0;\frac{1}{2},-\frac{1}{2}\rangle$	$\frac{1}{2}\omega_B$

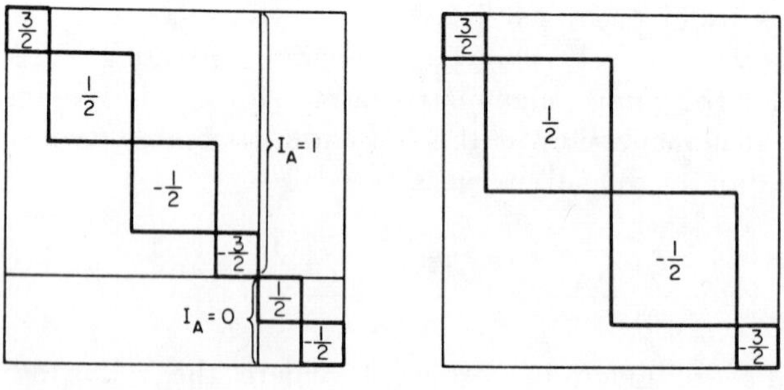

FIG. 6.5. Direct sum decompositions of the A_2B hamiltonian matrix relative to bases that diagonalize: (a) $\mathbf{I}_A^2$, $\mathbf{I}_B^2$, and I_z; (b) I_z alone.

would not have been incorrect to use some other basis; for example, the basis $\{|+++\rangle, |++-\rangle, ..., |---\rangle\}$. Although this basis may appear to be rather more obvious than the one actually used, it does not lead to optimum factorization of the secular determinant. In fact, the matrix for $\mathscr{H}$ would have the form shown in Fig. 6.5b. The blocks with

$m = \pm \frac{1}{2}$ are three-dimensional, so that one is confronted with a pair of cubic equations. It turns out that these cubics are easily factored into linear and quadratic equations, but the essential point here—and in more complicated systems—is that optimum factorization of the hamiltonian matrix is automatically achieved if the elements of the initial basis are eigenvectors of $\mathbf{I}_A{}^2$, $\mathbf{I}_B{}^2$, and I_z.

B. Spectra of A_2B Systems

The spectrum of the A_2B system is computed by the same procedure used for the AB system. In the present instance, transitions between states with different values of I_A are strictly forbidden. The resonance frequencies and their relative intensities are given in Table 6.5. The A transitions and the first three B transitions conserve $I_A = 1$; B_4 conserves $I_A = 0$.

The last transition recorded in Table 6.5 is a mixed transition, that is, a transition with $\Delta m = \Delta m_A + \Delta m_B = -1$, but with Δm_A and Δm_B nonvanishing. Mixed transitions are not usually detected in the spectra of two-group systems since Int $M_i \ll$ Int A_j, Int B_k (cf. the numerical data given in Appendix VI).

An interesting property of the A_2B spectrum is that transition B_4 leads to a resonance of unit intensity at the Larmor frequency of nucleus B. Since the arithmetic mean of A_2 and A_3 is ω_A,

$$\delta = \tfrac{1}{2}\{(A_2 - B_4) + (A_3 - B_4)\}.$$

The spin-spin coupling constant may be determined from the equation

$$J = \tfrac{1}{3}\{(A_1 - A_4) + (B_1 - B_3)\}.$$

If all the A and B transitions are not resolved J and δ are obtained by comparing the observed frequencies and integrated intensities with calculated spectra until the "best fit" is obtained. For this purpose, Figs. 6.6 through 6.8, and the numerical data in Appendix VI will be found most useful. Part (d) of Fig. 6.8 is drawn for $\delta \neq 0$ and J infinitely large compared to δ. The three components of the symmetrical triplet are at zero (i.e., ω_B), $2\,\delta/3$, and $4\,\delta/3$. When $\delta = 0$, only a single resonance can be observed. An example of an A_2B spectrum is shown in Fig. 6.9.

The A_2B system is a reducible two-group system; its irreducible components are the $A_0B_{1/2}$ system, whose spectrum is the single resonance of unit intensity at ω_B, and the $A_1B_{1/2}$ system, whose spectrum makes up

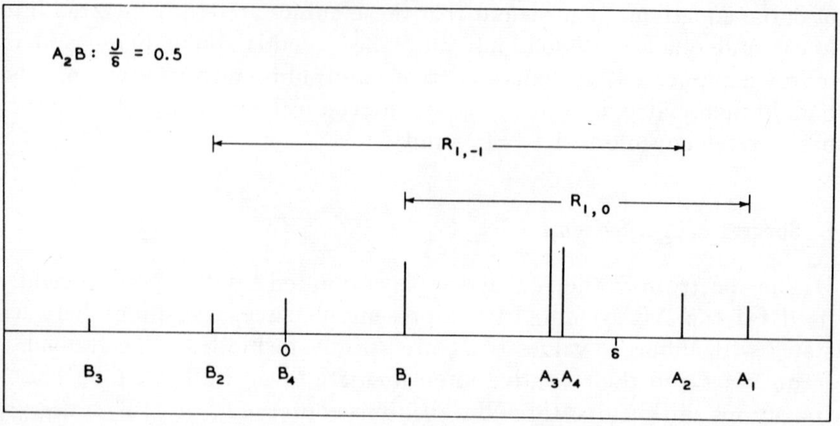

FIG. 6.6. Theoretical A_2B spectrum for $J/\delta = 0.5$. The frequency origin is at ω_B.

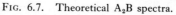

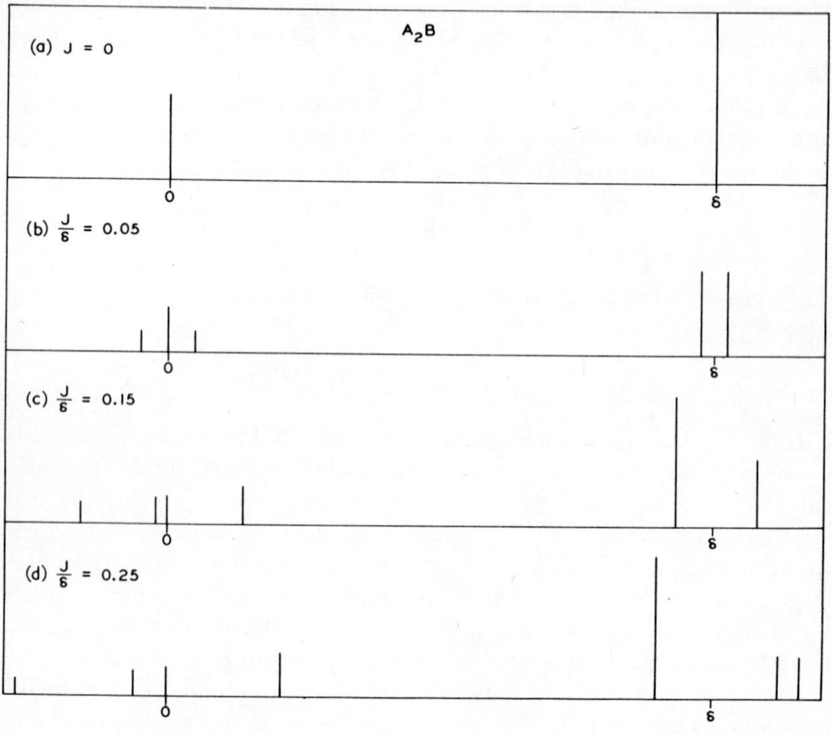

FIG. 6.7. Theoretical A_2B spectra.

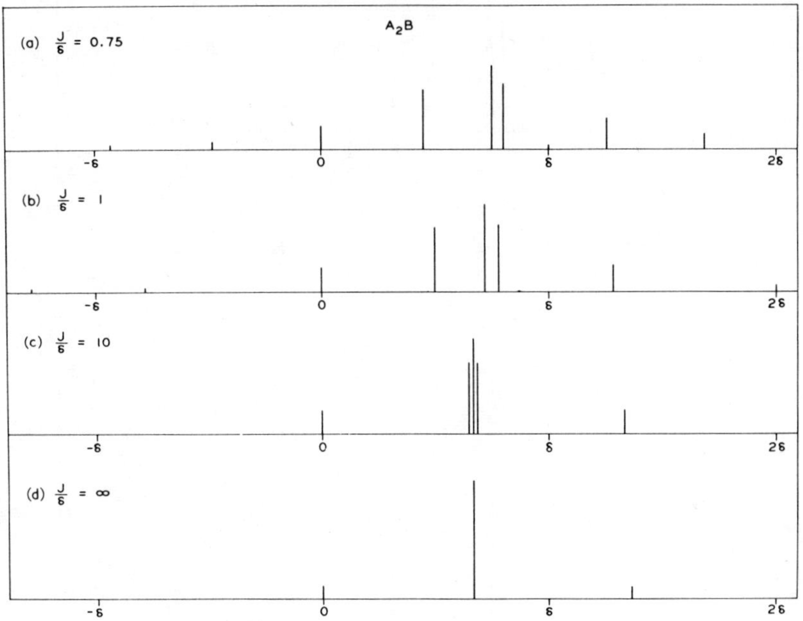

FIG. 6.8. Theoretical A_2B spectra.

the remaining eight lines of the A_2B spectrum. The decomposition of the A_2B system into its irreducible components is shown in Fig. 6.10 (the mixed transition is not shown).

The intensities of an A_2B system satisfy the following relations:

$$\text{Int } A_1 + \text{Int } B_1 = 3,$$
$$\text{Int } A_4 + \text{Int } B_3 = 3,$$
$$\text{Int } A_2 + \text{Int } A_3 + \text{Int } B_2 + \text{Int } M = 5.$$

The first two relations are deduced from the explicit expressions given in Table 6.5; the last relation follows from the first two and the fact that Int $A_1B_{1/2} = 11$, by (1.14).

Additional examples of A_2B spectra are provided by the 60 Mcps spectra of the $-CH_2OH$ protons of benzyl alcohol in acetone (Figs. 6.11 through 6.15). The chemical shift of the magnetically equivalent CH_2 protons, relative to that of the hydroxyl proton, varies from 48.6 cps in pure benzyl alcohol to -7.8 cps for an acetone : benzyl alcohol volume ratio (V_A/V_B) of 2.0. The coupling constant is 5.7 ± 0.1 cps and, within experimental error, independent of the acetone concentration. By varying the volume ratio, one can obtain spectra conforming to various

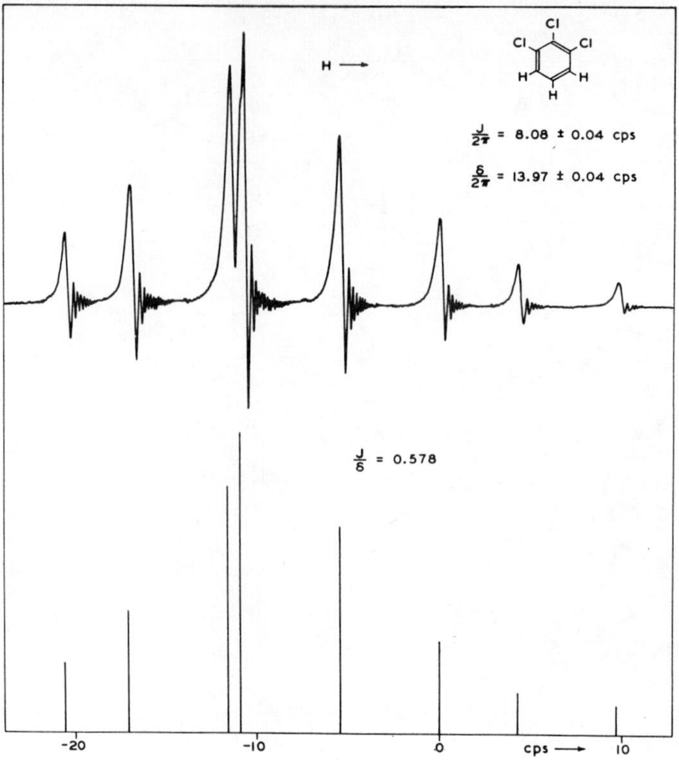

FIG. 6.9. Experimental and theoretical proton spectra of 1, 2, 3-trichlorobenzene in CS_2 at 60 Mcps.

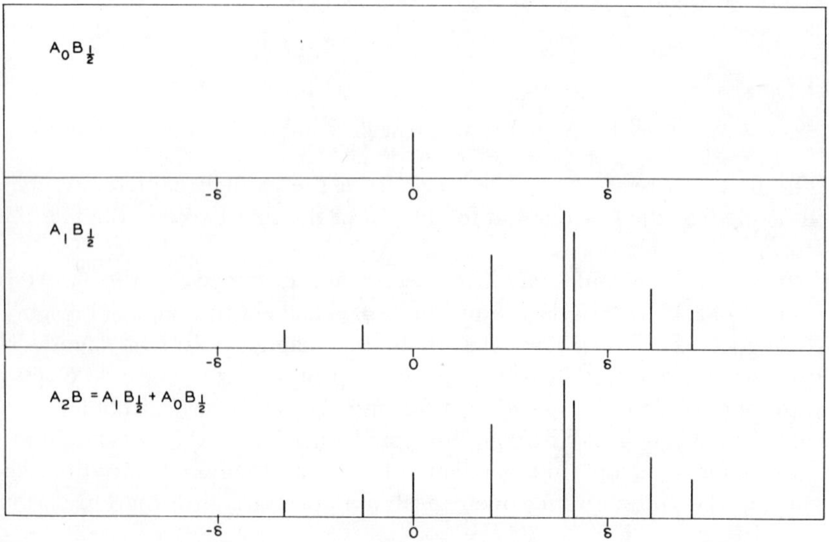

FIG. 6.10. Reduction of the A_2B system into its irreducible components.

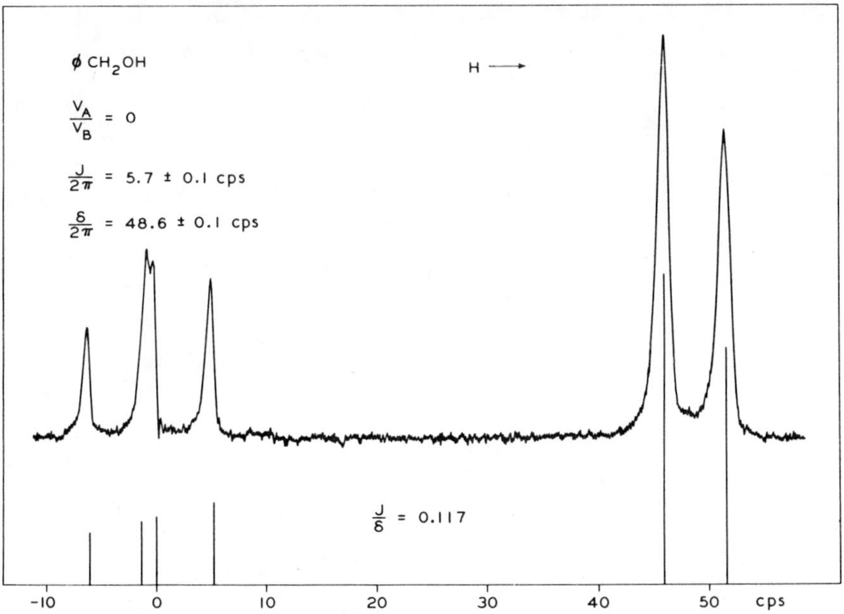

FIG. 6.11. Experimental and theoretical proton spectra of the methylene and hydroxyl group protons of benzyl alcohol in acetone at 60 Mcps.

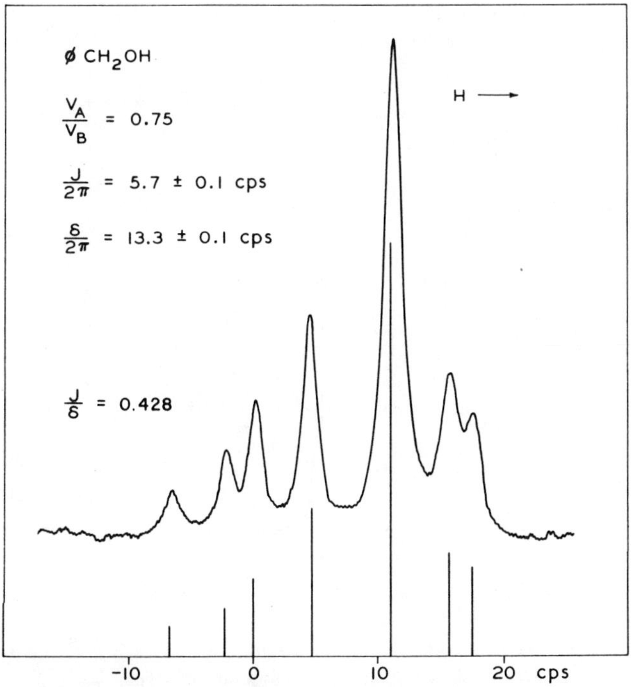

FIG. 6.12. Experimental and theoretical proton spectra of the methylene and hydroxyl group protons of benzyl alcohol in acetone at 60 Mcps.

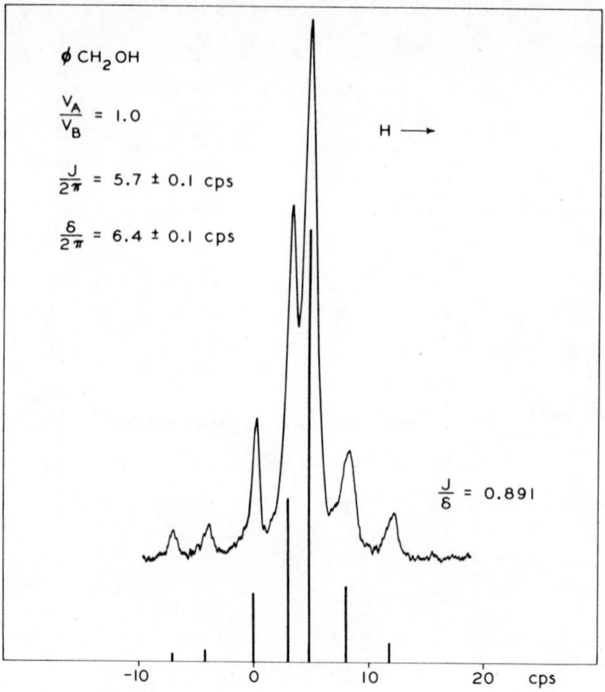

FIG. 6.13. Experimental and theoretical proton spectra of the methylene and hydroxyl group protons of benzyl alcohol in acetone at 60 Mcps.

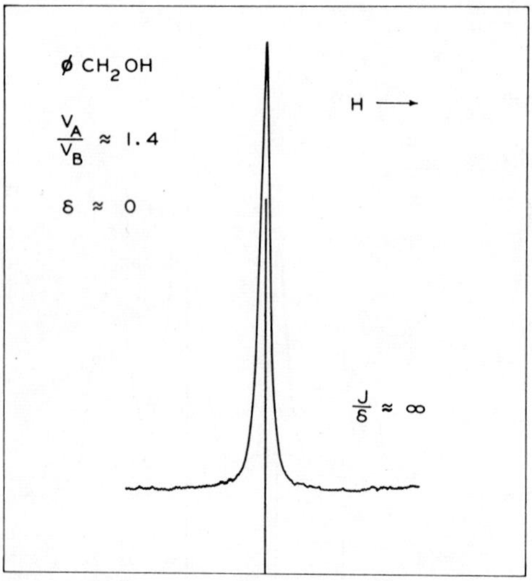

FIG. 6.14. Experimental and theoretical proton spectra of the methylene and hydroxyl group protons of benzyl alcohol in acetone at 60 Mcps.

TABLE 6.5 — RESONANCE FREQUENCIES AND RELATIVE INTENSITIES FOR THE A_2B SYSTEM

Transition[a]	Intensity	Frequency
	A *Transitions*	
A_1: $\|1, 1; \frac{1}{2}, \frac{1}{2}\rangle \rightarrow \|1, 0; \frac{1}{2}, \frac{1}{2}\rangle$	$\dfrac{\{\sqrt{2} - Q_{1,0}\}^2}{1 + Q^2_{1,0}}$	$\frac{1}{2}(\omega_A + \omega_B + \frac{3}{2}J + R_{1,0})$
A_2: $\|1, 0; \frac{1}{2}, \frac{1}{2}\rangle \rightarrow \|1, -1; \frac{1}{2}, \frac{1}{2}\rangle$	$\dfrac{\{Q_{1,-1}[\sqrt{2}\,Q_{1,0} - 1] + \sqrt{2}\}^2}{(1 + Q^2_{1,0})(1 + Q^2_{1,-1})}$	$\frac{1}{2}(2\omega_A + R_{1,-1} - R_{1,0})$
A_3: $\|1, 1; \frac{1}{2}, -\frac{1}{2}\rangle \rightarrow \|1, 0; \frac{1}{2}, -\frac{1}{2}\rangle$	$\dfrac{\{\sqrt{2} + Q_{1,0}[1 + \sqrt{2}\,Q_{1,-1}]\}^2}{(1 + Q^2_{1,0})(1 + Q^2_{1,-1})}$	$\frac{1}{2}(2\omega_A + R_{1,0} - R_{1,-1})$
A_4: $\|1, 0; \frac{1}{2}, -\frac{1}{2}\rangle \rightarrow \|1, -1; \frac{1}{2}, -\frac{1}{2}\rangle$	$\dfrac{\{\sqrt{2} + Q_{1,-1}\}^2}{1 + Q^2_{1,-1}}$	$\frac{1}{2}(\omega_A + \omega_B - \frac{3}{2}J + R_{1,-1})$
	B *Transitions*	
B_1: $\|1, 1; \frac{1}{2}, \frac{1}{2}\rangle \rightarrow \|1, 1; \frac{1}{2}, -\frac{1}{2}\rangle$	$\dfrac{\{1 + \sqrt{2}\,Q_{1,0}\}^2}{1 + Q^2_{1,0}}$	$\frac{1}{2}(\omega_A + \omega_B + \frac{3}{2}J - R_{1,0})$
B_2: $\|1, 0; \frac{1}{2}, \frac{1}{2}\rangle \rightarrow \|1, 0; \frac{1}{2}, -\frac{1}{2}\rangle$	$\dfrac{\{\sqrt{2}(Q_{1,0} - Q_{1,-1}) - 1\}^2}{(1 + Q^2_{1,0})(1 + Q^2_{1,-1})}$	$\frac{1}{2}(2\omega_A - R_{1,-1} - R_{1,0})$
B_3: $\|1, -1; \frac{1}{2}, \frac{1}{2}\rangle \rightarrow \|1, -1; \frac{1}{2}, -\frac{1}{2}\rangle$	$\dfrac{\{\sqrt{2}\,Q_{1,-1} - 1\}^2}{1 + Q^2_{1,-1}}$	$\frac{1}{2}(\omega_A + \omega_B - \frac{3}{2}J - R_{1,-1})$
B_4: $\|0, 0; \frac{1}{2}, \frac{1}{2}\rangle \rightarrow \|0, 0; \frac{1}{2}, -\frac{1}{2}\rangle$	1	ω_B
	M *Transition*	
M: $\|1, 1; \frac{1}{2}, -\frac{1}{2}\rangle \rightarrow \|1, -1; \frac{1}{2}, \frac{1}{2}\rangle$	$\dfrac{\{(Q_{1,-1} - \sqrt{2})\,Q_{1,0} + \sqrt{2}\,Q_{1,-1}\}^2}{(1 + Q^2_{1,-1})(1 + Q^2_{1,0})}$	$\frac{1}{2}(2\omega_A + R_{1,0} + R_{1,-1})$

[a] Transition in the limit $J \rightarrow 0$.

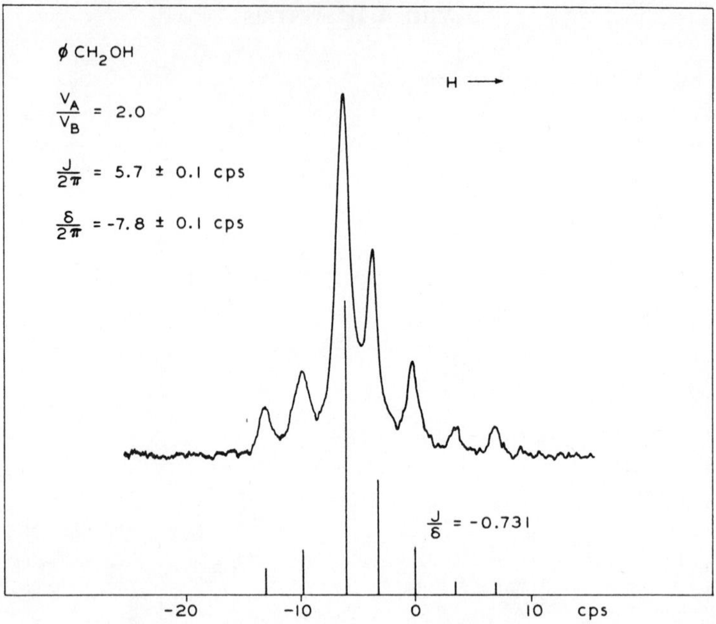

FIG. 6.15. Experimental and theoretical proton spectra of the methylene and hydroxyl group protons of benzyl alcohol in acetone at 60 Mcps.

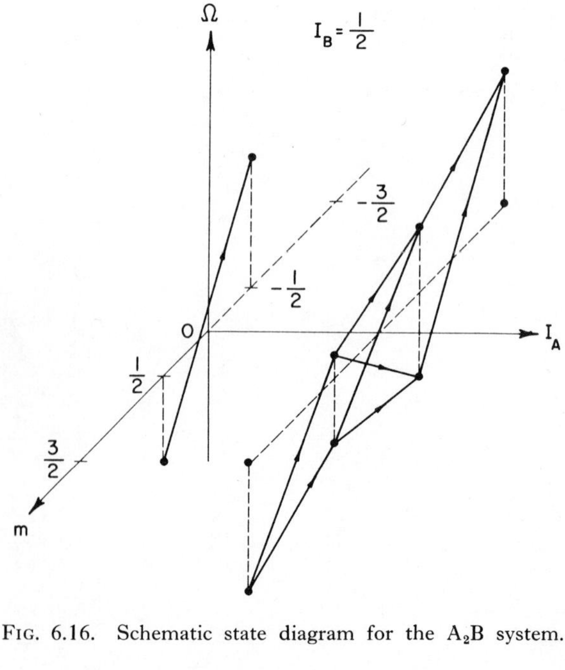

FIG. 6.16. Schematic state diagram for the A_2B system.

values of J/δ. In particular, one can observe the collapse of the spectrum to a single resonance when $\delta \approx 0$ (Fig. 6.14), and the reversal of the ordering of the groups when δ changes sign (Fig. 6.15).

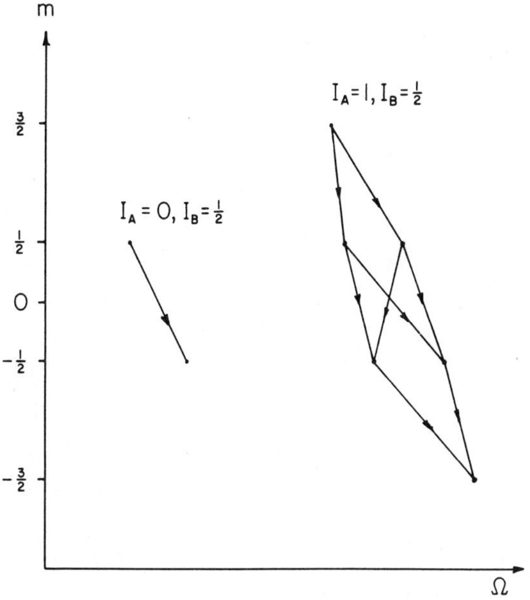

FIG. 6.17. Transition diagrams for the irreducible components of the A_2B system.

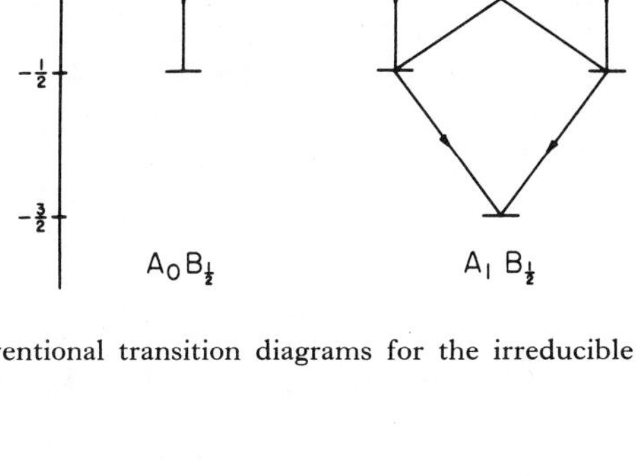

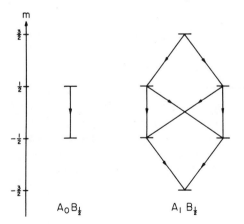

FIG. 6.18. Conventional transition diagrams for the irreducible components of the A_2B system.

C. Transition Diagrams

A stationary state of an A_2B system is defined by four eigenvalues: Ω, m, I_A, and I_B. An arbitrary state of the system can be represented by a point $\rho = (m, I_A, I_B, \Omega)$ in a real four-dimensional space. Since nucleus B is a spin-$\frac{1}{2}$ particle, all states of the system have $I_B = \frac{1}{2}$; hence the points of the four-dimensional space can be projected onto points in a real three-dimensional space with coordinates (m, I_A, Ω). The three-dimensional space is simply a "plane" of the four-dimensional space defined by the equation $I_B = \frac{1}{2}$. This projection yields the diagram shown in Fig. 6.16. This figure is purely schematic; no attempt has been made to indicate the correct relative magnitudes of the energies. The states of the system with $I_A = 0$ or $I_A = 1$ lie in the (two-dimensional) planes defined by these equations. The tie lines represent transitions satisfying the selection rules $\Delta I_A = 0$, $\Delta m = -1$. The selection rule $\Delta I_A = 0$ prohibits the existence of tie lines connecting points in the plane $I_A = 0$ to points in the plane $I_A = 1$.

The state diagram may be simplified by drawing separate graphs for the planes $I_A = 0$ and $I_A = 1$, as shown in Fig. 6.17. A further simplification results if one abandons the attempt to indicate differences in energies and adopts the symmetrical arrangements shown in Fig. 6.18. In this figure the points representing the states of the system have been expanded to finite line segments to suggest energy levels. However the description of such figures as "energy-level diagrams" is not correct; henceforth figures of this type will be called "transition diagrams."

3. The General $A_{n_A}B$ System

A. The Structure of the Hamiltonian Matrix

The AB and A_2B systems are special cases of the $A_{n_A}B$ system. The latter system provides an excellent illustration of the power and elegance of the concept of a group of magnetically equivalent nuclei. With the aid of this concept, exact recursive formulas for the resonance frequencies and line intensities can be derived for any value of n_A whatsoever.

The conservation of the total angular momentum for group A permits the description of its spin states in terms of the total spin quantum numbers

$$I_A = \tfrac{1}{2}n_A - k, \qquad k = \begin{cases} 0, 1, 2, \ldots, \tfrac{1}{2}n_A & \text{for } n_A \text{ even}, \\ 0, 1, 2, \ldots, \tfrac{1}{2}(n_A - 1) & \text{for } n_A \text{ odd}, \end{cases} \tag{3.1}$$

with spin multiplicities

$$g_{I_A} = \frac{n_A!\,(n_A - 2k + 1)}{(n_A - k + 1)!\,k!}\,. \tag{3.2}$$

A generic ket for group A will be denoted $|\,I_A\,, m_A\rangle$. The spin multiplicity indices, $s_{I_A} = 1, 2, ..., g_{I_A}$, need not be indicated in the kets for group A since the manner in which they enter the problem will be explicitly taken into account in the following discussion. However, one must keep in mind that there are $2I_A + 1$ kets for each choice of s_{I_A}.

The conservation of $\mathbf{I}_B{}^2$ is ensured by using $\{|\,\frac{1}{2}, \frac{1}{2}\rangle, |\,\frac{1}{2}, -\frac{1}{2}\rangle\}$ as a basis for the spin space of nucleus B alone. A basis for the spin space of the joint system is provided by the 2^{n_A+1} independent product kets

$$\{|\,I_A\,, m_A\rangle|\,\tfrac{1}{2}, \pm\tfrac{1}{2}\rangle\} \equiv \{|\,I_A\,, m_A\,; \tfrac{1}{2}, \pm\tfrac{1}{2}\rangle\}, \tag{3.3}$$

whose elements are simultaneous eigenvectors of $\mathbf{I}_A{}^2$, $\mathbf{I}_B{}^2$, and I_z.

The hamiltonian matrix is not diagonal with respect to the basis (3.3), but it is easy to describe its structure. Since $\mathbf{I}_A{}^2$ is a constant of the motion, the matrix elements of $\mathscr{H}$ connecting states with different values of I_A vanish, as indicated in Fig. 6.19 for $n_A = 3$. The only nonvanishing matrix elements of $\mathscr{H}$ are enclosed by the square blocks along the principal diagonal. Each of these "I_A blocks" is generated by product kets with the same value of I_A. The number of I_A blocks is equal to the number of distinct values of I_A; hence

$$\text{number of } I_A \text{ blocks} = \begin{cases} \frac{1}{2}n_A + 1 & \text{for} \quad n_A \text{ even}, \\ \frac{1}{2}(n_A + 1) & \text{for} \quad n_A \text{ odd}. \end{cases} \tag{3.4}$$

The product kets which generate an I_A block may be partitioned into g_{I_A} sets of $2(2I_A + 1)$ members; each set is characterized by a distinct value of the spin multiplicity index s_{I_A}, as shown in Fig. 6.20. The nonvanishing matrix elements within an I_A block are enclosed by the g_{I_A} subblocks along the principal diagonal. Each of these subblocks is generated by a subset of the basis, formed by taking the (Kronecker) product of the $2I_A + 1$ group-A kets with a fixed value of s_{I_A} and the two product kets for group B. Thus the dimension of each subblock is $2(2I_A + 1)$. Since there are g_{I_A} subblocks, it follows that the dimension of an I_A block is $2g_{I_A}(2I_A + 1)$.

The submatrices enclosed by the g_{I_A} subblocks of an I_A block are generated by sets of product kets described by the same quantum numbers. By suitably ordering the elements in the g_{I_A} sets $\{|\,I_A\,, m_A\,; 1\rangle|\,\frac{1}{2}, \pm\frac{1}{2}\rangle\}, \{|\,I_A\,, m_A\,; 2\rangle|\,\frac{1}{2}\,; \pm\frac{1}{2}\rangle\} \cdots$, all these submatrices

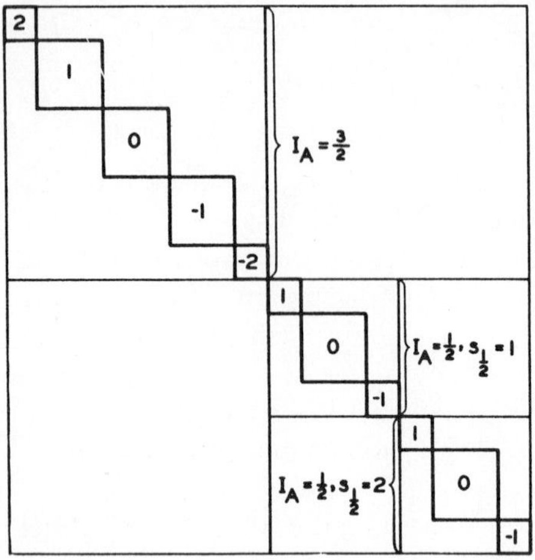

FIG. 6.19. Structure of the hamiltonian matrix for the A_3B system.

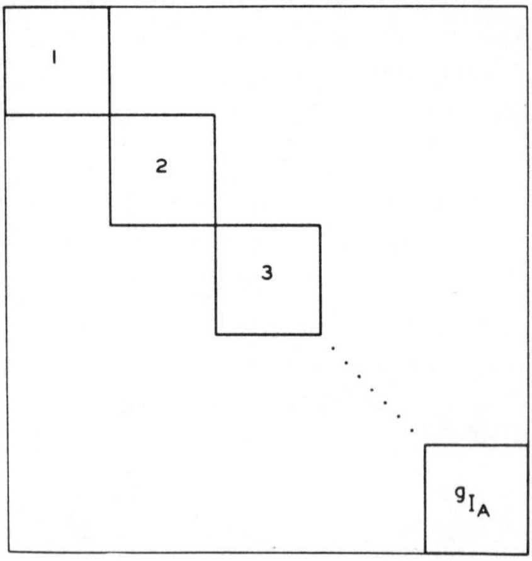

FIG. 6.20. Each I_A block of the hamiltonian matrix for the $A_{n_A}B$ system factors into g_{I_A} identical subblocks.

will be identical, so that one need only consider the structure of the submatrix enclosed by an arbitrary subblock. To this representative subblock one may apply the condition that the matrix elements of $\mathscr{H}$ connecting states with different values of $m = m_A + m_B$ must vanish.

The number of product kets corresponding to a given value of m in a typical subblock $(-I_A - \frac{1}{2} \leqslant m \leqslant I_A + \frac{1}{2})$ may be determined by first choosing any product ket, say

$$|I_A, m_A; \tfrac{1}{2}, \tfrac{1}{2}\rangle, \qquad m = m_A + \tfrac{1}{2}.$$

If there is another product ket in the set of $2(2I_A + 1)$ kets $\{|I_A, m_A; \frac{1}{2}, \pm\frac{1}{2}\rangle\}$ with the same value of m, the value of m_B must be $-\frac{1}{2}$, since otherwise the second product ket would be identical with the product ket already selected. It follows that there are at most two product kets corresponding to the I_z eigenvalue $m = m_A + \frac{1}{2}$:

$$\begin{array}{l} |I_A, m_A; \tfrac{1}{2}, \tfrac{1}{2}\rangle \\ |I_A, m_A + 1; \tfrac{1}{2}, -\tfrac{1}{2}\rangle \end{array} \qquad (m = m_A + \tfrac{1}{2}). \tag{3.5}$$

The second ket is not defined when $m_A = I_A$. This means that there is only one product ket with $m = I_A + \frac{1}{2}$, and it is an eigenvector of $\mathscr{H}$. Similarly, when $m_A = -I_A - 1$, the first ket is undefined, and the second ket is an eigenvector of $\mathscr{H}$ corresponding to $m = -I_A - \frac{1}{2}$.

The substructure of a typical subblock of an I_A block is now easily described. It commences with a 1×1 matrix in the upper left-hand corner, followed by a string of $2I_A$ 2×2 matrices along the principal diagonal, and terminates with a final 1×1 matrix in the lower right-hand corner (Fig. 6.21). The diagonalization of this subblock will be reduced to the solution of a single quadratic equation.

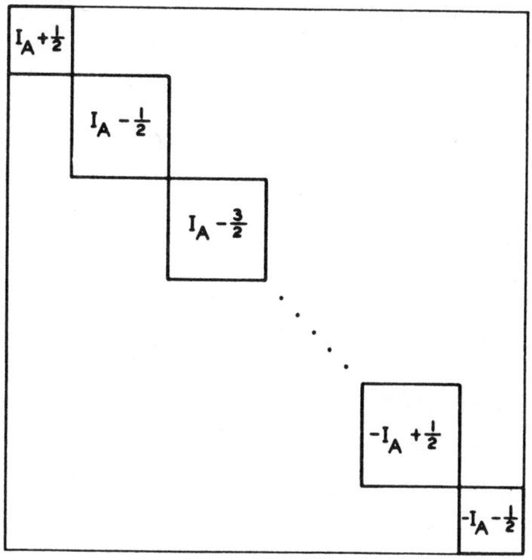

FIG. 6.21. Substructure of the g_{I_A} subblocks.

B. Diagonalization of the Hamiltonian Matrix

The 2×2 submatrix generated by the product kets (3.5) is obtained by operating on these kets with $\mathscr{H}$. One finds that

$$\mathscr{H}(I_A, m_A + \tfrac{1}{2}) = -\frac{1}{2}\begin{pmatrix} (2\omega_A + J)m_A + \omega_B & J[(I_A - m_A)(I_A + m_A + 1)]^{1/2} \\ J[(I_A - m_A)(I_A + m_A + 1)]^{1/2} & (2\omega_A - J)(m_A + 1) - \omega_B \end{pmatrix}. \quad (3.6)$$

The eigenvalues and eigenvectors of this matrix are

$$\begin{aligned} \Omega_1(I_A, m_A + \tfrac{1}{2}) &= -\tfrac{1}{2}[(2m_A + 1)\omega_A - \tfrac{1}{2}J - R_{I_A,m_A}], \\ \Omega_2(I_A, m_A + \tfrac{1}{2}) &= -\tfrac{1}{2}[(2m_A + 1)\omega_A - \tfrac{1}{2}J + R_{I_A,m_A}], \end{aligned} \quad (3.7)$$

$$\begin{aligned} &| I_A, m_A + \tfrac{1}{2}; 1\rangle \\ &= \frac{1}{(1 + Q^2_{I_A,m_A})^{1/2}}\{| I_A, m_A; \tfrac{1}{2}, \tfrac{1}{2}\rangle - Q_{I_A,m_A} | I_A, m_A + 1; \tfrac{1}{2}, -\tfrac{1}{2}\rangle\}, \\ &| I_A, m_A + \tfrac{1}{2}; 2\rangle \\ &= \frac{1}{(1 + Q^2_{I_A,m_A})^{1/2}}\{Q_{I_A,m_A} | I_A, m_A; \tfrac{1}{2}, \tfrac{1}{2}\rangle + | I_A, m_A + 1; \tfrac{1}{2}, -\tfrac{1}{2}\rangle\}, \end{aligned} \quad (3.8)$$

where

$$R_{I_A,m_A} = \{[\delta - \tfrac{1}{2}(2m_A + 1)J]^2 + J^2(I_A - m_A)(I_A + m_A + 1)\}^{1/2}, \quad (3.9)$$

$$Q_{I_A,m_A} = \frac{J[(I_A - m_A)(I_A + m_A + 1)]^{1/2}}{\delta - \tfrac{1}{2}(2m_A + 1)J + R_{I_A,m_A}}. \quad (3.10)$$

$$\text{If} \quad m_A = I_A, \quad Q_{I_A,I_A} = 0, \quad \text{and} \quad R_{I_A,I_A} = \delta - \tfrac{1}{2}(2I_A + 1)J,$$

so that

$$\left.\begin{aligned} |I_A, I_A + \tfrac{1}{2}; 1\rangle &= |I_A, I_A; \tfrac{1}{2}, \tfrac{1}{2}\rangle \\ \Omega_1(I_A, I_A + \tfrac{1}{2}) &= -\tfrac{1}{2}(2I_A\omega_A + \omega_B + I_A J) \end{aligned}\right\} \quad (m_A = I_A).$$

The reduction of $|I_A, m_A + \frac{1}{2}; 2\rangle$ and $\Omega_2(I_A, m_A + \frac{1}{2})$ need not be considered, since these quantities are undefined when $m_A = I_A$.

Similarly, for $m_A = -I_A - 1$,

$$\left.\begin{aligned} |I_A, -I_A - \tfrac{1}{2}; 2\rangle &= |I_A, -I_A; \tfrac{1}{2}, -\tfrac{1}{2}\rangle \\ \Omega_2(I_A, -I_A - \tfrac{1}{2}) &= \tfrac{1}{2}(2I_A\omega_A + \omega_B - I_A J) \end{aligned}\right\} \quad (m_A = -I_A - 1).$$

Thus the solution of the eigenvalue problem for the 2×2 matrix includes the solutions of the two 1×1 matrices as special cases.

Equations (3.7) through (3.10) can be used to obtain the solution of the eigenvalue problem for the complete subblock by allowing m_A to range from $+I_A$ to $-I_A - 1$ in integral steps. It is not necessary, however, to write down all these results; only the eigenvalues and eigenvectors for the case where m_A is replaced with $m_A - 1$ will be required. From (3.7) through (3.10) one finds that

$$\begin{aligned} \Omega_1(I_A, m_A - \tfrac{1}{2}) &= -\tfrac{1}{2}[(2m_A - 1)\omega_A - \tfrac{1}{2}J - R_{I_A,m_A-1}], \\ \Omega_2(I_A, m_A - \tfrac{1}{2}) &= -\tfrac{1}{2}[(2m_A - 1)\omega_A - \tfrac{1}{2}J + R_{I_A,m_A-1}], \end{aligned} \quad (3.11)$$

$$\begin{aligned} &|I_A, m_A - \tfrac{1}{2}; 1\rangle \\ &= \frac{1}{(1 + Q^2_{I_A,m_A-1})^{1/2}}\{|I_A, m_A - 1; \tfrac{1}{2}, \tfrac{1}{2}\rangle - Q_{I_A,m_A-1}|I_A, m_A; \tfrac{1}{2}, -\tfrac{1}{2}\rangle\}, \\ &|I_A, m_A - \tfrac{1}{2}; 2\rangle \\ &= \frac{1}{(1 + Q^2_{I_A,m_A-1})^{1/2}}\{Q_{I_A,m_A-1}|I_A, m_A - 1; \tfrac{1}{2}, \tfrac{1}{2}\rangle + |I_A, m_A; \tfrac{1}{2}, -\tfrac{1}{2}\rangle\}. \end{aligned} \quad (3.12)$$

From (3.12) it follows that

$$\begin{aligned}
&|I_A, m_A - 1; \tfrac{1}{2}, \tfrac{1}{2}\rangle \\
&\quad = \frac{1}{(1 + Q^2_{I_A, m_A - 1})^{1/2}} \{| I_A, m_A - \tfrac{1}{2}; 1\rangle + Q_{I_A, m_A - 1} | I_A, m_A - \tfrac{1}{2}; 2\rangle\}, \\
&|I_A, m_A; \tfrac{1}{2}, -\tfrac{1}{2}\rangle \\
&\quad = \frac{1}{(1 + Q^2_{I_A, m_A - 1})^{1/2}} \{-Q_{I_A, m_A - 1} | I_A, m_A - \tfrac{1}{2}; 1\rangle + | I_A, m_A - \tfrac{1}{2}; 2\rangle\}.
\end{aligned} \tag{3.13}$$

C. Spectra of $A_{n_A}B$ Systems

The allowed transitions of an $A_{n_A}B$ system satisfy the selection rules

$$I_A = I_A', \qquad s_{I_A} = s'_{I_A}. \tag{3.14}$$

The first of these forbids transitions between states "belonging to" distinct I_A blocks, the second forbids transitions between states with distinct values of s_{I_A} in the same I_A block. The transitions within a given subblock are duplicated in all the remaining subblocks, so that the intensity of any computed transition must be multiplied by g_{I_A}. Thus the relative intensities are given by

$$g_{I_A} |\langle I_A, m_A - \tfrac{1}{2}; j | I^- | I_A, m_A + \tfrac{1}{2}; j'\rangle|^2, \tag{3.15}$$

where $j, j' = 1, 2$. The corresponding resonance frequencies are

$$\Omega_j(I_A, m_A - \tfrac{1}{2}) - \Omega_{j'}(I_A, m_A + \tfrac{1}{2}). \tag{3.16}$$

The transitions between the states of a typical subblock are of the form

$$|I_A, m_A + \tfrac{1}{2}; 1\rangle \xrightarrow{\text{A}} |I_A, m_A - \tfrac{1}{2}; 1\rangle, \qquad |I_A, m_A + \tfrac{1}{2}; 1\rangle \xrightarrow{\text{B}} |I_A, m_A - \tfrac{1}{2}; 2\rangle,$$

$$|I_A, m_A + \tfrac{1}{2}; 2\rangle \xrightarrow{\text{M}} |I_A, m_A - \tfrac{1}{2}; 1\rangle, \qquad |I_A, m_A + \tfrac{1}{2}; 2\rangle \xrightarrow{\text{A}} |I_A, m_A - \tfrac{1}{2}; 2\rangle.$$

The indicated A, B, and M character of these transitions may be verified by examining the corresponding energy differences in the limit as $J \to 0$. Since there is only one state with $m = I_A + \frac{1}{2}$, it follows that only two transitions are possible from the state with $m = I_A + \frac{1}{2}$ to the pair of states with $m = I_A - \frac{1}{2}$. Similarly, there is only one state with $m = -I_A - \frac{1}{2}$, so that there are two transitions from the pair of states with $m = -I_A + \frac{1}{2}$ to the state with $m = -I_A - \frac{1}{2}$. For all other values of m, there are four transitions from the two states with $m = m_A + \frac{1}{2}$ to the pair of states with $m = m_A - \frac{1}{2}$.

To obtain explicit formulas for the relative intensities, one first applies I^- to the eigenvectors (3.8), obtaining

$$I^- | I_A, m_A + \tfrac{1}{2}; 1\rangle = \frac{1}{(1 + Q^2_{I_A, m_A})^{1/2}} \{[(I_A + m_A)(I_A - m_A + 1)]^{1/2} | I_A, m_A - 1; \tfrac{1}{2}, \tfrac{1}{2}\rangle + (1 - Q_{I_A, m_A}[(I_A - m_A)(I_A + m_A + 1)]^{1/2}) | I_A, m_A; \tfrac{1}{2}, -\tfrac{1}{2}\rangle\} \tag{3.17}$$

$$I^- | I_A, m_A + \tfrac{1}{2}; 2\rangle = \frac{1}{(1 + Q^2_{I_A, m_A})^{1/2}} \{Q_{I_A, m_A}[(I_A + m_A)(I_A - m_A + 1)]^{1/2} | I_A, m_A - 1; \tfrac{1}{2}, \tfrac{1}{2}\rangle + (Q_{I_A, m_A} + [(I_A - m_A)(I_A + m_A + 1)]^{1/2}) | I_A, m_A; \tfrac{1}{2}, -\tfrac{1}{2}\rangle\}. \tag{3.18}$$

If the product kets in the right-hand members of (3.17) and (3.18) are replaced by their equivalent expressions as given by (3.13), one can determine all the matrix elements required by (3.15). The results of this calculation are collected in Table 6.6, along with the resonance frequencies.

Table 6.6 gives only the general form of the A, B, and M transitions generated by an arbitrary value of I_A. To obtain all the A, B, and M transitions associated with I_A, it is necessary to insert the allowed values of m_A into the expressions for the intensities and frequencies, and then tabulate the results. The complete $A_{n_A}B$ spectrum is obtained by iterating this procedure for all values of I_A.

The total number of A, B, and M transitions may be determined as follows. For the first A transition, m_A ranges from I_A to $-I_A + 1$, and from $I_A - 1$ to $-I_A$ for the second A transition. Thus for a given I_A the number of A transitions is $4I_A$. The total number of A transitions is obtained by summing over all values of I_A,

$$N_A = 4 \sum I_A \qquad \text{(all distinct } I_A\text{)}.$$

TABLE 6.6. — RESONANCE FREQUENCIES AND RELATIVE INTENSITIES FOR THE $A_{n_A}B$ SPIN SYSTEM

Transition[a]	Intensity	Frequency
	A Transitions	
A: $\vert I_A, m_A; \frac{1}{2}, \frac{1}{2}\rangle \to \vert I_A, m_A - 1; \frac{1}{2}, \frac{1}{2}\rangle$	$\dfrac{g_{I_A}(Q_{I_A,m_A-1}\{Q_{I_A,m_A}[(I_A - m_A)(I_A + m_A + 1)]^{1/2} - 1\} + [(I_A + m_A)(I_A - m_A + 1)]^{1/2})^2}{(1 + Q^2_{I_A,m_A})(1 + Q^2_{I_A,m_A-1})}$	$\frac{1}{2}\{2\omega_A + R_{I_A,m_A-1} - R_{I_A,m_A}\}$
A′: $\vert I_A, m_A + 1; \frac{1}{2}, -\frac{1}{2}\rangle \to \vert I_A, m_A; \frac{1}{2}, -\frac{1}{2}\rangle$	$\dfrac{g_{I_A}([(I_A - m_A)(I_A + m_A + 1)]^{1/2} + Q_{I_A,m_A}\{1 + Q_{I_A,m_A-1}[(I_A + m_A)(I_A - m_A + 1)]^{1/2}\})^2}{(1 + Q^2_{I_A,m_A})(1 + Q^2_{I_A,m_A-1})}$	$\frac{1}{2}\{2\omega_A + R_{I_A,m_A} - R_{I_A,m_A-1}\}$
	B Transitions	
B: $\vert I_A, m_A; \frac{1}{2}, \frac{1}{2}\rangle \to \vert I_A, m_A; \frac{1}{2}, -\frac{1}{2}\rangle$	$\dfrac{g_{I_A}(Q_{I_A,m_A}[(I_A - m_A)(I_A + m_A + 1)]^{1/2} - \{1 + Q_{I_A,m_A-1}[(I_A + m_A)(I_A - m_A + 1)]^{1/2}\})^2}{(1 + Q^2_{I_A,m_A})(1 + Q^2_{I_A,m_A-1})}$	$\frac{1}{2}\{2\omega_A - R_{I_A,m_A-1} - R_{I_A,m_A}\}$
	M Transitions	
M: $\vert I_A, m_A + 1; \frac{1}{2}, -\frac{1}{2}\rangle \to \vert I_A, m_A - 1; \frac{1}{2}, \frac{1}{2}\rangle$	$\dfrac{g_{I_A}(Q_{I_A,m_A-1}\{Q_{I_A,m_A} + [(I_A - m_A)(I_A + m_A + 1)]^{1/2}\} - Q_{I_A,m_A}[(I_A + m_A)(I_A - m_A + 1)]^{1/2})^2}{(1 + Q^2_{I_A,m_A})(1 + Q^2_{I_A,m_A-1})}$	$\frac{1}{2}\{2\omega_A + R_{I_A,m_A} + R_{I_A,m_A-1}\}$

[a] Transition in the limit $J \to 0$.

Similarly, the number of B and M transitions for a given I_A are $2I_A + 1$ and $2I_A - 1$, respectively. Hence

$$N_B = \sum (2I_A + 1) \qquad \text{(all distinct } I_A\text{)},$$
$$N_M = \sum (2I_A - 1) \qquad \text{(all distinct } I_A \neq 0\text{)}.$$

From the values of I_A given by (3.1), one finds, after some elementary algebra,

$$N_A = \begin{cases} n_A\left(\frac{n_A}{2} + 1\right) & \text{for } n_A \text{ even,} \\ \frac{1}{2}(n_A + 1)^2 & \text{for } n_A \text{ odd,} \end{cases} \tag{3.19}$$

$$N_B = \begin{cases} \left(\frac{n_A}{2} + 1\right)^2 & \text{for } n_A \text{ even,} \\ \frac{1}{4}(n_A + 1)(n_A + 3) & \text{for } n_A \text{ odd,} \end{cases} \tag{3.20}$$

$$N_M = \begin{cases} \frac{1}{4}n_A^2 & \text{for } n_A \text{ even,} \\ \frac{1}{4}(n_A^2 - 1) & \text{for } n_A \text{ odd.} \end{cases} \tag{3.21}$$

It follows that for any n_A,

$$N_A + N_B + N_M = (n_A + 1)^2; \tag{3.22}$$

that is, the total number of resonances is the square of the total number of nuclei. The preceding equations will be found useful when one wishes to verify that all transitions defined by Table 6.6 have been determined.

D. Reduction to the A_3B and A_4B Systems

The preceding results are easily checked for the AB and A_2B systems. In this section, the general formulas will be reduced to the A_3B and A_4B systems.

A_3B. The values of I_A, g_{I_A}, N_A, N_B, and N_M are

$$I_A = \tfrac{3}{2}, \tfrac{1}{2}; \qquad g_{3/2} = 1, \quad g_{1/2} = 2;$$
$$N_A = 8; \qquad N_B = 6; \qquad N_M = 2.$$

The eight transitions in group A are obtained as two sets of transitions, four from each of the first and second A transitions of Table 6.6. The first set of four A transitions is obtained from the first A transition by putting $I_A = \frac{3}{2}$, $m_A = \frac{3}{2}, \frac{1}{2}, -\frac{1}{2}$; $I_A = m_A = \frac{1}{2}$. The remaining set of four A transitions is obtained from the second A transition with $I_A = \frac{3}{2}$, $m_A = \frac{1}{2}, -\frac{1}{2}, -\frac{3}{2}$; $I_A = \frac{1}{2}$, $m_A = -\frac{1}{2}$. The B transitions are defined by the quantum numbers $I_A = \frac{3}{2}$, $m_A = \frac{3}{2}, \frac{1}{2}, -\frac{1}{2}, -\frac{3}{2}$; $I_A = \frac{1}{2}$, $m_A = \pm\frac{1}{2}$. The mixed transitions are both characterized by $I_A = \frac{3}{2}$, $m_A = \pm\frac{1}{2}$. The resonance frequencies and relative intensities of all 16 transitions are given in Table 6.7. The R's and Q's used in these tables are, according to (3.9) and (3.10),

$$R_{3/2,3/2} = \delta - 2J, \qquad Q_{3/2,3/2} = 0;$$

$$R_{3/2,1/2} = [(\delta - J)^2 + 3J^2]^{1/2}, \qquad Q_{3/2,1/2} = \frac{J\sqrt{3}}{\delta - J + R_{3/2,1/2}};$$

$$R_{3/2,-1/2} = (\delta^2 + 4J^2)^{1/2}, \qquad Q_{3/2,-1/2} = \frac{2J}{\delta + R_{3/2,-1/2}};$$

$$R_{3/2,-3/2} = [(\delta + J)^2 + 3J^2]^{1/2}, \qquad Q_{3/2,-3/2} = \frac{J\sqrt{3}}{\delta + J + R_{3/2,-3/2}};$$

$$R_{3/2,-5/2} = \delta + 2J, \qquad Q_{3/2,-5/2} = 0;$$

$$R_{1/2,1/2} = \delta - J, \qquad Q_{1/2,1/2} = 0;$$

$$R_{1/2,-1/2} = (\delta^2 + J^2)^{1/2}, \qquad Q_{1/2,-1/2} = \frac{J}{\delta + R_{1/2,-1/2}};$$

$$R_{1/2,-3/2} = \delta + J, \qquad Q_{1/2,-3/2} = 0.$$

Theoretical A_3B spectra are sketched in Figs. 6.22 through 6.24, and Fig. 6.25 illustrates the decomposition of the A_3B spectrum into its irreducible components. Apart from an intensity factor, an A_3B spectrum includes an AB spectrum (transitions A_7, A_8, B_5, B_6), and the identification of these resonances can expedite the analysis of an A_3B system. Transition diagrams for the irreducible components of the A_3B system are shown in Fig. 6.26.

The proton magnetic resonance spectrum of methyl mercaptan, as observed at 40 Mcps, is shown in Fig. 6.27. Except for the two mixed transitions, all resonances are resolved.

The intensities of an A_3B system satisfy the following relations:

$$\text{Int } A_1 + \text{Int } B_1 = 4,$$

$$\text{Int } A_6 + \text{Int } B_4 = 4,$$

$$\text{Int } A_7 + \text{Int } A_8 = \text{Int } B_5 + \text{Int } B_6 = 4,$$

$$\sum_{i=2}^{5} \text{Int } A_i + \text{Int } B_2 + \text{Int } B_3 + \text{Int } M_1 + \text{Int } M_2 = 16.$$

The last relation follows from the first two and the fact that $\text{Int } A_{3/2}B_{1/2} = 24$.

TABLE 6.7

RESONANCE FREQUENCIES AND RELATIVE INTENSITIES FOR THE A_3B SYSTEM

Transition[a]	Intensity	Frequency
	A *Transitions*	
A_1 : $\lvert \frac{3}{2}, \frac{3}{2}; \frac{1}{2}, \frac{1}{2}\rangle \rightarrow \lvert \frac{3}{2}, \frac{1}{2}; \frac{1}{2}, \frac{1}{2}\rangle$	$\dfrac{(\sqrt{3} - Q_{3/2,1/2})^2}{1 + Q^2_{3/2,1/2}}$	$\frac{1}{2}(\omega_A + \omega_B + 2J + R_{3/2,1/2})$
A_2 : $\lvert \frac{3}{2}, \frac{1}{2}; \frac{1}{2}, \frac{1}{2}\rangle \rightarrow \lvert \frac{3}{2}, -\frac{1}{2}; \frac{1}{2}, \frac{1}{2}\rangle$	$\dfrac{\{Q_{3/2,-1/2}[\sqrt{3}\,Q_{3/2,1/2} - 1] + 2\}^2}{(1 + Q^2_{3/2,1/2})(1 + Q^2_{3/2,-1/2})}$	$\frac{1}{2}(2\omega_A + R_{3/2,-1/2} - R_{3/2,1/2})$
A_3 : $\lvert \frac{3}{2}, -\frac{1}{2}; \frac{1}{2}, \frac{1}{2}\rangle \rightarrow \lvert \frac{3}{2}, -\frac{3}{2}; \frac{1}{2}, \frac{1}{2}\rangle$	$\dfrac{\{Q_{3/2,-3/2}[2Q_{3/2,-1/2} - 1] + \sqrt{3}\}^2}{(1 + Q^2_{3/2,-1/2})(1 + Q^2_{3/2,-3/2})}$	$\frac{1}{2}(2\omega_A + R_{3/2,-3/2} - R_{3/2,-1/2})$
A_4 : $\lvert \frac{3}{2}, \frac{3}{2}; \frac{1}{2}, -\frac{1}{2}\rangle \rightarrow \lvert \frac{3}{2}, \frac{1}{2}; \frac{1}{2}, -\frac{1}{2}\rangle$	$\dfrac{\{\sqrt{3} + Q_{3/2,1/2}[1 + 2Q_{3/2,-1/2}]\}^2}{(1 + Q^2_{3/2,1/2})(1 + Q^2_{3/2,-1/2})}$	$\frac{1}{2}(2\omega_A + R_{3/2,1/2} - R_{3/2,-1/2})$
A_5 : $\lvert \frac{3}{2}, \frac{1}{2}; \frac{1}{2}, -\frac{1}{2}\rangle \rightarrow \lvert \frac{3}{2}, -\frac{1}{2}; \frac{1}{2}, -\frac{1}{2}\rangle$	$\dfrac{\{2 + Q_{3/2,-1/2}[1 + \sqrt{3}Q_{3/2,-3/2}]\}^2}{(1 + Q^2_{3/2,-1/2})(1 + Q^2_{3/2,-3/2})}$	$\frac{1}{2}(2\omega_A + R_{3/2,-1/2} - R_{3/2,-3/2})$
A_6 : $\lvert \frac{3}{2}, -\frac{1}{2}; \frac{1}{2}, -\frac{1}{2}\rangle \rightarrow \lvert \frac{3}{2}, -\frac{3}{2}; \frac{1}{2}, -\frac{1}{2}\rangle$	$\dfrac{\{\sqrt{3} + Q_{3/2,-3/2}\}^2}{1 + Q^2_{3/2,-3/2}}$	$\frac{1}{2}(\omega_A + \omega_B - 2J + R_{3/2,-3/2})$
A_7 : $\lvert \frac{1}{2}, \frac{1}{2}; \frac{1}{2}, \frac{1}{2}\rangle \rightarrow \lvert \frac{1}{2}, -\frac{1}{2}; \frac{1}{2}, \frac{1}{2}\rangle$	$2\left(1 - \dfrac{J}{R_{1/2,-1/2}}\right)$	$\frac{1}{2}(\omega_A + \omega_B + J + R_{1/2,-1/2})$
A_8 : $\lvert \frac{1}{2}, \frac{1}{2}; \frac{1}{2}, -\frac{1}{2}\rangle \rightarrow \lvert \frac{1}{2}, -\frac{1}{2}; \frac{1}{2}, -\frac{1}{2}\rangle$	$2\left(1 + \dfrac{J}{R_{1/2,-1/2}}\right)$	$\frac{1}{2}(\omega_A + \omega_B - J + R_{1/2,-1/2})$

Transition[a]	Intensity	Frequency
	B *Transitions*	
B_1: $\mid \frac{3}{2}, \frac{3}{2}; \frac{1}{2}, \frac{1}{2}\rangle \to \mid \frac{3}{2}, \frac{3}{2}; \frac{1}{2}, -\frac{1}{2}\rangle$	$\dfrac{(1 + \sqrt{3}\, Q_{3/2,1/2})^2}{1 + Q^2_{3/2,1/2}}$	$\frac{1}{2}(\omega_A + \omega_B + 2J - R_{3/2,1/2})$
B_2: $\mid \frac{3}{2}, \frac{1}{2}; \frac{1}{2}, \frac{1}{2}\rangle \to \mid \frac{3}{2}, \frac{1}{2}; \frac{1}{2}, -\frac{1}{2}\rangle$	$\dfrac{\{\sqrt{3}\, Q_{3/2,1/2} - [1 + 2Q_{3/2,-1/2}]\}^2}{(1 + Q^2_{3/2,1/2})(1 + Q^2_{3/2,-1/2})}$	$\frac{1}{2}(2\omega_A - R_{3/2,-1/2} - R_{3/2,1/2})$
B_3: $\mid \frac{3}{2}, -\frac{1}{2}; \frac{1}{2}, \frac{1}{2}\rangle \to \mid \frac{3}{2}, -\frac{1}{2}; \frac{1}{2}, -\frac{1}{2}\rangle$	$\dfrac{\{2Q_{3/2,-1/2} - [1 + \sqrt{3}\, Q_{3/2,-3/2}]\}^2}{(1 + Q_{3/2,-1/2})(1 + Q^2_{3/2,-3/2})}$	$\frac{1}{2}(2\omega_A - R_{3/2,-3/2} - R_{3/2,-1/2})$
B_4: $\mid \frac{3}{2}, -\frac{3}{2}; \frac{1}{2}, \frac{1}{2}\rangle \to \mid \frac{3}{2}, -\frac{3}{2}; \frac{1}{2}, -\frac{1}{2}\rangle$	$\dfrac{(\sqrt{3}\, Q_{3/2,-3/2} - 1)^2}{1 + Q^2_{3/2,-3/2}}$	$\frac{1}{2}(\omega_A + \omega_B - 2J - R_{3/2,-3/2})$
B_5: $\mid \frac{1}{2}, \frac{1}{2}; \frac{1}{2}, \frac{1}{2}\rangle \to \mid \frac{1}{2}, \frac{1}{2}; \frac{1}{2}, -\frac{1}{2}\rangle$	$2\left(1 + \dfrac{J}{R_{1/2,-1/2}}\right)$	$\frac{1}{2}(\omega_A + \omega_B + J - R_{1/2,-1/2})$
B_6: $\mid \frac{1}{2}, -\frac{1}{2}; \frac{1}{2}, \frac{1}{2}\rangle \to \mid \frac{1}{2}, -\frac{1}{2}; \frac{1}{2}, -\frac{1}{2}\rangle$	$2\left(1 - \dfrac{J}{R_{1/2,-1/2}}\right)$	$\frac{1}{2}(\omega_A + \omega_B - J - R_{1/2,-1/2})$
	M *Transitions*	
M_1: $\mid \frac{3}{2}, \frac{3}{2}; \frac{1}{2}, -\frac{1}{2}\rangle \to \mid \frac{3}{2}, -\frac{1}{2}; \frac{1}{2}, \frac{1}{2}\rangle$	$\dfrac{\{Q_{3/2,-1/2}[Q_{3/2,1/2} + \sqrt{3}] - 2Q_{3/2,1/2}\}^2}{(1 + Q^2_{3/2,1/2})(1 + Q^2_{3/2,-1/2})}$	$\frac{1}{2}(2\omega_A + R_{3/2,1/2} + R_{3/2,-1/2})$
M_2: $\mid \frac{3}{2}, \frac{1}{2}; \frac{1}{2}, -\frac{1}{2}\rangle \to \mid \frac{3}{2}, -\frac{3}{2}; \frac{1}{2}, \frac{1}{2}\rangle$	$\dfrac{\{Q_{3/2,-3/2}[Q_{3/2,-1/2} + 2] - \sqrt{3}\, Q_{3/2,-1/2}\}^2}{(1 + Q^2_{3/2,-1/2})(1 + Q^2_{3/2,-3/2})}$	$\frac{1}{2}(2\omega_A + R_{3/2,-1/2} + R_{3/2,-3/2})$

[a] Transition in the limit $J \to 0$.

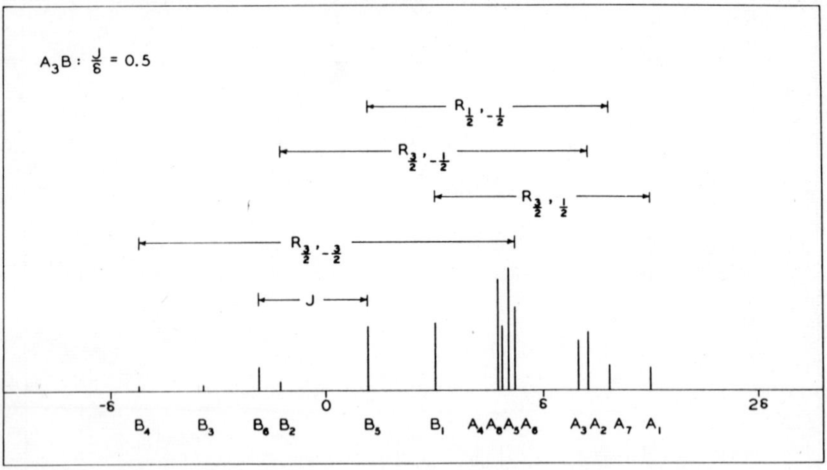

FIG. 6.22. Theoretical A_3B spectrum for $J/\delta = 0.5$.

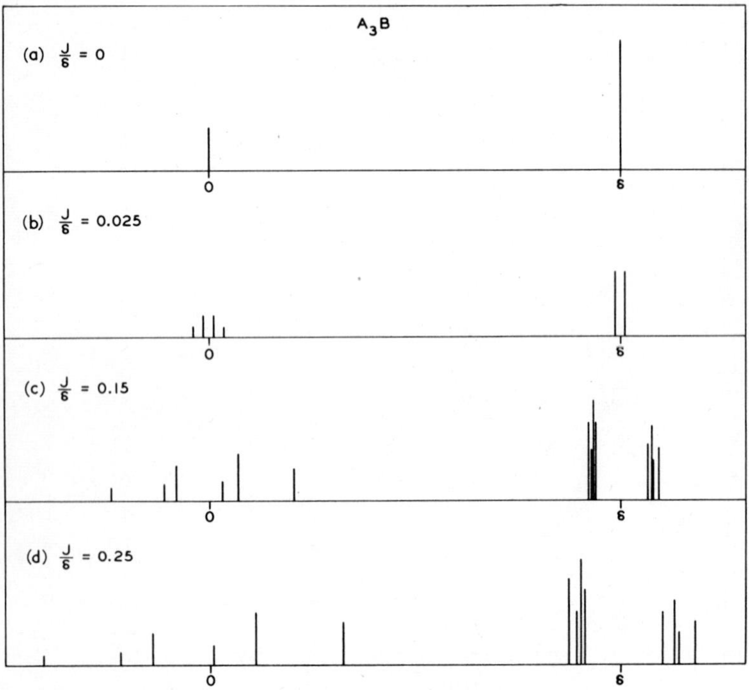

FIG. 6.23. Theoretical A_3B spectra.

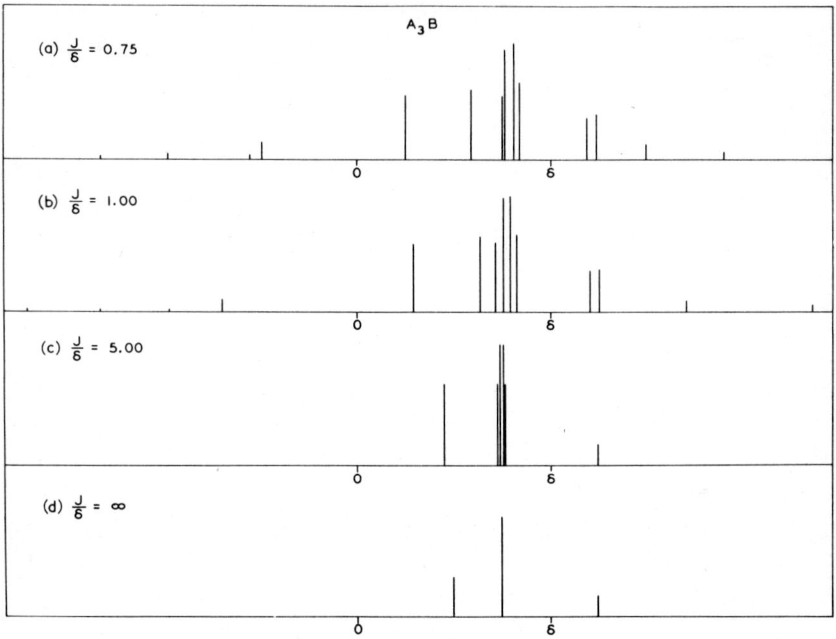

FIG. 6.24. Theoretical A_3B spectra.

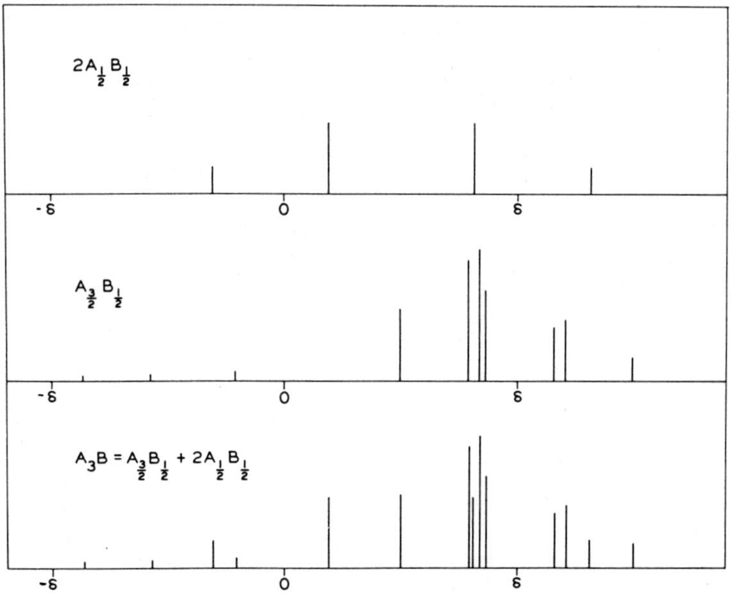

FIG. 6.25. Reduction of the A_3B system into its irreducible components.

TABLE 6.8 — RESONANCE FREQUENCIES AND RELATIVE INTENSITIES FOR THE A_4B SYSTEM

Transition[a]	Intensity	Frequency
	A *Transitions*	
A_1 : $\|2, 2; \frac{1}{2}, \frac{1}{2}\rangle \to \|2, 1; \frac{1}{2}, \frac{1}{2}\rangle$	$\frac{(2 - Q_{2,1})^2}{1 + Q_{2,1}^2}$	$\frac{1}{2}(\omega_A + \omega_B + \frac{5}{2}J + R_{2,1})$
A_2 : $\|2, 1; \frac{1}{2}, \frac{1}{2}\rangle \to \|2, 0; \frac{1}{2}, \frac{1}{2}\rangle$	$\frac{\{Q_{2,0}[2Q_{2,1} - 1] + \sqrt{6}\}^2}{(1 + Q_{2,1}^2)(1 + Q_{2,0}^2)}$	$\frac{1}{2}(2\omega_A + R_{2,0} - R_{2,1})$
A_3 : $\|2, 0; \frac{1}{2}, \frac{1}{2}\rangle \to \|2, -1; \frac{1}{2}, \frac{1}{2}\rangle$	$\frac{\{Q_{2,-1}[\sqrt{6}Q_{2,0} - 1] + \sqrt{6}\}^2}{(1 + Q_{2,0}^2)(1 + Q_{2,-1}^2)}$	$\frac{1}{2}(2\omega_A + R_{2,-1} - R_{2,0})$
A_4 : $\|2, -1; \frac{1}{2}, \frac{1}{2}\rangle \to \|2, -2; \frac{1}{2}, \frac{1}{2}\rangle$	$\frac{\{Q_{2,-2}[\sqrt{6}Q_{2,-1} - 1] + 2\}^2}{(1 + Q_{2,-1}^2)(1 + Q_{2,-2}^2)}$	$\frac{1}{2}(2\omega_A + R_{2,-2} - R_{2,-1})$
A_5 : $\|2, 2; \frac{1}{2}, -\frac{1}{2}\rangle \to \|2, 1; \frac{1}{2}, -\frac{1}{2}\rangle$	$\frac{\{2 + Q_{2,1}[1 + \sqrt{6}Q_{2,0}]\}^2}{(1 + Q_{2,1}^2)(1 + Q_{2,0}^2)}$	$\frac{1}{2}(2\omega_A + R_{2,1} - R_{2,0})$
A_6 : $\|2, 1; \frac{1}{2}, -\frac{1}{2}\rangle \to \|2, 0; \frac{1}{2}, -\frac{1}{2}\rangle$	$\frac{\{\sqrt{6} + Q_{2,0}[1 + \sqrt{6}Q_{2,-1}]\}^2}{(1 + Q_{2,0}^2)(1 + Q_{2,-1}^2)}$	$\frac{1}{2}(2\omega_A + R_{2,0} - R_{2,-1})$
A_7 : $\|2, 0; \frac{1}{2}, -\frac{1}{2}\rangle \to \|2, -1; \frac{1}{2}, -\frac{1}{2}\rangle$	$\frac{\{\sqrt{6} + Q_{2,-1}[1 + 2Q_{2,-2}]\}^2}{(1 + Q_{2,-1}^2)(1 + Q_{2,-2}^2)}$	$\frac{1}{2}(2\omega_A + R_{2,-1} - R_{2,-2})$
A_8 : $\|2, -1; \frac{1}{2}, -\frac{1}{2}\rangle \to \|2, -2; \frac{1}{2}, -\frac{1}{2}\rangle$	$\frac{(Q_{2,-2} + 2)^2}{1 + Q_{2,-2}^2}$	$\frac{1}{2}(\omega_A + \omega_B - \frac{5}{2}J + R_{2,-2})$
A_9 : $\|1, 1; \frac{1}{2}, \frac{1}{2}\rangle \to \|1, 0; \frac{1}{2}, \frac{1}{2}\rangle$	$\frac{3\{\sqrt{2} - Q_{1,0}\}^2}{1 + Q_{1,0}^2}$	$\frac{1}{2}(\omega_A + \omega_B + \frac{3}{2}J + R_{1,0})$
A_{10} : $\|1, 0; \frac{1}{2}, \frac{1}{2}\rangle \to \|1, -1; \frac{1}{2}, \frac{1}{2}\rangle$	$\frac{3\{Q_{1,-1}[\sqrt{2}Q_{1,0} - 1] + \sqrt{2}\}^2}{(1 + Q_{1,0}^2)(1 + Q_{1,-1}^2)}$	$\frac{1}{2}(2\omega_A + R_{1,-1} - R_{1,0})$
A_{11} : $\|1, 1; \frac{1}{2}, -\frac{1}{2}\rangle \to \|1, 0; \frac{1}{2}, -\frac{1}{2}\rangle$	$\frac{3\{\sqrt{2} + Q_{1,0}(1 + \sqrt{2}Q_{1,-1})\}^2}{(1 + Q_{1,0}^2)(1 + Q_{1,-1}^2)}$	$\frac{1}{2}(2\omega_A + R_{1,0} - R_{1,-1})$
A_{12} : $\|1, 0; \frac{1}{2}, -\frac{1}{2}\rangle \to \|1, -1; \frac{1}{2}, -\frac{1}{2}\rangle$	$\frac{3\{\sqrt{2} + Q_{1,-1}\}^2}{1 + Q_{1,-1}^2}$	$\frac{1}{2}(\omega_A + \omega_B - \frac{3}{2}J + R_{1,-1})$

Transition[a]	Intensity	Frequency
	B *Transitions*	
B_1 : $\lvert 2, 2; \frac{1}{2}, \frac{1}{2}\rangle \rightarrow \lvert 2, 2; \frac{1}{2}, -\frac{1}{2}\rangle$	$\dfrac{(1+2Q_{2,1})^2}{1+Q_{2,1}^2}$	$\frac{1}{2}(\omega_A+\omega_B+\frac{5}{2}J-R_{2,1})$
B_2 : $\lvert 2, 1; \frac{1}{2}, \frac{1}{2}\rangle \rightarrow \lvert 2, 1; \frac{1}{2}, -\frac{1}{2}\rangle$	$\dfrac{\{2Q_{2,1}-[1+\sqrt{6}\,Q_{2,0}]\}^2}{(1+Q_{2,1}^2)(1+Q_{2,0}^2)}$	$\frac{1}{2}(2\omega_A-R_{2,0}-R_{2,1})$
B_3 : $\lvert 2, 0; \frac{1}{2}, \frac{1}{2}\rangle \rightarrow \lvert 2, 0; \frac{1}{2}, -\frac{1}{2}\rangle$	$\dfrac{\{\sqrt{6}\,Q_{2,0}-[1+\sqrt{6}\,Q_{2,-1}]\}^2}{(1+Q_{2,0}^2)(1+Q_{2,-1}^2)}$	$\frac{1}{2}(2\omega_A-R_{2,-1}-R_{2,0})$
B_4 : $\lvert 2, -1; \frac{1}{2}, \frac{1}{2}\rangle \rightarrow \lvert 2, -1; \frac{1}{2}, -\frac{1}{2}\rangle$	$\dfrac{\{\sqrt{6}\,Q_{2,-1}-[1+2Q_{2,-2}]\}^2}{(1+Q_{2,-1}^2)(1+Q_{2,-2}^2)}$	$\frac{1}{2}(2\omega_A-R_{2,-2}-R_{2,-1})$
B_5 : $\lvert 2, -2; \frac{1}{2}, \frac{1}{2}\rangle \rightarrow \lvert 2, -2; \frac{1}{2}, -\frac{1}{2}\rangle$	$\dfrac{(2Q_{2,-2}-1)^2}{1+Q_{2,-2}^2}$	$\frac{1}{2}(\omega_A+\omega_B-\frac{5}{2}J-R_{2,-2})$
B_6 : $\lvert 1, 1; \frac{1}{2}, \frac{1}{2}\rangle \rightarrow \lvert 1, 1; \frac{1}{2}, -\frac{1}{2}\rangle$	$\dfrac{3\{1+\sqrt{2}\,Q_{1,0}\}^2}{1+Q_{1,0}^2}$	$\frac{1}{2}(\omega_A+\omega_B+\frac{3}{2}J-R_{1,0})$
B_7 : $\lvert 1, 0; \frac{1}{2}, \frac{1}{2}\rangle - \lvert 1, 0; \frac{1}{2}, -\frac{1}{2}\rangle$	$\dfrac{3\{\sqrt{2}\,(Q_{1,0}-Q_{1,-1})-1\}^2}{(1+Q_{1,0}^2)(1+Q_{1,-1}^2)}$	$\frac{1}{2}(2\omega_A-R_{1,-1}-R_{1,0})$
B_8 : $\lvert 1, -1; \frac{1}{2}, \frac{1}{2}\rangle \rightarrow \lvert 1, -1; \frac{1}{2}, -\frac{1}{2}\rangle$	$\dfrac{3\{\sqrt{2}\,Q_{1,-1}-1\}^2}{1+Q_{1,-1}^2}$	$\frac{1}{2}(\omega_A+\omega_B-\frac{3}{2}J-R_{1,-1})$
B_9 : $\lvert 0, 0; \frac{1}{2}, \frac{1}{2}\rangle \rightarrow \lvert 0, 0; \frac{1}{2}, -\frac{1}{2}\rangle$	2	ω_B
	M *Transitions*	
M_1 : $\lvert 2, 2; \frac{1}{2}, -\frac{1}{2}\rangle \rightarrow \lvert 2, 0; \frac{1}{2}, \frac{1}{2}\rangle$	$\dfrac{\{Q_{2,0}[Q_{2,1}+2]-\sqrt{6}\,Q_{2,1}\}^2}{(1+Q_{2,1}^2)(1+Q_{2,0}^2)}$	$\frac{1}{2}(2\omega_A+R_{2,1}+R_{2,0})$
M_2 : $\lvert 2, 1; \frac{1}{2}, -\frac{1}{2}\rangle \rightarrow \lvert 2, -1; \frac{1}{2}, \frac{1}{2}\rangle$	$\dfrac{\{Q_{2,-1}[Q_{2,0}+\sqrt{6}]-\sqrt{6}\,Q_{2,0}\}^2}{(1+Q_{2,0}^2)(1+Q_{2,-1}^2)}$	$\frac{1}{2}(2\omega_A+R_{2,0}+R_{2,-1})$
M_3 : $\lvert 2, 0; \frac{1}{2}, -\frac{1}{2}\rangle \rightarrow \lvert 2, -2; \frac{1}{2}, \frac{1}{2}\rangle$	$\dfrac{\{Q_{2,-2}[Q_{2,-1}+\sqrt{6}]-2Q_{2,-1}\}^2}{(1+Q_{2,-1}^2)(1+Q_{2,-2}^2)}$	$\frac{1}{2}(2\omega_A+R_{2,-1}+R_{2,-2})$
M_4 : $\lvert 1, 1; \frac{1}{2}, -\frac{1}{2}\rangle \rightarrow \lvert 1, -1; \frac{1}{2}, \frac{1}{2}\rangle$	$\dfrac{3\{(Q_{1,-1}-\sqrt{2})\,Q_{1,0}+\sqrt{2}\,Q_{1,-1}\}^2}{(1+Q_{1,-1}^2)(1+Q_{1,0}^2)}$	$\frac{1}{2}(2\omega_A+R_{1,0}+R_{1,-1})$

[a] Transition in the limit $J \rightarrow 0$.

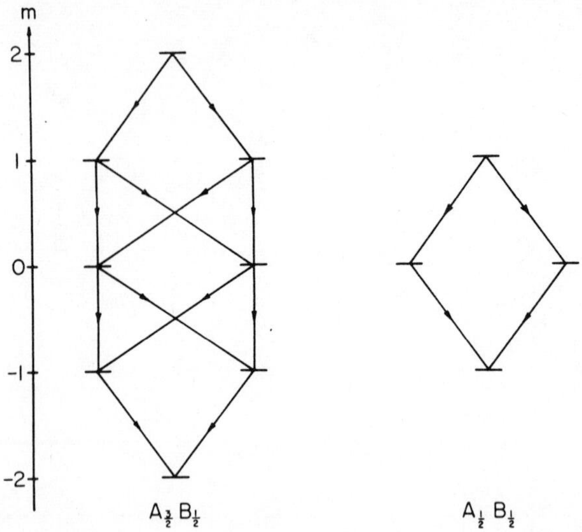

FIG. 6.26. Transition diagrams for the irreducible components of the A_3B system.

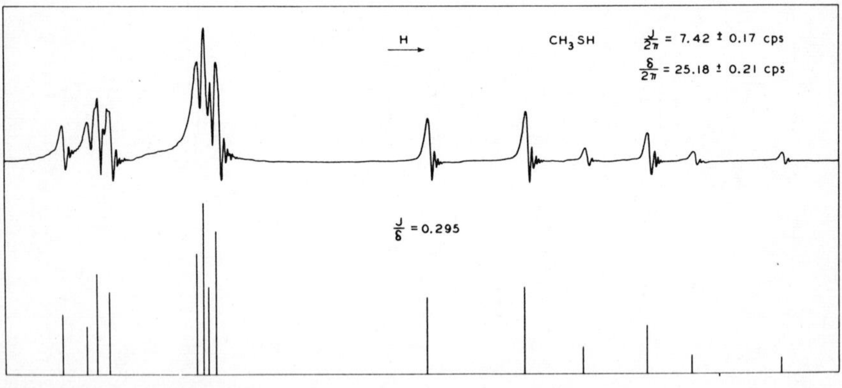

FIG. 6.27. Experimental and theoretical spectra of the protons in pure methyl mercaptan at 40 Mcps.

A_4B. The values of I_A, g_{I_A}, N_A, N_B, and N_M are

$$I_A = 2, 1, 0; \quad g_2 = 1, \quad g_1 = 3, \quad g_0 = 2;$$

$$N_A = 12; \quad N_B = 9; \quad N_M = 4.$$

The reduction of Table 6.6 is given in Table 6.8. The *R's* and *Q*'s for $I_A = 1$ are identical with those defined in Section 2 for the A_2B system.

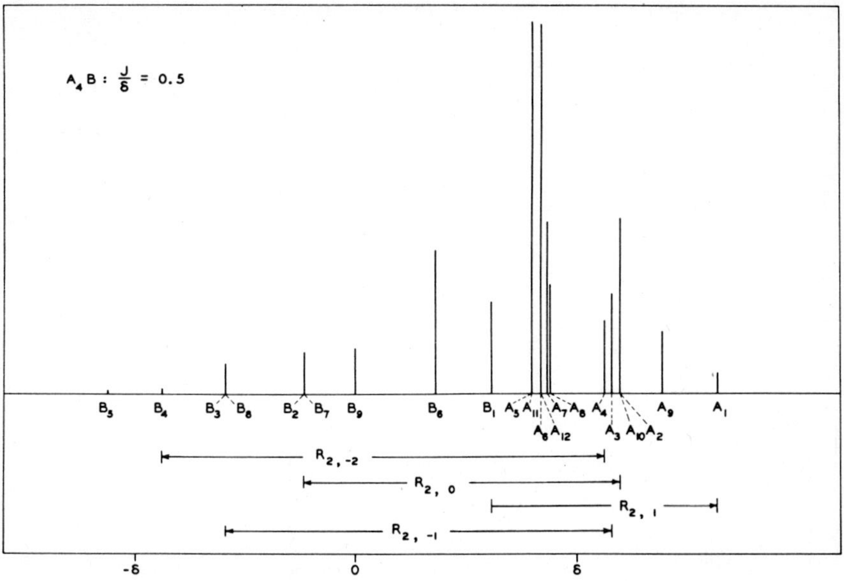

FIG. 6.28. Theoretical A_4B spectrum for $J/\delta = 0.5$.

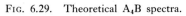

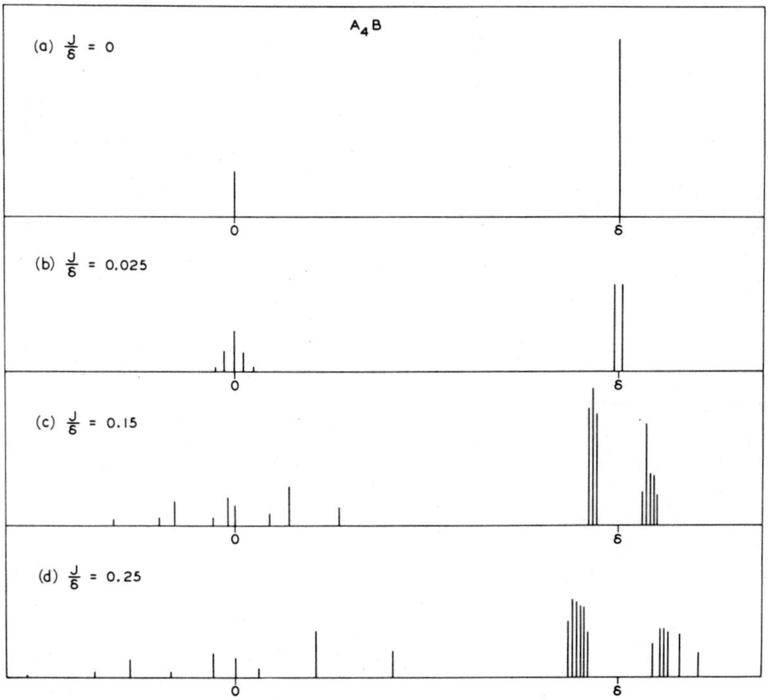

FIG. 6.29. Theoretical A_4B spectra.

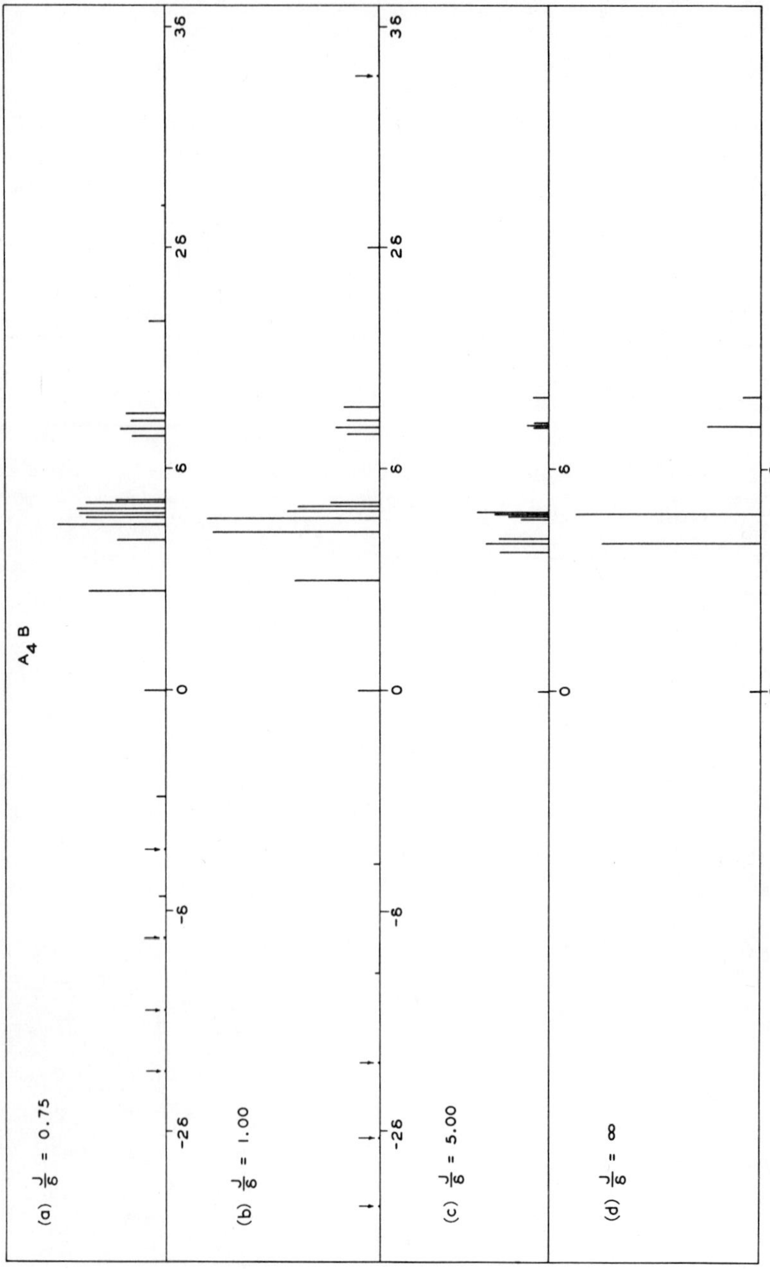

FIG. 6.30. Theoretical A_4B spectra.

The R's and Q's for $I_A = 2$ are given by

$$R_{2,2} = \delta - \tfrac{5}{2}J, \qquad Q_{2,2} = 0;$$

$$R_{2,1} = [(\delta - \tfrac{3}{2}J)^2 + 4J^2]^{1/2}, \qquad Q_{2,1} = \frac{2J}{\delta - \tfrac{3}{2}J + R_{2,1}};$$

$$R_{2,0} = [(\delta - \tfrac{1}{2}J)^2 + 6J^2]^{1/2}, \qquad Q_{2,0} = \frac{J\sqrt{6}}{\delta - \tfrac{1}{2}J + R_{2,0}};$$

$$R_{2,-1} = [(\delta + \tfrac{1}{2}J)^2 + 6J^2]^{1/2}, \qquad Q_{2,-1} = \frac{J\sqrt{6}}{\delta + \tfrac{1}{2}J + R_{2,-1}};$$

$$R_{2,-2} = [(\delta + \tfrac{3}{2}J)^2 + 4J^2]^{1/2}, \qquad Q_{2,-2} = \frac{2J}{\delta + \tfrac{3}{2}J + R_{2,-2}};$$

$$R_{2,-3} = \delta + \tfrac{5}{2}J, \qquad Q_{2,-3} = 0.$$

Theoretical A_4B spectra are sketched in Figs. 6.28 through 6.30. The transition diagrams are shown in Fig. 6.31.

The decomposition of the A_4B system is illustrated in Fig. 6.32. This figure indicates an important point concerning the decomposition of an A_4B system—that the A_4B system does not contain the A_2B system,

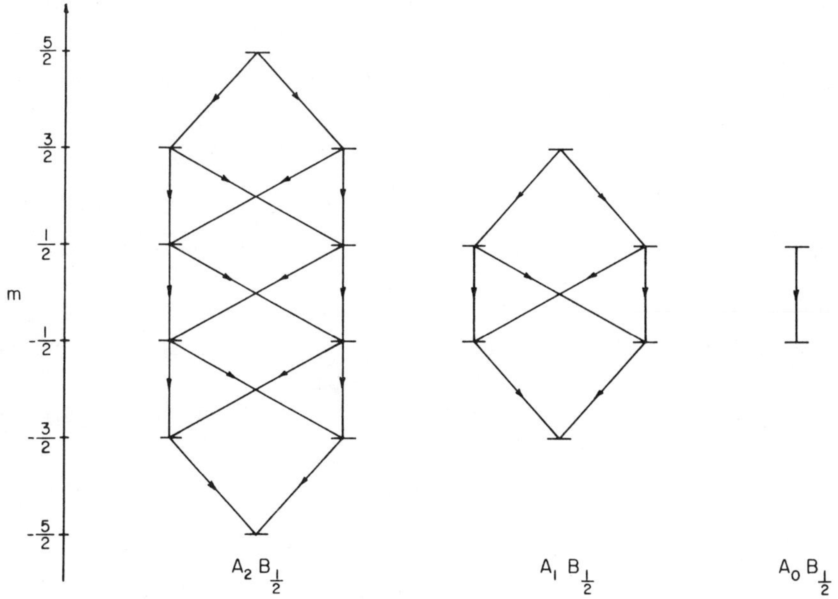

FIG. 6.31. Transition diagrams for the irreducible components of the A_4B system.

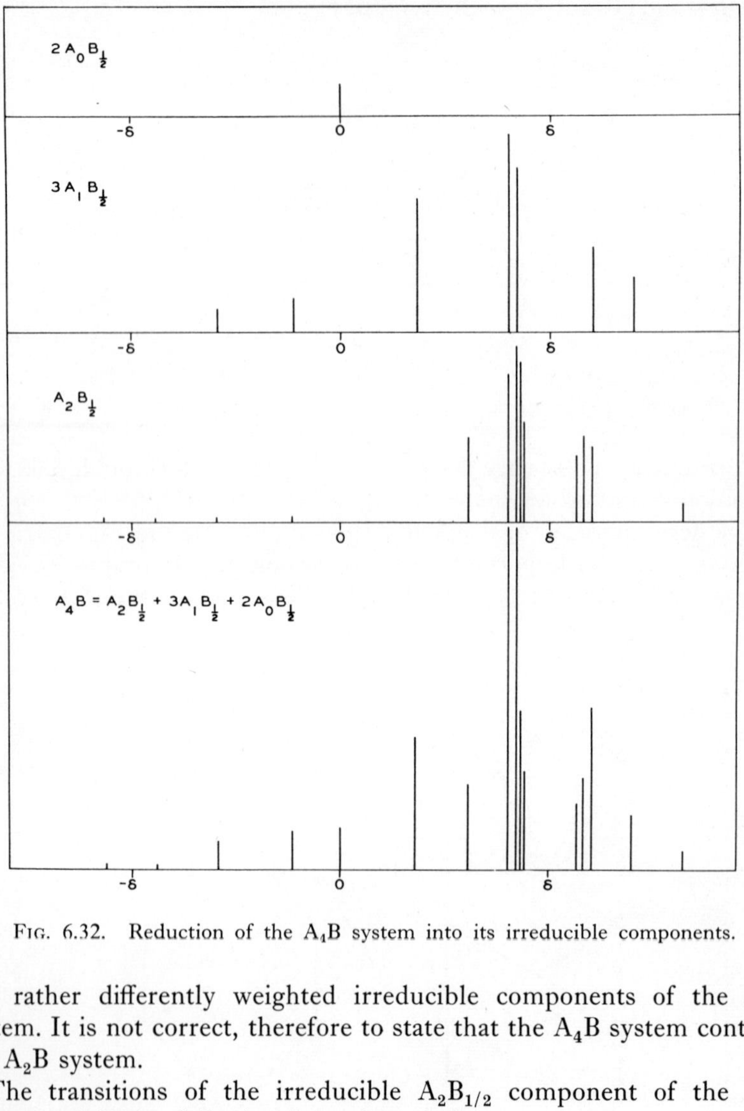

FIG. 6.32. Reduction of the A_4B system into its irreducible components.

but rather differently weighted irreducible components of the A_2B system. It is not correct, therefore to state that the A_4B system contains the A_2B system.

The transitions of the irreducible $A_2B_{1/2}$ component of the A_4B system satisfy the following intensity relations

$$\text{Int } A_1 + \text{Int } B_1 = 5,$$

$$\text{Int } A_8 + \text{Int } B_5 = 5,$$

$$\sum_{i=2}^{7} \text{Int } A_i + \sum_{i=2}^{4} \text{Int } B_i + \sum_{i=1}^{3} \text{Int } M_i = 35.$$

E. Properties of $A_{n_A}B$ Systems; Superposition

Table 6.6 permits the deduction of some properties of $A_{n_A}B$ systems that are often useful in the analysis of observed spectra. Some of these properties have already been noted for the AB, A_2B, and A_3B systems, but a number of them are generally valid.

The arithmetic mean of the frequencies of the two A transitions recorded in Table 6.6 is precisely ω_A. Note, however, that the quantum number $m_A + 1$, which is to be inserted into the second A transition, must be consistent with the quantum number I_A. This is not possible for the AB system, since the only value of m_A that can be used in the first A transition is $+\frac{1}{2}$; hence the value $m_A + 1 = \frac{3}{2}$ cannot be used for the second A transition. When $I_A > \frac{1}{2}$, the two transitions described always exist, so that

(1) For any $n_A > 1$, there are two A transitions whose arithmetic mean is ω_A.

Consider now the B transition of Table 6.6 when n_A is an even integer. In this case, $I_A = 0$ is a possible spin quantum number for group A and, upon putting $I_A = m_A = 0$ into the expressions for the intensity and frequency of the B transition, it follows that

(2) When n_A is even, there is a B transition at ω_B whose relative intensity is

$$g_{I_A=0} = \frac{n_A!}{(\frac{1}{2}n_A)!(\frac{1}{2}n_A + 1)!},$$

by (3.2) with $k = \frac{1}{2}n_A$.

Properties (1) and (2) may be combined to yield

(3) If $n_A \geqslant 2$ is an even integer, there are three resonances whose identification permits the direct determination of the internal chemical shifts.

The discussion of the AB and A_3B systems showed that both systems contain A and B transitions whose frequency separations are J. These observations are special cases of

(4) For n_A odd, there are two A transitions whose frequency separation is J, and a corresponding pair of B transitions, whose frequency separation is also J. The internal chemical shift is equal to the geometric mean of the frequency separations of the extreme and mean resonances.

This property follows at once from the decomposition

$$A_{n_A}B = \sum_{I_A} g_{I_A} A_{I_A} B_{1/2} .$$

Finally, by summing the four intensities given in Table 6.6, one obtains the following intensity relation:

(5) $\text{Int A} + \text{Int A}' + \text{Int B} + \text{Int M} = g_{I_A}\{2I_A(I_A + 1) - 2m_A{}^2 + 1\}.$

All the intensity relations derived above are special cases of this general formula. For example, if $m_A = I_A$, A′ and M are not defined, so that

$$\text{Int A} + \text{Int B} = g_{I_A}(2I_A + 1).$$

For $I_A = \frac{1}{2}, 1, \frac{3}{2}, 2$, and $g_{I_A} = 1$ for each choice of I_A, the right-hand member yields 2, 3, 4, and 5, in agreement with the results already derived. Other choices for m_A lead to additional relations.

4. The $A_{n_A}B_2$ System

A. Decomposition into Irreducible Components

The total spin quantum numbers for a group of two magnetically equivalent spin-$\frac{1}{2}$ nuclei are 1, 0, with spin multiplicities $g_1 = g_0 = 1$. It follows that the decomposition of the $A_{n_A}B_2$ system into its irreducible components is given by

$$A_{n_A}B_2 = \sum_{I_A} g_{I_A}(A_{I_A}B_0 + A_{I_A}B_1). \tag{4.1}$$

This equation reduces the study of the $A_{n_A}B_2$ system to a study of the irreducible components $A_{I_A}B_0$ and $A_{I_A}B_1$, with I_A given by (3.1).

(1) *Analysis of the* $A_{I_A}B_0$ *Component.* The product kets for the irreducible $A_{I_A}B_0$ system are of the form $|I_A, m_A\rangle|0, 0\rangle \equiv |I_A, m_A; 0, 0\rangle$. Every product ket of this form is an eigenvector of $\mathscr{H}$ with the eigenvalue $-m_A\omega_A$. Moreover, since $m = m_A + m_B = m_A + 0 = m_A$, the selection rule $\Delta m = -1$ is equivalent to $\Delta m_A = -1$. Thus the spectrum generated by an irreducible $A_{I_A}B_0$ component consists of a single resonance at

$$-\omega_A(m_A - 1) - (-\omega_A m_A) = \omega_A .$$

The relative intensity of a particular transition $|I_A, m_A; 0, 0\rangle \rightarrow |I_A, m_A - 1; 0, 0\rangle$ is

$$|\langle I_A, m_A - 1; 0, 0 | I^- | I_A, m_A; 0, 0\rangle|^2 = (I_A + m_A)(I_A - m_A + 1).$$

Since all transitions with $I_B = 0$ and $\Delta m = \Delta m_A = -1$ lead to a resonance at ω_A, the total intensity of the resonance at ω_A is obtained by multiplying this expression by g_{I_A}, summing over all m_A consistent with I_A, and then summing over all I_A. The sum over m_A is

$$\sum_{m_A} (I_A + m_A)(I_A - m_A + 1) = \tfrac{2}{3} I_A(I_A + 1)(2I_A + 1),$$

so that the total intensity is[4]

$$\tfrac{2}{3} \sum_{I_A} g_{I_A} I_A(I_A + 1)(2I_A + 1) = 2^{n_A - 1} n_A. \tag{4.2}$$

(2) *Analysis of* $A_{I_A}B_1$ *Component.* The dimension of the hamiltonian matrix for the irreducible $A_{I_A}B_1$ system is $(2I_A + 1)(2I_B + 1) = 3(2I_A + 1)$. This matrix is the direct sum of $2I_A + 3$ submatrices, one for each of the $2I_A + 3$ eigenvalues of $I_z : I_A + 1, I_A, \ldots, -I_A, -I_A - 1$.

The submatrices corresponding to $m = \pm(I_A + 1)$ are one-dimensional, those corresponding to $m = \pm I_A$ are two-dimensional. The eigenvalues and eigenvectors defined by these submatrices are given in Table 6.9, where

$$R_\pm = \{[\delta \pm J(I_A - 1)]^2 + 4I_A J^2\}^{1/2}, \qquad Q_\pm = \frac{2J(I_A)^{1/2}}{\delta \pm J(I_A - 1) + R_\pm}.$$

The remaining $3(2I_A - 1)$ submatrices have their m values in the range

$$-I_A + 1 \leqslant m \leqslant I_A - 1.$$

The product kets whose m values are in this range generate precisely $2I_A - 1$ three-dimensional submatrices, so that the analysis of the eigenvalue problem requires the solution of $2I_A - 1$ cubic equations. To prove this, consider the product ket $|I_A, m_A\rangle|1, 0\rangle$, whose I_z eigenvalue, by choice of $m_B = 0$, is m_A. The only other eigenvalues of I_{Az} and I_{Bz} that generate independent product kets with $m = m_A$ are:

I_{Az}	I_{Bz}
$m_A + 1$	-1
$m_A - 1$	1

[4] The sum over I_A may be evaluated with the help of equation (22) of Appendix V.

TABLE 6.9

EIGENVALUES AND EIGENVECTORS OF THE $A_{I_A}B_1$ SUBSYSTEM

Eigenvector	m	Eigenvalue
$\lvert I_A, I_A; 1, 1\rangle$	$I_A + 1$	$-\{\omega_A I_A + \omega_B + JI_A\}$
$\frac{1}{(1+Q_-^2)^{1/2}}\{\lvert I_A, I_A - 1; 1, 1\rangle - Q_- \lvert I_A, I_A; 1, 0\rangle\}$	I_A	$-\frac{1}{2}\{(2I_A - 1)\omega_A + \omega_B + J(I_A - 1) - R_-\}$
$\frac{1}{(1+Q_-^2)^{1/2}}\{Q_- \lvert I_A, I_A - 1; 1, 1\rangle + \lvert I_A, I_A; 1, 0\rangle\}$	I_A	$-\frac{1}{2}\{(2I_A - 1)\omega_A + \omega_B + J(I_A - 1) + R_-\}$
$\vdots$	$\vdots$	$\vdots$
$a_{11} \lvert I_A, m_A + 1; 1, -1\rangle + a_{21} \lvert I_A, m_A; 1, 0\rangle + a_{31} \lvert I_A, m_A - 1; 1, 1\rangle$	m_A	Ω_1
$a_{12} \lvert I_A, m_A + 1; 1, -1\rangle + a_{22} \lvert I_A, m_A; 1, 0\rangle + a_{32} \lvert I_A, m_A - 1; 1, 1\rangle$	m_A	Ω_2
$a_{13} \lvert I_A, m_A + 1; 1, -1\rangle + a_{23} \lvert I_A, m_A; 1, 0\rangle + a_{33} \lvert I_A, m_A - 1; 1, 1\rangle$	m_A	Ω_3
$\vdots$	$\vdots$	$\vdots$
$\frac{1}{(1+Q_+^2)^{1/2}}\{\lvert I_A, -I_A; I_B, -I_B + 1\rangle - Q_+ \lvert I_A, -I_A + 1; I_B, -I_B\rangle\}$	$-I_A$	$\frac{1}{2}\{(2I_A - 1)\omega_A + \omega_B - J(I_A - 1) + R_+\}$
$\frac{1}{(1+Q_+^2)^{1/2}}\{Q_+ \lvert I_A, -I_A; I_B, -I_B + 1\rangle + \lvert I_A, -I_A + 1; I_B, -I_B\rangle\}$	$-I_A$	$\frac{1}{2}\{(2I_A - 1)\omega_A + \omega_B - J(I_A - 1) - R_+\}$
$\lvert I_A, -I_A; 1, -1\rangle$	$-I_A - 1$	$\{\omega_A I_A + \omega_B - JI_A\}$

The 3×3 submatrix corresponding to an arbitrary value of $m = m_A$ is obtained by applying $\mathscr{H}$ to the appropriate product kets:

$$\begin{aligned}
&\mathscr{H} \mid I_A, m_A + 1; 1, -1\rangle \\
&\quad = -\{[(m_A + 1)\omega_A - \omega_B - J(m_A + 1)] \mid I_A, m_A + 1; 1, -1\rangle \\
&\qquad + J[\tfrac{1}{2}(I_A - m_A)(I_A + m_A + 1)]^{1/2} \mid I_A, m_A; 1, 0\rangle\},
\end{aligned}$$

$$\begin{aligned}
&\mathscr{H} \mid I_A, m_A; 1, 0\rangle \\
&\quad = -(m_A\omega_A \mid I_A, m_A; 1, 0\rangle \\
&\qquad + J\{[\tfrac{1}{2}(I_A - m_A)(I_A + m_A + 1)]^{1/2} \mid I_A, m_A + 1; 1, -1\rangle \\
&\qquad + [\tfrac{1}{2}(I_A + m_A)(I_A - m_A + 1)]^{1/2} \mid I_A, m_A - 1; 1, 1\rangle\}),
\end{aligned}$$

$$\begin{aligned}
&\mathscr{H} \mid I_A, m_A - 1; 1, 1\rangle \\
&\quad = -\{[\omega_A(m_A - 1) + \omega_B + J(m_A - 1)] \mid I_A, m_A - 1; 1, 1\rangle \\
&\qquad + J[\tfrac{1}{2}(I_A + m_A)(I_A - m_A + 1)]^{1/2} \mid I_A, m_A; 1, -1\rangle\}.
\end{aligned}$$

From these equations, it follows that

$$\mathscr{H}(m_A) = -\begin{pmatrix} (\omega_A - J)(m_A + 1) - \omega_B & J[\tfrac{1}{2}(I_A - m_A)(I_A + m_A + 1)]^{1/2} & 0 \\ J[\tfrac{1}{2}(I_A - m_A)(I_A + m_A + 1)]^{1/2} & m_A\omega_A & J[\tfrac{1}{2}(I_A + m_A)(I_A - m_A + 1)]^{1/2} \\ 0 & J[\tfrac{1}{2}(I_A + m_A)(I_A - m_A + 1)]^{1/2} & (\omega_A + J)(m_A - 1) + \omega_B \end{pmatrix}. \tag{4.3}$$

All the 3×3 submatrices of the irreducible $A_{I_A}B_1$ system are obtained from (4.3) by allowing m_A to range from $I_A - 1$ to $-I_A + 1$ in integral steps.

The eigenvectors of $\mathscr{H}(m_A)$ have the form indicated in Table 6.9. Since $\mathscr{H}(m_A)$ is a real symmetric matrix, there is no essential loss of generality in supposing that the expansion coefficients are the components of an orthogonal matrix

$$\sum_j a_{ij}a_{kj} = \delta_{ik}.$$

For $J \ll \delta$, the eigenvalues of (4.3) are[5]

$$\begin{aligned}
\Omega_1 &= -m_A\omega_A - \delta + J(m_A + 1), \\
\Omega_2 &= -m_A\omega_A, \\
\Omega_3 &= -m_A\omega_A + \delta - J(m_A - 1),
\end{aligned}$$

[5] The results cited here for $J \ll \delta$ and $J \gg \delta$ may be obtained by the perturbation method described in Chapter 7.

and the matrix $(a_{ij}) = (\delta_{ij})$. For $J \gg \delta$, the eigenvalues are [5]

$$\Omega_1 = -m_A\omega_A - I_A\left\{J + \frac{(2m_A + 1)\,\delta}{(I_A + 1)(2I_A + 1)}\right\},$$

$$\Omega_2 = -m_A\omega_A + J - \frac{(2m_A + 1)\,\delta}{I_A(I_A + 1)},$$

$$\Omega_3 = -m_A\omega_A + (I_A + 1)\left\{J + \frac{(2m_A + 1)\,\delta}{I_A(I_A + 1)}\right\},$$

and the ratios of the expansion coefficients are

$$\frac{a_{i1}}{a_{i2}} = \frac{1}{\sqrt{2}}\left\{\frac{[(I_A - m_A)(I_A + m_A + 1)]^{1/2}}{m_A + \lambda_i - 1}\right\},$$

$$\frac{a_{i2}}{a_{i3}} = \sqrt{2}\left\{\frac{m_A - \lambda_i - 1}{[(I_A + m_A)(I_A - m_A + 1)]^{1/2}}\right\},$$

$$\lambda_1 = -I_A, \qquad \lambda_2 = 1, \qquad \lambda_3 = I_A + 1.$$

When J is comparable to δ, the determination of the eigenvalues and eigenvectors requires the solution of the determinantal equation $\det[\mathscr{H}(m_A) - \Omega I] = 0$. The expansion of the determinantal equation yields

$$\Omega^3 + a\Omega^2 + b\Omega + c = 0, \tag{4.4}$$

where $a = -\mathrm{tr}\,\mathscr{H}(m_A)$, b is the sum of the cofactors of the diagonal elements of $\mathscr{H}(m_A)$, and $c = -\det \mathscr{H}(m_A)$. The roots of this equation are given by[6] (7)

$$\Omega_i = -\frac{1}{3}a + 2r^{1/3}\cos\frac{\theta + 2\pi(i-1)}{3} \qquad (i = 1, 2, 3),$$

where

$$r = \left(-\frac{p^3}{27}\right)^{1/2}, \qquad \cos\theta = -\frac{q}{2r}, \qquad p = b - \frac{a^2}{3}, \qquad q = c - \frac{ab}{3} + \frac{2a^3}{27}.$$

These relations can be used to derive explicit expressions for the resonance frequencies and relative intensities of the $A_{I_A}B_1$ system, but the resulting expressions are quite complicated and of limited practical value. The analysis of an eigenvalue problem involving determinantal

---

[6] These formulas apply if the roots of (4.4) are real and unequal, that is, when the discriminant $-(4p^3 + 27q^2) > 0$.

equations of degrees exceeding two is usually carried out numerically (*8–10*).

The numerical analysis of an experimental spectrum is carried through by comparing the observed frequencies and intensities with those computed for trial values of J and δ until the "best fit" is obtained. In particular cases, it may be possible to determine δ and/or J directly. For example, if n_A is an even integer, $I_A = 0$ is a possible spin quantum number for group A. It follows, by an argument similar to that used in the discussion of the $A_{I_A}B_0$ component, that there is an unshifted resonance at ω_B whose relative intensity is

$$2^{n_B-1}n_B g_{I_A=0} = \frac{8n_A!}{(n_A+2)[(\frac{1}{2}n_A)!]^2}. \tag{4.5}$$

Hence the $A_{n_A}B_2$ system, where n_A is an even integer, contains two resonances whose frequency separation is δ, and whose relative intensities are given by (4.2) and (4.5). More generally, the spectrum of an $A_{n_A}B_{n_B}$ system, where n_A and n_B are even integers, includes two unshifted resonances whose relative intensities are in the ratio

$$2^{n_A-n_B}\left(\frac{n_A g_{I_B=0}}{n_B g_{I_A=0}}\right) = 2^{n_A-n_B}\left(\frac{n_A+2}{n_B+2}\right)\frac{(n_B-1)!}{(n_A-1)!}\left[\frac{(\frac{1}{2}n_A)!}{(\frac{1}{2}n_B)!}\right]^2.$$

In the following sections it will be shown that it is often possible to obtain both J and δ without solving any of the $2I_A - 1$ cubic equations.

B. The A_2B_2 System

For the A_2B_2 system, $I_A = 1, 0, g_1 = g_0 = 1$. Only one 3×3 submatrix appears in the eigenvalue problem for the A_1B_1 component; it is obtained from (4.3) by setting $I_A = 1$, $m_A = 0$:

$$\mathscr{H}(0) = \begin{pmatrix} -\delta + J & -J & 0 \\ -J & 0 & -J \\ 0 & -J & \delta + J \end{pmatrix}$$

Although the complete analysis of the A_2B_2 system requires the solution of a cubic equation, some useful information can be deduced by putting $I_A = 1$ in Table 6.9, and then formally calculating a table of resonance frequencies and relative intensities. These calculations show that the spectrum consists of 18 transitions, $N_A = N_B = 7$, $N_M = 4$, and is symmetrical with respect to $\frac{1}{2}(\omega_A + \omega_B)$. The seven A transitions and two of the mixed transitions are given in Table 6.10, where

$$R_+ = R_- = R = (\delta^2 + 4J^2)^{1/2}, \qquad Q_+ = Q_- = Q = \frac{2J}{\delta + R}.$$

TABLE 6.10

RESONANCE FREQUENCIES AND RELATIVE INTENSITIES FOR THE A_2B_2 SYSTEM

Transition[a]	Intensity	Frequency[b]
A_1 : $\vert 1, 1; 1, 1\rangle \rightarrow \vert 1, 0; 1, 1\rangle$	$2\left(1 - \frac{2J}{R}\right)$	$J + \frac{1}{2}R$
A_2 : $\vert 1, 0; 1, 1\rangle \rightarrow \vert 1, -1; 1, 1\rangle$	$\frac{2[Q(a_{13} + a_{23}) - (a_{33} + a_{23})]^2}{1 + Q^2}$	$\Omega_3 - \frac{1}{2}R$
A_3 : $\vert 1, 1; 1, 0\rangle \rightarrow \vert 1, 0; 1, 0\rangle$	$\frac{2[Q(a_{22} + a_{32}) + (a_{22} + a_{12})]^2}{1 + Q^2}$	$\Omega_2 + \frac{1}{2}R$
A_4 : $\vert 1, 0; 1, 0\rangle \rightarrow \vert 1, -1; 1, 0\rangle$	$\frac{2[Q(a_{12} + a_{22}) - (a_{22} + a_{32})]^2}{1 + Q^2}$	$-\Omega_2 + \frac{1}{2}R$
A_5 : $\vert 1, 1; 1, -1\rangle \rightarrow \vert 1, 0; 1, -1\rangle$	$\frac{2[Q(a_{21} + a_{31}) + (a_{11} + a_{21})]^2}{1 + Q^2}$	$-\Omega_1 - \frac{1}{2}R$
A_6 : $\vert 1, 0; 1, -1\rangle \rightarrow \vert 1, -1; 1, -1\rangle$	$2\left(1 + \frac{2J}{R}\right)$	$-J + \frac{1}{2}R$
A_7 : $\vert 1, 1; 0, 0\rangle \rightarrow \vert 1, 0; 0, 0\rangle$, $\vert 1, 0; 0, 0\rangle \rightarrow \vert 1, -1; 0, 0\rangle$	4	$\frac{1}{2}\delta$
M_1 : $\vert 1, 1; 1, -1\rangle \rightarrow \vert 1, -1; 1, 0\rangle$	$\frac{2[Q(a_{11} + a_{21}) - (a_{21} + a_{31})]^2}{1 + Q^2}$	$-\Omega_1 + \frac{1}{2}R$
M_2 : $\vert 1, 1; 1, 0\rangle \rightarrow \vert 1, -1; 1, 1\rangle$	$\frac{2[(a_{23} + a_{13}) + Q(a_{23} + a_{33})]^2}{1 + Q^2}$	$\Omega_3 + \frac{1}{2}R$

[a] In the limit $J \rightarrow 0$.
[b] Relative to $\frac{1}{2}(\omega_A + \omega_B)$.

The transition diagrams for the irreducible components of the A_2B_2 system are shown in Fig. 6.33. The spectra generated by the irreducible components are illustrated in Fig. 6.34 for $J/\delta = 0.5$. Additional theoretical spectra[7] are sketched in Figs. 6.35 and 6.36.

[7] Tables of the resonance frequencies and relative intensities for the A_2B_2 and A_3B_2 systems are given in Appendix VI.

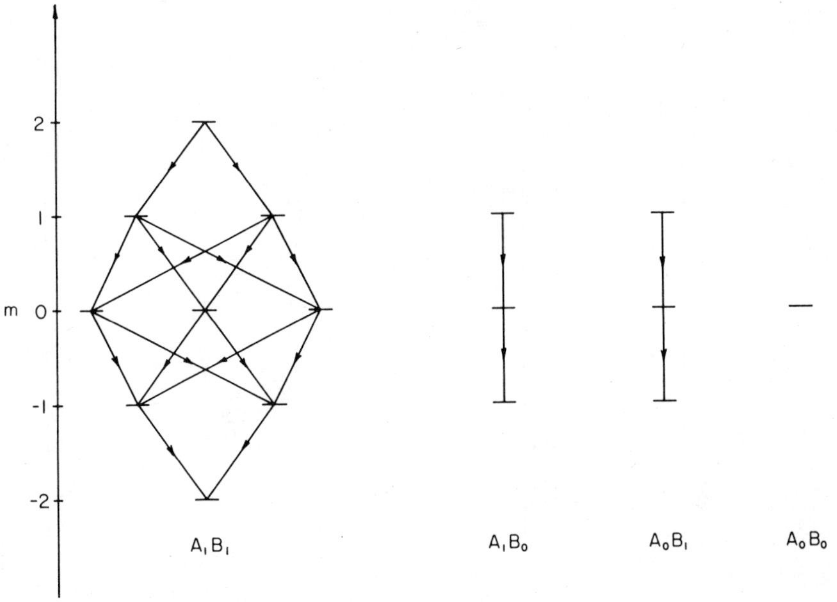

FIG. 6.33. Transition diagrams for the irreducible components of the A_2B_2 system.

From the expressions given in Table 6.10 and the orthogonality conditions satisfied by the a_{ij}, it follows that

$$A_7 - B_7 = \delta, \qquad \tfrac{1}{2}(A_1 - A_6) = J,$$

$$\text{Int } A_1 + \text{Int } A_6 = 4,$$

$$\text{Int } A_3 + \text{Int } A_5 + \text{Int } M_2 = 4\left(1 + \frac{J}{R}\right),$$

$$\text{Int } A_2 + \text{Int } A_4 + \text{Int } M_1 = 4\left(1 - \frac{J}{R}\right).$$

If transitions A_1, A_6, A_7, and B_7 are resolved and identified in an experimental spectrum, J and δ can be directly determined.

Figure 6.37 shows the experimental spectrum of ethylene monothiocarbonate as observed at 40 Mcps. The theoretical spectrum was calculated on the assumption that the protons form two sets of magnetically equivalent nuclei with $n_A = n_B = 2$. It should be noted, however, that the structure of the molecule precludes the realization of magnetic equivalence by rapid internal rotation. The spin system is actually of the AA′BB′ type (cf. Chapter 8), which is described by five parameters: δ, $J_{AA'}$, $J_{BB'}$, J_{AB}, and $J_{AB'}$. When $J_{AB} = J_{AB'}$, the

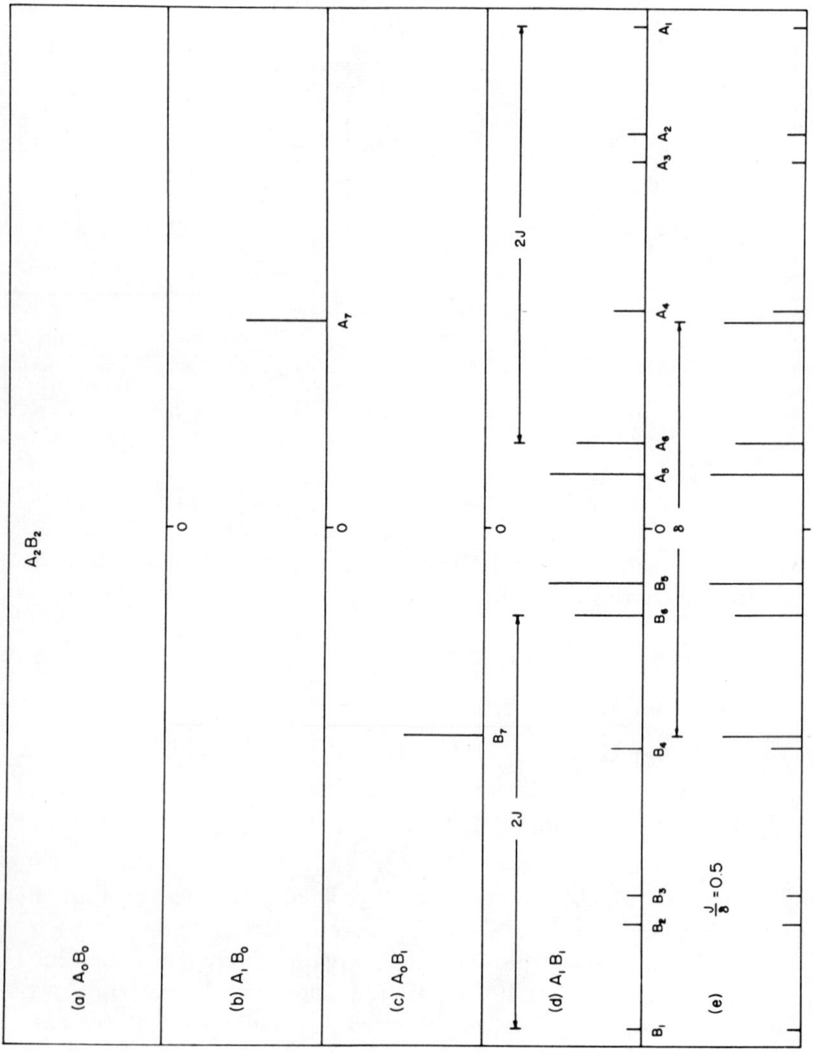

FIG. 6.34. The A_2B_2 system reduced into its irreducible components; (e) shows the A_2B_2 spectrum for $J/\delta = 0.5$.

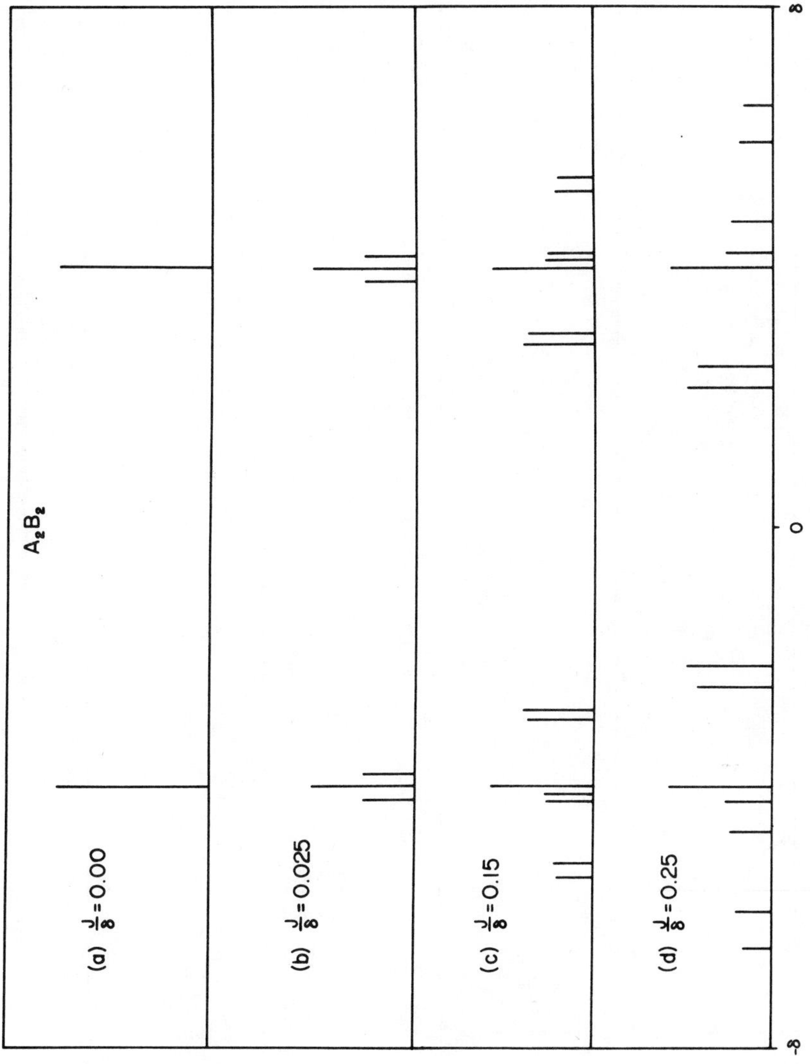

FIG. 6.35. Theoretical A_2B_2 spectra.

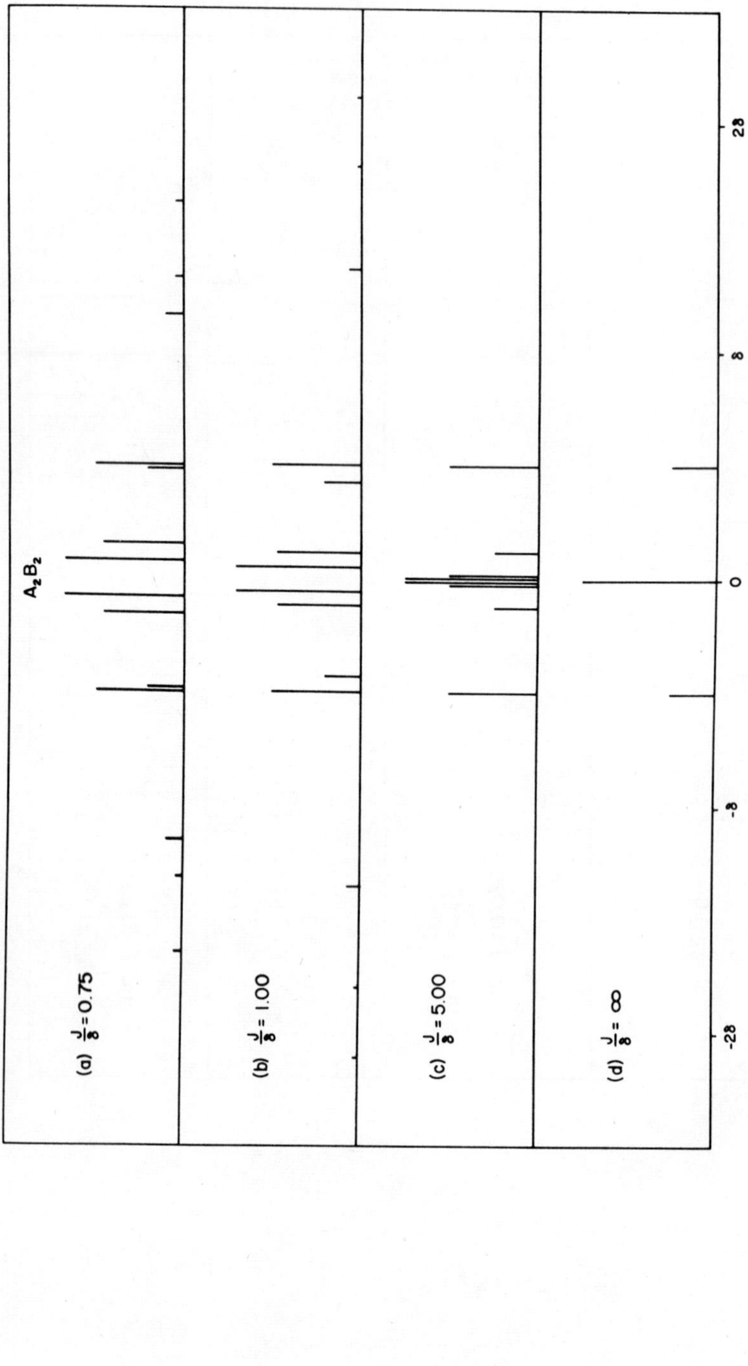

FIG 6.36. Theoretical A_2B_2 spectra.

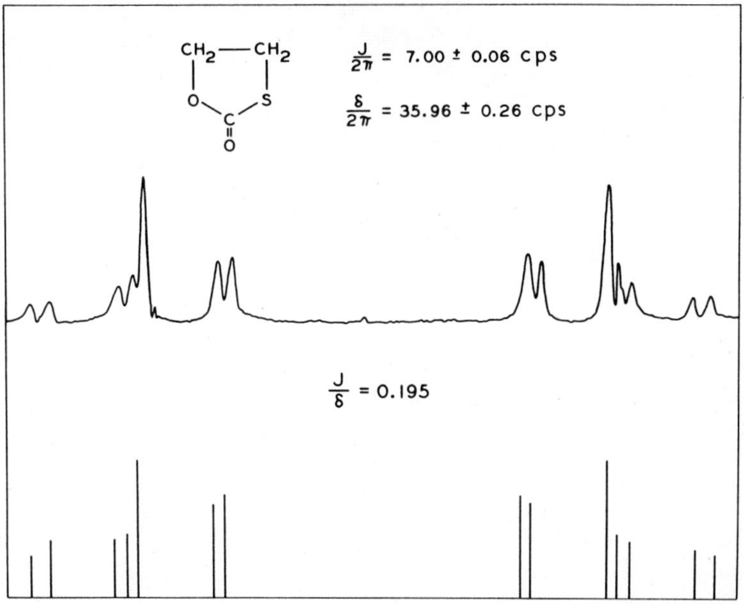

FIG. 6.37. Experimental and theoretical spectra for the protons in pure ethylene monothiocarbonate at 40 Mcps.

AA'BB' system reduces to an A_2B_2 system, which can be described by only two parameters: $J_{AB} \equiv J$ and δ, the effects of the couplings $J_{AA'}$ and $J_{BB'}$ being unobservable, owing to the magnetic equivalence of groups A and B. Even when $J_{AB} \neq J_{AB'}$, it is possible for the spectrum of an AA'BB' to be quite similar to that of an A_2B_2 system (*11*). It is conceivable, therefore, that the protons in ethylene monothiocarbonate do not constitute two groups of magnetically equivalent nuclei.

C. The A_3B_2 System

In the A_3B_2 system, $I_A = \frac{3}{2}, \frac{1}{2}, g_{3/2} = 1, g_{1/2} = 2$. The analysis of the eigenvalue problem for the irreducible $A_{3/2}B_1$ component requires the diagonalization of the two 3×3 submatrices obtained from (4.3) by setting $I_A = \frac{3}{2}, m_A = \pm\frac{1}{2}$. After some elementary row and column operations on the matrix corresponding to $m_A = -\frac{1}{2}$, one finds that

$$\mathscr{H}(\pm\tfrac{1}{2}) = -\begin{pmatrix} \pm(\frac{1}{2}\omega_A + \delta) - \frac{3}{2}J & J\sqrt{\frac{3}{2}} & 0 \\ J\sqrt{\frac{3}{2}} & \pm\frac{1}{2}\omega_A & J\sqrt{2} \\ 0 & J\sqrt{2} & \pm(\frac{1}{2}\omega_A - \delta) - \frac{1}{2}J \end{pmatrix}.$$

TABLE 6.11

RESONANCE FREQUENCIES AND RELATIVE INTENSITIES FOR THE A_3B_2 SYSTEM TRANSITIONS IN GROUP A

Transition[a]	Intensity	Frequency[b]
A_1: $\lvert \frac{3}{2}, \frac{3}{2}; 1, 1\rangle \rightarrow \lvert \frac{3}{2}, \frac{1}{2}; 1, 1\rangle$	$\dfrac{[\sqrt{3} - Q_- \sqrt{2}]^2}{1 + Q_-^2}$	$\frac{1}{2}(\delta + \frac{5}{2} J + R_-)$
A_2: $\lvert \frac{3}{2}, \frac{1}{2}; 1, 1\rangle \rightarrow \lvert \frac{3}{2}, -\frac{1}{2}; 1, 1\rangle$	$\dfrac{[Q_- a_{13} \sqrt{2} + (Q_- \sqrt{3} - \sqrt{2})a_{23} - 2a_{33}]^2}{1 + Q_-^2}$	$\delta + \Omega_3 + \frac{1}{4} J - \frac{1}{2} R_-$
A_3: $\lvert \frac{3}{2}, -\frac{1}{2}; 1, 1\rangle \rightarrow \lvert \frac{3}{2}, -\frac{3}{2}; 1, 1\rangle$	$[a_{33}b_{11} \sqrt{3} + (2a_{23} + a_{33} \sqrt{2})b_{21} + (a_{13} \sqrt{3} + a_{23} \sqrt{2})\, b_{31}]^2$	$\Omega_1' - \Omega_3$
A_4: $\lvert \frac{3}{2}, \frac{3}{2}; 1, 0\rangle \rightarrow \lvert \frac{3}{2}, \frac{1}{2}; 1, 0\rangle$	$\dfrac{[a_{12} \sqrt{2} + (\sqrt{3} + Q_- \sqrt{2})\, a_{22} + 2Q_- a_{32}]^2}{1 + Q_-^2}$	$\delta + \Omega_2 + \frac{1}{4} J + \frac{1}{2} R_-$
A_5: $\lvert \frac{3}{2}, \frac{1}{2}; 1, 0\rangle \rightarrow \lvert \frac{3}{2}, -\frac{1}{2}; 1, 0\rangle$	$[a_{32}b_{12} \sqrt{3} + (2a_{23} + a_{32} \sqrt{2})b_{22} + (a_{12} \sqrt{3} + a_{22} \sqrt{2})b_{31}]^2$	$\Omega_2' - \Omega_3$
A_6: $\lvert \frac{3}{2}, -\frac{1}{2}; 1, 0\rangle \rightarrow \lvert \frac{3}{2}, -\frac{3}{2}; 1, 0\rangle$	$\dfrac{[b_{12} \sqrt{2} + (\sqrt{3} - Q_+ \sqrt{2})b_{22} - 2Q_+ b_{32}]^2}{1 + Q_+^2}$	$\delta - \Omega_2' - \frac{1}{4} J + \frac{1}{2} R_+$
A_7: $\lvert \frac{3}{2}, \frac{3}{2}; 1, -1\rangle \rightarrow \lvert \frac{3}{2}, \frac{1}{2}; 1, -1\rangle$	$[a_{31}b_{13} \sqrt{3} + (2a_{21} + a_{31} \sqrt{2})b_{23} + (a_{11} \sqrt{3} + a_{21} \sqrt{2})b_{33}]^2$	$\Omega_3' - \Omega_1$
A_8: $\lvert \frac{3}{2}, \frac{1}{2}; 1, -1\rangle \rightarrow \lvert \frac{3}{2}, -\frac{1}{2}; 1, -1\rangle$	$\dfrac{[Q_+ b_{13} \sqrt{2} + (Q_+ \sqrt{3} + \sqrt{2})b_{23} + 2b_{33}]^2}{1 + Q_+^2}$	$\delta - \Omega_3' - \frac{1}{4} J - \frac{1}{2} R_+$

Transition[a]	Intensity	Frequency[b]
A_9 : $\mid \frac{3}{2}, -\frac{1}{2}; 1, -1) \rightarrow \mid \frac{3}{2}, -\frac{3}{2}; 1, -1\rangle$	$\frac{[\sqrt{3} + Q_+ \sqrt{2}]}{1 + Q_+{}^2}$	$\frac{1}{2}(\delta - \frac{5}{2}J + R_+)$
A_{10} : $\mid \frac{1}{2}, \frac{1}{2}; 1, 1\rangle \rightarrow \mid \frac{1}{2}, -\frac{1}{2}; 1, 1\rangle$	$\frac{2[\sqrt{2}Q_{1,-1} - 1]^2}{1 + Q^2_{1,-1}}$	$\frac{1}{2}(\delta + \frac{3}{2}J + R_{1,-1})$
A_{11} : $\mid \frac{1}{2}, \frac{1}{2}; 1, 0\rangle \rightarrow \mid \frac{1}{2}, -\frac{1}{2}; 1, 0\rangle$	$\frac{2[\sqrt{2}(Q_{1,0} - Q_{1,-1}) - 1]^2}{(1 + Q^2_{1,-1})(1 + Q^2_{1,0})}$	$\frac{1}{2}(R_{1,0} + R_{1,-1})$
A_{12} : $\mid \frac{1}{2}, \frac{1}{2}; 1, -1\rangle \rightarrow \mid \frac{1}{2}, -\frac{1}{2}; 1, -1\rangle$	$\frac{2[\sqrt{2}Q_{1,0} + 1]^2}{1 + Q^2_{1,0}}$	$\frac{1}{2}(\delta - \frac{3}{2}J + R_{1,0})$
A_{13} : $\mid \frac{3}{2}, \frac{3}{2}; 0, 0\rangle \rightarrow \mid \frac{3}{2}, \frac{1}{2}; 0, 0\rangle$	3 } 12	} δ
$\mid \frac{3}{2}, \frac{1}{2}; 0, 0\rangle \rightarrow \mid \frac{3}{2}, -\frac{1}{2}; 0, 0\rangle$	4	
$\mid \frac{3}{2}, -\frac{1}{2}; 0, 0\rangle \rightarrow \mid \frac{3}{2}, -\frac{3}{2}; 0, 0\rangle$	3	
$\mid \frac{1}{2}, \frac{1}{2}; 0, 0\rangle \rightarrow \mid \frac{1}{2}, -\frac{1}{2}; 0, 0\rangle$	2	

[a] In the limit $J \rightarrow 0$.
[b] Relative to ω_B.

TABLE 6.12 — RESONANCE FREQUENCIES AND RELATIVE INTENSITIES FOR THE A_3B_2 SYSTEM TRANSITIONS IN GROUP B

	Transition[a]	Intensity	Frequency[b]
B_1 :	$\lvert \frac{3}{2}, \frac{3}{2}; 1, 1\rangle \rightarrow \lvert \frac{3}{2}, \frac{3}{2}; 1, 0\rangle$	$\dfrac{(\sqrt{2} + Q_- \sqrt{3})^2}{1 + Q_-^2}$	$\frac{1}{2}(\delta + \frac{5}{2} J - R_-)$
B_2 :	$\lvert \frac{3}{2}, \frac{1}{2}; 1, 1\rangle \rightarrow \lvert \frac{3}{2}, \frac{1}{2}; 1, 0\rangle$	$\dfrac{[Q_- a_{12} \sqrt{2} + (Q_- \sqrt{3} - \sqrt{2})\, a_{22} - 2a_{32}]^2}{1 + Q_-^2}$	$\delta + \Omega_2 + \frac{1}{4} J - \frac{1}{2} R_-$
B_3 :	$\lvert \frac{3}{2}, -\frac{1}{2}; 1, 1\rangle \rightarrow \lvert \frac{3}{2}, -\frac{1}{2}; 1, 0\rangle$	$\dfrac{[Q_+ b_{12} \sqrt{2} + (Q_+ \sqrt{3} + \sqrt{2}) b_{22} + 2b_{32}]^2}{1 + Q_+^2}$	$\delta - \Omega_2' - \frac{1}{4} J - \frac{1}{2} R_+$
B_4 :	$\lvert \frac{3}{2}, -\frac{3}{2}; 1, 1\rangle \rightarrow \lvert \frac{3}{2}, -\frac{3}{2}; 1, 0\rangle$	$\dfrac{[b_{11} \sqrt{2} + (\sqrt{3} - Q_+ \sqrt{2}) b_{21} - 2Q_+ b_{31}]^2}{1 + Q_+^2}$	$\delta - \Omega_1' - \frac{1}{4} J + \frac{1}{2} R_+$
B_5 :	$\lvert \frac{3}{2}, \frac{3}{2}; 1, 0\rangle \rightarrow \lvert \frac{3}{2}, \frac{3}{2}; 1, -1\rangle$	$\dfrac{[a_{11} \sqrt{2} + (\sqrt{3} + Q_- \sqrt{2})\, a_{21} + 2Q_- a_{31}]^2}{1 + Q_-^2}$	$\delta + \Omega_1 + \frac{1}{4} J + \frac{1}{2} R_-$
B_6 :	$\lvert \frac{3}{2}, \frac{1}{2}; 1, 0\rangle \rightarrow \lvert \frac{3}{2}, \frac{1}{2}; 1, -1\rangle$	$[a_{32} b_{13} \sqrt{3} + (2a_{22} + a_{32} \sqrt{3}) b_{33} + (a_{12} \sqrt{3} + a_{22} \sqrt{2}) b_{33}]^2$	$\Omega_3' - \Omega_2$
B_7 :	$\lvert \frac{3}{2}, -\frac{1}{2}; 1, 0\rangle \rightarrow \lvert \frac{3}{2}, -\frac{1}{2}; 1, -1\rangle$	$[a_{33} b_{12} \sqrt{3} + (2a_{23} + a_{33} \sqrt{2}) b_{22} + (a_{13} \sqrt{3} + a_{23} \sqrt{2}) b_{32}]^2$	$\Omega_2' - \Omega_3$
B_8 :	$\lvert \frac{3}{2}, -\frac{3}{2}; 1, 0\rangle \rightarrow \lvert \frac{3}{2}, -\frac{3}{2}; 1, -1\rangle$	$\dfrac{(\sqrt{2} - Q_+ \sqrt{3})^2}{1 + Q_+^2}$	$\frac{1}{2}(\delta - \frac{5}{2} J - R_+)$
B_9 :	$\lvert \frac{1}{2}, \frac{1}{2}; 1, 1\rangle \rightarrow \lvert \frac{1}{2}, \frac{1}{2}; 1, 0\rangle$	$\dfrac{2(Q_{1,-1} + \sqrt{2})^2}{1 + Q_{1,-1}^2}$	$\frac{1}{2}(\delta + \frac{3}{2} J - R_{1,-1})$
B_{10} :	$\lvert \frac{1}{2}, \frac{1}{2}; 1, 0\rangle \rightarrow \lvert \frac{1}{2}, \frac{1}{2}; 1, -1\rangle$	$\dfrac{2[Q_{1,0}(Q_{1,-1} \sqrt{2} + 1) + \sqrt{2}]^2}{(1 + Q_{1,0}^2)(1 + Q_{1,-1}^2)}$	$\frac{1}{2}(R_{1,-1} - R_{1,0})$
B_{11} :	$\lvert \frac{1}{2}, -\frac{1}{2}; 1, 1\rangle \rightarrow \lvert \frac{1}{2}, -\frac{1}{2}; 1, 0\rangle$	$\dfrac{2[Q_{1,-1}(1 - Q_{1,0} \sqrt{2}) - \sqrt{2}]^2}{(1 + Q_{1,0}^2)(1 + Q_{1,-1}^2)}$	$\frac{1}{2}(R_{1,0} - R_{1,-1})$
B_{12} :	$\lvert \frac{1}{2}, -\frac{1}{2}; 1, 0\rangle \rightarrow \lvert \frac{1}{2}, -\frac{1}{2}; 1, -1\rangle$	$\dfrac{2(Q_{1,0} - \sqrt{2})^2}{1 + Q_{1,0}^2}$	$\frac{1}{2}(\delta - \frac{3}{2} J - R_{1,0})$

[a] In the limit $J \rightarrow 0$. [b] Relative to ω_B.

TABLE 6.13

RESONANCE FREQUENCIES AND RELATIVE INTENSITIES FOR THE A_3B_2 SYSTEM
MIXED TRANSITIONS

Transition[a]	Intensity	Frequency[b]
M_1 : $\mid \frac{3}{2}, \frac{3}{2}; 1, -1\rangle \to \mid \frac{3}{2}, -\frac{3}{2}; 1, 1\rangle$	$[a_{31}b_{11}\sqrt{3} + (2a_{21} + a_{31}\sqrt{2})b_{21} + (a_{11}\sqrt{3} + a_{21}\sqrt{2})b_{31}]^2$	$\Omega_1' - \Omega_1$
M_2 : $\mid \frac{3}{2}, \frac{3}{2}; 1, 0\rangle \to \mid \frac{3}{2}, -\frac{1}{2}; 1, 1\rangle$	$\dfrac{[a_{13}\sqrt{2} + (Q_-\sqrt{2} + \sqrt{3})a_{23} + 2a_{33}Q_-]^2}{1 + Q_-^2}$	$\delta + \Omega_3 + \frac{1}{4}J + \frac{1}{2}R_-$
M_3 : $\mid \frac{3}{2}, \frac{1}{2}; 1, 0\rangle \to \mid \frac{3}{2}, -\frac{3}{2}; 1, 1\rangle$	$[a_{32}b_{11}\sqrt{3} + (2a_{22} + a_{32}\sqrt{2})b_{21} + (a_{12}\sqrt{3} + a_{22}\sqrt{2})b_{31}]^2$	$\Omega_1' - \Omega_2$
M_4 : $\mid \frac{3}{2}, \frac{1}{2}; 1, -1\rangle \to \mid \frac{3}{2}, -\frac{3}{2}; 1, 0\rangle$	$\dfrac{[b_{13}\sqrt{2} + (\sqrt{3} - Q_+\sqrt{2})b_{23} - 2Q_+b_{33}]^2}{1 + Q_+^2}$	$\delta - \Omega_3' - \frac{1}{4}J + \frac{1}{2}R_+$
M_5 : $\mid \frac{3}{2}, \frac{3}{2}; 1, -1\rangle \to \mid \frac{3}{2}, -\frac{1}{2}; 1, 0\rangle$	$[a_{31}b_{12}\sqrt{3} + (2a_{21} + a_{31}\sqrt{2})b_{22} + (a_{11}\sqrt{3} + a_{21}\sqrt{2})b_{32}]^2$	$\Omega_2' - \Omega_1$
M_6 : $\mid \frac{3}{2}, \frac{1}{2}; 1, 1\rangle \to \mid \frac{3}{2}, \frac{3}{2}; 1, -1\rangle$	$\dfrac{[Q_-a_{11}\sqrt{2} + (Q_-\sqrt{3} - \sqrt{2})a_{21} - 2a_{31}]^2}{1 + Q_-^2}$	$\delta + \Omega_1 + \frac{1}{4}J - \frac{1}{2}R_-$
M_7 : $\mid \frac{3}{2}, -\frac{1}{2}; 1, 1\rangle \to \mid \frac{3}{2}, \frac{1}{2}; 1, -1\rangle$	$[a_{33}b_{13}\sqrt{3} + (2a_{23} + a_{33}\sqrt{2})b_{23} + (a_{13}\sqrt{3} + a_{23}\sqrt{2})b_{33}]^2$	$\Omega_3' - \Omega_3$
M_8 : $\mid \frac{3}{2}, -\frac{3}{2}; 1, 1\rangle \to \mid \frac{3}{2}, -\frac{1}{2}; 1, -1\rangle$	$\dfrac{[Q_+b_{11}\sqrt{2} + (Q_+\sqrt{3} + \sqrt{2})b_{21} + 2b_{31}]^2}{1 + Q_+^2}$	$\delta - \Omega_1' - \frac{1}{4}J - \frac{1}{2}R_+$
M_9 : $\mid \frac{1}{2}, -\frac{1}{2}; 1, 1\rangle \to \mid \frac{1}{2}, \frac{1}{2}; 1, -1\rangle$	$\dfrac{2[(\sqrt{2} - Q_{1,-1})Q_{1,0} - Q_{1,-1}\sqrt{2}]^2}{(1 + Q_{1,0}^2)(1 + Q_{1,-1}^2)}$	$-\frac{1}{2}(R_{1,0} + R_{1,-1})$

[a] In the limit $J \to 0$.
[b] Relative to ω_B.

The eigenvalues of $\mathscr{H}(\frac{1}{2})$ will be denoted $\Omega_1, \Omega_2, \Omega_3$, and the 3×3 orthogonal matrix that diagonalizes $\mathscr{H}(\frac{1}{2})$ will be denoted (a_{ij}); the corresponding quantities for $\mathscr{H}(-\frac{1}{2})$ will be denoted $\Omega_1', \Omega_2', \Omega_3'$, (b_{ij}). With these definitions, one can construct Tables 6.11 through 6.13, where

$$R_\pm = [(\delta \pm \tfrac{1}{2}J)^2 + 6J^2]^{1/2}, \qquad Q_\pm = \frac{J\sqrt{6}}{\delta \pm \frac{1}{2}J + R_\pm}.$$

The remaining R's and Q's are those defined for the A_2B system. In fact, the A_3B_2 system contains each irreducible component of the AB_2 system twice, as shown in Fig. 6.38. The analysis of an A_3B_2 system is quite

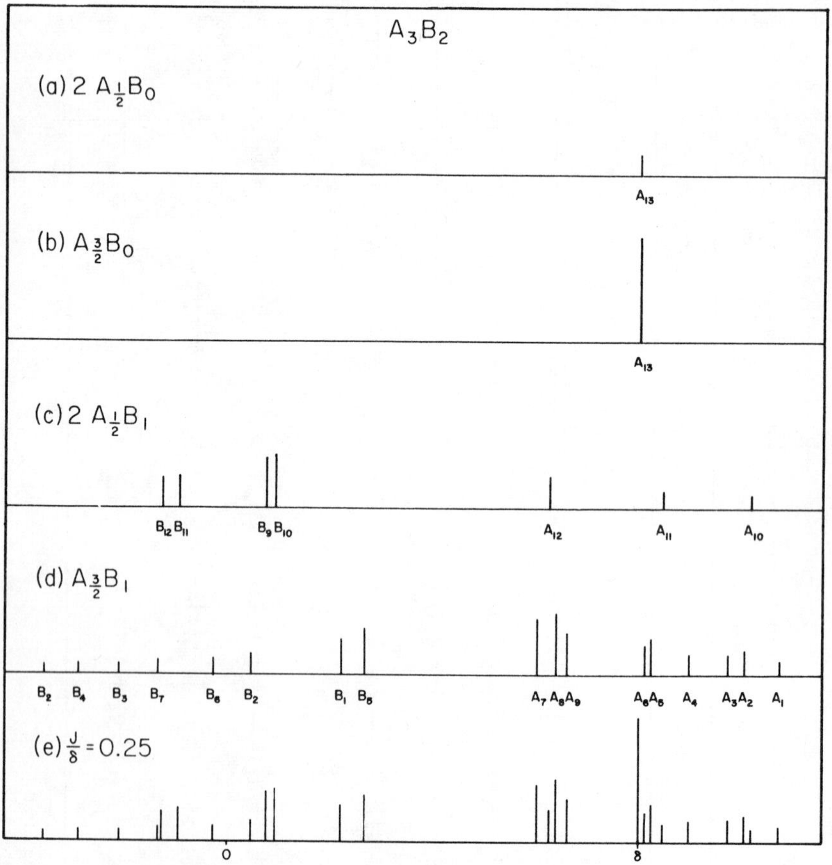

FIG. 6.38. Reduction of the A_3B_2 system into its irreducible components. Part (e) shows the theoretical A_3B_2 spectrum for $J/\delta = 0.25$.

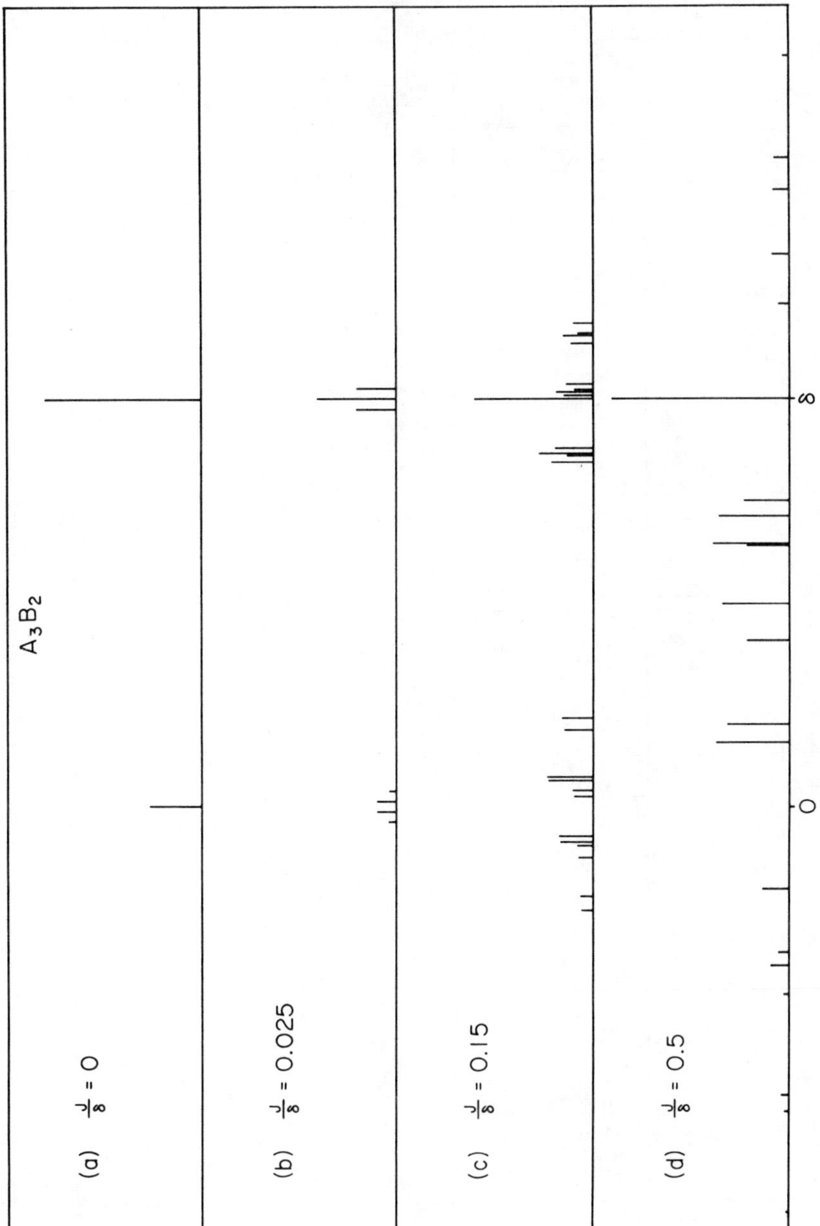

FIG. 6.39. Theoretical A_3B_2 spectra.

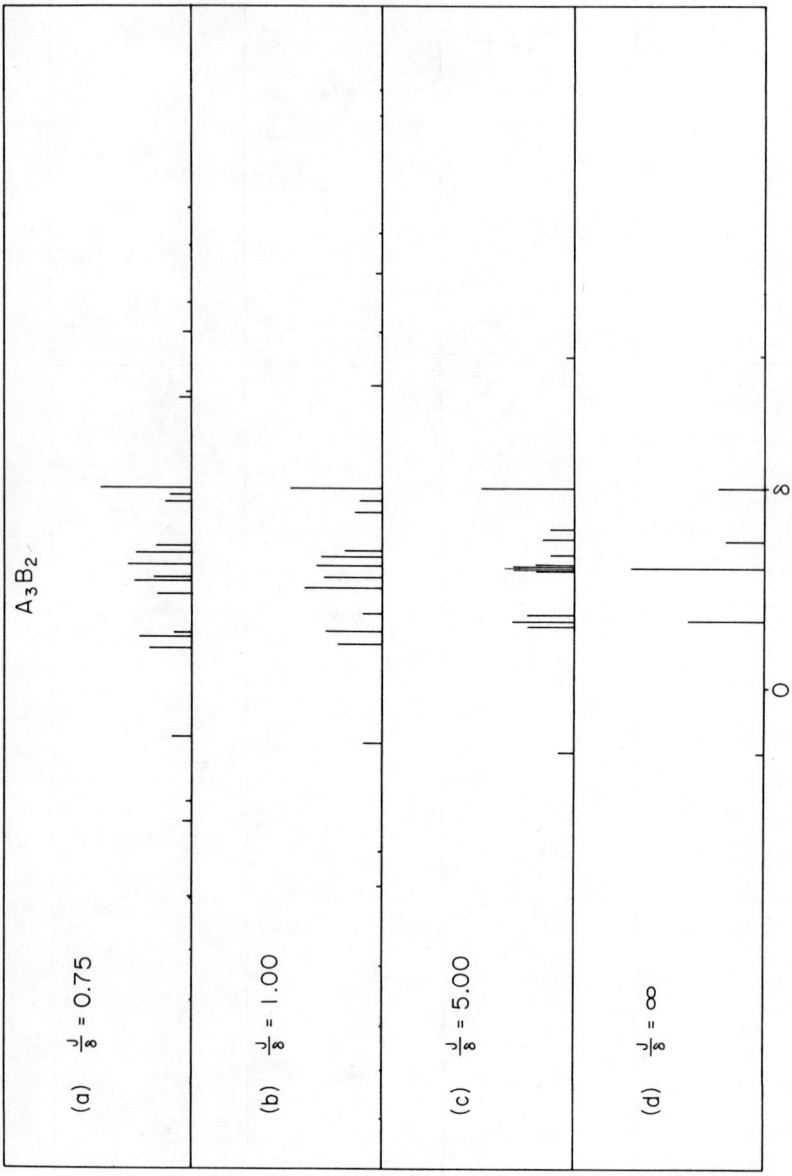

FIG. 6.40. Theoretical A_3B_2 spectra.

simple if the transitions of the $A_{1/2}B_1$ component can be distinguished from those of the $A_{3/2}B_1$ component.

The intensities of the $A_{3/2}B_1$ resonances satisfy the equations

$$\begin{aligned}
\text{Int } A_1 + \text{Int } B_1 &= 5,\\
\text{Int } A_9 + \text{Int } B_8 &= 5,\\
\text{Int } A_2 + \text{Int } A_4 + \text{Int } B_2 + \text{Int } B_5 + \text{Int } M_2 + \text{Int } M_6 &= 11,\\
\text{Int } A_6 + \text{Int } A_8 + \text{Int } B_3 + \text{Int } B_4 + \text{Int } M_4 + \text{Int } M_8 &= 11,\\
\text{Int } A_3 + \text{Int } A_5 + \text{Int } A_7 + \text{Int } B_6 + \text{Int } B_7 + \text{Int } M_1 + \text{Int } M_3 + \text{Int } M_5 &= 14.
\end{aligned}$$

Aside from some trivial changes in notation, the $A_{1/2}B_1$ transitions satisfy the intensity rules given for the $A_1B_{1/2}$ system with each numerical constant multiplied by a factor of two.

Theoretical A_3B_2 spectra are sketched in Figs. 6.39 and 6.40; Fig. 6.41 shows the transition diagrams for the irreducible components. The experimental and theoretical spectra for the protons in ethyl iodide are shown in Figs. 6.42 and 6.43. The unshifted resonance at ω_A and the B resonances of the irreducible $A_{1/2}B_1$ component are well resolved and lead at once to the values

$$\frac{J}{2\pi} = 7.5 \pm 0.3 \quad \text{cps}, \qquad \frac{\delta}{2\pi} = 54.1 \pm 0.2 \quad \text{cps}$$

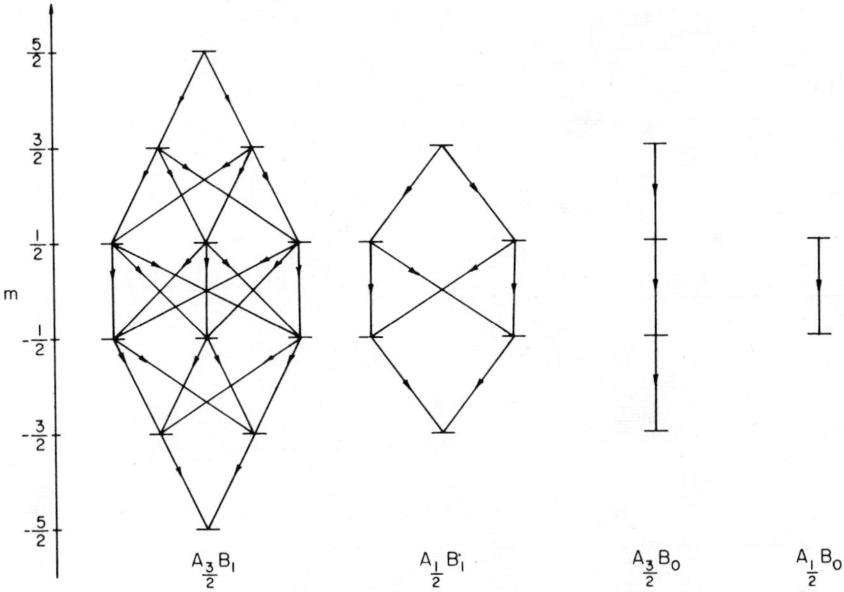

FIG. 6.41. Transition diagrams for the irreducible components of the A_3B_2 system.

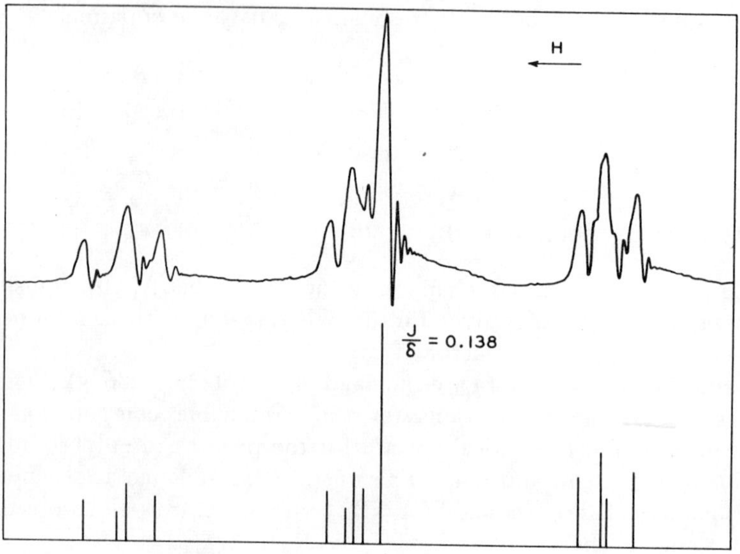

FIG. 6.42. Experimental and theoretical spectra of the methyl group protons of pure ethyl iodide at 40 Mcps.

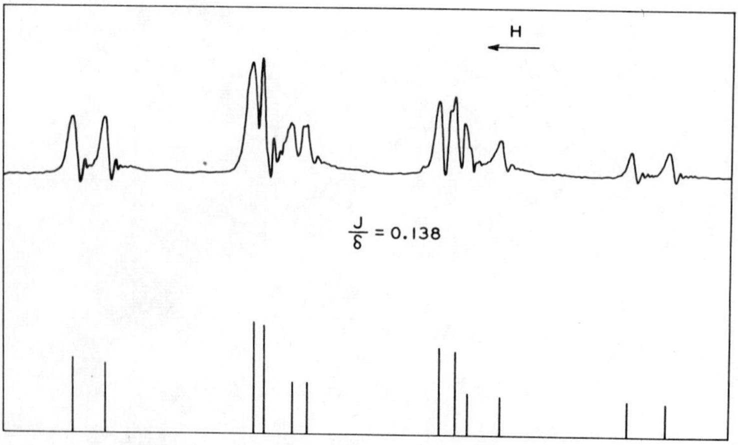

FIG. 6.43. Experimental and theoretical spectra of the methylene group protons of pure ethyl iodide at 40 Mcps.

D. General Properties of the $A_{n_A}B_{n_B}$ System

The decomposition of an $A_{n_A}B_{n_B}$ system into its irreducible components is given by

$$A_{n_A}B_{n_B} = \sum_{I_A}\sum_{I_B} g_{I_A}g_{I_B}A_{I_A}B_{I_B}\,. \tag{4.6}$$

This decomposition shows that whatever the parities (i.e., odd or even character) of n_A and n_B, the spectrum of an $A_{n_A}B_{n_B}$ system always contains subspectra of irreducible systems already analyzed. If the spectrum of an $A_{n_A}B_{n_B}$ system is sufficiently well resolved to permit the identification of its simpler irreducible components, it is possible to determine the chemical shift and spin-spin coupling constant from the known properties of these component systems. This is an important practical consideration, since the degrees of the determinantal equations increase rapidly with n_A or n_B, whichever is smaller.

The structure of the hamiltonian submatrix for an (I_A, I_B)-block (i.e., for an $A_{I_A}B_{I_B}$ component system) follows at once from the discussion in Section 3.E of Chapter 4. Indeed, Table 4.8 shows that, for $I_A \geqslant I_B$, an (I_A, I_B)-block is the direct sum of exactly $2(I_A + I_B) + 1$ matrices of dimensions $1 \times 1, 2 \times 2, ..., (2I_B + 1) \times (2I_B + 1)$. There are two each of the $1 \times 1, 2 \times 2, ..., (2I_B) \times (2I_B)$ matrices, and $2(I_A - I_B) + 1$ matrices of dimension $(2I_B + 1) \times (2I_B + 1)$. Since $(I_B)_{\max} = \frac{1}{2}n_B$, it follows that the highest-order secular equation(s) for the $A_{n_A}B_{n_B}$ system $(n_A \geqslant n_B)$ is $2(I_B)_{\max} + 1 = n_B + 1$.

The eigenvalues and eigenvectors corresponding to the 1×1 and 2×2 matrices are given in Table 6.14, where

$$R_\pm = \{[\delta \pm J(I_A - I_B)]^2 + 4I_AI_BJ^2\}^{1/2}, \qquad Q_\pm = \frac{2J(I_AI_B)^{1/2}}{\delta \pm J(I_A - I_B) + R_\pm}\,.$$

From these results one can construct Table 6.15, which gives four transitions for each distinct choice of (I_A, I_B).

An $A_{n_A}B_{n_B}$ system for which n_A and n_B are both odd or both even will contain at least one irreducible component system with $I_A = I_B = I$. In this case,

$$R_+ = R_- \equiv R_I = [\delta^2 + (2IJ)^2]^{1/2}, \qquad Q_+ = Q_- \equiv Q_I = \frac{2IJ}{\delta + R_I},$$

and Table 6.15 reduces to Table 6.16. Apart from the intensity factor $2Ig_{I_A}g_{I_B}$, the spectrum generated by these transitions is similar to that of an AB spectrum with J replaced by $2IJ$.

TABLE 6.14

SOME EIGENVECTORS AND EIGENVALUES FOR THE $A_{I_A}B_{I_B}$ SYSTEM

Eigenvector	Eigenvalue
$\mid I_A, I_A; I_B, I_B\rangle$	$-\{\omega_A I_A + \omega_B I_B + J I_A I_B\}$
$\frac{1}{(1+Q_-^2)^{1/2}}\{\mid I_A, I_A - 1; I_B, I_B\rangle - Q_- \mid I_A, I_A; I_B, I_B - 1\rangle\}$	$-\frac{1}{2}\{\omega_A(2I_A - 1) + \omega_B(2I_B - 1) + J[I_A(I_B - 1) + I_B(I_A - 1)] - R_-\}$
$\frac{1}{(1+Q_-^2)^{1/2}}\{Q_- \mid I_A, I_A - 1; I_B, I_B\rangle + \mid I_A, I_A; I_B, I_B - 1\rangle\}$	$-\frac{1}{2}\{\omega_A(2I_A - 1) + \omega_B(2I_B - 1) + J[I_A(I_B - 1) + I_B(I_A - 1)] + R_-\}$
$\frac{1}{(1+Q_+^2)^{1/2}}\{\mid I_A, -I_A; I_B, -I_B + 1\rangle - Q_+ \mid I_A, -I_A + 1; I_B, -I_B\rangle\}$	$\frac{1}{2}\{\omega_A(2I_A - 1) + \omega_B(2I_B - 1) - J[I_A(I_B - 1) + I_B(I_A - 1)] + R_+\}$
$\frac{1}{(1+Q_+^2)^{1/2}}\{Q_+ \mid I_A, -I_A; I_B, -I_B + 1\rangle + \mid I_A, -I_A + 1; I_B, -I_B\rangle\}$	$\frac{1}{2}\{\omega_A(2I_A - 1) + \omega_B(2I_B - 1) - J[I_A(I_B - 1) + I_B(I_A - 1)] - R_+\}$
$\mid I_A, -I_A; I_B, -I_B\rangle$	$\{\omega_A I_A + \omega_B I_B - J I_A I_B\}$

TABLE 6.15

SOME RESONANCE FREQUENCIES AND RELATIVE INTENSITIES FOR THE $A_{I_A}B_{I_B}$ SYSTEM

Transition[a]	Intensity	Frequency
A_1 : $\mid I_A, I_B; I_B, I_B\rangle \rightarrow \mid I_A, I_A - 1; I_B, I_B\rangle$	$\dfrac{g_{I_A} g_{I_B}[(2I_A)^{1/2} - Q_- (2I_B)^{1/2}]^2}{1 + Q_-^2}$	$\frac{1}{2}\{\omega_A + \omega_B + J(I_A + I_B) + R_-\}$
A_2 : $\mid I_A, -I_A + 1; I_B, -I_B\rangle \rightarrow \mid I_A, -I_A; I_B, -I_B\rangle$	$\dfrac{g_{I_A} g_{I_B}[(2I_A)^{1/2} + Q_+ (2I_B)^{1/2}]^2}{1 + Q_+^2}$	$\frac{1}{2}\{\omega_A + \omega_B - J(I_A + I_B) + R_+\}$
B_1 : $\mid I_A, I_A; I_B, I_B\rangle \rightarrow \mid I_A, I_B; I_B, I_B - 1\rangle$	$\dfrac{g_{I_A} g_{I_B}[(2I_B)^{1/2} + Q_- (2I_A)^{1/2}]^2}{1 + Q_-^2}$	$\frac{1}{2}\{\omega_A + \omega_B + J(I_A + I_B) - R_-\}$
B_2 : $\mid I_A, -I_A; I_B, -I_B + 1\rangle \rightarrow \mid I_A, -I_A; I_B, -I_B\rangle$	$\dfrac{g_{I_A} g_{I_B}[(2I_B)^{1/2} - Q_+ (2I_A)^{1/2}]^2}{1 + Q_+^2}$	$\frac{1}{2}\{\omega_A + \omega_B - J(I_A + I_B) - R_+\}$

[a] In the limit $J \rightarrow 0$

TABLE 6.16

SOME RESONANCE FREQUENCIES AND RELATIVE INTENSITIES OF THE $A_I B_I$ SYSTEM

Transition[a]	Intensity / $g_{I_A} g_{I_B}$	Frequency
$A_1: \lvert I, I; I, I\rangle \to \lvert I, I-1; I, I\rangle$	$2I\left(1 - \frac{2IJ}{R_I}\right)$	$\frac{1}{2}\{\omega_A + \omega_B + 2IJ + R_I\}$
$A_2: \lvert I, -I+1; I, -I\rangle \to \lvert I, -I; I, -I\rangle$	$2I\left(1 + \frac{2IJ}{R_I}\right)$	$\frac{1}{2}\{\omega_A + \omega_B - 2IJ + R_I\}$
$B_1: \lvert I, I; I, I\rangle \to \lvert I, I; I, I-1\rangle$	$2I\left(1 + \frac{2IJ}{R_I}\right)$	$\frac{1}{2}\{\omega_A + \omega_B + 2IJ - R_I\}$
$B_2: \lvert I, -I; I, -I+1\rangle \to \lvert I, -I; I, -I\rangle$	$2I\left(1 - \frac{2IJ}{R_I}\right)$	$\frac{1}{2}\{\omega_A + \omega_B - 2IJ - R_I\}$

[a] In the limit $J \to 0$.

An interesting application occurs with two-group systems of the form $A_n B_n$, when $g_{I_A} g_{I_B} = g_I^2$. This system contains irreducible components of the form $A_I B_I$, where $I = n/2, n/2 - 1, \ldots$. Hence the spectrum of an $A_n B_n$ system contains, aside from intensity factors, spectra of the AB type, except that the apparent coupling constants are

$$2IJ = nJ, \quad (n-2)J, \quad (n-4)J, \ldots .$$

If n is odd, there will be $\frac{1}{2}(n+1)$ of these pseudo AB quartets with apparent coupling constants J, $3J$, $5J$, ... If n is even, there will be $\frac{1}{2}n$ pseudo AB quartets with apparent coupling constants $2J$, $4J$, $6J$, ... The AB ($n = 1$) and A_2B_2 ($n = 2$) systems are special cases of this general result.

E. Symmetry Theorem for $A_n B_n$ Systems

The pseudo AB spectra contained in the spectrum of an $A_n B_n$ system are symmetrical with respect to the mean resonance frequency $\langle\omega\rangle = \frac{1}{2}(\omega_A + \omega_B)$. In fact, the entire spectrum of an $A_n B_n$ is symmetrical with respect to $\langle\omega\rangle$. To prove this theorem, consider the decomposition of the system into its irreducible components

$$A_n B_n = \sum_{I_A} \sum_{I_B} g_{I_A} g_{I_B} A_{I_A} B_{I_B} .$$

Since the total spin quantum numbers for groups A and B range over the same set of values, the decomposition can be written in the form

$$A_nB_n = \sum_I g_I^2 A_IB_I + \sum_{I_A<I_B}\sum g_{I_A}g_{I_B}(A_{I_A}B_{I_B} + A_{I_B}B_{I_A}).$$

The first sum represents the superposition of spectra generated by irreducible components with $I_A = I_B = I$; the double sum represents the superposition of spectra of pairs of irreducible components with I_A and I_B interchanged. Since the spectrum of $A_{I_A}B_{I_B} + A_{I_B}B_{I_A}$ will be symmetrical with respect to $\langle\omega\rangle$, it is only necessary to prove that the spectrum of any A_IB_I system is symmetrical with respect to $\langle\omega\rangle$. For this purpose, it is convenient to introduce the hamiltonian operator

$$\bar{\mathscr{H}} = \mathscr{H} + \langle\omega\rangle I_z = -\left\{\frac{\delta}{2}(I_{Az} - I_{Bz}) + J\mathbf{I}_A \cdot \mathbf{I}_B\right\}.$$

The eigenvalues of $\bar{\mathscr{H}}$ are $\Omega_m + \langle\omega\rangle m$.

The spectrum of an A_IB_I system, as computed with the eigenvalues and eigenvectors of $\bar{\mathscr{H}}$, is identical to that computed with the eigenvalues and eigenvectors of

$$\bar{\mathscr{H}}' = -\left\{\frac{\delta}{2}(I_{Bz} - I_{Az}) + J\mathbf{I}_A \cdot \mathbf{I}_B\right\},$$

which is obtained from $\bar{\mathscr{H}}$ by interchanging A and B. For since $I_A = I_B = I$, m_A and m_B range over the same set of values, specifically $I, I-1, \ldots, -I$. Hence, if $| I, m_A; I, m_B\rangle$ is a product ket for the system, so is $| I, m_B; I, m_A\rangle$, unless $m_A = m_B = 0$, when there is only one such ket. It follows that the matrices of $\bar{\mathscr{H}}'$ and $\bar{\mathscr{H}}$ are, except for the ordering of rows and columns, identical. The symmetry theorem now follows from the fact that

$$\Lambda\bar{\mathscr{H}}\Lambda = \bar{\mathscr{H}}',$$

where Λ is the spin-inversion operator introduced in Chapter 5. Thus if $\{| m)\}$ and $\{\Omega_m + \langle\omega\rangle m\}$ are the eigenvectors and eigenvalues of $\bar{\mathscr{H}}$, those of $\bar{\mathscr{H}}'$ are $\{\Lambda| m)\}$ and $\{\Omega_m + \langle\omega\rangle m\}$. It now follows, by an argument analogous to that used in Section 3.F of Chapter 5, that for each transition predicted by $\bar{\mathscr{H}}$, $\bar{\mathscr{H}}'$ predicts a transition with the same intensity, but with the opposite sign for the resonance frequency.

F. Three-Group Systems

The analysis of a spin system containing three groups of magnetically equivalent nuclei can be carried out by straightforward applications of the general principles developed in Chapter 5. The hamiltonian matrix will be a function of six parameters: ω_A, ω_B, ω_C, J_{AB}, J_{AC}, and J_{BC}, but one parameter can be eliminated by choosing a new frequency origin at ω_A, ω_B, or ω_C. In some instances it may be more appropriate to take the frequency origin at the mean resonance frequency

$$\langle\omega\rangle = \frac{1}{N}(n_A\omega_A + n_B\omega_B + n_C\omega_C),$$

where $N = n_A + n_B + n_C$ (cf. Section 4, Chapter 7). Whatever the choice of origin, the direct sum decomposition of the hamiltonian matrix always contains submatrices whose dimensions exceed two, so that a complete analysis of the eigenvalue problem requires the solution of algebraic equations whose degrees are greater than two. For this reason it is usually necessary to compute the spectra of three-group systems numerically, that is, numerical values are assigned to the internal chemical shifts and coupling constants, and these parameters are used to compute numerical values for the resonance frequencies and the relative intensities.[8]

The numerical computation of a spectrum is not an inherently difficult problem—the calculations may be lengthy and tedious, but the resolution of numerical equations can be carried out by well-known algorithms (*8–11*). On the other hand, the problem of obtaining a set of chemical shifts and coupling constants that accurately describes an experimental spectrum is rather more difficult. The iterative method of analysis attacks this problem by attempting to "fit" the observed spectrum through comparisons of the experimental resonance frequencies and signal intensities with those computed for several sets of chemical shifts and coupling constants. Although "goodness of fit" is certainly a desirable criterion for the acceptability of a descriptive set of parameters, criteria such as stability and uniqueness should not be overlooked.

The preceding remarks lend importance to any special techniques which permit the direct determination of chemical shifts and coupling constants. One or more of these parameters can often be directly extracted from sufficiently well-resolved spectra of particular three-group systems. Suppose, for example, that one number of the triple (n_A, n_B, n_C), say n_C, is an even integer. In this event, the states with $I_C = 0$ generate the spectra of irreducible $A_{I_A}B_{I_B}$ components, whose identification can be used to determine $|J_{AB}|$ and $|\omega_{AB}|$. In particular, if n_A and n_B are both odd, the spectrum will contain the AB system.

[8] Electronic computers provide considerable relief in the numerical analysis of complex spectra; the interested reader should consult the references given in Appendix VI.

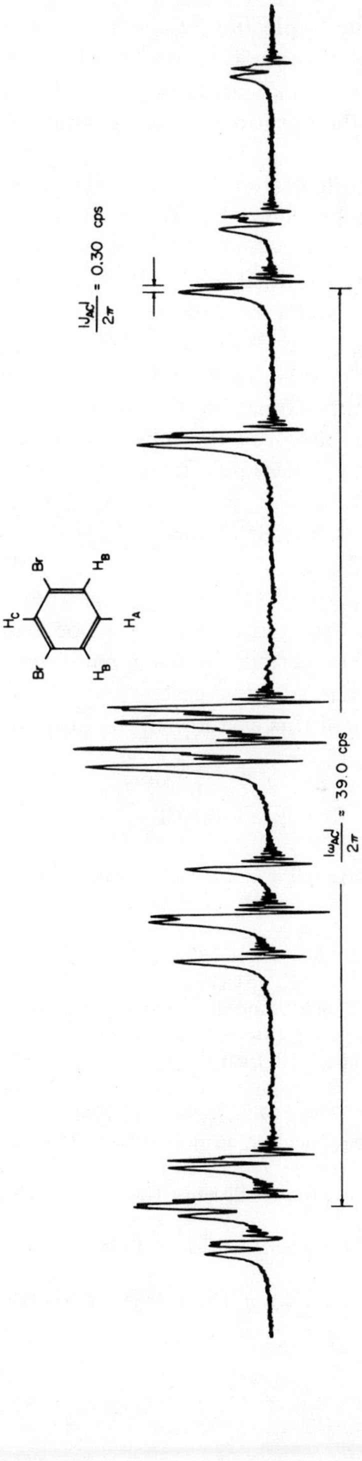

FIG. 6.44. Experimental spectrum of pure *m*-dibromobenzene at 60 Mcps.

If two integers in the triple (n_A, n_B, n_C), say n_B and n_C, are even, then the spectrum will contain the spectra of irreducible $A_{I_A}B_{I_B}$ and $A_{I_A}C_{I_C}$ systems. If n_A, n_B, and n_C are all even integers, the spectrum will include the spectra of the irreducible $A_{I_A}B_{I_B}$, $A_{I_A}C_{I_C}$, and $B_{I_B}C_{I_C}$ systems.

These remarks are illustrated by the proton magnetic resonance spectrum of *m*-dibromobenzene (Fig. 6.44). By symmetry, the protons form an AB_2C system, for which $AB_2C = A_{1/2}B_1C_{1/2} + A_{1/2}B_0C_{1/2}$. The resonances of the irreducible $A_{1/2}B_0C_{1/2}$ component, which are equivalent to an AC spectrum, can be located in the experimental spectrum by the following considerations. If the couplings of nucleus C to A and B are neglected, the A and B nuclei would constitute an AB_2 system. To a first approximation, the coupling of A and B to nucleus C should lead to a "doubling" of the AB_2 resonances, and this effect is evident in the experimental trace. It is now easy to pick out two resonances of the AC quartet whose separation yields $|J_{AC}|$. The remaining AC doublet is buried in the multiplet at the extreme left of the figure, so that $\omega_{AC}/2\pi \approx 39$ cps, which is probably correct to within ± 0.5 cps.

When n_A, n_B, and n_C are odd integers, the spectrum will not include two-group spectra unless certain limiting conditions are satisfied (cf. Section 3, Chapter 7). The simplest case is the irreducible ABC system. Some general properties of this system will be described in Chapter 7.

REFERENCES

1. E. L. Hahn and D. E. Maxwell, *Phys. Rev.* **84**, 1246 (1951).
2. M. K. Bannerjee, T. P. Das, and A. K. Saha, *Proc. Roy. Soc.* (*London*) **A226**, 490 (1954).
3. H. M. McConnell, A. D. McLean, and C. A. Reilly, *J. Chem. Phys.* **23**, 68 (1955).
4. W. A. Anderson, *Phys. Rev.* **102**, 151 (1956).
5. J. A. Pople, W. G. Schneider, and H. J. Bernstein, "High-Resolution Nuclear Magnetic Resonance," Chap. 6, McGraw-Hill, New York, 1959.
6. P. L. Corio, *Chem. Rev.* **60**, 363 (1960).
7. I. S. Sokolnikoff and E. S. Sokolnikoff, "Higher Mathematics for Engineers and Physicists," Chap. III. McGraw-Hill, New York, 1941.
8. W. E. Milne, "Numerical Calculus." Princeton Univ. Press, Princeton, New Jersey, 1949.
9. C. Lanczos, "Applied Analysis." Prentice-Hall, Englewood Cliffs, New Jersey, 1956.
10. V. N. Faddeeva, "Computational Methods of Linear Algebra." Dover, New York, 1959.
11. D. M. Grant and H. S. Gutowsky, *J. Chem. Phys.* **34**, 699 (1961).

CHAPTER 7

Perturbation and Moment Calculations

1. Perturbation Theory

A. Perturbation Expansions

The calculations carried out in the preceding chapter were based upon exact determinations of the eigenvalues and eigenvectors of the hamiltonian operator. There are, however, many spin systems whose magnetic resonance spectra can be analyzed by approximate calculations based on perturbation theory (*1*). Perturbation calculations can also be used to provide a set of approximate chemical shifts and coupling constants for use as initial parameters in an iterative analysis.

The perturbation method assumes that the stationary hamiltonian operator

$$\mathscr{H} = -\left\{\sum_{\mathrm{G}} \omega_{\mathrm{G}} I_{\mathrm{G}z} + \sum_{\mathrm{G}<\mathrm{G}'}\sum J_{\mathrm{GG}'} \mathbf{I}_{\mathrm{G}} \cdot \mathbf{I}_{\mathrm{G}'}\right\} \tag{1.1}$$

can be written in the form

$$\mathscr{H} = \mathscr{H}^{(0)} + V, \tag{1.2}$$

where $\mathscr{H}^{(0)}$ is the so-called *zero-order hamiltonian operator*, whose eigenvalues $\{\Omega_r^{(0)}\}$ and eigenvectors $\{u_r^{(0)}\}$ are known or exactly calculable, and V is a small correction to $\mathscr{H}^{(0)}$ called the *perturbation operator*. When the unperturbed eigenvalues are nondegenerate, the rth eigenvector and its associated eigenvalue are given by the expansions (*2*)

$$u_r = u_r^{(0)} + u_r^{(1)} + u_r^{(2)} + \cdots, \tag{1.3}$$

$$\Omega_r = \Omega_r^{(0)} + \Omega_r^{(1)} + \Omega_r^{(2)} + \Omega_r^{(3)} + \cdots, \tag{1.4}$$

$$u_r^{(1)} = \sum_s{}' \frac{V_{sr}}{\Delta_{rs}} u_s^{(0)}, \tag{1.5}$$

$$u_r^{(2)} = \sum_s{}' \sum_t{}' \frac{V_{st}V_{tr}}{\Delta_{rt}\Delta_{rs}} u_s^{(0)} - \sum_s{}' \frac{V_{rr}V_{sr}}{\Delta_{rs}^2} u_s^{(0)}$$

$$- \tfrac{1}{2} u_r^{(0)} \sum_s{}' \frac{|V_{rs}|^2}{\Delta_{rs}^2}, \tag{1.6}$$

$$\Omega_r^{(1)} = V_{rr}, \tag{1.7}$$

$$\Omega_r^{(2)} = \sum_s{}' \frac{|V_{rs}|^2}{\Delta_{rs}}, \tag{1.8}$$

$$\Omega_r^{(3)} = \sum_s{}' \sum_t{}' \frac{V_{rt}V_{ts}V_{sr}}{\Delta_{tr}\Delta_{sr}} - V_{rr} \sum_s{}' \frac{|V_{rs}|^2}{\Delta_{rs}^2}, \tag{1.9}$$

where

$$\Delta_{rs} = \Omega_r^{(0)} - \Omega_s^{(0)}, \qquad V_{rs} = (u_r^{(0)}, V u_s^{(0)}), \tag{1.10}$$

and the primes on the summation signs mean that all terms with vanishing denominators are to be omitted. The superscripts appended to the u's and Ω's refer to the "order" of the perturbation calculation (*2*). In general, the calculation of Ω_r to the kth order requires only a knowledge of u_r to order $k - 1$, so that a kth-order perturbation calculation ($k \neq 0$) means that (1.3) is to be terminated after k terms, (1.4) after $k + 1$ terms.

Equations (1.3) to (1.9) represent the energy eigenvalues and the expansion coefficients of the unperturbed basis vectors mixed by the perturbation operator as power series in the ratios V_{pq}/Δ_{rs} ($r \neq s$). Hence a kth-order perturbation calculation approximates the eigenvalues and expansion coefficients by polynomials of degree $k - 1$ in these ratios.

From a practical point of view, the perturbation method is most useful when the series expansions converge rapidly enough to be terminated after two or three terms. The convergence of these series can be expected to be fairly rapid whenever the absolute values of the matrix elements of V are small compared to the absolute values of the differences of the unperturbed energies. However, when the former are comparable to the latter, the perturbation expansions may diverge, or converge so slowly as to require a calculation of very high order. It is not uncommon for the convergence to be quite rapid for some eigenvalues and eigenvectors, whereas the expansions for other eigenvalues and eigenvectors may converge very slowly or diverge. In such instances it is necessary to diagonalize all submatrices of the hamiltonian matrix generated by unperturbed basis vectors too strongly mixed by V to be accurately described by perturbation theory. Similar remarks apply when there is a complete or partial degeneracy of the unperturbed energies (*2*).

The application of the perturbation method to a particular system requires the specification of $\mathscr{H}^{(0)}$ and a determination of the zero-order eigenvalues and eigenvectors satisfying

$$\mathscr{H}^{(0)}u_r^{(0)} = \Omega_r^{(0)}u_r^{(0)} \qquad (r = 1, 2, \ldots). \tag{1.11}$$

The choice of $\mathscr{H}^{(0)}$ will depend upon the properties of the system under consideration, and this section will be restricted to the two limiting cases described by the inequalities:

$$| J_{\mathrm{GG'}} | \ll | \omega_{\mathrm{GG'}} |, \tag{1.12}$$

$$| J_{\mathrm{GG'}} | \gg | \omega_{\mathrm{GG'}} |, \tag{1.13}$$

for all G, G′ = A, B, ... (G ≠ G′).[1] A spin system will be said to be weakly coupled or strongly coupled, accordingly as its internal shifts and coupling constants satisfy (1.12) or (1.13). This classification is introduced only for the purpose of distinguishing between the various orders of perturbation in the two limiting cases, for example, first-order perturbation theory—weak coupling; first-order perturbation theory—strong coupling, etc.[2]

1. *Weakly Coupled Systems.* For a weakly coupled system, the spin-spin interactions are collectively treated as the perturbation operator, so that

$$\mathscr{H}^{(0)} = -\sum_{\mathrm{G}} \omega_{\mathrm{G}} I_{\mathrm{G}z}, \qquad V = -\sum_{\mathrm{G}<\mathrm{G'}}\sum J_{\mathrm{GG'}} \mathbf{I}_{\mathrm{G}} \cdot \mathbf{I}_{\mathrm{G'}}. \tag{1.14}$$

The zero-order eigenvalue problem is trivial since the eigenvectors of $\mathscr{H}^{(0)}$ are just the product kets

$$\{| I_{\mathrm{A}}, m_{\mathrm{A}}; \ldots; I_{\mathrm{G}}, m_{\mathrm{G}}; \ldots; m\rangle\}, \qquad m = m_{\mathrm{A}} + m_{\mathrm{B}} + \cdots. \tag{1.15}$$

The corresponding eigenvalues are

$$\Omega_m^{(0)} = -\sum_{\mathrm{G}} \omega_{\mathrm{G}} m_{\mathrm{G}}, \tag{1.16}$$

[1] The application of perturbation theory to spin systems whose internal chemical shifts and spin-spin coupling constants do not conform to (1.12) or (1.13) will be discussed in Sections 2 and 3. The treatment of symmetrical systems will be deferred to Chapter 8.

[2] In the literature, the term "strongly coupled" is often used to describe a system for which $| J_{\mathrm{GG'}} | \approx | \omega_{\mathrm{GG'}} |$, for all G, G′(G ≠ G′).

and the nonvanishing matrix elements of the perturbation operator are

$$\langle \cdots I_G, m_G; \cdots I_{G'}, m_{G'}; \cdots; m \mid V \mid \cdots I_G, m_G; \cdots I_{G'}, m_{G'}; \cdots; m\rangle$$

$$= -\sum_{G<G'}\sum J_{GG'}m_G m_{G'}, \tag{1.17}$$

$$\langle \cdots I_G, m_G; \cdots I_{G'}, m_{G'}; \cdots; m \mid V \mid \cdots I_G, m_G - 1; \cdots I_{G'}, m_{G'} + 1; \cdots; m\rangle$$

$$= -\tfrac{1}{2}J_{GG'}F(I_G, -m_G)F(I_{G'}, m_{G'}), \tag{1.18}$$

where

$$F(I_G, m_G) = [(I_G - m_G)(I_G + m_G + 1)]^{1/2}. \tag{1.19}$$

2. *Srongly Coupled Systems.* For a strongly coupled system, $\mathscr{H}^{(0)}$ and V are given by

$$\mathscr{H}^{(0)} = -\Big\{\omega_0 I_z + \sum_{G<G'}\sum J_{GG'}\mathbf{I}_G \cdot \mathbf{I}_{G'}\Big\}, \qquad V \equiv \delta Z = -\sum_G \delta\omega_G I_{Gz}, \tag{1.20}$$

where $\mathscr{H}^{(0)}$ is obtained from (1.1) by setting $\omega_A = \omega_B = \cdots = \omega_0$. The symbol δ denotes a small increment in the quantity immediately following it. For example, the frequencies $\delta\omega_G$ represent small deviations of the ω_G from ω_0 ($\omega_G = \omega_0 + \delta\omega_G$).

The zero-order hamiltonian admits the following constants of the motion:

$$\mathbf{I}^2, \quad \mathbf{I}_A^2, \quad \mathbf{I}_B^2, \ldots, I_z, \quad \sum_{G<G'}\sum J_{GG'}\mathbf{I}_G \cdot \mathbf{I}_{G'}.$$

The eigenvectors of the square and z component of the total angular momentum are also eigenvectors of $\mathbf{I}_G^2$, G = A, B, ..., but, excepting the special case of two groups, they are not eigenvectors of the coupling operator. The general solution of the zero-order eigenvalue problem requires rather lengthy calculations and will not be considered here. The analysis will be illustrated for the ABC system in Section 1.F.

In the special case of two groups, the simultaneous eigenvectors of $\mathbf{I}^2$, $\mathbf{I}_A^2$, $\mathbf{I}_B^2$, and I_z, which will be denoted[3] $\{| I, I_A, I_B, m\rangle\}$, are eigenvectors of $\mathscr{H}^{(0)}$. For $\mathbf{I}^2 = \mathbf{I}_A^2 + \mathbf{I}_B^2 + 2\mathbf{I}_A \cdot \mathbf{I}_B$, so that

$$\mathscr{H}^{(0)} = -\{\omega_0 I_z + \tfrac{1}{2}J(\mathbf{I}^2 - \mathbf{I}_A^2 - \mathbf{I}_B^2)\}. \tag{1.21}$$

[3] To simplify the notation, the spin multiplicity index s_I will not be explicitly indicated in the elements of the basis.

Hence the eigenvalues of $\mathscr{H}^{(0)}$ are

$$\Omega^{(0)}_{I,I_A,I_B,m} = -\{\omega_0 m + \tfrac{1}{2}J[I(I+1) - I_A(I_A+1) - I_B(I_B+1)]\}. \quad (1.22)$$

To complete the theoretical basis for the case of two groups, it is necessary to calculate the matrix elements of I_{Az} and I_{Bz}. Since $[I_{Gz}, I_z] = 0$, (G = A, B), and $I_{Az} + I_{Bz} = I_z$, it follows that[4]

$$\langle I', I_A, I_B, m' \mid I_{Gz} \mid I, I_A, I_B, m\rangle = 0 \qquad \text{for } m' \neq m,$$

$$\langle I', I_A, I_B, m' \mid I_{Az} \mid I, I_A, I_B, m\rangle + \langle I', I_A, I_B, m' \mid I_{Bz} \mid I, I_A, I_B, m\rangle = m\,\delta_{m'm}\,\delta_{I'I}.$$

Hence

$$\langle I, I_A, I_B, m \mid I_{Bz} \mid I, I_A, I_B, m\rangle = m - \langle I, I_A, I_B, m \mid I_{Az} \mid I, I_A, I_B, m\rangle, \quad (1.23)$$

$$\langle I', I_A, I_B, m \mid I_{Bz} \mid I, I_A, I_B, m\rangle = -\langle I', I_A, I_B, m \mid I_{Az} \mid I, I_A, I_B, m\rangle. \quad (1.24)$$

Consider now the operator identity:

$$[\mathbf{I}^2, [\mathbf{I}^2, I_{Az}]] = \mathbf{I}^4 I_{Az} - 2\mathbf{I}^2 I_{Az}\mathbf{I}^2 + I_{Az}\mathbf{I}^4$$
$$= 2\{\mathbf{I}^2 I_{Az} + I_{Az}\mathbf{I}^2 - I_z(\mathbf{I}^2 - \mathbf{I}_B{}^2 + \mathbf{I}_A{}^2)\}, \quad (1.25)$$

which may be verified by a straightforward calculation based on the commutation rules for the spin operators. Computing the matrix elements of this identity that are diagonal in m but nondiagonal in I and I', one obtains

$$[(I + I' + 1)^2 - 1][(I - I')^2 - 1]\langle I', I_A, I_B, m \mid I_{Az} \mid I, I_A, I_B, m\rangle = 0,$$

by virtue of the fact that the matrix elements of $I_z(\mathbf{I}^2 - \mathbf{I}_B{}^2 + \mathbf{I}_A{}^2)$ vanish for $I' \neq I$. The matrix elements of I_{Az} for $I \neq I'$ will be non-vanishing if $(I + I' + 1)^2 - 1 = 0$, which implies that $I + I' = 0$ or $I + I' = -2$, or if $(I - I')^2 - 1 = 0$, which implies that $I' = I \pm 1$. Since the spin quantum numbers are nonnegative, the only possibilities are

$$I' = I \pm 1. \quad (1.26)$$

[4] The total spin quantum numbers I and I' are here understood to be taken from the series $I_A + I_B$, $I_A + I_B - 1, \ldots, |I_A - I_B|$. The multiplicities of these quantum numbers may be deduced by the procedure described in Section 3.E, Chapter 4.

The matrix elements of I_{Az} diagonal in I and m are, by (1.25),

$$\langle I, I_A, I_B, m \mid I_{Az} \mid I, I_A, I_B, m\rangle = \frac{m[I(I+1) - I_B(I_B+1) + I_A(I_A+1)]}{2I(I+1)}. \tag{1.27}$$

When $I_A = I_B$, the right side reduces to $m/2$, so that the matrix elements are not explicit functions of I; however, their number is delimited by I. This leads to the conclusion that the diagonal matrix elements of I_{Az} vanish if $I = 0$. For $I = 0$ can result only by the addition of two equal spin quantum numbers: $I_A = I_B \neq 0$ (i.e., $I = I_A - I_A = 0$) or $I_A = I_B = 0$. The value of m is zero in either case, so the matrix elements vanish, as asserted.

The diagonal matrix elements of δZ may be obtained from (1.23), (1.24), and (1.27):

$$\langle I, I_A, I_B, m \mid \delta Z \mid I, I_A, I_B, m\rangle$$
$$= -m\left\{\delta\omega_A + \frac{\omega_{AB}[I_A(I_A+1) - I_B(I_B+1) - I(I+1)]}{2I(I+1)}\right\}, \tag{1.28}$$

where $\omega_{AB} = \delta\omega_A - \delta\omega_B$. These matrix elements may be used to calculate the first-order spectrum of two strongly coupled groups. Second-order theory requires the matrix elements of I_{Az} connecting states with $I' - I = \pm 1$. The second-order theory is rather lengthy and seldom used, so that the derivation of these matrix elements will be omitted.[5] The results are

$$\langle I+1, I_A, I_B, m \mid I_{Az} \mid I, I_A, I_B, m\rangle = C(I+1, I; I_A, I_B)[(I+1)^2 - m^2]^{1/2},$$
$$\langle I-1, I_A, I_B, m \mid I_{Az} \mid I, I_A, I_B, m\rangle = C(I-1, I; I_A, I_B)(I^2 - m^2)^{1/2}, \tag{1.29}$$

where

$$C(I-1, I; I_A, I_B)$$
$$= C(I, I-1; I_A, I_B)$$
$$= \frac{[(I - I_A + I_B)(I + I_A - I_B)(I_A + I_B + I + 1)(I_A + I_B - I + 1)]^{1/2}}{4I^2(2I-1)(2I+1)}. \tag{1.30}$$

[5] The derivation is given in reference 3(d) of Chapter 4.

B. Zero-Order Spectra

The zero-order hamiltonian operator for a strongly coupled system is identical to the hamiltonian operator for the A_N system (cf. Section 4.A, Chapter 5). The theory of the A_N system shows that the zero-order spectrum of any strongly coupled system consists of a single resonance at ω_0.

The zero-order spectrum of a weakly coupled system is also quite simple. Transitions are allowed between any two states (i.e., product kets) for which the matrix element of I^- is nonvanishing. In particular, group-G transitions are characterized by the selection rules

$$\Delta I_G = 0, \qquad \Delta m_G = -1, \qquad \Delta m_{G'} = 0. \tag{1.31}$$

From (1.16) and (1.31), it follows that the frequency of a group G transition is ω_G.

The relative intensity of a group-G transition is

$$\begin{aligned} g_{I_G} &|\langle \ldots I_G, m_G - 1; \ldots; m - 1 \mid I^- \mid \ldots I_G, m_G; \ldots; m\rangle|^2 \\ &= g_{I_G}(I_G + m_G)(I_G - m_G + 1), \end{aligned} \tag{1.32}$$

where g_{I_G} is the multiplicity of I_G. Each transition in group G leads to a resonance at ω_G, so that the total intensity of the resonance is

$$(\text{Int})_G = 2^{N-n_G} \sum_{I_G} \sum_{m_G} g_{I_G}(I_G + m_G)(I_G - m_G + 1) = 2^{N-1} n_G. \tag{1.33}$$

The factor

$$2^{N-n_G} = \prod_{G' \neq G} g_{I_{G'}}(2I_{G'} + 1),$$

introduced in (1.33), is the number of choices for all kets $| I_{G'}, m_{G'}\rangle$, other than $| I_G, m_G\rangle$, in the product ket $| I_A, m_A; \ldots; I_G, m_G; \ldots; m\rangle$. It follows that

$$(\text{Int})_A : (\text{Int})_B : (\text{Int})_C \cdots = n_A : n_B : n_C : \cdots, \tag{1.34}$$

$$\sum_G (\text{Int})_G = 2^{N-1} N. \tag{1.35}$$

Thus the zero-order spectrum of a weakly coupled system containing n groups of magnetically equivalent nuclei consists of n resonances, one at each of the Larmor frequencies ω_A, ω_B, ..., with relative intensities proportional to n_A, n_B, ...

C. First-Order Spectra—Weak Coupling

In the first-order approximation, the off-diagonal elements of the hamiltonian matrix are neglected, so that the first-order energies for weak coupling are

$$\Omega_m^{(0)} + \Omega_m^{(1)} = -\left\{\sum_{\mathrm{G}} \omega_{\mathrm{G}} m_{\mathrm{G}} + \sum_{\mathrm{G}<\mathrm{G}'}\sum J_{\mathrm{GG}'} m_{\mathrm{G}} m_{\mathrm{G}'}\right\}. \tag{1.36}$$

The selection rules (1.31) are still valid and their application to (1.36) leads to the following expression for the frequency of a generic transition in group G:

$$\omega_{\mathrm{G}} + \sum_{\mathrm{G}' \neq \mathrm{G}} J_{\mathrm{GG}'} m_{\mathrm{G}'}, \tag{1.37}$$

where $\mathrm{G}' = \mathrm{A}, \mathrm{B}, \ldots \neq \mathrm{G}$.

There is one group-G resonance for each choice of the quantum numbers $m_{\mathrm{G}'}$. Since the resonance frequencies are not explicit functions of the total spin quantum numbers, the correct number of group-G transitions is obtained by allowing each spin variable to range from its maximum to its minimum value. In particular, $m_{\mathrm{G}'}$ may range from $I_{\mathrm{G}'}(\max) = \frac{1}{2}n_{\mathrm{G}'}$ to $-I_{\mathrm{G}'}(\max)$, so that the coupling of group G to group G′ results in $2I_{\mathrm{G}'}(\max) + 1 = n_{\mathrm{G}'} + 1$ resonances in group G. If group G is also coupled to a second group G″, each of the $n_{\mathrm{G}'} + 1$ resonances is split into $n_{\mathrm{G}''} + 1$ lines, and so on. The coupling of group G to groups G′, G″, ... results in

$$\prod_{\mathrm{G}' \neq \mathrm{G}} (n_{\mathrm{G}'} + 1)$$

resonances in group G.

The relative intensity of a group-G transition is

$$\prod_{\mathrm{G}' \neq \mathrm{G}} \nu(m_{\mathrm{G}'}) \left\{\sum_{I_{\mathrm{G}}}\sum_{m_{\mathrm{G}}} g_{I_{\mathrm{G}}} (I_{\mathrm{G}} + m_{\mathrm{G}})(I_{\mathrm{G}} - m_{\mathrm{G}} + 1)\right\}$$

$$= 2^{n_{\mathrm{G}}-1} n_{\mathrm{G}} \prod_{\mathrm{G}' \neq \mathrm{G}} \nu(m_{\mathrm{G}'}), \tag{1.38}$$

where

$$\binom{n_{\mathrm{G}'}}{\frac{1}{2}n_{\mathrm{G}'} + m_{\mathrm{G}'}} = \nu(m_{\mathrm{G}'})$$

is the degree of degeneracy of $m_{\mathrm{G}'}$. On summing (1.38) over all $m_{\mathrm{G}'} \neq m_{\mathrm{G}}$, one obtains (1.35).

To illustrate the use of (1.37) and (1.38), consider the resonances in group C of a weakly coupled system with $n_A = 2$, $n_B = 1$, $n_C = 3$. There are $(n_A + 1)(n_B + 1) = 6$ resonances in group C, corresponding to the six ways of pairing m_A and m_B : $(m_A, m_B) = (1, \frac{1}{2}), (0, \frac{1}{2}), (-1, \frac{1}{2}), (1, -\frac{1}{2}), (0, -\frac{1}{2}), (-1, -\frac{1}{2})$. Inserting the values of n_A, n_B, m_A, and m_B in (1.37) and (1.38), one obtains the results given in the accompanying tabulation.

m_A	m_B	Intensity	Frequency
1	$\frac{1}{2}$	8	$\omega_C + J_{AC} + \frac{1}{2}J_{BC}$
0	$\frac{1}{2}$	16	$\omega_C + \frac{1}{2}J_{BC}$
-1	$\frac{1}{2}$	8	$\omega_C - J_{AC} + \frac{1}{2}J_{BC}$
1	$-\frac{1}{2}$	8	$\omega_C + J_{AC} - \frac{1}{2}J_{BC}$
0	$-\frac{1}{2}$	16	$\omega_C - \frac{1}{2}J_{BC}$
-1	$-\frac{1}{2}$	8	$\omega_C - J_{AC} - \frac{1}{2}J_{BC}$

Examples of high-resolution spectra that conform to first-order theory for weak coupling have been given in Chapter 5. The only remaining problem is the determination of the conditions for which the first-order approximation is valid.

A perturbation calculation of arbitrary order will be meaningful only if the series expansions for the eigenvalues and the expansion coefficients for the eigenvectors converge. For weak coupling, the perturbation expansions are power series in the ratios $J_{GG'}/\omega_{RS}$, so that if $| J_{GG'}/\omega_{RS} | \ll 1$ $(R \neq S)$, terms of degree greater than unity in these ratios can be neglected. However, these conditions relate only to matters of convergence. The validity of a first-order calculation of the resonance frequencies and relative intensities also requires that the corrections to these quantities predicted by a second-order calculation be unobservable. More generally, if one performs a perturbation calculation to order $n - 1$, the frequency corrections $\Omega_{m-1}^{(n)} - \Omega_m^{(n)}$ must be unobservable and corrections to the line intensities of degree $n - 1$ in the ratios $J_{GG'}/\omega_{RS}$ must be unobservable. Similar remarks apply to strongly coupled systems and, more generally, to any system whose theoretical spectrum is to be calculated by the perturbation method.

Consider, for example, an A_2B system with $| J/\delta | = 0.067$. Since $J^2/\delta^2 = 0.004$, it would appear, from the condition $| J/\delta | \ll 1$ alone, that a first-order calculation would suffice. However, an examination of the fluorine magnetic resonance spectrum of ClF_3 at 56.4 Mcps (Fig. 7.1) shows that the anticipated 1 : 1 doublet and 1 : 2 : 1 triplet are not observed. The second-order splittings, which are of the order of

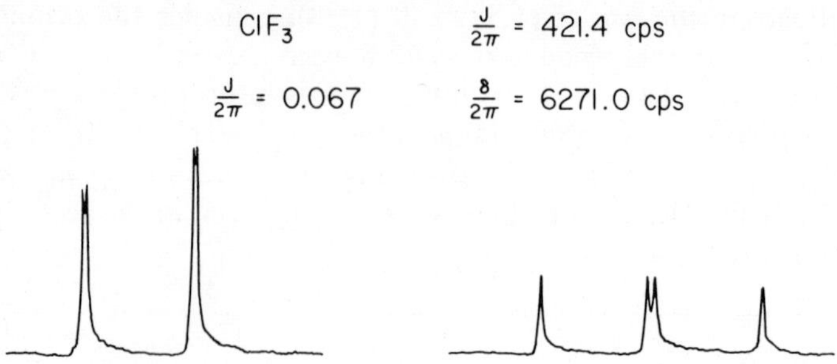

FIG. 7.1. Fluorine magnetic resonance spectrum of ClF_3 at 56.4 Mcps.

$J^2/2\delta = 14$ cps, are barely resolved. The third-order frequency corrections ($J^3/2\delta^2 \approx 2.2$ cps) are less than the observed line widths, so that a second-order calculation is sufficient.

D. First-Order Spectra—Strong Coupling

The first-order energies for two strongly coupled groups are, by (1.22) and (1.28),

$$-\left\{m\omega_A + \tfrac{1}{2}J[I(I+1) - I_A(I_A+1) - I_B(I_B+1)] + \frac{m\omega_{AB}[I_A(I_A+1) - I_B(I_B+1) - I(I+1)]}{2I(I+1)}\right\}. \quad (1.39)$$

Since first-order theory neglects the off-diagonal elements of δZ, $\mathbf{I}^2$ is still conserved; hence the selection rules for first-order transitions are

$$\Delta I_A = \Delta I_B = \Delta I = \Delta s_I = 0, \qquad \Delta m = -1. \quad (1.40)$$

It follows that the frequency of the transition $|I, I_A, I_B, m\rangle \rightarrow |I, I_A, I_B, m-1\rangle$ is given by

$$\omega_A + \frac{\omega_{AB}[I_A(I_A+1) - I_B(I_B+1) - I(I+1)]}{2I(I+1)} \qquad (I \neq 0), \quad (1.41)$$

which is independent of the spin-spin coupling constant. Furthermore, (1.41) is independent of m, so that the resonance frequencies of the $2I$ transitions defined by $m = I, I-1, ..., -I+1$ coincide. Thus the intensity of the resonance is

$$\sum_m g_I |\langle I, I_A, I_B, m-1 | I^- | I, I_A, I_B, m\rangle|^2 = g_I \sum_m (I+m)(I-m+1) = \tfrac{2}{3}\{g_I I(I+1)(2I+1)\}. \quad (1.42)$$

The application of (1.42) and (1.41) requires the calculation of I and g_I from given values of I_A and I_B. Consider, for example, an A_3B_2 system, for which $I_A = \frac{3}{2}, \frac{1}{2}$ $(g_{1/2} = 2)$, $I_B = 1, 0$. For convenience, the frequency origin will be taken at ω_B, so that $\omega_A \to \omega_A - \omega_B = \delta \equiv \omega_{AB}$. The values of I, g_I, the resonance frequencies, and their relative intensities are given in the accompanying tabulation. These results should be compared with the numerical data for the A_3B_2 system given in Appendix VI.

I_A	I_B	I	g_I	Intensity	Frequency
$\frac{3}{2}$	1	$\frac{5}{2}$	1	35	$\frac{3}{5}\delta$
$\frac{3}{2}$	1	$\frac{3}{2}$	1	10	$\frac{11}{15}\delta$
$\frac{3}{2}$	1	$\frac{1}{2}$	1	1	$\frac{5}{3}\delta$
$\frac{3}{2}$	0	$\frac{3}{2}$	1	10	δ
$\frac{1}{2}$	1	$\frac{3}{2}$	2	20	$\frac{1}{3}\delta$
$\frac{1}{2}$	1	$\frac{1}{2}$	2	2	$-\frac{1}{3}\delta$
$\frac{1}{2}$	0	$\frac{1}{2}$	2	2	δ

E. Second-Order Spectra—Weak Coupling

In second-order perturbation theory, u_r is approximated by the first two terms of (1.3), and Ω_r is approximated by the first three terms of (1.4). The corrections to $u_r^{(1)}$ and $\Omega_r^{(2)}$ for weak coupling are obtained by substituting (1.17) and (1.18) in (1.5) and (1.8). The second-order approximations to the eigenvectors and the eigenvalues are

$$|I_A, I_B, ..., m) = |\, ... I_G, m_G ...; m\rangle$$
$$-\frac{1}{2}\sum_{G<G'}\sum \frac{J_{GG'}}{\omega_{GG'}}\{F(I_{G'}, -m_{G'})F(I_G, m_G)|\, ... I_G, m_G+1 ... I_{G'}, m_{G'}-1 ...; m\rangle$$
$$- F(I_{G'}, m_{G'})F(I_G, -m_G)|\, ... I_G, m_G-1 ... I_{G'}, m_{G'}+1 ...; m\rangle\}, \tag{1.43}$$

$$\Omega_m^{(0)} + \Omega_m^{(1)} + \Omega_m^{(2)} = -\sum_G \omega_G m_G - \sum_{G<G'}\sum J_{GG'} m_G m_{G'}$$
$$-\frac{1}{2}\sum_{G<G'}\sum \frac{J_{GG'}^2}{\omega_{GG'}}\{m_G(I_{G'}^2 + I_{G'} - m_{G'}^2) - m_{G'}(I_G^2 + I_G - m_G^2)\}. \tag{1.44}$$

The selection rules for allowed transition are $\Delta I_G = 0$, $G = A, B, \ldots$, and $\Delta m = -1$. It follows that the resonance frequencies and relative intensities of group-G transitions are given by

$$\omega_G + \sum_{G' \neq G} J_{GG'} m_{G'} + \frac{1}{2} \sum_{G' \neq G} \frac{J_{GG'}^2}{\omega_{GG'}} \{I_{G'}(I_{G'} + 1) - m_{G'}(m_{G'} + 1) + 2m_G m_{G'}\}, \tag{1.45}$$

$$g_{I_G}(I_G - m_G + 1)(I_G + m_G) \left\{1 - \sum_{G' \neq G} \frac{2J_{GG'} m_{G'}}{\omega_{GG'}}\right\} \prod_{G' \neq G} g_{I_{G'}}, \tag{1.46}$$

where all terms of degree greater than unity in the ratios $J_{GG'}/\omega_{GG'}$ have been dropped from the expansion of $|(I_A, I_B, \ldots, m-1\,|I^-|\, I_A, I_B, \ldots, m)|^2$.

Summing (1.46) over all quantum numbers gives (1.33). But, (1.33) is not valid when the intensities are calculated with higher-order eigenvectors. For the intensities associated with mixed transitions—which vanish when computed with the zero-order eigenvectors, and are negligibly small when computed with the first-order eigenvectors—are not necessarily negligible in higher order. Since the total intensity is constant, an increase in the intensities of mixed transitions requires a compensating decrease in the intensities of the remaining transitions.

For two groups, (1.45) and (1.46) reduce to

$$\omega_A + Jm_B + \frac{1}{2}\frac{J^2}{\delta}\{I_B(I_B + 1) - m_B(m_B + 1) + 2m_A m_B\}, \tag{1.47}$$

$$g_{I_A} g_{I_B}(I_A + m_A)(I_A - m_A + 1)\left\{1 - \frac{2Jm_B}{\delta}\right\}. \tag{1.48}$$

These results may be checked for the $A_{n_A}B$ systems by expanding the exact expressions for the resonance frequencies and relative intensities given in Chapter 6.

F. Application to the ABC System

The hamiltonian operator for the ABC system is

$$\mathscr{H} = -\{\omega_A I_{Az} + \omega_B I_{Bz} + \omega_C I_{Cz} + J_{AB}\mathbf{I}_A \cdot \mathbf{I}_B + J_{AC}\mathbf{I}_A \cdot \mathbf{I}_C + J_{BC}\mathbf{I}_B \cdot \mathbf{I}_C\}. \tag{1.49}$$

Relative to the product basis $\{|+++\rangle, |++-\rangle, \ldots, |---\rangle\}$, the matrix for $\mathscr{H}$ is the direct sum of four submatrices of dimensions 1, 3, 3, 1, corresponding to the I_z eigenvalues $m = \frac{3}{2}, \frac{1}{2}, -\frac{1}{2}, -\frac{3}{2}$, respectively. The two 1×1 submatrices are generated by the product kets $|+++\rangle$ and $|---\rangle$. These kets are eigenvectors of $\mathscr{H}$: $\mathscr{H}|+++\rangle = \Omega_0|+++\rangle$, $\mathscr{H}|---\rangle = \Omega_0'|---\rangle$, where

$$\Omega_0 = -\tfrac{1}{2}\{\omega_A + \omega_B + \omega_C + \tfrac{1}{2}(J_{AB} + J_{AC} + J_{BC})\}, \tag{1.50}$$

$$\Omega_0' = \tfrac{1}{2}\{\omega_A + \omega_B + \omega_C - \tfrac{1}{2}(J_{AB} + J_{AC} + J_{BC})\}. \tag{1.51}$$

The 3×3 submatrix of $\mathscr{H}$ generated by the product kets with $m = +\tfrac{1}{2}$ is of the form

$$\mathscr{H}(\tfrac{1}{2}) = \begin{pmatrix} Z_{11} + V_{11} & V_{12} & V_{13} \\ V_{21} & Z_{22} + V_{22} & V_{23} \\ V_{31} & V_{32} & Z_{33} + V_{33} \end{pmatrix}, \tag{1.52}$$

where

$$Z_{11} = -\tfrac{1}{2}(\omega_A + \omega_B - \omega_C), \qquad Z_{22} = -\tfrac{1}{2}(\omega_A - \omega_B + \omega_C),$$

$$Z_{33} = -\tfrac{1}{2}(-\omega_A + \omega_B + \omega_C),$$

$$V_{11} = -\tfrac{1}{4}(J_{AB} - J_{AC} - J_{BC}), \qquad V_{22} = \tfrac{1}{4}(J_{AB} - J_{AC} + J_{BC}),$$

$$V_{33} = \tfrac{1}{4}(J_{AB} + J_{AC} - J_{BC}),$$

$$V_{12} = V_{21} = -\tfrac{1}{2}J_{BC}, \qquad V_{13} = V_{31} = -\tfrac{1}{2}J_{AC},$$

$$V_{23} = V_{32} = -\tfrac{1}{2}J_{AB}.$$

The matrix for $\mathscr{H}(-\tfrac{1}{2})$ is obtained from (1.52) by replacing Z_{ii} with $-Z_{ii}$.

The eigenvalues of $\mathscr{H}(\tfrac{1}{2})$ will be denoted Ω_1, Ω_2, Ω_3, ($\Omega_i \to Z_{ii}$, as all $J_{GG'} \to 0$), and the corresponding eigenvectors will be denoted

$$a_{11}|++-\rangle + a_{21}|+-+\rangle + a_{31}|-++\rangle,$$

$$a_{12}|++-\rangle + a_{22}|+-+\rangle + a_{32}|-++\rangle,$$

$$a_{13}|++-\rangle + a_{23}|+-+\rangle + a_{33}|-++\rangle.$$

Since $\mathscr{H}(\tfrac{1}{2})$ is real and symmetric, it will be assumed that the matrix (a_{ij}) is orthogonal. In the limit as all $J_{GG'} \to 0$, $a_{ij} \to \delta_{ij}$, where δ_{ij} is the Kronecker delta.

The eigenvalues and the coefficient matrix for the states with $m = -\tfrac{1}{2}$ will be denoted Ω_1', Ω_2', Ω_3', (a_{ij}'). According to the theorem of Section 3.F, Chapter 5, the Ω_i, Ω_i', a_{ij}, and a_{ij}' are related by the following identities:

$$\begin{aligned} \Omega_i'(J_{AB}, J_{AC}, J_{BC}) &= -\Omega_i(-J_{AB}, -J_{AC}, -J_{BC}), \\ a_{ij}'(J_{AB}, J_{AC}, J_{BC}) &= a_{ij}(-J_{AB}, -J_{AC}, -J_{BC}). \end{aligned} \tag{1.53}$$

These identities are very useful in perturbation calculations of order >2.

TABLE 7.1

RESONANCE FREQUENCIES AND RELATIVE INTENSITIES FOR THE ABC SYSTEM

Transition[a]	Relative intensity	Frequency
A_1 : $\vert +++\rangle \to \vert -++\rangle$	$[a_{13} + a_{23} + a_{33}]^2$	$\Omega_3 - \Omega_0$
A_2 : $\vert ++-\rangle \to \vert -+-\rangle$	$[a'_{12}(a_{21} + a_{31}) + a'_{22}(a_{11} + a_{31}) + a'_{32}(a_{11} + a_{21})]^2$	$\Omega_2' - \Omega_1$
A_3 : $\vert +-+\rangle \to \vert --+\rangle$	$[a_{12}(a'_{21} + a'_{31}) + a_{22}(a'_{11} + a'_{31}) + a_{32}(a'_{11} + a'_{21})]^2$	$\Omega_1' - \Omega_2$
A_4 : $\vert +--\rangle \to \vert ---\rangle$	$[a'_{13} + a'_{23} + a'_{33}]^2$	$\Omega_0' - \Omega_3'$
B_1 : $\vert +++\rangle \to \vert +-+\rangle$	$[a_{12} + a_{22} + a_{32}]^2$	$\Omega_2 - \Omega_0$
B_2 : $\vert ++-\rangle \to \vert +--\rangle$	$[a'_{13}(a_{21} + a_{31}) + a'_{23}(a_{11} + a_{31}) + a'_{33}(a_{11} + a_{21})]^2$	$\Omega_3' - \Omega_1$
B_3 : $\vert -++\rangle \to \vert --+\rangle$	$[a_{13}(a'_{21} + a'_{31}) + a_{23}(a'_{11} + a'_{31}) + a_{33}(a'_{11} + a'_{21})]^2$	$\Omega_1' - \Omega_3$
B_4 : $\vert -+-\rangle \to \vert ---\rangle$	$[a'_{12} + a'_{22} + a'_{32}]^2$	$\Omega_0' - \Omega_2'$
C_1 : $\vert +++\rangle \to \vert ++-\rangle$	$[a_{11} + a_{21} + a_{31}]^2$	$\Omega_1 - \Omega_0$
C_2 : $\vert +-+\rangle \to \vert +--\rangle$	$[a_{12}(a'_{23} + a'_{33}) + a_{22}(a'_{13} + a'_{33}) + a_{32}(a'_{13} + a'_{23})]^2$	$\Omega_3' - \Omega_2$
C_3 : $\vert -++\rangle \to \vert -+-\rangle$	$[a'_{12}(a_{23} + a_{33}) + a'_{22}(a_{13} + a_{33}) + a'_{32}(a_{13} + a_{23})]^2$	$\Omega_2' - \Omega_3$
C_4 : $\vert --+\rangle \to \vert ---\rangle$	$[a'_{11} + a'_{21} + a'_{31}]^2$	$\Omega_0' - \Omega_1'$
M_1 : $\vert ++-\rangle \to \vert --+\rangle$	$[a'_{11}(a_{21} + a_{31}) + a'_{21}(a_{11} + a_{31}) + a'_{31}(a_{11} + a_{21})]^2$	$\Omega_1' - \Omega_1$
M_2 : $\vert +-+\rangle \to \vert -+-\rangle$	$[a'_{12}(a_{22} + a_{32}) + a'_{22}(a_{12} + a_{32}) + a'_{32}(a_{12} + a_{22})]^2$	$\Omega_2' - \Omega_2$
M_3 : $\vert -++\rangle \to \vert +--\rangle$	$[a'_{13}(a_{23} + a_{33}) + a'_{23}(a_{13} + a_{33}) + a'_{33}(a_{13} + a_{23})]^2$	$\Omega_3' - \Omega_3$

[a] In the limit as all $J_{GG'} \to 0$.

From the preceding definitions, it is not difficult to construct Table 7.1, which clearly indicates the transformation of the spectrum into itself when $J_{GG'} \to -J_{GG'}$: $G_1 \to G_4$, $G_2 \to G_3$, G = A, B, C; $M_i \to M_i$, $i = 1, 2, 3$.

1. *Weak Coupling.* The resonance frequencies and relative intensities for group A of the ABC system, as determined by second-order perturbation theory, are given in Table 7.2. The results for groups B and C may be obtained from those for group A by cyclical permutation of A, B, and C. The mixed transitions are not included, since their intensities are of the second degree in $J_{GG'}/\omega_{RS}$ and, therefore, negligible in the second-order approximation. The first-order ABC spectrum follows from Table 7.2 by omitting all terms containing the ratios $J_{GG'}/\omega_{GG'}$.

TABLE 7.2

SECOND-ORDER PERTURBATION ANALYSIS OF THE ABC SYSTEM FOR WEAK COUPLING

Frequency	Relative intensity
$\omega_A + \frac{1}{2}(J_{AB} + J_{AC}) + \frac{1}{4}\left\{\frac{J_{AB}^2}{\omega_{AB}} + \frac{J_{AC}^2}{\omega_{AC}}\right\}$	$1 - \frac{J_{AB}}{\omega_{AB}} - \frac{J_{AC}}{\omega_{AC}}$
$\omega_A + \frac{1}{2}(J_{AB} - J_{AC}) + \frac{1}{4}\left\{\frac{J_{AB}^2}{\omega_{AB}} + \frac{J_{AC}^2}{\omega_{AC}}\right\}$	$1 - \frac{J_{AB}}{\omega_{AB}} + \frac{J_{AC}}{\omega_{AC}}$
$\omega_A - \frac{1}{2}(J_{AB} - J_{AC}) + \frac{1}{4}\left\{\frac{J_{AB}^2}{\omega_{AB}} + \frac{J_{AC}^2}{\omega_{AC}}\right\}$	$1 + \frac{J_{AB}}{\omega_{AB}} - \frac{J_{AC}}{\omega_{AC}}$
$\omega_A - \frac{1}{2}(J_{AB} + J_{AC}) + \frac{1}{4}\left\{\frac{J_{AB}^2}{\omega_{AB}} + \frac{J_{AC}^2}{\omega_{AC}}\right\}$	$1 + \frac{J_{AB}}{\omega_{AB}} + \frac{J_{AC}}{\omega_{AC}}$

Table 7.2 shows that the second-order ABC spectrum is invariant with respect to a change in the sign of any coupling constant. The relative signs of the coupling constants begin to influence the appearance of an ABC spectrum in the third order, that is, when terms of the second degree in the ratios $J_{GG'}/\omega_{RS}$ make observable contributions to the resonance frequencies and relative intensities. Calculated ABC spectra in the zero-, first- and second-order approximations are shown in Fig. 7.2. In the first-order spectrum, the magnitudes of the coupling constants appear as repeated spacings in the A, B, and C quartets. Table 7.2 shows that the same repeated spacings occur in the second-order spectrum.

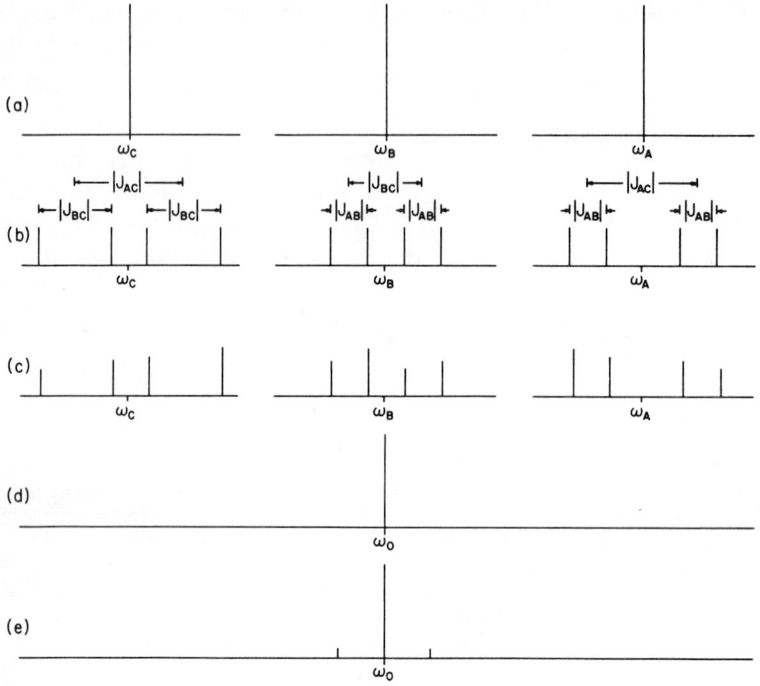

FIG. 7.2. Calculated ABC spectra: (a), (b), and (c) show the zero-, first-, and second-order spectra for $|J_{GG'}| \ll |\omega_{GG'}|$; (d) and (e) show the zero- and first-order spectra for $|\omega_{GG'}| \gg |J_{GG'}|$. Part (e) is drawn for $(\delta\omega_A + \delta\omega_B + \delta\omega_C)/3 = 0$.

An example of an ABC system that conforms to second-order theory is provided by the vinyl protons of vinyl acetate at 60 Mcps (Fig. 7.3). An exact analysis of this system at 29.92 Mcps (*3*) indicates that $-s_{AB} = s_{BC} = s_{AC}$, where $s_{GG'}$ denotes the algebraic sign of $J_{GG'}$.

2. *Strong Coupling*. The zero-order hamiltonian operator for strong coupling is

$$\mathscr{H}^{(0)} = -\{\omega_0 I_z + J_{AB}\mathbf{I}_A \cdot \mathbf{I}_B + J_{AC}\mathbf{I}_A \cdot \mathbf{I}_C + J_{BC}\mathbf{I}_B \cdot \mathbf{I}_C\},$$

and the perturbation operator is

$$\delta Z = -\{\delta\omega_A I_{Az} + \delta\omega_B I_{Bz} + \delta\omega_C I_{Cz}\}.$$

Since the square and z component of the total angular momentum are constants of the motion with respect to $\mathscr{H}^{(0)}$, the calculation of the unperturbed eigenvalues and eigenvectors is facilitated by using the

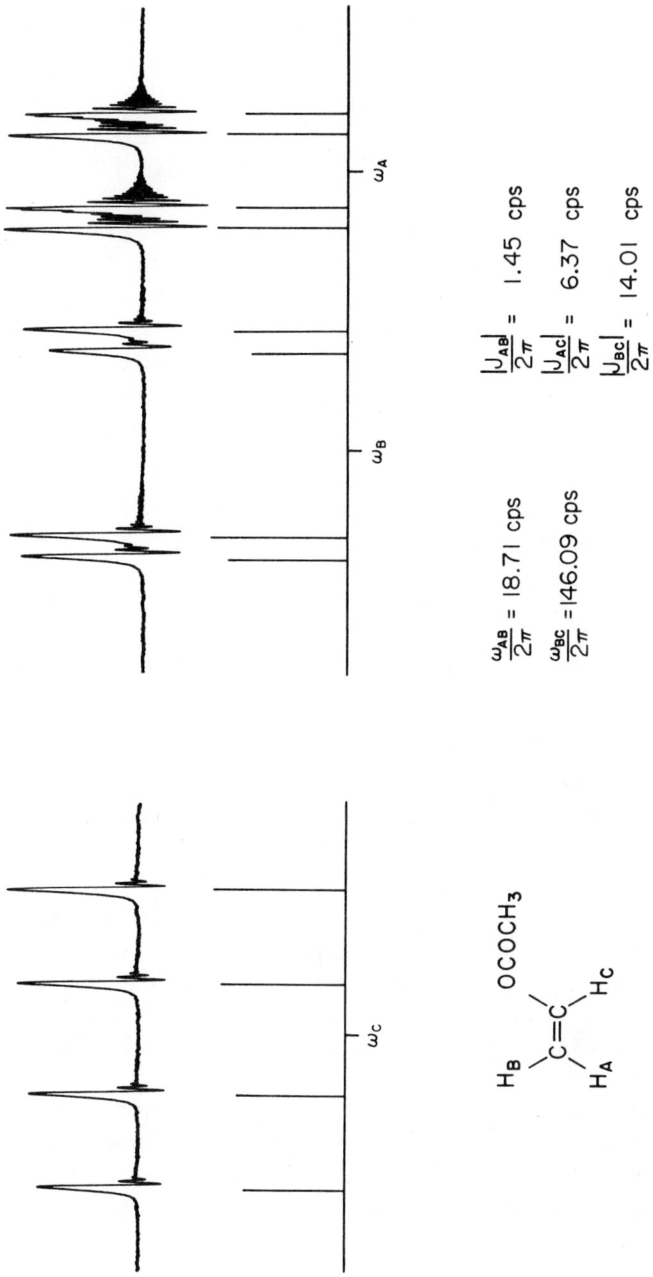

FIG. 7.3. Experimental and theoretical proton spectra of the vinyl-group protons of pure vinyl acetate at 60 Mcps.

basis given in Table 4.6. The results of this calculation are given in Table 7.3, where

$$Q = \frac{(J_{AB} - J_{AC})\sqrt{3}}{J_{AB} + J_{AC} - 2J_{BC} + R},$$

$$R = [(J_{AB} + J_{AC} - 2J_{BC})^2 + 3(J_{AB} - J_{AC})^2]^{1/2}.$$

TABLE 7.3

ZERO-ORDER EIGENVECTORS AND EIGENVALUES OF THE ABC SYSTEM FOR STRONG COUPLING

Eigenvector	Eigenvalue
$\mid \frac{3}{2}, \frac{3}{2}\rangle$	$-\frac{1}{4}\{6\omega_0 + J_{AB} + J_{AC} + J_{BC}\}$
$\mid \frac{3}{2}, \frac{1}{2}\rangle$	$-\frac{1}{4}\{2\omega_0 + J_{AB} + J_{AC} + J_{BC}\}$
$\mid \frac{3}{2}, -\frac{1}{2}\rangle$	$-\frac{1}{4}\{-2\omega_0 + J_{AB} + J_{AC} + J_{BC}\}$
$\mid \frac{3}{2}, -\frac{3}{2}\rangle$	$-\frac{1}{4}\{-6\omega_0 + J_{AB} + J_{AC} + J_{BC}\}$
$\frac{1}{(1+Q^2)^{1/2}}\{\mid \frac{1}{2}, \frac{1}{2}; 1\rangle - Q \mid \frac{1}{2}, \frac{1}{2}; 2\rangle\}$	$\frac{1}{4}\{-2\omega_0 + J_{AB} + J_{AC} + J_{BC} + R\}$
$\frac{1}{(1+Q^2)^{1/2}}\{Q \mid \frac{1}{2}, \frac{1}{2}; 1\rangle + \mid \frac{1}{2}, \frac{1}{2}; 2\rangle\}$	$\frac{1}{4}\{-2\omega_0 + J_{AB} + J_{AC} + J_{BC} - R\}$
$\frac{1}{(1+Q^2)^{1/2}}\{\mid \frac{1}{2}, -\frac{1}{2}; 1\rangle - Q \mid \frac{1}{2}, -\frac{1}{2}; 2\rangle\}$	$\frac{1}{4}\{2\omega_0 + J_{AB} + J_{AC} + J_{BC} + R\}$
$\frac{1}{(1+Q^2)^{1/2}}\{Q \mid \frac{1}{2}, -\frac{1}{2}; 1\rangle + \mid \frac{1}{2}, -\frac{1}{2}; 2\rangle\}$	$\frac{1}{4}\{2\omega_0 + J_{AB} + J_{AC} + J_{BC} - R\}$

The zero-order strongly coupled ABC spectrum is obtained by applying the usual rules for the computation of resonance frequencies and relative intensities, together with the selection rules $\Delta I = \Delta s_I = 0$, $\Delta m = -1$. The theoretical spectrum is given in Table 7.4, which shows that the resonance frequency of all transitions with nonvanishing intensities is ω_0.

The first-order corrections to the energies are given in Table 7.5. From these results it can be shown that the first-order strongly coupled ABC spectrum [Fig. 7. 2(e)] consists of a symmetrical 1 : 10 : 1 triplet. The frequencies of the two satellite resonances, relative to the central resonance, are

$$\frac{\pm 1}{1+Q^2}\left\{\frac{1-Q^2}{3}(2\,\delta\omega_A - \delta\omega_B - \delta\omega_C) + \frac{2Q}{\sqrt{3}}(\delta\omega_B - \delta\omega_C)\right\}.$$

TABLE 7.4

ZERO-ORDER ABC SPECTRUM FOR STRONG COUPLING

Transition	Intensity	Frequency
$\lvert \frac{3}{2}, \frac{3}{2}\rangle \rightarrow \lvert \frac{3}{2}, \frac{1}{2}\rangle$	3	ω_0
$\lvert \frac{3}{2}, \frac{1}{2}\rangle \rightarrow \lvert \frac{3}{2}, -\frac{1}{2}\rangle$	4	ω_0
$\lvert \frac{3}{2}, -\frac{1}{2}\rangle \rightarrow \lvert \frac{3}{2}, -\frac{3}{2}\rangle$	3	ω_0
$\lvert \frac{3}{2}, \frac{3}{2}\rangle \rightarrow \lvert \frac{1}{2}, \frac{1}{2}; 1)$	0	$\omega_0 + \frac{1}{2}(J_{AB} + J_{AC} + J_{BC}) + \frac{1}{4}R$
$\lvert \frac{3}{2}, \frac{3}{2}\rangle \rightarrow \lvert \frac{1}{2}, \frac{1}{2}; 2)$	0	$\omega_0 + \frac{1}{2}(J_{AB} + J_{AC} + J_{BC}) - \frac{1}{4}R$
$\lvert \frac{3}{2}, \frac{1}{2}\rangle \rightarrow \lvert \frac{1}{2}, -\frac{1}{2}; 1)$	0	$\omega_0 + \frac{1}{2}(J_{AB} + J_{AC} + J_{BC}) + \frac{1}{4}R$
$\lvert \frac{3}{2}, \frac{1}{2}\rangle \rightarrow \lvert \frac{1}{2}, -\frac{1}{2}; 2)$	0	$\omega_0 + \frac{1}{2}(J_{AB} + J_{AC} + J_{BC}) - \frac{1}{4}R$
$\lvert \frac{1}{2}, \frac{1}{2}; 1) \rightarrow \lvert \frac{1}{2}, -\frac{1}{2}; 1)$	1	ω_0
$\lvert \frac{1}{2}, \frac{1}{2}; 1) \rightarrow \lvert \frac{1}{2}, -\frac{1}{2}; 2)$	0	$\omega_0 - \frac{1}{2}R$
$\lvert \frac{1}{2}, \frac{1}{2}; 2) \rightarrow \lvert \frac{1}{2}, -\frac{1}{2}; 1)$	0	$\omega_0 + \frac{1}{2}R$
$\lvert \frac{1}{2}, \frac{1}{2}; 2) \rightarrow \lvert \frac{1}{2}, -\frac{1}{2}; 2)$	1	ω_0
$\lvert \frac{1}{2}, \frac{1}{2}; 1) \rightarrow \lvert \frac{3}{2}, -\frac{1}{2}\rangle$	0	$\omega_0 - \frac{1}{2}(J_{AB} + J_{AC} + J_{BC}) - \frac{1}{4}R$
$\lvert \frac{1}{2}, \frac{1}{2}; 2) \rightarrow \lvert \frac{3}{2}, -\frac{1}{2}\rangle$	0	$\omega_0 - \frac{1}{2}(J_{AB} + J_{AC} + J_{BC}) + \frac{1}{4}R$
$\lvert \frac{1}{2}, -\frac{1}{2}; 1) \rightarrow \lvert \frac{3}{2}, -\frac{3}{2}\rangle$	0	$\omega_0 - \frac{1}{2}(J_{AB} + J_{AC} + J_{BC}) - \frac{1}{4}R$
$\lvert \frac{1}{2}, -\frac{1}{2}; 2) \rightarrow \lvert \frac{3}{2}, -\frac{3}{2}\rangle$	0	$\omega_0 - \frac{1}{2}(J_{AB} + J_{AC} + J_{BC}) + \frac{1}{4}R$

TABLE 7.5

FIRST-ORDER ENERGY CORRECTIONS FOR THE STRONGLY COUPLED ABC SYSTEM

State	First-order energy correction
$\lvert \frac{3}{2}, \frac{3}{2}\rangle$	$-\frac{1}{2}(\delta\omega_A + \delta\omega_B + \delta\omega_C)$
$\lvert \frac{3}{2}, \frac{1}{2}\rangle$	$-\frac{1}{6}(\delta\omega_A + \delta\omega_B + \delta\omega_C)$
$\lvert \frac{3}{2}, -\frac{1}{2}\rangle$	$\frac{1}{6}(\delta\omega_A + \delta\omega_B + \delta\omega_C)$
$\lvert \frac{3}{2}, -\frac{3}{2}\rangle$	$\frac{1}{2}(\delta\omega_A + \delta\omega_B + \delta\omega_C)$
$\lvert \frac{1}{2}, \frac{1}{2}; 1)$	$\frac{1}{1+Q^2}\left\{\frac{1}{6}(\delta\omega_A - 2\delta\omega_B - 2\delta\omega_C) + \frac{Q}{\sqrt{3}}(\delta\omega_B - \delta\omega_C) - \frac{1}{2}Q^2\,\delta\omega_A\right\}$
$\lvert \frac{1}{2}, \frac{1}{2}; 2)$	$\frac{1}{1+Q^2}\left\{\frac{Q^2}{6}(\delta\omega_A - 2\delta\omega_B - 2\delta\omega_C) - \frac{Q}{\sqrt{3}}(\delta\omega_B - \delta\omega_C) - \frac{1}{2}\,\delta\omega_A\right\}$
$\lvert \frac{1}{2}, -\frac{1}{2}; 1)$	$-\frac{1}{1+Q^2}\left\{\frac{1}{6}(\delta\omega_A - 2\delta\omega_B - 2\delta\omega_C) + \frac{Q}{\sqrt{3}}(\delta\omega_B - \delta\omega_C) - \frac{1}{2}Q^2\,\delta\omega_A\right\}$
$\lvert \frac{1}{2}, -\frac{1}{2}; 2)$	$-\frac{1}{1+Q^2}\left\{\frac{Q^2}{6}(\delta\omega_A - 2\delta\omega_B - 2\delta\omega_C) - \frac{Q}{\sqrt{3}}(\delta\omega_B - \delta\omega_C) - \frac{1}{2}\,\delta\omega_A\right\}$

If $J_{AB} = J_{AC}$ and $\delta\omega_B = \delta\omega_C$, then $Q = 0$, and the strongly coupled ABC system reduces to a strongly coupled AB_2 system with $\delta = \delta\omega_B - \delta\omega_A$. In this case, the spectrum reduces to a 1 : 10 : 1 triplet with resonances at $-2\,\delta/3$, 0, $2\,\delta/3$, in agreement with the results obtained in Chapter 6.

When the perturbation analysis is extended to higher orders, the total angular momentum is no longer conserved and transitions are allowed between any two states for which $\Delta m = -1$. The calculations are straightforward, but the expressions for the resonance frequencies and relative intensities are quite complicated and will not be given here.

3. *Exact Analysis.* Explicit expressions for the resonance frequencies and relative intensities of the ABC system can be derived by using the well-known algebraic formulas for the roots of a cubic equation (cf. Section 6.4). The resulting expressions are rather cumbersome (*4*) and reveal little about the general properties of ABC systems that cannot be deduced by other means. For example, Table 7.1, equations (1.50) and (1.51), and the trace relations

$$\operatorname{tr} \mathscr{H}(\pm\tfrac{1}{2}) = \mp\tfrac{1}{2}(\omega_A + \omega_B + \omega_C) + \tfrac{1}{4}(J_{AB} + J_{AC} + J_{BC})$$

can be used to establish the relations:

$$\begin{aligned} A_1 - A_2 &= A_3 - A_4 = C_1 - C_3 = C_2 - C_4 = a, \\ A_1 - A_3 &= A_2 - A_4 = B_2 - B_4 = B_1 - B_3 = b, \\ B_1 - B_2 &= B_3 - B_4 = C_1 - C_2 = C_3 - C_4 = c, \end{aligned} \tag{1.54}$$

where

$$\begin{aligned} a &= \Omega_3 - \Omega_0 - \Omega_2' + \Omega_1\,, \\ b &= \Omega_3 - \Omega_0 - \Omega_1' + \Omega_2\,, \\ c &= \Omega_2 - \Omega_0 - \Omega_3' + \Omega_1\,. \end{aligned}$$

Equations (1.54) show that the decomposition of Table 7.1 into three quartets and three mixed transitions possesses the repeated spacing property already noted in the perturbation analysis. Unfortunately, this decomposition is not unique. It can be shown (*5*) that there are fifteen independent groupings into three quartets and three mixed transitions. In weakly coupled spectra, the correct decomposition is usually obvious (Fig. 7.3), because conditions (1.12) preclude the overlapping of resonances associated with different nuclei. The decomposition becomes more difficult when overlapping occurs (Figs. 7.4 and 7.5), and is by no means obvious when the intensities of some of the quartet resonances are vanishingly small (Fig. 7.6).

$$\frac{\omega_{AB}}{2\pi} = 13.92 \text{ cps}$$

$$\frac{\omega_{AC}}{2\pi} = 18.57 \text{ cps}$$

$$\frac{J_{AB}}{2\pi} = 3.65 \text{ cps}$$

$$\frac{J_{AC}}{2\pi} = 5.63 \text{ cps}$$

$$\frac{J_{BC}}{2\pi} = 1.39 \text{ cps}$$

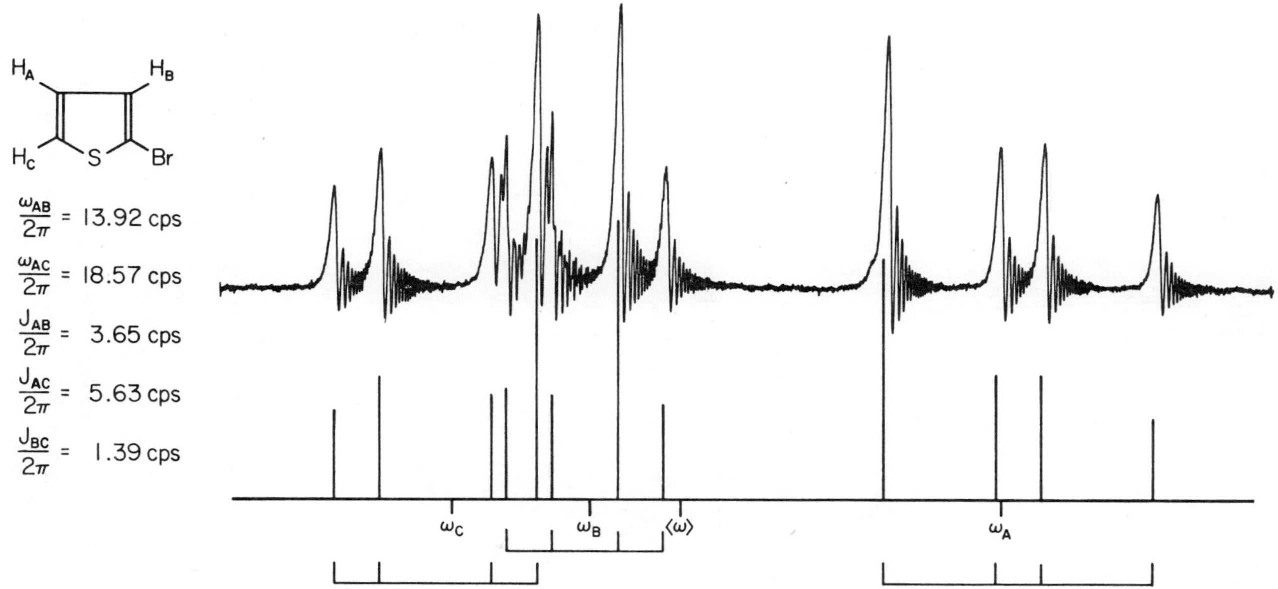

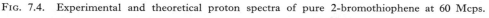

FIG. 7.4. Experimental and theoretical proton spectra of pure 2-bromothiophene at 60 Mcps.

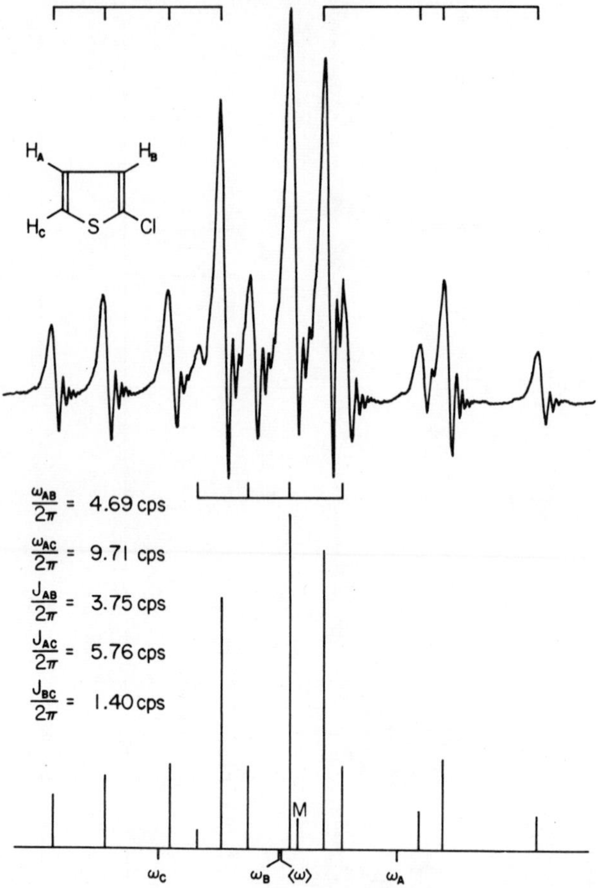

FIG. 7.5. Experimental and theoretical proton spectra of pure 2-chlorothiophene at 60 Mcps. M denotes a mixed transition.

The repeated spacings a, b, c, are called the *characteristic spacings* of the ABC system. Their algebraic sum is equal to the sum of the coupling constants:

$$a + b + c = -3\Omega_0 + 2\,\mathrm{tr}\,\mathscr{H}(\tfrac{1}{2}) - \mathrm{tr}\,\mathscr{H}(-\tfrac{1}{2})$$
$$= J_{AB} + J_{AC} + J_{BC}\,.$$

Unless the correspondence between the observed resonances and those given in Table 7.1 is known, or assumed, the signs of a, b, and c are undetermined. In weakly coupled spectra, the characteristic spacings are good approximations to the magnitudes of the spin-spin coupling constants: $|a| \approx |J_{AC}|$, $|b| \approx |J_{AB}|$, $|c| \approx |J_{BC}|$.

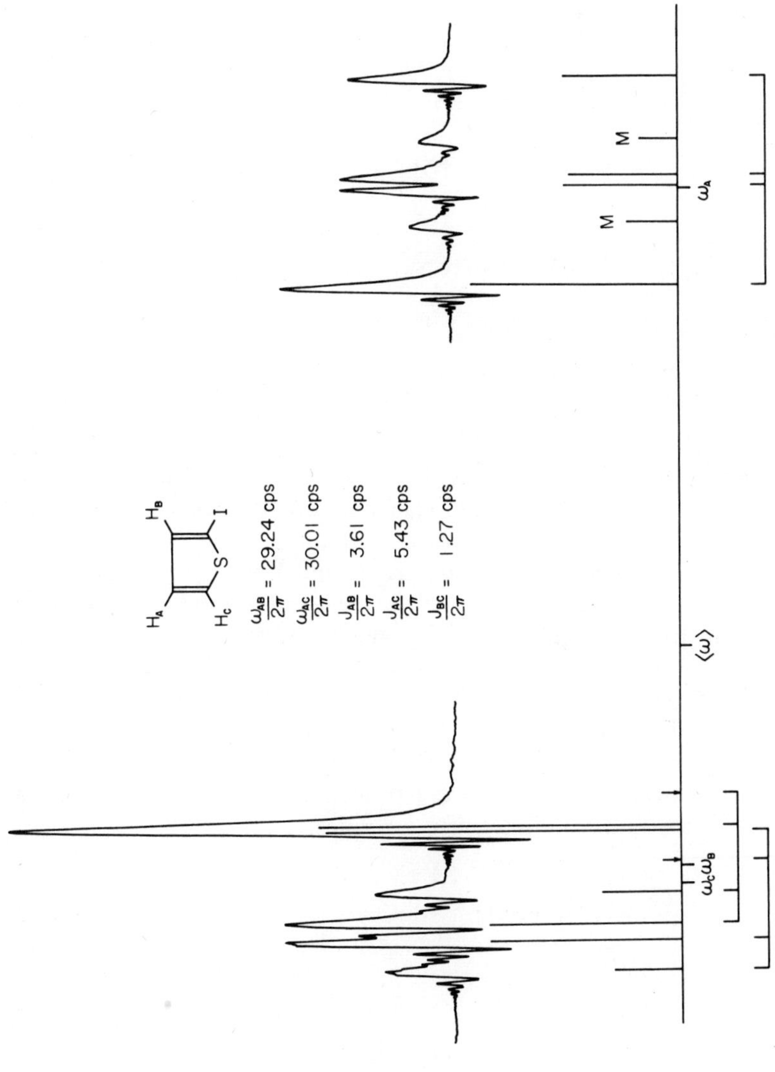

FIG. 7.6. Experimental and theoretical proton spectra of pure 2-iodothiophene at 60 Mcps. In the theoretical spectrum, the M's denoted mixed transitions.

The procedure used to establish equations (1.54) can also be used to show that the theoretical frequencies of an ABC system satisfy the relations

$$\sum_{i=1}^{4} \sum_{G} G_i = 12\langle\omega\rangle \qquad (G = A, B, C),$$

$$\sum_{i=1}^{3} M_i = 3\langle\omega\rangle,$$

$$A_1 + A_4 = A_2 + A_3 = 3\langle\omega\rangle - M_3\,,$$

$$B_1 + B_4 = B_2 + B_3 = 3\langle\omega\rangle - M_2\,,$$

$$C_1 + C_4 = C_2 + C_3 = 3\langle\omega\rangle - M_1\,,$$

$$2M_3 + \sum_{i=1}^{4} A_i = 6\langle\omega\rangle, \qquad 2M_2 + \sum_{i=1}^{4} B_i = 6\langle\omega\rangle, \qquad 2M_1 + \sum_{i=1}^{4} C_i = 6\langle\omega\rangle,$$

where

$$\langle\omega\rangle = \tfrac{1}{3}(\omega_A + \omega_B + \omega_C).$$

In Section 4 it will be shown that $\langle\omega\rangle$ is the mean resonance frequency of the ABC system. If all twelve resonances of the three quartets are observed, $\langle\omega\rangle$ can be determined by summing their frequencies (as measured with respect to an arbitrary origin) and dividing the result by 12.

The preceding frequency conditions become more suitable for practical applications by choosing a new frequency origin at $\langle\omega\rangle$. One may formally refer these conditions to an origin at $\langle\omega\rangle$ by setting $\langle\omega\rangle = 0$, it being understood that all A_i, B_i, C_i, and M_i then denote resonance frequencies relative to $\langle\omega\rangle$.

The frequency conditions can be used to check a trial decomposition into three quartets and three mixed transitions. Additional checks are provided by the following intensity sum rules:

$$\text{Int}\,A_1 + \text{Int}\,B_1 + \text{Int}\,C_1 = 3,$$
$$\text{Int}\,A_4 + \text{Int}\,B_4 + \text{Int}\,C_4 = 3,$$

$$\text{Int}\,M_1 + \text{Int}\,A_2 + \text{Int}\,B_2 = 1 + \text{Int}\,C_1\,,$$
$$\text{Int}\,A_3 + \text{Int}\,M_2 + \text{Int}\,C_2 = 1 + \text{Int}\,B_1\,,$$
$$\text{Int}\,B_3 + \text{Int}\,C_3 + \text{Int}\,M_3 = 1 + \text{Int}\,A_1\,,$$

$$\text{Int}\,M_1 + \text{Int}\,A_3 + \text{Int}\,B_3 = 1 + \text{Int}\,C_4\,,$$
$$\text{Int}\,A_2 + \text{Int}\,M_2 + \text{Int}\,C_3 = 1 + \text{Int}\,B_4\,,$$
$$\text{Int}\,B_2 + \text{Int}\,C_2 + \text{Int}\,M_3 = 1 + \text{Int}\,A_4\,.$$

These equations can be verified by direct expansions of the expressions given in Table 7.1, together with the orthogonality conditions satisfied by the a_{ij} and a'_{ij}. Since Int ABC $=$ Int $A_{1/2}B_{1/2}C_{1/2} = 12$, it will usually be convenient to normalize the observed intensities so that their sum is 12.

The general properties of the ABC system have been incorporated in a computational scheme for the exact analysis of ABC spectra (*5*). The input data for this method consists of the magnitudes of the characteristic spacings and the frequencies of the quartet centers relative to the mean resonance frequency. This scheme yields 40 sets of chemical shifts and spin-spin coupling constants. Each of these sets is consistent with the observed resonance frequencies, but many of them can be eliminated at an early stage of the analysis. The line intensities calculated with acceptable sets of parameters are then compared with the observed intensities to obtain the parameters consistent with the observed frequencies and intensities. This method of analysis is usually much more expeditious than the trial-and-error method based upon direct numerical diagonalizations of the cubic equations appearing in the ABC system. The calculated spectra of the 2-halothiophenes (Figs. 7.4 through 7.6) are examples of the results obtainable by this method (*6*). The mathematical details of the method are quite lengthy and will not be discussed here. For a complete discussion and illustrative calculations, the reader is referred to reference *5*.

2. The X Approximation and Its Generalizations

A. Approximate Constants of the Motion

Consider a spin system composed of groups of magnetically equivalent nuclei A, B, ..., X, such that

$$|\omega_{GX}| \gg |\omega_{GG'}|, \quad |J_{GG'}|, \quad |J_{GX}|, \tag{2.1}$$

where G, G′ $=$ A, B, ..., and G $\neq$ G′ $\neq$ X. When these conditions are satisfied, (1.43) shows that the interactions of group X with each of the remaining groups may be treated by first-order perturbation theory in the weak-coupling limit. Indeed, conditions (2.1) show that all terms in (1.43) multiplied by the factor J_{GX}/ω_{GX} may be omitted from the double summation; hence all eigenvectors of the system are of the form

$$|I_A, I_B, ...; m_A + m_B + \cdots\rangle | I_X, m_X\rangle.$$

It follows that I_{Xz} is a constant of the motion in a steady z field, so that the stationary hamiltonian operator for the system is

$$\mathscr{H} = -\left\{\sum_{G} \omega_G I_{Gz} + \sum_{G<G'}\sum J_{GG'} \mathbf{I}_G \cdot \mathbf{I}_{G'} + \omega_X I_{Xz} + \sum_{G \neq X} J_{GX} I_{Gz} I_{Xz}\right\}. \quad (2.2)$$

The first two sums within the brackets represent the hamiltonian operator for groups A, B, ...; the third term is the Zeeman energy for group X, and the last summation is the first-order approximation to the spin-spin interactions between group X and the remaining groups.

The validity of (2.2) for the calculation of theoretical spectra requires, in addition to (2.1), that corrections to the resonance frequencies and relative intensities of the first degree in the ratios J_{GX}/ω_{GX} ($G \neq X$) be unobservable. Systems for which both sets of conditions are satisfied are denoted $A_{n_A}B_{n_B} \cdots X_{n_X}$, and the calculation of theoretical spectra based on the hamiltonian operator (2.2) is called the *X approximation*[6] (*7–10*).

The z component of the total spin angular momentum is always a constant of the motion in a stationary z field, so that I_z still commutes with (2.2). Since I_{Xz} is a constant of the motion, the z component of the total angular momentum of groups A, B, ..., is also a constant of the motion. Thus the hamiltonian (2.2) admits the following constants of the motion:

$$\begin{gathered} I_z(\mathrm{AB}\cdots) = I_{Az} + I_{Bz} + \cdots, \qquad \mathbf{I}_A{}^2, \ \ \mathbf{I}_B{}^2, \ldots, \mathbf{I}_X{}^2, \\ I_{Xz}, \qquad I_z = I_{Az} + I_{Bz} + \cdots + I_{Xz}. \end{gathered} \quad (2.3)$$

The 2^N product kets $\{|I_A, m_A\rangle| I_B, m_B\rangle \cdots | I_X, m_X\rangle\}$ are eigenvectors of these operators, and provide a suitable initial basis for the analysis of the eigenvalue problem. Relative to this basis, the hamiltonian matrix decomposes into $(I_A, I_B, ..., I_X)$-blocks (cf. Section 4.D, Chapter 5), each block in the decomposition corresponding to a particular choice of total spin quantum numbers $I_A, I_B, ..., I_X$. Each $(I_A, I_B, ..., I_X)$-block decomposes into $2I(\max) + 1$ submatrices $[I(\max) = I_A + I_B + \cdots + I_X]$ characterized by the eigenvalues of I_z, which range from $+I(\max)$ to $-I(\max)$ in integral steps. This "factorization" of the hamiltonian matrix is always realized. However, when the X approximation is valid, the conservation of $I_z(\mathrm{AB}\cdots)$ and I_{Xz} leads to the conclusion that the submatrix of an $(I_A, I_B, ..., I_X)$-block belonging to a particular eigen-

[6] The approximate nature of (2.2) is betrayed at once by the fact that the interactions between group X and the remaining groups are not invariant under arbitrary rotations of the coordinate axes—they are invariant only under rotations about the z axis.

value of I_z decomposes into submatrices generated by product kets belonging to fixed eigenvalues of $m_{AB\cdots} = m_A + m_B + \cdots$ and m_X. As an illustration, consider the ABX system. Each group consists of a single spin-$\frac{1}{2}$ nucleus, so there is only one (I_A, I_B, I_X)-subblock—the complete 8×8 hamiltonian matrix. This matrix decomposes into four submatrices of dimensions 1, 3, 3, 1, corresponding, respectively, to the I_z eigenvalues $\frac{3}{2}, \frac{1}{2}, -\frac{1}{2}, -\frac{3}{2}$. The product kets corresponding to $m = +\frac{1}{2}$ are $|++-\rangle$, $|+-+\rangle$, $|-++\rangle$, but $|++-\rangle$ does not mix with $|+-+\rangle$ or $|-++\rangle$, since the last two kets belong to the I_{Xz} eigenvalue $+\frac{1}{2}$, whereas the I_{Xz} eigenvalue of $|++-\rangle$ is $-\frac{1}{2}$. Hence the submatrix for $m = \frac{1}{2}$ decomposes into submatrices of dimensions 1×1 and 2×2. A similar decomposition occurs for the three kets corresponding to $m = -\frac{1}{2}$.

The generalization of (2.1) through (2.3) is straightforward. For example, if there are two collections of magnetically equivalent groups {A, B, ...}, {X, Y, ...}, such that

$$|\omega_{GS}| \gg |\omega_{GG'}|, \quad |\omega_{SS'}|, \quad |J_{GG'}|, \quad |J_{SS'}|, \quad |J_{GS}|, \qquad (G, G' = A, B, \ldots; S, S' = X, Y, \ldots), \tag{2.4}$$

and corrections to the resonance frequencies and relative intensities of the first degree in the ratio J_{GS}/ω_{GS} can be neglected, the calculation of theoretical spectra may be based on the hamiltonian operator[7]

$$\mathscr{H} = -\Big\{\sum_G \omega_G I_{Gz} + \sum_{G<G'}\sum J_{GG'}\mathbf{I}_G \cdot \mathbf{I}_{G'} + \sum_S \omega_S I_{Sz} + \sum_{S<S'}\sum J_{SS'}\mathbf{I}_S \cdot \mathbf{I}_{S'} + \sum_S \sum_G J_{GS} I_{Gz} I_{Sz}\Big\}. \tag{2.5}$$

This hamiltonian admits the following constants of the motion:

$$\mathbf{I}_A{}^2, \quad \mathbf{I}_B{}^2, \ldots, \mathbf{I}_X{}^2, \quad \mathbf{I}_Y{}^2, \ldots, \qquad I_z(XY\cdots) = I_{Xz} + I_{Yz} + \cdots,$$
$$I_z(AB\cdots) = I_{Az} + I_{Bz} + \cdots, \qquad I_z = I_{Az} + I_{Bz} + \cdots + I_{Xz} + I_{Yz} + \cdots. \tag{2.6}$$

By analogy with the terminology introduced above, the calculation of theoretical spectra using (2.5) and (2.6) may be described as the XY $\cdots$ approximation.

[7] Throughout this section, G and G′ denote generic groups in the set {A, B, ...}. In sums or products, the range of G and G′ will be understood to be A, B, ..., unless otherwise noted. Similar remarks apply to S and S′, which will be used to denote generic groups in the set {X, Y, ...}.

The preceding considerations immediately suggest other variations of the X and XY approximations. For example, if there are two groups X and P, coupled to groups G = A, B, ..., and

$$|\omega_{XP}|, \quad |\omega_{GX}|, \quad |\omega_{GP}| \gg |\omega_{GG'}|, \quad |J_{GG'}|, \quad |J_{GP}|, \quad |J_{GX}|, \quad |J_{XP}|,$$

then $I_z(AB\cdots)$, I_{Xz}, and I_{Pz} commute with the stationary hamiltonian. Similarly, one may study three collections of magnetically equivalent groups {A, B, ...}, {P, Q, ...}, {X, Y, ...}, such that the coupling of a group in one collection to that in a second collection may be treated by first-order perturbation theory in the weak-coupling limit. The mathematical analysis of these and other generalizations of the X and XY approximations can be inferred from the treatment of the systems discussed in later sections of this chapter.

B. Selection Rules

Although X and XY approximations are often applicable to systems composed of nuclei with the same gyromagnetic ratio, the conditions for their validity are almost always satisfied when the gyromagnetic ratio of the nuclei in group X, or in groups X, Y, ... is different from that of the nuclei in groups A, B, ...[8] The separation theorem alluded to in Section 3.G of Chapter 5 rests upon this property. For simplicity, consider two collections of magnetically equivalent groups {A, B, ...}, {X, Y, ...}, and let the common gyromagnetic ratio for the nuclei of the first collection be denoted γ, that of the second collection γ'. Transitions are allowed between any pair of states for which the matrix elements of

$$\gamma \sum_{G} I_G^- + \gamma' \sum_{S} I_S^- \equiv \gamma I^-(AB\cdots) + \gamma' I^-(XY\cdots) \tag{2.7}$$

are nonzero. Now $I_z(AB\cdots)$ and $I_z(XY\cdots)$ are constants of the motion for the unperturbed problem, so the eigenvectors of $\mathscr{H}$ may be denoted $|m_{AB\cdots}, m_{XY\cdots})$, where $m_{AB\cdots}$ and $m_{XY\cdots}$ are the eigenvalues of $I_z(AB\cdots)$ and $I_z(XY\cdots)$, and where all other labels have been omitted to simplify the notation. The matrix elements of (2.7) are of the form

$$\gamma(m'_{AB\cdots}, m'_{XY\cdots} | I^-(AB\cdots)| m_{AB\cdots}, m_{XY\cdots})$$
$$+ \gamma'(m'_{AB\cdots}, m'_{XY\cdots} | I^-(XY\cdots)| m_{AB\cdots}, m_{XY\cdots}).$$

[8] This is certainly true for polarizing fields in the kilogauss range, but in very weak polarizing fields the X or XY approximations for mixed nuclear spin systems may not be valid.

But

$$[I^-(\text{AB}\cdots), I_z(\text{AB}\cdots)] = I^-(\text{AB}\cdots), \qquad [I^-(\text{AB}\cdots), I_z(\text{XY}\cdots)] = 0,$$

$$[I^-(\text{XY}\cdots), I_z(\text{XY}\cdots)] = I^-(\text{XY}\cdots), \qquad [I^-(\text{XY}\cdots), I_z(\text{AB}\cdots)] = 0,$$

so that

$$(m'_{\text{AB}\cdots}, m'_{\text{XY}\cdots} \mid I^-(\text{AB}\cdots) \mid m_{\text{AB}\cdots}, m_{\text{XY}\cdots}) = 0,$$

unless

$$m'_{\text{AB}\cdots} = m_{\text{AB}\cdots} - 1, \qquad m'_{\text{XY}\cdots} = m_{\text{XY}\cdots}; \tag{2.8}$$

$$(m'_{\text{AB}\cdots}, m'_{\text{XY}\cdots} \mid I^-(\text{XY}\cdots) \mid m_{\text{AB}\cdots}, m_{\text{XY}\cdots}) = 0,$$

unless

$$m'_{\text{AB}\cdots} = m_{\text{AB}\cdots}, \qquad m'_{\text{XY}\cdots} = m_{\text{XY}\cdots} - 1. \tag{2.9}$$

It follows that allowed transitions may be divided into two classes: (1) those for which $\Delta m_{\text{AB}\cdots} = -1$, and $\Delta m_{\text{XY}\cdots} = 0$; (2) those for which $\Delta m_{\text{XY}\cdots} = -1$, and $\Delta m_{\text{AB}\cdots} = 0$. These selection rules are consistent with the selection rule for the eigenvalues of I_z: $\Delta m = \Delta m_{\text{AB}\cdots} + \Delta m_{\text{XY}\cdots} = -1$.

Since the intensities of transitions associated with nuclei of different gyromagnetic ratios are not ordinarily compared, γ and γ' may be omitted from (2.7). It is permissible, therefore, to apply the results established in Section 4 of Chapter 5 to mixed nuclear spin systems, with the understanding that only the intensities for transitions associated with a given nuclear species may be directly compared.

The selection rules (2.8) and (2.9) are illustrated in Fig. 7.7(a) for

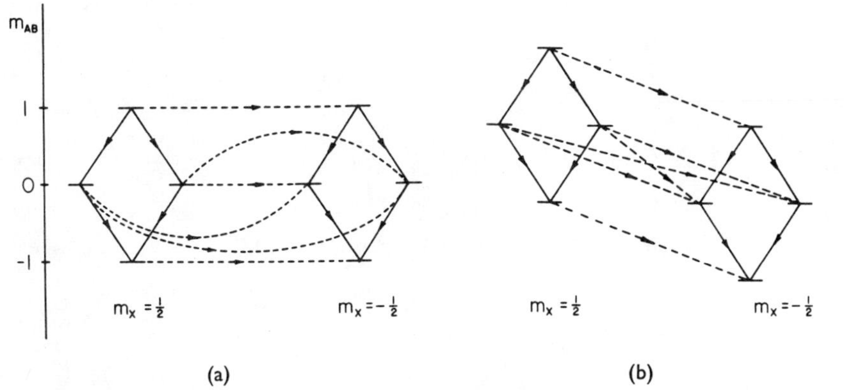

FIG. 7.7. Transition diagrams for the ABX system.

the ABX system. The solid lines indicate transitions that conserve $m_{\rm X}$ and appear in the AB region of the spectrum; the dashed lines conserve $m_{\rm AB}$ and appear in the X region of the spectrum. The use of curved lines to denote transitions in the X region can be avoided by displacing one set of "levels," as shown in part (b) of the figure.

C. Intensity Theorems

A spin system of the form $\mathrm{A}_{n_\mathrm{A}}\mathrm{B}_{n_\mathrm{B}} \cdots \mathrm{X}_{n_\mathrm{X}}\mathrm{Y}_{n_\mathrm{Y}} \cdots$ can always be decomposed into its irreducible components $\mathrm{A}_{I_\mathrm{A}}\mathrm{B}_{I_\mathrm{B}} \cdots \mathrm{X}_{I_\mathrm{X}}\mathrm{Y}_{I_\mathrm{Y}} \cdots$. According to the discussion in Section 4.F of Chapter 5, the total intensity of an irreducible component is

$$\mathrm{Int}\, \mathrm{A}_{I_\mathrm{A}}\mathrm{B}_{I_\mathrm{B}} \cdots \mathrm{X}_{I_\mathrm{X}}\mathrm{Y}_{I_\mathrm{Y}} \cdots = \tfrac{2}{3}\prod_{\mathrm{G}}(2I_\mathrm{G}+1)\prod_{\mathrm{S}}(2I_\mathrm{S}+1)\Big\{\sum_{\mathrm{G}} I_\mathrm{G}(I_\mathrm{G}+1) + \sum_{\mathrm{S}} I_\mathrm{S}(I_\mathrm{S}+1)\Big\}. \quad (2.10)$$

If a given irreducible component occurs more than once in the decomposition, its contribution to the total intensity is obtained through multiplication of (2.10) by $g_{I_\mathrm{A}} g_{I_\mathrm{B}} \cdots g_{I_\mathrm{X}} g_{I_\mathrm{Y}} \cdots$.

In the XY $\cdots$ approximation, it follows, from (2.8) and (2.9), that the total intensity of an irreducible component is equal to the sum of the spectral intensities of the AB $\cdots$ regions and XY $\cdots$ regions:

$$\mathrm{Int}\, \mathrm{A}_{I_\mathrm{A}}\mathrm{B}_{I_\mathrm{B}} \cdots \mathrm{X}_{I_\mathrm{X}}\mathrm{Y}_{I_\mathrm{Y}} \cdots = \mathrm{Int}\{\mathrm{A}_{I_\mathrm{A}}\mathrm{B}_{I_\mathrm{B}} \cdots \mathrm{X}_{I_\mathrm{X}}\mathrm{Y}_{I_\mathrm{Y}} \cdots\}_{\mathrm{AB}\cdots} + \mathrm{Int}\{\mathrm{A}_{I_\mathrm{A}}\mathrm{B}_{I_\mathrm{B}} \cdots \mathrm{X}_{I_\mathrm{X}}\mathrm{Y}_{I_\mathrm{Y}} \cdots\}_{\mathrm{XY}\cdots}, \quad (2.11)$$

where[9]

$$\mathrm{Int}\{\mathrm{A}_{I_\mathrm{A}}\mathrm{B}_{I_\mathrm{B}} \cdots \mathrm{X}_{I_\mathrm{X}}\mathrm{Y}_{I_\mathrm{Y}} \cdots\}_{\mathrm{AB}\cdots} = \mathrm{tr}\, I^+(\mathrm{AB}\cdots)I^-(\mathrm{AB}\cdots) = \tfrac{2}{3}\prod_{\mathrm{S}}(2I_\mathrm{S}+1)\prod_{\mathrm{G}}(2I_\mathrm{G}+1)\Big\{\sum_{\mathrm{G}} I_\mathrm{G}(I_\mathrm{G}+1)\Big\}, \quad (2.12)$$

$$\mathrm{Int}\{\mathrm{A}_{I_\mathrm{A}}\mathrm{B}_{I_\mathrm{B}} \cdots \mathrm{X}_{I_\mathrm{X}}\mathrm{Y}_{I_\mathrm{Y}} \cdots\}_{\mathrm{XY}\cdots} = \mathrm{tr}\, I^+(\mathrm{XY}\cdots)I^-(\mathrm{XY}\cdots) = \tfrac{2}{3}\prod_{\mathrm{G}}(2I_\mathrm{G}+1)\prod_{\mathrm{S}}(2I_\mathrm{S}+1)\Big\{\sum_{\mathrm{S}} I_\mathrm{S}(I_\mathrm{S}+1)\Big\}. \quad (2.13)$$

[9] See Appendix V.

If the irreducible component $A_{I_A}B_{I_B} \cdots X_{I_X}Y_{I_Y} \cdots$ occurs more than once in the decomposition of the system, (2.11) through (2.13) must be multiplied by $g_{I_A}g_{I_B} \cdots g_{I_X}g_{I_Y} \cdots$.

The total intensity of any system composed of N spin-$\frac{1}{2}$ nuclei is $2^{N-1}N$. In the XY $\cdots$ approximation, the total intensity decomposes as follows:

$$\text{Int}\{A_{n_A}B_{n_B} \cdots X_{n_X}Y_{n_Y}\}_{AB\cdots} = 2^{N-1}(n_A + n_B + \cdots), \tag{2.14}$$

$$\text{Int}\{A_{n_A}B_{n_B} \cdots X_{n_X}Y_{n_Y}\}_{XY\cdots} = 2^{N-1}(n_X + n_Y + \cdots). \tag{2.15}$$

To illustrate these relations, consider the $ABX(\equiv A_{1/2}B_{1/2}X_{1/2})$ system. Equations (2.10), (2.12), and (2.13) yield

$$\text{Int}\, A_{1/2}B_{1/2}X_{1/2} = 12, \qquad \text{Int}\{A_{1/2}B_{1/2}X_{1/2}\}_{AB} = 8, \qquad \text{Int}\{A_{1/2}B_{1/2}X_{1/2}\}_X = 4.$$

If the ABX system is considered as an irreducible component of an A_3BX_3 system, each of these numbers must be increased by a factor of four.

D. Effective Chemical Shifts

The AB $\cdots$ region of an $A_{n_A}B_{n_B} \cdots X_{n_X}$ system can be decomposed into subspectra of the $A_{n_A}B_{n_B} \cdots$ type, by virtue of the conservation of I_{Xz} for all transitions in the AB $\cdots$-region of the spectrum. For since these transitions conserve I_{Xz}, it is permissible to replace I_{Xz} in (2.2) with one of its eigenvalues, say m_X, to obtain

$$\mathscr{H}(m_X) = -\left\{\sum_G (\omega_G + J_{GX}m_X)I_{Gz} + \sum_{G<G'}\sum J_{GG'}\mathbf{I}_G \cdot \mathbf{I}_{G'}\right\}. \tag{2.16}$$

The term $\omega_X m_X$ has been omitted from (2.16) since it is canceled in all energy differences that yield frequencies in the AB $\cdots$ region of the spectrum.

Equation (2.16) has the form of the hamiltonian operator for an $A_{n_A}B_{n_B} \cdots$ system with effective Larmor frequencies (*9*)

$$\omega_G{}^* = \omega_G + J_{GX}m_X. \tag{2.17}$$

For each value of m_X, equations (2.16) and (2.17), together with the usual rules for the calculation of resonance frequencies and relative intensities, define a pseudo $A_{n_A}B_{n_B} \cdots$ system whose spectrum is identical with that of a "normal" $A_{n_A}B_{n_B} \cdots$ system, except for the replacement of ω_G with $\omega_G{}^*$. If m_X is $\nu(m_X)$-fold degenerate, the pseudo $A_{n_A}B_{n_B}\cdots$ system associated with the eigenvalue m_X will appear in the spectrum with relative weight $\nu(m_X)$. The total number of pseudo $A_{n_A}B_{n_B}\cdots$ systems is $2I_X(\max) + 1 = n_X + 1$. For example, the AB region of an ABX_3 system will include four pseudo AB quartets with relative weights 1 : 3 : 3 : 1, and effective internal chemical shifts $\delta \pm \frac{3}{2}(J_{AX} - J_{BX})$, $\delta \pm \frac{1}{2}(J_{AX} - J_{BX})$.

The preceding considerations also apply to the $A_{n_A}B_{n_B}\cdots P_{n_P}X_{n_X}$ systems, where both I_{Pz} and I_{Xz} are conserved for all transitions in the AB $\cdots$ region of the spectrum. The effective Larmor frequencies are

$$\omega_G{}^* = \omega_G + J_{GX}m_X + J_{GP}m_P\,. \tag{2.18}$$

The AB $\cdots$ region of the spectrum will include the spectra of $(n_X + 1)(n_P + 1)$ pseudo $A_{n_A}B_{n_B}\cdots$ systems, corresponding to the $(n_X + 1)(n_P + 1)$ ways of choosing the eigenvalues m_X and m_P. The spectrum of the pseudo $A_{n_A}B_{n_B}\cdots$ system associated with a particular choice of m_X and m_P will appear with relative weight $\nu(m_X)\nu(m_P)$.

These remarks are not generally applicable to systems of the type $A_{n_A}B_{n_B}\cdots X_{n_X}Y_{n_Y}\cdots$, since $I_{Xz}, I_{Yz}, \ldots$ are not constants of motion for every stationary state of the system. However, for each choice of the total spin quantum numbers, there will always be two states which conserve $I_{Xz}, I_{Yz}, \ldots$, namely $| I_A, I_B, \ldots, m_{AB} \cdots; I_X, \pm I_X, I_Y, \pm I_Y, \ldots\rangle$. These states lead to spectra of the $A_{n_A}B_{n_B}\cdots$ type in the AB $\cdots$ region with effective Larmor frequencies $\omega_G \pm J_{GX}I_X \pm J_{GY}I_Y \cdots$. Similarly, the states $| I_A, \pm I_A, I_B, \pm I_B, \ldots, I_X, I_Y, \ldots, m_{XY} \cdots\rangle$ lead to spectra of the $X_{n_X}Y_{n_Y}\cdots$ type in the XY $\cdots$ region with effective Larmor frequencies $\omega_S \pm J_{SA}I_A \pm J_{SB}I_B \cdots$.

3. The $A_{n_A}BX_{n_X}$ System

A. Diagonalization of the Hamiltonian Matrix

The study of the $A_{n_A}BX_{n_X}$ system can be carried through by a simple generalization of the method used in the study of the $A_{n_A}B$ system. The hamiltonian operator is

$$\mathscr{H} = -\{\omega_A I_{Az} + \omega_B I_{Bz} + \omega_X I_{Xz} + J_{AB}\mathbf{I}_A \cdot \mathbf{I}_B + J_{AX}I_{Az}I_{Xz} + J_{BX}I_{Bz}I_{Xz}\}, \tag{3.1}$$

so that $\mathbf{I}_A{}^2$, $\mathbf{I}_B{}^2$, $\mathbf{I}_X{}^2$, I_z, $I_{Az} + I_{Bz}$, and I_{Xz} are constants of the motion.

The total spin quantum numbers and spin multiplicities of groups A and X are given by the following expressions with G = A or X:

$$I_G = \tfrac{1}{2}n_G - k, \qquad g_{I_G} = \frac{n_G!(n_G - 2k + 1)}{(n_G - k + 1)!k!}, \qquad k = \begin{cases} 0, 1, \ldots, n_G/2 & \text{for } n_G \text{ even}, \\ 0, 1, \ldots, (n_G - 1)/2 & \text{for } n_G \text{ odd}. \end{cases} \tag{3.2}$$

Since group B consists of a single nucleus with $I_B = \frac{1}{2}$, $g_{1/2} = 1$, a suitable initial basis for an irreducible $A_{I_A}B_{1/2}X_{I_X}$ component system is generated by product kets of the form

$$|I_A, m_A\rangle|\tfrac{1}{2}, \pm\tfrac{1}{2}\rangle|I_X, m_X\rangle \equiv |I_A, m_A; \tfrac{1}{2}, \pm\tfrac{1}{2}; I_X, m_X\rangle.$$

Mixing occurs only between product kets with the same eigenvalue of I_z. Furthermore, since $I_{Az} + I_{Bz}$ and I_{Xz} also commute with $\mathscr{H}$, each submatrix of $\mathscr{H}$ characterized by a given value of m must admit a further decomposition into submatrices characterized by fixed values of $m_A + m_B$ and m_X. It follows that mixing occurs only between pairs of product kets of the form

$$\left.\begin{array}{l} |I_A, m_A; \tfrac{1}{2}, \tfrac{1}{2}; I_X, m_X\rangle \\ |I_A, m_A + 1; \tfrac{1}{2}, -\tfrac{1}{2}; I_X, m_X\rangle \end{array}\right. \qquad (m = m_A + \tfrac{1}{2} + m_X). \tag{3.3}$$

Hence the diagonalization of $\mathscr{H}$ requires the solution of algebraic equations of, at most, the second degree.

The 2×2 submatrix for a generic pair of states with $m = m_A + \frac{1}{2} + m_X$ may be obtained by computing the matrix elements of $\mathscr{H}$ with respect to the kets (3.3)

$$\langle I_A, m_A; \tfrac{1}{2}, \tfrac{1}{2}; I_X, m_X | \mathscr{H} | I_A, m_A; \tfrac{1}{2}, \tfrac{1}{2}; I_X, m_X\rangle$$
$$= -\{m_A\omega_A + \tfrac{1}{2}\omega_B + m_X\omega_X + \tfrac{1}{2}m_A J_{AB} + \tfrac{1}{2}m_X J_{BX} + m_A m_X J_{AX}\},$$

$$\langle I_A, m_A + 1; \tfrac{1}{2}, -\tfrac{1}{2}; I_X, m_X | \mathscr{H} | I_A, m_A + 1; \tfrac{1}{2}, -\tfrac{1}{2}; I_X, m_X\rangle$$
$$= -\{(m_A + 1)\omega_A - \tfrac{1}{2}\omega_B + m_X\omega_X - \tfrac{1}{2}(m_A + 1)J_{AB} - \tfrac{1}{2}m_X J_{BX}$$
$$+ m_X(m_A + 1)J_{AX}\},$$

$$\langle I_A, m_A; \tfrac{1}{2}, \tfrac{1}{2}; I_X, m_X | \mathscr{H} | I_A, m_A + 1; \tfrac{1}{2}, -\tfrac{1}{2}; I_X, m_X\rangle$$
$$= \langle I_A, m_A + 1; \tfrac{1}{2}, -\tfrac{1}{2}; I_X, m_X | \mathscr{H} | I_A, m_A; \tfrac{1}{2}, \tfrac{1}{2}; I_X, m_X\rangle$$
$$= -\tfrac{1}{2}J_{AB}[(I_A - m_A)(I_A + m_A + 1)]^{1/2}.$$

The diagonalization of the 2×2 matrix defined by these equations yields the eigenvalues and eigenvectors given in Table 7.6, where

$$\begin{aligned} R(I_A, m_A, m_X) &= \{[\delta - \tfrac{1}{2}(2m_A + 1)J_{AB} + (J_{AX} - J_{BX})m_X]^2 \\ &\quad + J_{AB}^2(I_A - m_A)(I_A + m_A + 1)\}^{1/2}, \\ Q(I_A, m_A, m_X) &= \frac{J_{AB}[(I_A - m_A)(I_A + m_A + 1)]^{1/2}}{\delta - \tfrac{1}{2}(2m_A + 1)J_{AB} + (J_{AX} - J_{BX})m_X + R(I_A, m_A, m_X)}, \\ \delta &= \omega_A - \omega_B . \end{aligned} \tag{3.4}$$

B. Spectra of $A_{n_A}BX_{n_X}$ Systems

The spectrum of the irreducible $A_{I_A}B_{1/2}X_{I_X}$ system may be determined by calculations similar to those used in the analysis of the $A_{n_A}B$ system. The results of these calculations are recorded in Table 7.7, where $F(I_G, m_G)$ is given by (1.19). The spectrum of an $A_{n_A}BX_{n_X}$ spin system is determined by assigning values to I_A and I_X, consistent with n_A and n_X, and computing a partial spectrum by permitting m_A and m_X to assume all values allowed by the first column of the table. The intensity of every resonance computed with a particular choice of I_A and I_X must be multiplied by the factor $g_{I_A}g_{I_X}$. The complete spectrum is obtained by iterating this process until all possible pairings of I_A and I_X have been exhausted.

The number of A, B, X, and M transitions defined by Table 7.7 may be determined as follows. For the first A transition of Table 7.7, m_A may assume any of the $2I_A$ values $I_A - 1, I_A - 2, \ldots, -I_A$. There are also $2I_A$ possible values of m_A for the second A transition. For each A transition, there are $2I_X + 1$ possible values of m_X, so that

$$N_A = \sum_{I_A} \sum_{I_X} 4I_A(2I_X + 1). \tag{3.5}$$

The double sum may be evaluated with the help of (3.2) and the formula for the sum of the first n integers. Similar remarks apply to the calculation of N_B, N_X, and N_M, except that $I_A = 0$ is excluded as a possible spin quantum number in the first M transition, and $I_A = I_X = 0$ are excluded as spin quantum numbers for the last two M transitions. The results are given in Table 7.8, where e denotes an even integer, o an odd integer. The principal use of this table is to verify that all transitions of the $A_{n_A}BX_{n_X}$ system defined by Table 7.7 have been calculated—it is not intended as a guide for testing experimental spectra.

TABLE 7.6

EIGENVALUES AND EIGENVECTORS FOR THE IRREDUCIBLE $A_{I_A}B_{1/2}X_{I_X}$ SYSTEM

Eigenvector	Eigenvalue
$\frac{1}{[1 + Q^2(I_A, m_A, m_X)]^{1/2}} \{\| I_A, m_A + 1; \frac{1}{2}, -\frac{1}{2}; I_X, m_X\rangle + Q(I_A, m_A, m_X) \| I_A, m_A; \frac{1}{2}, \frac{1}{2}; I_X, m_X\rangle\}$	$-\frac{1}{2}\{(2m_A + 1)\omega_A + 2m_X\omega_X - \frac{1}{2}J_{AB} + J_{AX}m_X(2m_A + 1) + R(I_A, m_A, m_X)\}$
$\frac{1}{[1 + Q^2(I_A, m_A, m_X)]^{1/2}} \{Q(I_A, m_A, m_X) \| I_A, m_A + 1; \frac{1}{2}, -\frac{1}{2}; I_X, m_X\rangle - \| I_A, m_A; \frac{1}{2}, \frac{1}{2}; I_X, m_X\rangle\}$	$-\frac{1}{2}\{(2m_A + 1)\omega_A + 2m_X\omega_X - \frac{1}{2}J_{AB} + J_{AX}m_X(2m_A + 1) - R(I_A, m_A, m_X)\}$

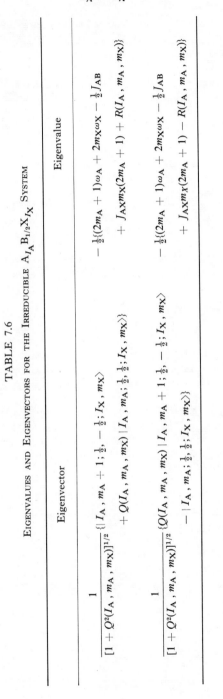

TABLE 7.7 — RESONANCE FREQUENCIES AND RELATIVE

	Transition[a]	Frequency
A_1:	$\vert I_A, m_A+1; \frac{1}{2}, -\frac{1}{2}; I_X, m_X\rangle \rightarrow \vert I_A, m_A; \frac{1}{2}, -\frac{1}{2}; I_X, m_X\rangle$	$\omega_A + J_{AX}m_X + \frac{1}{2}\{R(I_A, m_A, m_X) - R(I_A, m_A-1, m_X)\}$
A_2:	$\vert I_A, m_A; \frac{1}{2}, \frac{1}{2}; I_X, m_X\rangle \rightarrow \vert I_A, m_A-1; \frac{1}{2}, \frac{1}{2}; I_X, m_X\rangle$	$\omega_A + J_{AX}m_X + \frac{1}{2}\{R(I_A, m_A-1, m_X) - R(I_A, m_A, m_X)\}$
B :	$\vert I_A, m_A; \frac{1}{2}, \frac{1}{2}; I_X, m_X\rangle \rightarrow \vert I_A, m_A; \frac{1}{2}, -\frac{1}{2}; I_X, m_X\rangle$	$\omega_A + J_{AX}m_X - \frac{1}{2}\{R(I_A, m_A, m_X) + R(I_A, m_A-1, m_X)\}$
X_1:	$\vert I_A, m_A+1; \frac{1}{2}, -\frac{1}{2}; I_X, m_X\rangle \rightarrow \vert I_A, m_A+1; \frac{1}{2}, -\frac{1}{2}; I_X, m_X-1\rangle$	$\omega_X + \frac{1}{2}J_{AX}(2m_A+1) + \frac{1}{2}\{R(I_A, m_A, m_X) - R(I_A, m_A, m_X-1)\}$
X_2:	$\vert I_A, m_A; \frac{1}{2}, \frac{1}{2}; I_X, m_X\rangle \rightarrow \vert I_A, m_A; \frac{1}{2}, \frac{1}{2}; I_X, m_X-1\rangle$	$\omega_X + \frac{1}{2}J_{AX}(2m_A+1) + \frac{1}{2}\{R(I_A, m_A, m_X-1) - R(I_A, m_A, m_X)\}$
M_1:	$\vert I_A, m_A+1; \frac{1}{2}, -\frac{1}{2}; I_X, m_X\rangle \rightarrow \vert I_A, m_A-1; \frac{1}{2}, \frac{1}{2}; I_X, m_X\rangle$	$\omega_A + J_{AX}m_X + \frac{1}{2}\{R(I_A, m_A, m_X) + R(I_A, m_A-1, m_X)\}$
M_2:	$\vert I_A, m_A+1; \frac{1}{2}, -\frac{1}{2}; I_X, m_X\rangle \rightarrow \vert I_A, m_A; \frac{1}{2}, \frac{1}{2}; I_X, m_X-1\rangle$	$\omega_X + \frac{1}{2}J_{AX}(2m_A+1) + \frac{1}{2}\{R(I_A, m_A, m_X-1) + R(I_A, m_A, m_X)\}$
M_3:	$\vert I_A, m_A; \frac{1}{2}, \frac{1}{2}; I_X, m_X\rangle \rightarrow \vert I_A, m_A+1; \frac{1}{2}, -\frac{1}{2}; I_X, m_X-1\rangle$	$\omega_X + \frac{1}{2}J_{AX}(2m_A+1) - \frac{1}{2}\{R(I_A, m_A, m_X-1) + R(I_A, m_A, m_X)\}$

[a] In the limit as all $J_{ij} \rightarrow 0$.

TABLE 7.8 — NUMBER OF A, B, X, AND

(n_A, n_X)	N_A	N_B
(e, e)	$n_A\left(\frac{n_A}{2}+1\right)\left(\frac{n_X}{2}+1\right)^2$	$\left(\frac{n_A}{2}+1\right)^2\left(\frac{n_X}{2}+1\right)^2$
(e, o)	$\frac{n_A}{4}\left(\frac{n_A}{2}+1\right)(n_X+1)(n_X+3)$	$\left(\frac{n_A}{2}+1\right)^2 \frac{(n_X+1)(n_X+3)}{4}$
(o, e)	$\frac{1}{2}(n_A+1)^2\left(\frac{n_X}{2}+1\right)^2$	$\frac{(n_A+1)(n_A+3)}{4}\left(\frac{n_X}{2}+1\right)^2$
(o, o)	$\frac{1}{8}(n_A+1)^2(n_X+1)(n_X+3)$	$\frac{(n_A+1)(n_A+3)(n_X+1)(n_X+3)}{16}$

INTENSITIES FOR THE IRREDUCIBLE $A_{I_A}B_{1/2}X_{I_X}$ SYSTEM

Intensity
$\dfrac{\{F(I_A, m_A) + Q(I_A, m_A, m_X)[1 + Q(I_A, m_A - 1, m_X)F(I_A, m_A - 1)]\}^2}{[1 + Q^2(I_A, m_A, m_X)][1 + Q^2(I_A, m_A - 1, m_X)]}$
$\dfrac{\{Q(I_A, m_A - 1, m_X)[Q(I_A, m_A, m_X)F(I_A, m_A) - 1] + F(I_A, m_A - 1)\}^2}{[1 + Q^2(I_A, m_A, m_X)][1 + Q^2(I_A, m_A - 1, m_X)]}$
$\dfrac{\{F(I_A, m_A)Q(I_A, m_A, m_X) - [1 + F(I_A, m_A - 1)Q(I_A, m_A - 1, m_X)]\}^2}{[1 + Q^2(I_A, m_A, m_X)][1 + Q^2(I_A, m_A - 1, m_X)]}$
$\dfrac{[1 + Q(I_A, m_A, m_X)Q(I_A, m_A, m_X - 1)]^2F^2(I_X, m_X - 1)}{[1 + Q^2(I_A, m_A, m_X)][1 + Q^2(I_A, m_A, m_X - 1)]}$
$\dfrac{[1 + Q(I_A, m_A, m_X)Q(I_A, m_A, m_X - 1)]^2F^2(I_X, m_X - 1)}{[1 + Q^2(I_A, m_A, m_X)][1 + Q^2(I_A, m_A, m_X - 1)]}$
$\dfrac{\{[F(I_A, m_A) + Q(I_A, m_A, m_X)]Q(I_A, m_A - 1, m_X) - Q(I_A, m_A, m_X)F(I_A, m_A - 1)\}^2}{[1 + Q^2(I_A, m_A, m_X)][1 + Q^2(I_A, m_A - 1, m_X)]}$
$\dfrac{[Q(I_A, m_A, m_X - 1) - Q(I_A, m_A, m_X)]^2F^2(I_X, m_X - 1)}{[1 + Q^2(I_A, m_A, m_X - 1)][1 + Q^2(I_A, m_A, m_X)]}$
$\dfrac{[Q(I_A, m_A, m_X - 1) - Q(I_A, m_A, m_X)]^2F^2(I_X, m_X - 1)}{[1 + Q^2(I_A, m_A, m_X - 1)][1 + Q^2(I_A, m_A, m_X)]}$

M TRANSITIONS FOR THE $A_{n_A}BX_{n_X}$ SPIN SYSTEM

N_X	N_M
$n_X\left(\frac{n_X}{2}+1\right)\left(\frac{n_A}{2}+1\right)^2$	$\frac{n_A}{2}\left(\frac{n_X}{2}+1\right)\left[\frac{n_A}{2}\left(\frac{n_X}{2}+1\right)+n_X\left(\frac{n_A}{2}+1\right)\right]$
$\frac{1}{2}(n_X+1)^2\left(\frac{n_A}{2}+1\right)^2$	$\frac{n_A}{2}\left(\frac{n_X+1}{4}\right)\left[\frac{n_A(n_X+3)}{2}+2(n_X+1)\left(\frac{n_A}{2}+1\right)\right]$
$\frac{n_X}{4}\left(\frac{n_X}{2}+1\right)(n_A+1)(n_A+3)$	$\frac{1}{4}\left(\frac{n_X}{2}+1\right)\left[(n_A^2-1)\left(\frac{n_X}{2}+1\right)+n_X(n_A+1)^2\right]$
$\frac{1}{8}(n_X+1)^2(n_A+1)(n_A+3)$	$\frac{1}{16}(n_X+1)(n_A^2-1)(n_X+3)+2(n_A+1)^2(n_X+1)]$

C. Properties of $A_{n_A}BX_{n_X}$ Spectra

The allowed values of m_A for the first X transition of Table 7.7 are $m_A = I_A - 1, I_A - 2, \ldots, -I_A, -I_A - 1$, while $m_A = I_A, I_A - 1, \ldots, -I_A$, for the second X transition. Now

$$Q(I_A, I_A, m_X) = Q(I_A, -I_A - 1, m_X) = 0,$$

$$R(I_A, I_A, m_X) = \delta - \tfrac{1}{2}(2I_A + 1)J_{AB} + (J_{AX} - J_{BX})m_X,$$

$$R(I_A, -I_A - 1, m_X) = \delta + \tfrac{1}{2}(2I_A + 1)J_{AB} + (J_{AX} - J_{BX})m_X,$$

so that the resonance frequencies and relative intensities of the two X transitions corresponding to $m_A = -I_A - 1$, and $m_A = I_A$ are as given in the accompanying tabulation. These resonances constitute a symmetrical doublet whose mean frequency is ω_X. Their frequency separation is $|2I_AJ_{AX} + J_{BX}|$, which is independent of the applied field. The complete $A_{n_A}BX_{n_X}$ spectrum will contain $\frac{1}{2}(n_A + 1)$ or $\frac{1}{2}n_A + 1$ doublets of this type, accordingly as n_A is odd or even.

m_A	Relative intensity	Frequency
$-I_A - 1$	$(I_X + m_X)(I_X - m_X + 1)$	$\omega_X - \frac{1}{2}\{(2I_A + 1)J_{AX} - (J_{AX} - J_{BX})\}$
I_A	$(I_X + m_X)(I_X - m_X + 1)$	$\omega_X + \frac{1}{2}\{(2I_A + 1)J_{AX} - (J_{AX} - J_{BX})\}$

The remaining values of m_A (viz., $I_A - 1, I_A - 2, \ldots, -I_A$) are used in both X transitions, and an examination of the expressions for the resonance frequencies and relative intensities shows that these quantum numbers generate symmetrical doublets whose mean frequencies are $\omega_X + \frac{1}{2}(2m_A + 1)J_{AX}$. It can also be shown that the last two mixed transitions in Table 7.7 also generate symmetrical doublets in the X region of the spectrum.

The remaining transitions of Table 7.7 occur in the AB region of the spectrum. According to the discussion of Section 2.D, the AB region consists of $n_X + 1$ pseudo $A_{n_A}B$ systems with effective Larmor frequencies and internal chemical shift:

$$\omega_A^*(m_X) = \omega_A + J_{AX}m_X, \qquad \omega_B^*(m_X) = \omega_B + J_{BX}m_X, \tag{3.6}$$

$$\delta^*(m_X) = \delta + (J_{AX} - J_{BX})m_X. \tag{3.7}$$

D. Signs of the Coupling Constants

The spin-spin interactions of an $A_{n_A}BX_{n_X}$ system are described by three coupling constants, so that the study of an experimental spectrum must include an investigation of the relative signs of the spin-spin coupling constants. Let Λ_0 denote the spin inversion operator for the AB nuclei, and Λ_1 the spin inversion operator for nucleus X, so that $\Lambda = \Lambda_0 \Lambda_1$. If $\mathscr{H}'$ denotes the hamiltonian operator for the $A_{n_A}BX_{n_X}$ system when the sign of J_{AB} is reversed, i.e.,

$$\mathscr{H}' = -\{\omega_A I_{Az} + \omega_B I_{Bz} + \omega_X I_{Xz} - J_{AB}\mathbf{I}_A \cdot \mathbf{I}_B + J_{AX} I_{Az} I_{Xz} + J_{BX} I_{Bz} I_{Xz}\},$$

then (cf. Section 3.F, Chapter 5)

$$\mathscr{H}'\Lambda_0 = -\Lambda_0 \mathscr{H} - 2\omega_X \Lambda_0 I_{Xz} .$$

Thus if $\{| m_{AB} ; m_X)\}$ and $\{\Omega(m_{AB}, m_X)\}$ are the eigenvectors and eigenvalues of $\mathscr{H}$, those of $\mathscr{H}'$ are $\{\Lambda_0 | m_{AB} ; m_X)\}$, $\{-\Omega(m_{AB}, m_X) - 2\omega_X m_X\}$.

The AB and X regions of the spectrum as computed with respect to the eigenvalues and eigenvectors of $\mathscr{H}$ are given by transitions of the form indicated in Scheme I. The corresponding scheme for the spectrum computed with the eigenvalues and eigenvectors of $\mathscr{H}'$ is shown in Scheme II.

If the frequency of the X transition in the first scheme is written in the form

$$\Omega(m_{AB}, m_X - 1) - \Omega(m_{AB}, m_X) = \omega_X + f(m_{AB}, m_X - 1) - f(m_{AB}, m_X),$$

SCHEME I

Transition	Intensity	Frequency
$\| m_{AB}; m_X) \rightarrow \| m_{AB} - 1; m_X)$	$\| (m_{AB} - 1; m_X \| I_x(AB) \| m_{AB}; m_X) \|^2$	$\Omega(m_{AB} - 1, m_X) - \Omega(m_{AB}, m_X)$
$\| m_{AB}; m_X) \rightarrow \| m_{AB}; m_X - 1)$	$\| (m_{AB}; m_X - 1 \| I_x(X) \| m_{AB}; m_X) \|^2$	$\Omega(m_{AB}, m_X - 1) - \Omega(m_{AB}, m_X)$

SCHEME II

Transition	Intensity	Frequency
$\Lambda_0 \| m_{AB} - 1; m_X) \rightarrow \Lambda_0 \| m_A; m_X)$	$\| (m_{AB} - 1; m_X \| I_x(AB) \| m_{AB}; m_X) \|^2$	$\Omega(m_{AB} - 1, m_X) - \Omega(m_{AB}, m_X)$
$\Lambda_0 \| m_{AB}; m_X) \rightarrow \Lambda_0 \| m_A; m_X - 1)$	$\| (m_{AB}; m_X - 1 \| I_x(X) \| m_{AB}; m_X) \|^2$	$2\omega_X + \Omega(m_{AB}, m_X) - \Omega(m_{AB}, m_X - 1)$

the frequency of the X transition in the second table may be written in the form

$$\Omega(m_{AB}, m_X) - \Omega(m_{AB}, m_X - 1) = \omega_X - f(m_{AB}, m_X - 1) + f(m_{AB}, m_X).$$

A comparison of both schemes now shows that

(1) The AB region of an $A_{n_A}BX_{n_X}$ spectrum is invariant with respect to the transformation $J_{AB} \to -J_{AB}$.

(2) The X region of an $A_{n_A}BX_{n_X}$ spectrum is reflected in the line $\omega = \omega_X$ when $J_{AB} \to -J_{AB}$.

These properties also hold for the transformation $J_{AX} \to -J_{AX}$, $J_{BX} \to -J_{BX}$. For the complete spectrum is invariant with respect to a change in the signs of all coupling constants, so that a change in the sign of J_{AB} is equivalent to reversing the signs of J_{AX} and J_{BX}.

The preceding analysis leads to the conclusion that all relative signs may be determined if the theoretical spectrum for the X region is not symmetrical with respect to ω_X, provided, of course, that the predicted asymmetry can be observed experimentally. If the X region is symmetrical with respect to ω_X, the complete spectrum will be independent of the sign of J_{AB}. However, it may be possible to determine the sign of J_{AX} relative to that of J_{BX}. These remarks also hold for the $A_{n_A}B_{n_B}X_{n_X}$ system, and, more generally, for the $A_{n_A}B_{n_B} \cdots X_{n_X}$ system. In the latter case, properties (1) and (2) refer to a change in the signs of J_{AB}, $J_{AC} \cdots$. The determination of some or all the signs of J_{GX}, G = A, B, ..., relative to J_{AB}, J_{AC}, ..., thus requires an observable asymmetry in the X region of the spectrum.

E. Reduction to Special Cases

When the quantum numbers I_X and m_X are identically zero, the formulas for the $A_{n_A}BX_{n_X}$ system correctly reduce to those of the $A_{n_A}B$ system. If I_A and m_A are identically zero, the resonance frequencies and relative intensities of the $A_{n_A}BX_{n_X}$ system reduce to the first-order expressions for the weakly coupled BX_{n_X} system.

The reduction of Table 7.7 when n_A and n_X are nonzero is carried through by a procedure analogous to that used in the discussion of the $A_{n_A}B$ system.

The ABX_{n_X} *System*

The spectrum of the ABX_{n_X} system is obtained from Table 7.7 by setting $I_A = \frac{1}{2}$ and inserting the appropriate values for m_A. The required values of m_A are $A_1: m_A = -\frac{1}{2}$; $A_2: m_A = +\frac{1}{2}$; B: $m_A = \pm\frac{1}{2}$; $X_1: m_A = -\frac{3}{2}, -\frac{1}{2}$; $X_2: m_A = \pm\frac{1}{2}$; $M_2: m_A = -\frac{1}{2}$; $M_3: m_A = -\frac{1}{2}$. The transition M_1 need not be considered, since its intensity vanishes identically for any ABX_{n_X} system.

The resonance frequencies and relative intensities for generic values of I_X and m_X are given in Table 7.9, where

$$\begin{aligned} R(\tfrac{1}{2}, \tfrac{1}{2}, m_X) &= \delta - J_{AB} + (J_{AX} - J_{BX})m_X, \\ R(\tfrac{1}{2}, -\tfrac{1}{2}, m_X) &= \{[\delta + (J_{AX} - J_{BX})m_X]^2 + J_{AB}^2\}^{1/2}, \\ R(\tfrac{1}{2}, -\tfrac{3}{2}, m_X) &= \delta + J_{AB} + (J_{AX} - J_{BX})m_X, \\ Q(\tfrac{1}{2}, \tfrac{1}{2}, m_X) &= Q(\tfrac{1}{2}, -\tfrac{3}{2}, m_X) = 0, \\ Q(\tfrac{1}{2}, -\tfrac{1}{2}, m_X) &= \frac{J_{AB}}{\delta + (J_{AX} - J_{BX})m_X + R(\tfrac{1}{2}, -\tfrac{1}{2}, m_X)}. \end{aligned} \tag{3.8}$$

Note that each line of the table provides two transitions for given values of I_X and m_X.

The transformation of the ABX_{n_X} spectrum into itself when J_{AB} is replaced by $-J_{AB}$ follows at once from the definitions of the R's and Q's, and the manner in which these quantities appear in the expressions for the relative intensities and resonance frequencies. The invariance of the AB region of the spectrum with respect to the transformation $J_{AX} \to -J_{AX}$, $J_{BX} \to -J_{BX}$, follows from the fact that this transformation is equivalent to a change in the sign of m_X, which merely effects a relabeling of the A and B transitions associated with the I_{Xz} eigenvalues $+m_X$ and $-m_X$.

An examination of the X and M transitions recorded in Table 7.9 shows that the X region of the spectrum is symmetrical with respect to ω_X. According to the discussion in Section 3.D, the X region of the spectrum should be transformed into itself when the signs of J_{AX} and and J_{BX} are reversed. The verification of this property rests upon the fact that for every transition in the X region of the spectrum such that the change in m_X is $m_X \to m_X - 1$, there is a corresponding transition in the X region defined by $-m_X + 1 \to -m_X$.

Finally, Table 7.9 shows that the AB region of the spectrum consists of $2I_X(\max) + 1 = n_X + 1$ quartets of the AB type with effective Larmor frequencies and internal chemical shifts defined by (3.6) and (3.7).

The ABX *System*

The theoretical spectrum of the ABX system is given in Table 7.10. The AB region consists of two pseudo AB quartets, corresponding

TABLE 7.9

RESONANCE FREQUENCIES AND RELATIVE INTENSITIES FOR THE ABX_{n_X} SYSTEM

Transition[a]	Relative intensity	Resonance frequency
	A Transitions	
$\vert\frac{1}{2}, \frac{1}{2}; \frac{1}{2}, \mp\frac{1}{2}; I_X, m_X\rangle \to \vert\frac{1}{2}, -\frac{1}{2}; \frac{1}{2}, \mp\frac{1}{2}; I_X, m_X\rangle$	$g_{I_X}\left\{1 \pm \frac{J_{AB}}{R(\frac{1}{2}, -\frac{1}{2}, m_X)}\right\}$	$\frac{1}{2}\{\omega_A + \omega_B \mp J_{AB} + (J_{AX} + J_{BX})m_X + R(\frac{1}{2}, -\frac{1}{2}, m_X)\}$
	B Transitions	
$\vert\frac{1}{2}, \pm\frac{1}{2}; \frac{1}{2}, \frac{1}{2}; I_X, m_X\rangle \to \vert\frac{1}{2}, \pm\frac{1}{2}; \frac{1}{2}, -\frac{1}{2}; I_X, m_X\rangle$	$g_{I_X}\left\{1 \pm \frac{J_{AB}}{R(\frac{1}{2}, -\frac{1}{2}, m_X)}\right\}$	$\frac{1}{2}\{\omega_A + \omega_B \pm J_{AB} + (J_{AX} + J_{BX})m_X - R(\frac{1}{2}, -\frac{1}{2}, m_X)\}$
	X Transitions	
$\vert\frac{1}{2}, \mp\frac{1}{2}; \frac{1}{2}, \pm\frac{1}{2}; I_X, m_X\rangle \to \vert\frac{1}{2}, \mp\frac{1}{2}; \frac{1}{2}, \pm\frac{1}{2}; I_X, m_X - 1\rangle$	$\frac{g_{I_X}(I_X + m_X)(I_X - m_X + 1)[Q(\frac{1}{2}, -\frac{1}{2}, m_X)Q(\frac{1}{2}, -\frac{1}{2}, m_X - 1) + 1]^2}{[1 + Q^2(\frac{1}{2}, -\frac{1}{2}, m_X)][1 + Q^2(\frac{1}{2}, -\frac{1}{2}, m_X - 1)]}$	$\frac{1}{2}\{2\omega_X \pm R(\frac{1}{2}, -\frac{1}{2}, m_X - 1) \mp R(\frac{1}{2}, -\frac{1}{2}, m_X)\}$
$\vert\frac{1}{2}, \pm\frac{1}{2}; \frac{1}{2}, \pm\frac{1}{2}; I_X, m_X\rangle \to \vert\frac{1}{2}, \pm\frac{1}{2}; \frac{1}{2}, \pm\frac{1}{2}; I_X, m_X - 1\rangle$	$g_{I_X}(I_X + m_X)(I_X - m_X + 1)$	$\frac{1}{2}\{2\omega_X \pm J_{AX} \pm J_{BX}\}$
	M Transitions	
$\vert\frac{1}{2}, \pm\frac{1}{2}; \frac{1}{2}, \mp\frac{1}{2}; I_X, m_X\rangle \to \vert\frac{1}{2}, \mp\frac{1}{2}; \frac{1}{2}, \pm\frac{1}{2}; I_X, m_X - 1\rangle$	$\frac{g_{I_X}(I_X + m_X)(I_X - m_X + 1)[Q(\frac{1}{2}, -\frac{1}{2}, m_X) - Q(\frac{1}{2}, -\frac{1}{2}, m_X - 1)]^2}{[1 + Q^2(\frac{1}{2}, -\frac{1}{2}, m_X)][1 + Q^2(\frac{1}{2}, -\frac{1}{2}, m_X - 1]}$	$\frac{1}{2}\{2\omega_X \pm R(\frac{1}{2}, -\frac{1}{2}, m_X - 1) \pm R(\frac{1}{2}, -\frac{1}{2}, m_X)\}$

[a] In the limit as all $J_{ij} \to 0$.

TABLE 7.10 — RESONANCE FREQUENCIES AND RELATIVE INTENSITIES FOR THE ABX SYSTEM

Transition[a]	Relative intensity	Resonance frequency
	A *Transitions*	
$\lvert\frac{1}{2},\frac{1}{2};\frac{1}{2},\mp\frac{1}{2};\frac{1}{2},\frac{1}{2}\rangle \to \lvert\frac{1}{2},-\frac{1}{2};\frac{1}{2},\mp\frac{1}{2};\frac{1}{2},\frac{1}{2}\rangle$	$1 \pm \dfrac{J_{AB}}{R(\frac{1}{2},-\frac{1}{2},\frac{1}{2})}$	$\frac{1}{2}\{\omega_A+\omega_B \mp J_{AB}+\frac{1}{2}(J_{AX}+J_{BX}) + R(\frac{1}{2},-\frac{1}{2},\frac{1}{2})\}$
$\lvert\frac{1}{2},\frac{1}{2};\frac{1}{2},\mp\frac{1}{2};\frac{1}{2},-\frac{1}{2}\rangle \to \lvert\frac{1}{2},-\frac{1}{2};\frac{1}{2},\mp\frac{1}{2};\frac{1}{2},-\frac{1}{2}\rangle$	$1 \pm \dfrac{J_{AB}}{R(\frac{1}{2},-\frac{1}{2},-\frac{1}{2})}$	$\frac{1}{2}\{\omega_A+\omega_B \mp J_{AB}-\frac{1}{2}(J_{AX}+J_{BX}) + R(\frac{1}{2},-\frac{1}{2},-\frac{1}{2})\}$
	B *Transitions*	
$\lvert\frac{1}{2},\pm\frac{1}{2};\frac{1}{2},\frac{1}{2};\frac{1}{2},\frac{1}{2}\rangle \to \lvert\frac{1}{2},\pm\frac{1}{2};\frac{1}{2},-\frac{1}{2};\frac{1}{2},\frac{1}{2}\rangle$	$1 \pm \dfrac{J_{AB}}{R(\frac{1}{2},-\frac{1}{2},\frac{1}{2})}$	$\frac{1}{2}\{\omega_A+\omega_B \pm J_{AB}+\frac{1}{2}(J_{AX}+J_{BX}) - R(\frac{1}{2},-\frac{1}{2},\frac{1}{2})\}$
$\lvert\frac{1}{2},\pm\frac{1}{2};\frac{1}{2},\frac{1}{2};\frac{1}{2},-\frac{1}{2}\rangle \to \lvert\frac{1}{2},\pm\frac{1}{2};\frac{1}{2},-\frac{1}{2};\frac{1}{2},-\frac{1}{2}\rangle$	$1 \pm \dfrac{J_{AB}}{R(\frac{1}{2},-\frac{1}{2},-\frac{1}{2})}$	$\frac{1}{2}\{\omega_A+\omega_B \pm J_{AB}-\frac{1}{2}(J_{AX}+J_{BX}) - R(\frac{1}{2},-\frac{1}{2},-\frac{1}{2})\}$
	X *Transitions*	
$\lvert\frac{1}{2},\mp\frac{1}{2};\frac{1}{2},\pm\frac{1}{2};\frac{1}{2},\frac{1}{2}\rangle \to \lvert\frac{1}{2},\mp\frac{1}{2};\frac{1}{2},\pm\frac{1}{2};\frac{1}{2},-\frac{1}{2}\rangle$	$\dfrac{[Q(\frac{1}{2},-\frac{1}{2},\frac{1}{2})Q(\frac{1}{2},-\frac{1}{2},-\frac{1}{2})+1]^2}{[1+Q^2(\frac{1}{2},-\frac{1}{2},\frac{1}{2})][1+Q^2(\frac{1}{2},-\frac{1}{2},-\frac{1}{2})]}$	$\frac{1}{2}\{2\omega_X \pm R(\frac{1}{2},-\frac{1}{2},-\frac{1}{2}) \mp R(\frac{1}{2},-\frac{1}{2},\frac{1}{2})\}$
$\lvert\frac{1}{2},\pm\frac{1}{2};\frac{1}{2},\pm\frac{1}{2};\frac{1}{2},\frac{1}{2}\rangle \to \lvert\frac{1}{2},\pm\frac{1}{2};\frac{1}{2},\pm\frac{1}{2};\frac{1}{2},-\frac{1}{2}\rangle$	1	$\frac{1}{2}\{2\omega_X \pm J_{AX} \pm J_{BX}\}$
	M *Transitions*	
$\lvert\frac{1}{2},\pm\frac{1}{2};\frac{1}{2},\mp\frac{1}{2};\frac{1}{2},\frac{1}{2}\rangle \to \lvert\frac{1}{2},\mp\frac{1}{2};\frac{1}{2},\pm\frac{1}{2};\frac{1}{2},-\frac{1}{2}\rangle$	$\dfrac{[Q(\frac{1}{2},-\frac{1}{2},\frac{1}{2})-Q(\frac{1}{2},-\frac{1}{2},-\frac{1}{2})]^2}{[1+Q^2(\frac{1}{2},-\frac{1}{2},\frac{1}{2})][1+Q^2(\frac{1}{2},-\frac{1}{2},-\frac{1}{2})]}$	$\frac{1}{2}\{2\omega_X \pm R(\frac{1}{2},-\frac{1}{2},-\frac{1}{2}) \pm R(\frac{1}{2},-\frac{1}{2},\frac{1}{2})\}$

[a] In the limit as all $J_{ij} \to 0$.

to $m_X = \pm \frac{1}{2}$. Both quartets appear with equal weights, since $\nu(\frac{1}{2}) = \nu(-\frac{1}{2}) = 1$. The identification of these quartets in an experimental spectrum will not be difficult, provided that all eight resonances are resolved, and intensity differences arising from a difference in $R(\frac{1}{2}, -\frac{1}{2}, \frac{1}{2})$ and $R(\frac{1}{2}, -\frac{1}{2}, -\frac{1}{2})$ are observable.

The X region consists of six lines, four X transitions and two M transitions. The frequency separation of the two X transitions of unit intensity is $|J_{AX} + J_{BX}|$, in agreement with the general results established in Section 3.C.

An excellent example of an ABX system is provided by the ring protons (AB) and the fluorine nucleus (X) of 2-fluoro-4, 6-dichlorophenol (*10a*). The proton resonances are shown in Fig. 7.8. Parts (b) and (c) of the figure illustrate the decomposition of the spectrum into pseudo AB quartets; the corresponding quartets of the experimental spectrum will be described as the "*b*" and "*c*" quartets. Part (d) of the figure is the superposition of parts (b) and (c).

The value of $|J_{AB}|/2\pi$, which may be determined from either the *b* quartet or the *c* quartet, is

$$\frac{|J_{AB}|}{2\pi} = 2.49 \quad \text{cps.} \tag{3.9}$$

The absolute value of $J_{AX} + J_{BX}$ is twice the frequency separation of the quartet centers:

$$\frac{1}{2\pi}|J_{AX} + J_{BX}| = 8.15 \quad \text{cps.} \tag{3.10}$$

However, as the experimental spectrum cannot reveal which quartet corresponds to $m_X = +\frac{1}{2}$, it will be arbitrarily assumed that the *b* quartet corresponds to $m_X = +\frac{1}{2}$. On the basis of this assumption, a comparison of line intensities shows that $R(\frac{1}{2}, -\frac{1}{2}, \frac{1}{2}) < R(\frac{1}{2}, -\frac{1}{2}, -\frac{1}{2})$. Hence

$$|\delta + \tfrac{1}{2}(J_{AX} - J_{BX})| < |\delta - \tfrac{1}{2}(J_{AX} - J_{BX})|,$$

so that δ and $J_{AX} - J_{BX}$ are of opposite sign. Since the spectrum is independent of the sign of $J_{AX} - J_{BX}$, only the absolute value of δ can be determined.

The absolute values of the effective internal shifts are given by (cf. Fig. 7.8 and the discussion of the AB system in Chapter 6)

$$\frac{1}{2\pi}|\delta + \tfrac{1}{2}(J_{AX} - J_{BX})| = (ab)^{1/2} = 3.55 \quad \text{cps},$$

$$\frac{1}{2\pi}|\delta - \tfrac{1}{2}(J_{AX} - J_{BX})| = (a'b')^{1/2} = 8.66 \quad \text{cps}.$$

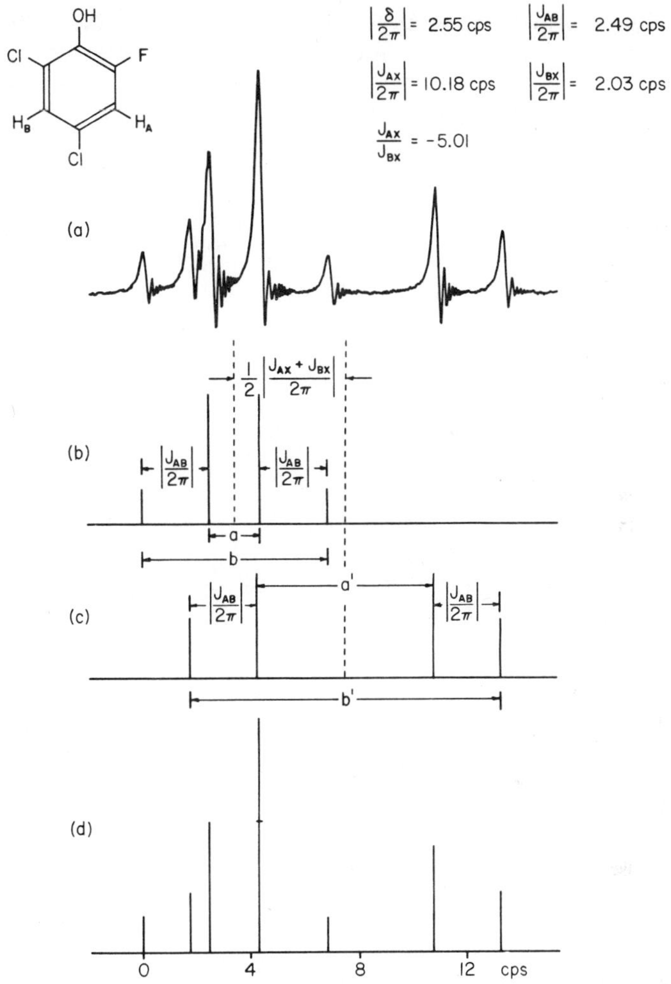

FIG. 7.8. Experimental and theoretical spectra for the ring protons of 2-fluoro-4,6-dichlorophenol in acetone at 60 Mcps.

From these data, one obtains

$$(1)\quad \frac{\delta}{2\pi} = \pm 2.55 \quad \text{cps}, \qquad \frac{1}{2\pi}(J_{AX} - J_{BX}) = \mp 12.21 \quad \text{cps};$$

$$(2)\quad \frac{\delta}{2\pi} = \pm 6.11 \quad \text{cps}, \qquad \frac{1}{2\pi}(J_{AX} - J_{BX}) = \mp 5.11 \quad \text{cps}.$$

Both (1) and (2) are consistent with the observed intensities and frequencies in the AB region.

The fluorine spectrum is shown in Fig. 7.9. All six predicted resonances in the X region are observed, and since (see Table 7.9)

$$\frac{[Q(\tfrac{1}{2}, -\tfrac{1}{2}, \tfrac{1}{2})Q(\tfrac{1}{2}, -\tfrac{1}{2}, -\tfrac{1}{2}) + 1]^2 + [Q(\tfrac{1}{2}, -\tfrac{1}{2}, \tfrac{1}{2}) - Q(\tfrac{1}{2}, -\tfrac{1}{2}, -\tfrac{1}{2})]^2}{[1 + Q^2(\tfrac{1}{2}, -\tfrac{1}{2}, \tfrac{1}{2})][1 + Q^2(\tfrac{1}{2}, -\tfrac{1}{2}, -\tfrac{1}{2})]} = 1,$$

the two lines of greatest intensity correspond to the theoretically predicted X transitions of unit intensity. The frequency separation of these lines is 8.15 cps, in agreement with (3.10).

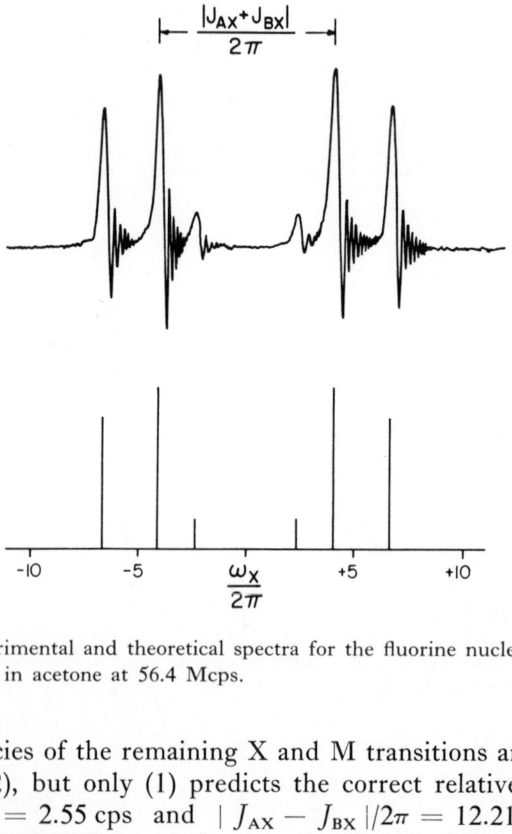

FIG. 7.9. Experimental and theoretical spectra for the fluorine nucleus of 2-fluoro-4,6-dichlorophenol in acetone at 56.4 Mcps.

The frequencies of the remaining X and M transitions are consistent with (1) and (2), but only (1) predicts the correct relative intensities. Hence $|\delta/2\pi| = 2.55$ cps and $|J_{AX} - J_{BX}|/2\pi = 12.21$ cps. From (3.10) it follows that J_{AX} and J_{BX} are of opposite sign, and that the magnitudes of these coupling constants are 10.18 and 2.03 cps. Studies of related molecules indicate that the larger coupling constant is associated with the interaction of the fluorine nucleus and the proton in the "3" position. Denoting the latter A, and the other ring proton B, the spectrum is described by any one of the following four sets of parameters:

$$\frac{\delta}{2\pi} = \pm 2.55 \quad \text{cps}, \qquad \frac{J_{AX}}{2\pi} = \mp 10.18 \quad \text{cps},$$

$$\frac{J_{BX}}{2\pi} = \pm 2.03 \quad \text{cps}, \qquad \frac{J_{AB}}{2\pi} = +2.49 \quad \text{cps};$$

$$\frac{\delta}{2\pi} = \pm 2.55 \quad \text{cps}, \qquad \frac{J_{AX}}{2\pi} = \mp 10.18 \quad \text{cps},$$

$$\frac{J_{BX}}{2\pi} = \pm 2.03 \quad \text{cps}, \qquad \frac{J_{AB}}{2\pi} = -2.49 \quad \text{cps}.$$

The same numerical values for the spectral parameters are obtained if the preceding analysis is carried through on the assumption that the b quartet corresponds to $m_X = -\frac{1}{2}$. In this case, however, $R(\frac{1}{2}, -\frac{1}{2}, -\frac{1}{2}) < R(\frac{1}{2}, -\frac{1}{2}, \frac{1}{2})$, so that δ and $J_{AX} - J_{BX}$ have the same sign.

The ABX_2 *System*

The theoretical spectrum for the ABX_2 system is given in Table 7.11. The only point worthy of special comment for this system is the fact that $I_X = 0$ is a possible total spin quantum number for group X. If the AB quartet corresponding to $I_X = 0$ can be identified in the experimental spectrum, $|\omega_{AB}|$ and $|J_{AB}|$ may be determined exactly.

The $A_2BX_{n_X}$ *System*

The theoretical spectrum of the $A_2BX_{n_X}$ system is given in Table 7.12. The R's and Q's for this system are

$$R(1, 1, m_X) = \delta - \tfrac{3}{2}J_{AB} + (J_{AX} - J_{BX})m_X,$$

$$R(1, 0, m_X) = \{[\delta - \tfrac{1}{2}J_{AB} + (J_{AX} - J_{BX})m_X]^2 + 2J_{AB}^2\}^{1/2},$$

$$R(1, -1, m_X) = \{[\delta + \tfrac{1}{2}J_{AB} + (J_{AX} - J_{BX})m_X]^2 + 2J_{AB}^2\}^{1/2},$$

$$R(1, -2, m_X) = \delta + \tfrac{3}{2}J_{AB} + (J_{AX} - J_{BX})m_X,$$

$$R(0, 0, m_X) = \delta - \tfrac{1}{2}J_{AB} + (J_{AX} - J_{BX})m_X,$$

$$Q(1, 1, m_X) = Q(1, -2, m_X) = Q(0, 0, m_X) = 0,$$

TABLE 7.11

RESONANCE FREQUENCIES AND RELATIVE INTENSITIES FOR THE ABX_2 SYSTEM

Transition[a]	Relative intensity	Resonance frequency
	A *Transitions*	
$\lvert \frac{1}{2}, \frac{1}{2}; \frac{1}{2}, \mp \frac{1}{2}; 1, 1\rangle \to \lvert \frac{1}{2}, -\frac{1}{2}; \frac{1}{2}, \mp \frac{1}{2}; 1, 1\rangle$	$1 \pm \frac{J_{AB}}{R(\frac{1}{2}, -\frac{1}{2}, 1)}$	$\frac{1}{2}\{\omega_A + \omega_B \mp J_{AB} + (J_{AX} + J_{BX}) + R(\frac{1}{2}, -\frac{1}{2}, 1)\}$
$\lvert \frac{1}{2}, \frac{1}{2}; \frac{1}{2}, \mp \frac{1}{2}; 1, 0\rangle \to \lvert \frac{1}{2}, -\frac{1}{2}; \frac{1}{2}, \mp \frac{1}{2}; 1, 0\rangle$	$1 \pm \frac{J_{AB}}{R(\frac{1}{2}, -\frac{1}{2}, 0)}$	$\frac{1}{2}\{\omega_A + \omega_B \mp J_{AB} + R(\frac{1}{2}, -\frac{1}{2}, 0)\}$
$\lvert \frac{1}{2}, \frac{1}{2}; \frac{1}{2}, \mp \frac{1}{2}; 1, -1\rangle \to \lvert \frac{1}{2}, -\frac{1}{2}; \frac{1}{2}, \mp \frac{1}{2}; 1, -1\rangle$	$1 \pm \frac{J_{AB}}{R(\frac{1}{2}, -\frac{1}{2}, -1)}$	$\frac{1}{2}\{\omega_A + \omega_B \mp J_{AB} - (J_{AX} + J_{BX}) + R(\frac{1}{2}, -\frac{1}{2}, -1)\}$
$\lvert \frac{1}{2}, \frac{1}{2}; \frac{1}{2}, \mp \frac{1}{2}; 0, 0\rangle \to \lvert \frac{1}{2}, -\frac{1}{2}; \frac{1}{2}, \mp \frac{1}{2}; 0, 0\rangle$	$1 \pm \frac{J_{AB}}{R(\frac{1}{2}, -\frac{1}{2}, 0)}$	$\frac{1}{2}\{\omega_A + \omega_B \mp J_{AB} + R(\frac{1}{2}, -\frac{1}{2}, 0)\}$
	B *Transitions*	
$\lvert \frac{1}{2}, \pm \frac{1}{2}; \frac{1}{2}, \frac{1}{2}; 1, 1\rangle \to \lvert \frac{1}{2}, \pm \frac{1}{2}; \frac{1}{2}, -\frac{1}{2}; 1, 1\rangle$	$1 \pm \frac{J_{AB}}{R(\frac{1}{2}, -\frac{1}{2}, 1)}$	$\frac{1}{2}\{\omega_A + \omega_B \pm J_{AB} + (J_{AX} + J_{BX}) - R(\frac{1}{2}, -\frac{1}{2}, 1)\}$
$\lvert \frac{1}{2}, \pm \frac{1}{2}; \frac{1}{2}, \frac{1}{2}; 1, 0\rangle \to \lvert \frac{1}{2}, \pm \frac{1}{2}; \frac{1}{2}, -\frac{1}{2}; 1, 0\rangle$	$1 \pm \frac{J_{AB}}{R(\frac{1}{2}, -\frac{1}{2}, 0)}$	$\frac{1}{2}\{\omega_A + \omega_B \pm J_{AB} - R(\frac{1}{2}, -\frac{1}{2}, 0)\}$
$\lvert \frac{1}{2}, \pm \frac{1}{2}; \frac{1}{2}, \frac{1}{2}; 1, -1\rangle \to \lvert \frac{1}{2}, \pm \frac{1}{2}; \frac{1}{2}, -\frac{1}{2}; 1, -1\rangle$	$1 \pm \frac{J_{AB}}{R(\frac{1}{2}, -\frac{1}{2}, -1)}$	$\frac{1}{2}\{\omega_A + \omega_B \pm J_{AB} - (J_{AX} + J_{BX}) - R(\frac{1}{2}, -\frac{1}{2}, -1)\}$
$\lvert \frac{1}{2}, \pm \frac{1}{2}; \frac{1}{2}, \frac{1}{2}; 0, 0\rangle \to \lvert \frac{1}{2}, \pm \frac{1}{2}; \frac{1}{2}, -\frac{1}{2}; 0, 0\rangle$	$1 \pm \frac{J_{AB}}{R(\frac{1}{2}, -\frac{1}{2}, 0)}$	$\frac{1}{2}\{\omega_A + \omega_B \pm J_{AB} - R(\frac{1}{2}, -\frac{1}{2}, 0)\}$

TABLE 7.11 *(Continued)*

Transition[a]	Relative intensity	Resonance frequency
	X *Transitions*	
$\lvert \frac{1}{2}, \mp\frac{1}{2}; \frac{1}{2}, \pm\frac{1}{2}; 1, 1\rangle \to \lvert \frac{1}{2}, \mp\frac{1}{2}; \frac{1}{2}, \pm\frac{1}{2}; 1, 0\rangle$	$\frac{2[Q(\frac{1}{2}, -\frac{1}{2}, 1)Q(\frac{1}{2}, -\frac{1}{2}, 0) + 1]^2}{[1 + Q^2(\frac{1}{2}, -\frac{1}{2}, 1)][1 + Q^2(\frac{1}{2}, -\frac{1}{2}, 0)]}$	$\frac{1}{2}\{2\omega_X \pm R(\frac{1}{2}, -\frac{1}{2}, 0) \mp R(\frac{1}{2}, -\frac{1}{2}, 1)\}$
$\lvert \frac{1}{2}, \mp\frac{1}{2}; \frac{1}{2}, \pm\frac{1}{2}; 1, 0\rangle \to \lvert \frac{1}{2}, \mp\frac{1}{2}; \frac{1}{2}, \pm\frac{1}{2}; 1, -1\rangle$	$\frac{2[Q(\frac{1}{2}, -\frac{1}{2}, 0)Q(\frac{1}{2}, -\frac{1}{2}, -1) + 1]^2}{[1 + Q^2(\frac{1}{2}, -\frac{1}{2}, 0)][1 + Q^2(\frac{1}{2}, -\frac{1}{2}, -1)]}$	$\frac{1}{2}\{2\omega_X \pm R(\frac{1}{2}, -\frac{1}{2}, -1) \mp R(\frac{1}{2}, -\frac{1}{2}, 0)\}$
$\lvert \frac{1}{2}, \pm\frac{1}{2}; \frac{1}{2}, \pm\frac{1}{2}; 1, 1\rangle \to \lvert \frac{1}{2}, \pm\frac{1}{2}; \frac{1}{2}, \pm\frac{1}{2}; 1, 0\rangle$	2	$\frac{1}{2}\{2\omega_X \pm J_{AX} \pm J_{BX}\}$
$\lvert \frac{1}{2}, \pm\frac{1}{2}; \frac{1}{2}, \pm\frac{1}{2}; 1, 0\rangle \to \lvert \frac{1}{2}, \pm\frac{1}{2}; \frac{1}{2}, \pm\frac{1}{2}; 1, -1\rangle$	2	$\frac{1}{2}\{2\omega_X \pm J_{AX} \pm J_{BX}\}$
	M *Transitions*	
$\lvert \frac{1}{2}, \pm\frac{1}{2}; \frac{1}{2}, \mp\frac{1}{2}; 1, 1\rangle \to \lvert \frac{1}{2}, \mp\frac{1}{2}; \frac{1}{2}, \pm\frac{1}{2}; 1, 0\rangle$	$\frac{2[Q(\frac{1}{2}, -\frac{1}{2}, 1) - Q(\frac{1}{2}, -\frac{1}{2}, 0)]^2}{[1 + Q^2(\frac{1}{2}, -\frac{1}{2}, 1)][1 + Q^2(\frac{1}{2}, -\frac{1}{2}, 0)]}$	$\frac{1}{2}\{2\omega_X \pm R(\frac{1}{2}, -\frac{1}{2}, 0) \pm R(\frac{1}{2}, -\frac{1}{2}, 1)\}$
$\lvert \frac{1}{2}, \pm\frac{1}{2}; \frac{1}{2}, \mp\frac{1}{2}; 1, 0\rangle \to \lvert \frac{1}{2}, \mp\frac{1}{2}; \frac{1}{2}, \pm\frac{1}{2}; 1, -1\rangle$	$\frac{2[Q(\frac{1}{2}, -\frac{1}{2}, 0) - Q(\frac{1}{2}, -\frac{1}{2}, -1)]^2}{[1 + Q^2(\frac{1}{2}, -\frac{1}{2}, 0)][1 + Q^2(\frac{1}{2}, -\frac{1}{2}, -1)]}$	$\frac{1}{2}\{2\omega_X \pm R(\frac{1}{2}, -\frac{1}{2}, -1) \pm R(\frac{1}{2}, -\frac{1}{2}, 0)\}$

[a] Transition in the limit as all $J_{ij} \to 0$.

TABLE 7.12

RESONANCE FREQUENCIES AND RELATIVE INTENSITIES FOR THE $A_2BX_{n_X}$ SYSTEM

Transition[a]	Relative intensity	Resonance frequency
	A *Transitions*	
$\|1, 1; \frac{1}{2}, -\frac{1}{2}; I_X, m_X\rangle \to$ $\|1, 0; \frac{1}{2}, -\frac{1}{2}; I_X, m_X\rangle$	$\dfrac{g_{I_X}\{\sqrt{2} + Q(1, 0, m_X)[1 + \sqrt{2}Q(1, -1, m_X]\}^2}{[1 + Q^2(1, 0, m_X)][1 + Q^2(1, -1, m_X)]}$	$\omega_A + J_{AX}m_X + \frac{1}{2}\{R(1, 0, m_X) - R(1, -1, m_X)\}$
$\|1, 0; \frac{1}{2}, -\frac{1}{2}; I_X, m_X\rangle \to$ $\|1, -1; \frac{1}{2}, -\frac{1}{2}; I_X, m_X\rangle$	$\dfrac{g_{I_X}\{\sqrt{2} + Q(1, -1, m_X)\}^2}{1 + Q^2(1, -1, m_X)}$	$\frac{1}{2}\{\omega_A + \omega_B - \frac{3}{2}J_{AB} + (J_{AX} + J_{BX})m_X + R(1, -1, m_X)\}$
$\|1, 1; \frac{1}{2}, \frac{1}{2}; I_X, m_X\rangle \to$ $\|1, 0; \frac{1}{2}, \frac{1}{2}; I_X, m_X\rangle$	$\dfrac{g_{I_X}\{\sqrt{2} - Q(1, 0, m_X)\}^2}{1 + Q^2(1, 0, m_X)}$	$\frac{1}{2}\{\omega_A + \omega_B + \frac{3}{2}J_{AB} + (J_{AX} + J_{BX})m_X + R(1, 0, m_X)\}$
$\|1, 0; \frac{1}{2}, \frac{1}{2}; I_X, m_X\rangle \to$ $\|1, -1; \frac{1}{2}, \frac{1}{2}; I_X, m_X\rangle$	$\dfrac{g_{I_X}\{Q(1, -1, m_X)[\sqrt{2}Q(1, 0, m_X) - 1] + \sqrt{2}\}^2}{[1 + Q^2(1, 0, m_X)][1 + Q^2(1, -1, m_X)]}$	$\omega_A + J_{AX}m_X + \frac{1}{2}\{R(1, -1, m_X) - R(1, 0, m_X)\}$
	B *Transitions*	
$\|1, 1; \frac{1}{2}, \frac{1}{2}; I_X, m_X\rangle \to$ $\|1, 1; \frac{1}{2}, -\frac{1}{2}; I_X, m_X\rangle$	$\dfrac{g_{I_X}\{1 + \sqrt{2}Q(1, 0, m_X)\}^2}{1 + Q^2(1, 0, m_X)}$	$\frac{1}{2}\{\omega_A + \omega_B + \frac{3}{2}J_{AB} + (J_{AX} + J_{BX})m_X - R(1, 0, m_X)\}$
$\|1, 0; \frac{1}{2}, \frac{1}{2}; I_X, m_X\rangle \to$ $\|1, 0; \frac{1}{2}, -\frac{1}{2}; I_X, m_X\rangle$	$\dfrac{g_{I_X}\{\sqrt{2}Q(1, 0, m_X) - [1 + \sqrt{2}Q(1, -1, m_X)]\}^2}{[1 + Q^2(1, 0, m_X)][1 + Q^2(1, -1, m_X)]}$	$\omega_A + J_{AX}m_X - \frac{1}{2}\{R(1, 0, m_X) + R(1, -1, m_X)\}$

TABLE 7.12 *(Continued)*

Transition[a]	Relative intensity	Resonance frequency
	B *Transitions*	
$\lvert 1, -1; \frac{1}{2}, \frac{1}{2}; I_X, m_X\rangle \rightarrow \lvert 1, -1; \frac{1}{2}, -\frac{1}{2}; I_X, m_X\rangle$	$\frac{g_{I_X}\{1 - \sqrt{2}\,Q(1, -1, m_X)\}^2}{1 + Q^2(1, -1, m_X)}$	$\frac{1}{2}\{\omega_A + \omega_B - \frac{3}{2}J_{AB} + (J_{AX} + J_{BX})m_X - R(1, -1, m_X)\}$
$\lvert 0, 0; \frac{1}{2}, \frac{1}{2}; I_X, m_X\rangle \rightarrow \lvert 0, 0; \frac{1}{2}, -\frac{1}{2}; I_X, m_X\rangle$	g_{I_X}	$\omega_B + J_{BX}m_X$
	X *Transitions*	
$\lvert 1, 1; \frac{1}{2}, -\frac{1}{2}; I_X, m_X\rangle \rightarrow \lvert 1, 1; \frac{1}{2}, -\frac{1}{2}; I_X, m_X - 1\rangle$	$\frac{g_{I_X}(I_X + m_X)(I_X - m_X + 1)[1 + Q(1, 0, m_X)Q(1, 0, m_X - 1)]^2}{[1 + Q^2(1, 0, m_X)][1 + Q^2(1, 0, m_X - 1)]}$	$\omega_X + \frac{1}{2}\{J_{AX} + R(1, 0, m_X) - R(1, 0, m_X - 1)\}$
$\lvert 1, 0; \frac{1}{2}, -\frac{1}{2}; I_X, m_X\rangle \rightarrow \lvert 1, 0; \frac{1}{2}, -\frac{1}{2}; I_X, m_X - 1\rangle$	$\frac{g_{I_X}(I_X + m_X)(I_X - m_X + 1)[1 + Q(1, -1, m_X)Q(1, -1, m_X - 1)]^2}{[1 + Q^2(1, -1, m_X)][1 + Q^2(1, -1, m_X - 1)]}$	$\omega_X + \frac{1}{2}\{-J_{AX} + R(1, -1, m_X) - R(1, -1, m_X - 1)\}$
$\lvert 1, -1; \frac{1}{2}, -\frac{1}{2}; I_X, m_X\rangle \rightarrow \lvert 1, -1; \frac{1}{2}, -\frac{1}{2}; I_X, m_X - 1\rangle$	$g_{I_X}(I_X + m_X)(I_X - m_X + 1)$	$\omega_X - \frac{1}{2}(2J_{AX} + J_{BX})$
$\lvert 0, 0; \frac{1}{2}, -\frac{1}{2}; I_X, m_X\rangle \rightarrow \lvert 0, 0; \frac{1}{2}, -\frac{1}{2}; I_X, m_X - 1\rangle$	$g_{I_X}(I_X + m_X)(I_X - m_X + 1)$	$\omega_X - \frac{1}{2}J_{BX}$
$\lvert 1, 1; \frac{1}{2}, \frac{1}{2}; I_X, m_X\rangle \rightarrow \lvert 1, 1; \frac{1}{2}, \frac{1}{2}; I_X, m_X - 1\rangle$	$g_{I_X}(I_X + m_X)(I_X - m_X + 1)$	$\omega_X + \frac{1}{2}(2J_{AX} + J_{BX})$

TABLE 7.12 *(Continued)* RESONANCE FREQUENCIES AND RELATIVE INTENSITIES FOR THE $A_2BX_{n_X}$ SYSTEM

Transition[a]	Relative intensity	Resonance frequency
	X *Transitions*	
$\vert 1, 0; \frac{1}{2}, \frac{1}{2}; I_X, m_X\rangle \to \vert 1, 0; \frac{1}{2}, \frac{1}{2}; I_X, m_X - 1\rangle$	$\frac{g_{I_X}(I_X + m_X)(I_X - m_X + 1)[1 + Q(1, 0, m_X)Q(1, 0, m_X - 1)]^2}{[1 + Q^2(1, 0, m_X)][1 + Q^2(1, 0, m_X - 1)]}$	$\omega_X + \frac{1}{2}\{J_{AX} + R(1, 0, m_X - 1) - R(1, 0, m_X)\}$
$\vert 1, -1; \frac{1}{2}, \frac{1}{2}; I_X, m_X\rangle \to \vert 1, -1; \frac{1}{2}, \frac{1}{2}; I_X, m_X - 1\rangle$	$\frac{g_{I_X}(I_X + m_X)(I_X - m_X + 1)[1 + Q(1, -1, m_X)Q(1, -1, m_X - 1)]^2}{[1 + Q^2(1, -1, m_X)][1 + Q^2(1, -1, m_X - 1)]}$	$\omega_X + \frac{1}{2}\{-J_{AX} + R(1, -1, m_X - 1) - R(1, -1, m_X)\}$
$\vert 0, 0; \frac{1}{2}, \frac{1}{2}; I_X, m_X\rangle \to \vert 0, 0; \frac{1}{2}, \frac{1}{2}; I_X, m_X - 1\rangle$	$g_{I_X}(I_X + m_X)(I_X - m_X + 1)$	$\omega_X + \frac{1}{2}J_{BX}$
	M *Transitions*	
$\vert 1, 1; \frac{1}{2}, -\frac{1}{2}; I_X, m_X\rangle \to \vert 1, -1; \frac{1}{2}, \frac{1}{2}; I_X, m_X\rangle$	$\frac{g_{I_X}\{[\sqrt{2} + Q(1, 0, m_X)]Q(1, -1, m_X) - \sqrt{2}Q(1, 0, m_X)\}^2}{[1 + Q^2(1, 0, m_X)][1 + Q^2(1, -1, m_X)]}$	$\omega_A + J_{AX}m_X + \frac{1}{2}\{R(1, 0, m_X) + R(1, -1, m_X)\}$
$\vert 1, 1; \frac{1}{2}, -\frac{1}{2}; I_X, m_X\rangle \to \vert 1, 0; \frac{1}{2}, \frac{1}{2}; I_X, m_X - 1\rangle$	$\frac{g_{I_X}(I_X + m_X)(I_X - m_X + 1)[Q(1, 0, m_X - 1) - Q(1, 0, m_X)]^2}{[1 + Q^2(1, 0, m_X - 1)][1 + Q^2(1, 0, m_X)]}$	$\omega_X + \frac{1}{2}\{J_{AX} + R(1, 0, m_X - 1) + R(1, 0, m_X)\}$
$\vert 1, 0; \frac{1}{2}, -\frac{1}{2}; I_X, m_X\rangle \to \vert 1, -1; \frac{1}{2}, \frac{1}{2}; I_X, m_X - 1\rangle$	$\frac{g_{I_X}(I_X + m_X)(I_X - m_X + 1)[Q(1, -1, m_X - 1) - Q(1, -1, m_X)]^2}{[1 + Q^2(1, -1, m_X - 1)][1 + Q^2(1, -1, m_X)]}$	$\omega_X + \frac{1}{2}\{-J_{AX} + R(1, -1, m_X - 1) + R(1, -1, m_X)\}$
$\vert 1, -1; \frac{1}{2}, \frac{1}{2}; I_X, m_X\rangle \to \vert 1, 0; \frac{1}{2}, -\frac{1}{2}; I_X, m_X - 1\rangle$	$\frac{g_{I_X}(I_X + m_X)(I_X - m_X + 1)[Q(1, -1, m_X - 1) - Q(1, -1, m_X)]^2}{[1 + Q^2(1, -1, m_X - 1)][1 + Q^2(1, -1, m_X)]}$	$\omega_X - \frac{1}{2}\{J_{AX} + R(1, -1, m_X - 1) + R(1, -1, m_X)\}$
$\vert 1, 0; \frac{1}{2}, \frac{1}{2}; I_X, m_X\rangle \to \vert 1, 1; \frac{1}{2}, -\frac{1}{2}; I_X, m_X - 1\rangle$	$\frac{g_{I_X}(I_X + m_X)(I_X - m_X + 1)[Q(1, 0, m_X - 1) - Q(1, 0, m_X)]^2}{[1 + Q^2(1, 0, m_X - 1)][1 + Q^2(1, 0, m_X)]}$	$\omega_X + \frac{1}{2}\{J_{AX} - R(1, 0, m_X - 1) - R(1, 0, m_X)\}$

[a] In the limit as all $J_{ij} \to 0$.

$$Q(1, 0, m_X) = \frac{J_{AB}2^{1/2}}{\delta - \frac{1}{2}J_{AB} + (J_{AX} - J_{BX})m_X + R(1, 0, m_X)},$$

$$Q(1, -1, m_X) = \frac{J_{AB}2^{1/2}}{\delta + \frac{1}{2}J_{AB} + (J_{AX} - J_{BX})m_X + R(1, -1, m_X)}.$$

With the help of these expressions, one may easily obtain the resonance frequencies and relative intensities for any value of n_X.

An example of the case $n_X = 1$ is provided by the proton and fluorine resonances of 2,6-dichlorofluorobenzene (*11*). The experimental and theoretical proton spectra are shown in Fig. 7.10; the theoretical spectrum shows the subspectra associated with the two pseudo A_2B systems. The experimental and theoretical fluorine spectra are shown in Fig. 7.11. The asymmetry of the spectrum with respect to ω_X makes it possible to relate the sign of J_{AB}, arbitrarily assumed to be positive, to those of J_{AX} and J_{BX}.

The preceding examples illustrate the practical utility of the X approximation and the concept of effective chemical shifts. Even when

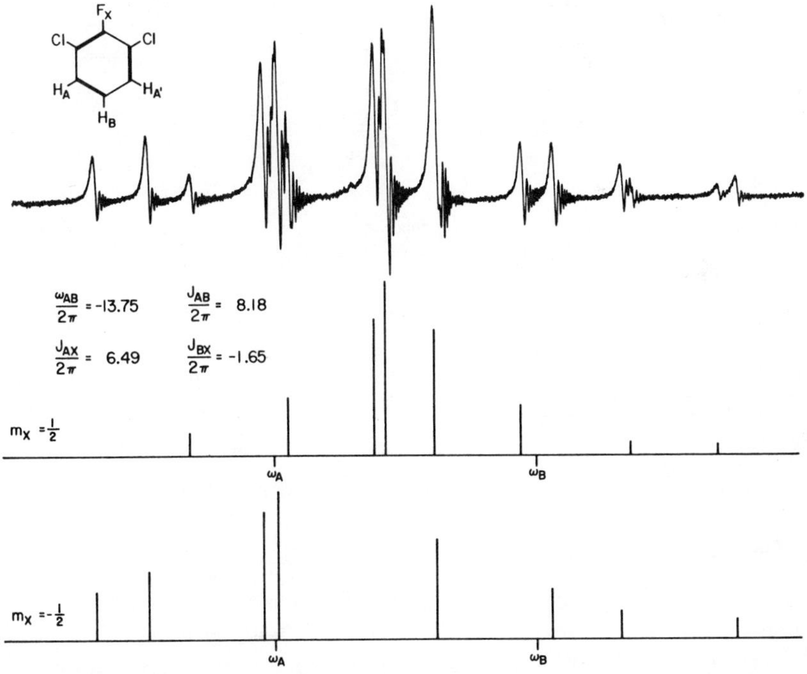

FIG. 7.10. Experimental and theoretical proton spectra of 2,6-dichlorofluorobenzene in hexafluorobenzene at 60 Mcps.

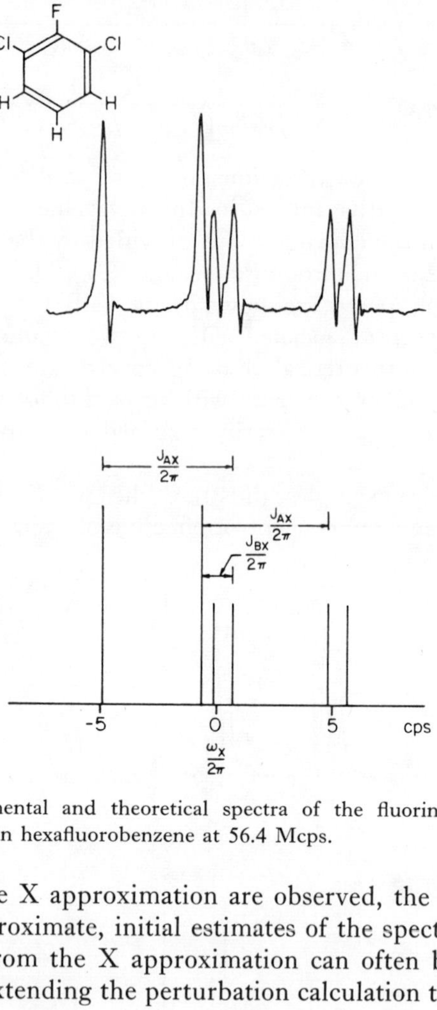

FIG. 7.11. Experimental and theoretical spectra of the fluorine nucleus of 2,6-dichlorofluorobenzene in hexafluorobenzene at 56.4 Mcps.

deviations from the X approximation are observed, the method can be used to obtain approximate, initial estimates of the spectral parameters. Small deviations from the X approximation can often be satisfactorily accounted for by extending the perturbation calculation to second order.

4. Moment Analysis of High-Resolution Spectra

A. Definition of Spectral Moments

The perturbation method, although often useful, is of limited value when the absolute values of the ratios $J_{GG'}/\omega_{GG'}$ are comparable to unity. For this reason the analysis of such systems is usually based upon exact numerical diagonalizations of the hamiltonian matrix. However, the analysis of a spectrum that is a function of several chemical shifts and coupling constants can be a problem of some difficulty, even with the aid of electronic computers. It is not surprising, therefore, that attempts have been made to devise methods of analysis that either entirely obviate the diagonalization of the hamiltonian matrix, or provide relations between the chemical shifts and coupling constants that can be used to simplify the analysis (*5*, *12–14*). That such procedures may be possible is already evident from previous discussions of systems containing two or more nontrivial groups of magnetically equivalent nuclei. In this section an alternative method of spectral analysis—the so-called *moment method*—will be described. This method (*12*) does not require the solution of the eigenvalue problem and, in principle, is applicable to all spin systems.

The essential idea of the moment method is to compute theoretical expressions for the frequency moments of a high-resolution spectrum which are then equated to the corresponding frequency moments calculated from the observed spectrum. This procedure yields a set of simultaneous algebraic equations for the chemical shifts and coupling constants. The basic problem is the computation of the theoretical moments, and it is indeed remarkable that this calculation can be carried out with comparative ease. Unfortunately, the inherent assumptions of the method and the difficulties encountered in the determination of experimental moments considerably limit its applicability. In favorable cases, the moment method can provide significant information.

The nth moment of an arbitrary spectrum is defined by the equation

$$\langle \omega^n \rangle = \frac{\sum_j \sum_k (\Omega_k - \Omega_j)^n \mid I_{kj}^+ \mid^2}{\sum_j \sum_k \mid I_{kj}^+ \mid^2}, \tag{4.1}$$

where $\Omega_k - \Omega_j$ is the frequency associated with the transition $\mid j) \rightarrow \mid k)$, and $\mid I_{kj}^+ \mid^2 = \mid I_{kj}^- \mid^2$ the corresponding relative intensity. The denominator of (4.1) is the total intensity, so that

$$\frac{\mid I_{kj}^+ \mid^2}{\sum_j \sum_k \mid I_{kj}^+ \mid^2}$$

may be interpreted as the probability of observing the frequency $(\Omega_k - \Omega_j)$. Thus $\langle \omega^n \rangle$ is the mathematical expectation of the nth power of the frequency, $\langle \omega \rangle$ is the mean frequency, $\langle \omega^2 \rangle$ the mean square frequency, and so on.

The denominator of (4.1) is equivalent to

$$\sum_j \sum_k \mid I_{kj}^+ \mid^2 = \sum_j \sum_k I_{kj}^+ I_{jk}^- = \operatorname{tr} I^+ I^-$$

where $\operatorname{tr} I^+ I^-$ denotes the trace of the matrix product $I^+ I^-$.

The numerators of the various moments can also be expressed as traces of matrix products upon noting that $\mathscr{H}_{jk} = \Omega_j \delta_{jk}$. For example, when $n = 1$,

$$\sum_{j,k} (\Omega_k - \Omega_j) | I_{kj}^+ |^2 = \sum_{j,k} (\mathscr{H}_{kk} I_{kj}^+ - I_{kj}^+ \mathscr{H}_{jj}) I_{jk}^-$$

$$= \sum_{j,k} [\mathscr{H}, I^+]_{kj} I_{jk}^- = \mathrm{tr}[\mathscr{H}, I^+] I^-.$$

Similar calculations lead to the following expressions for the first four moments:

$$\langle \omega \rangle = \frac{\mathrm{tr}[\mathscr{H}, I^+]I^-}{\mathrm{tr}\, I^+I^-}, \qquad \langle \omega^3 \rangle = \frac{\mathrm{tr}[\mathscr{H}, [\mathscr{H}, I^+]][I^-, \mathscr{H}]}{\mathrm{tr}\, I^+I^-},$$

$$\langle \omega^2 \rangle = \frac{\mathrm{tr}[\mathscr{H}, I^+][I^-, \mathscr{H}]}{\mathrm{tr}\, I^+I^-}, \qquad \langle \omega^4 \rangle = \frac{\mathrm{tr}[\mathscr{H}, [\mathscr{H}, I^+]][[I^-, \mathscr{H}], \mathscr{H}]}{\mathrm{tr}\, I^+I^-}. \tag{4.2}$$

These equations reveal a pattern of formation that can be used to write down the equations for all higher moments.

The distinguishing feature of equations (4.2) is that they are all expressed in terms of trace operations and, since the trace is a matrix invariant, it is not necessary to solve a complicated eigenvalue problem to evaluate the moments—any matrix representation of the operators will suffice.[9]

B. Calculation of Spectral Moments

The derivation of explicit formulas for the theoretical moments requires the specification of the hamiltonian operator and the evaluation of the necessary commutators and traces. The hamiltonian operator will be taken to be

$$\mathscr{H} = \sum_{\mathrm{G}} \omega_{\mathrm{G}} I_{\mathrm{G}z} + \sum_{\mathrm{G}<\mathrm{G}'}\sum J_{\mathrm{GG}'} \mathbf{I}_{\mathrm{G}} \cdot \mathbf{I}_{\mathrm{G}'}, \tag{4.3}$$

the minus signs usually prefixed to the right-hand members being omitted for convenience. It will be assumed that the total spin quantum numbers for each group G arise by addition of n_{G} angular momenta with spin I, and that all nuclei are identical.

[9] See Appendix V.

The theoretical moments will first be computed for the irreducible components of the system, the nth moment of the rth irreducible component being denoted $\langle \omega_r^n \rangle$. The integral index r is an abbreviation for the total spin quantum numbers defining the irreducible component: $r \leftrightarrow (I_A, I_B, \ldots)$. For example, the irreducible components of the A_2BC system ($I = \frac{1}{2}$) are $A_1B_{1/2}C_{1/2}$, $A_0B_{1/2}C_{1/2}$, and these may be arbitrarily distinguished by assigning $r = 1$ to the former, $r = 2$ to the latter.

The spectrum of the $A_{I_A}B_{I_B} \cdots$ component appears with weight $g_{I_A}g_{I_B} \cdots$ in the complete $A_{n_A}B_{n_B} \cdots$ spectrum, but as these weights occur as multiplicative factors in the numerators and denominators of all moment equations, the moments of the irreducible components do not depend upon these weighting factors. Therefore the common denominator of equations (4.2) for the irreducible $A_{I_A}B_{I_B} \cdots$ component is

$$\operatorname{tr} I^+I^- = \tfrac{2}{3} \prod_G (2I_G + 1) \sum_G I_G(I_G + 1).$$

On the other hand, the appropriate common denominator required for the moments of the complete system is

$$\operatorname{tr} I^+I^- = \tfrac{2}{3} \prod_j (2I_j + 1) \sum_j I_j(I_j + 1) = \tfrac{2}{3} NI(I + 1)(2I + 1)^N,$$

since $I^\pm = I_1^\pm + I_2^\pm + \cdots + I_N^\pm$, and $I_1 = I_2 = \cdots = I$. This result may also be obtained by multiplying $\operatorname{tr} I^+I^-$ for the irreducible $A_{I_A}B_{I_B} \cdots$ system by $g_{I_A}g_{I_B} \cdots$ and summing the result over all values of $I_A, I_B, \ldots$.

The commutators required for the calculation of the first four moments are

$$\begin{aligned}
[\mathscr{H}, I^+] &= \sum_G \omega_G I_G^+, \\
[I^-, \mathscr{H}] &= \sum_G \omega_G I_G^-, \\
[\mathscr{H}, [\mathscr{H}, I^+]] &= \sum_G \omega_G^2 I_G^+ + \sum_{G<G'}\sum J_{GG'}\omega_{GG'}(I_G^+ I_{G'z} - I_{G'}^+ I_{Gz}), \\
[[I^-, \mathscr{H}], \mathscr{H}] &= \sum_G \omega_G^2 I_G^- + \sum_{G<G'}\sum J_{GG'}\omega_{GG'}(I_G^- I_{G'z} - I_{G'}^- I_{Gz}).
\end{aligned} \tag{4.4}$$

Only the first and third commutators need be explicitly calculated, since $[I^-, \mathscr{H}] = [\mathscr{H}, I^+]^\dagger$, and $[[I^-, \mathscr{H}], \mathscr{H}] = [\mathscr{H}, [\mathscr{H}, I^+]]^\dagger$. With these results and the trace relations derived in Appendix V, it is not difficult to show that

$$\sum_{G} \omega_G I_G(I_G+1) = \Big\{\sum_{G} I_G(I_G+1)\Big\} \langle\omega_r\rangle,$$

$$\sum_{G} \omega_G^2 I_G(I_G+1) = \Big\{\sum_{G} I_G(I_G+1)\Big\} \langle\omega_r^2\rangle,$$

$$\sum_{G} \omega_G^3 I_G(I_G+1) = \Big\{\sum_{G} I_G(I_G+1)\Big\} \langle\omega_r^3\rangle,$$

$$\sum_{G} \omega_G^4 I_G(I_G+1) + \tfrac{2}{3}\sum_{G<G'}\sum J_{GG'}^2 \omega_{GG'}^2 I_G I_{G'}(I_G+1)(I_{G'}+1)$$
$$= \Big\{\sum_{G} I_G(I_G+1)\Big\} \langle\omega_r^4\rangle.$$

These equations show that the first three moments of any irreducible component are independent of the spin-spin interactions.

Equations (4.4) may also be used to compute the moments for the complete system, but in this case the numerators in (4.2) must be multiplied by $g_{I_A} g_{I_B} \cdots$ and the results summed over all irreducible components, that is, over all distinct values of I_A, I_B, … . The summations may be easily carried out by observing that, for any group G,

$$\sum_{\text{all } I_G} g_{I_G}(2I_G+1) = (2I+1)^{n_G},$$

and, by equation (23) of Appendix V,

$$\sum_{\text{all } I_G} g_{I_G} I_G(I_G+1)(2I_G+1) = n_G I(I+1)(2I+1)^{n_G}.$$

To illustrate the procedure, consider the summations required for the first moment:

$$\sum_{I_A}\sum_{I_B} \cdots \{g_{I_A} g_{I_B} \cdots \operatorname{tr}[\mathscr{H}, I^+]I^-\}$$

$$= \sum_{I_A}\sum_{I_B} \cdots \Big\{g_{I_A} g_{I_B} \cdots \sum_{G} \omega_G \operatorname{tr} I_G^+ I_G^-\Big\}$$

$$= \tfrac{2}{3}\sum_{I_A}\sum_{I_B} \cdots \Big\{g_{I_A} g_{I_B} \cdots \prod_{G} (2I_G+1) \sum_{G} \omega_G I_G(I_G+1)\Big\}$$

$$= \tfrac{2}{3} I(I+1)(2I+1)^N \sum_{G} n_G \omega_G .$$

The summations required for the other moments are performed similarly, and one obtains the following formulas for the first four moments of the complete system:

$$\sum_{G} n_G \omega_G = N\langle \omega \rangle, \qquad \sum_{G} n_G {\omega_G}^2 = N\langle \omega^2 \rangle, \qquad \sum_{G} n_G {\omega_G}^3 = N\langle \omega^3 \rangle,$$

$$\sum_{G} n_G {\omega_G}^4 + \tfrac{2}{3} I(I+1) \sum_{G<G'}\sum n_G n_{G'} J^2_{GG'} \omega^2_{GG'} = N\langle \omega^4 \rangle.$$

The application of the moment method to the study of practical problems is facilitated by referring the spectral moments to a new frequency origin at the mean resonance frequency. Experimentally, this may be accomplished by measuring $\langle \omega \rangle$ relative to some arbitrary origin (e.g., relative to some prominent resonance in the spectrum), and then choosing a new origin at the mean frequency. For the special case $I = \frac{1}{2}$, the moments about the mean are

$$\sum_{G} n_G \Delta\omega_G = 0, \qquad \sum_{G} n_G (\Delta\omega_G)^2 = N\langle \Delta\omega^2 \rangle, \qquad \sum_{G} n_G (\Delta\omega_G)^3 = N\langle \Delta\omega^3 \rangle,$$

$$\sum_{G} n_G (\Delta\omega_G)^4 + \frac{1}{2} \sum_{G<G'}\sum n_G n_{G'} J^2_{GG'} \omega^2_{GG'} = N\langle \Delta\omega^4 \rangle, \tag{4.5}$$

where $\langle \Delta\omega^n \rangle$ denotes the nth spectral moment of the complete system, and $\Delta\omega_G = \omega_G - \langle \omega \rangle$.

C. Two-Group Systems

When the spin system consists of two groups of magnetically equivalent nuclei, equations (4.5) reduce to

$$n_A \Delta\omega_A + n_B \Delta\omega_B = 0, \tag{4.6}$$

$$n_A (\Delta\omega_A)^2 + n_B (\Delta\omega_B)^2 = N\langle \Delta\omega^2 \rangle, \tag{4.7}$$

$$n_A (\Delta\omega_A)^3 + n_B (\Delta\omega_B)^3 = N\langle \Delta\omega^3 \rangle, \tag{4.8}$$

$$n_A (\Delta\omega_A)^4 + n_B (\Delta\omega_B)^4 + \tfrac{1}{2}(n_A n_B J^2 \delta^2) = N\langle \Delta\omega^4 \rangle, \tag{4.9}$$

$$n_A + n_B = N, \qquad \delta = \Delta\omega_A - \Delta\omega_B . \tag{4.10}$$

Equations (4.6) and (4.7) provide simultaneous equations for $\Delta\omega_A$ and $\Delta\omega_B$, whose solutions are

$$\Delta\omega_A = \pm \left(\frac{n_B}{n_A} \langle \Delta\omega^2 \rangle \right)^{1/2}, \qquad \Delta\omega_B = \mp \left(\frac{n_A}{n_B} \langle \Delta\omega^2 \rangle \right)^{1/2}. \tag{4.11}$$

The geometric interpretation of these solutions is simple. If all pairs of numbers $(\Delta\omega_A, \Delta\omega_B)$ are interpreted as points in the cartesian plane, then (4.6) is the equation of a line through the origin with slope $-(n_B/n_A)$, and (4.7) is the equation of an ellipse with semiaxes $(N\langle\Delta\omega^2\rangle/n_A)^{1/2}$, $(N\langle\Delta\omega^2\rangle/n_B)^{1/2}$. The solutions (4.11) represent the points of intersection of the line (4.6) with the ellipse (4.7).

The signs of $\Delta\omega_A$ and $\Delta\omega_B$ are determined by the sign of the third moment, provided that $n_A \neq n_B$. For if (4.11) is substituted in (4.8), one obtains

$$\langle\Delta\omega^3\rangle = \pm \frac{\langle\Delta\omega^2\rangle^{3/2}}{(n_A n_B)^{1/2}}(n_B - n_A),$$

where the upper and lower signs correspond to the upper and lower signs for $\Delta\omega_A$ in (4.11). The sign of $n_B - n_A$ is known in any particular instance, so that the sign of $\langle\Delta\omega^3\rangle$ dictates the correct choice of signs for $\Delta\omega_A$ and $\Delta\omega_B$. The several contingencies are indicated in the accompanying tabulation. When $n_A = n_B$, $\langle\Delta\omega^3\rangle = 0$, so that the signs of $\Delta\omega_A$ and $\Delta\omega_B$ are not determined.

$n_B - n_A$	$\langle\Delta\omega^3\rangle$	$\Delta\omega_A$	$\Delta\omega_B$
+	+	+	−
+	−	−	+
−	+	−	+
−	−	+	−

The square of the internal chemical shift and the square of the spin-spin coupling constant are determined by eliminating $\Delta\omega_A$ and $\Delta\omega_B$ from $\delta^2 = (\Delta\omega_A - \Delta\omega_B)^2$ and (4.9):

$$\delta^2 = \frac{N^2}{n_A n_B}\langle\Delta\omega^2\rangle, \tag{4.12}$$

$$J^2 = \frac{2}{N^2\langle\Delta\omega^2\rangle}\left\{N\langle\Delta\omega^4\rangle - \frac{n_A{}^3 + n_B{}^3}{n_A n_B}\langle\Delta\omega^2\rangle^2\right\}. \tag{4.13}$$

Equation (4.12) shows that δ is proportional to the root-mean-square frequency, and (4.13) shows that the ratio $\langle\Delta\omega^2\rangle^2/\langle\Delta\omega^4\rangle$ cannot exceed $Nn_An_B/(n_A{}^3 + n_B{}^3)$.

When $n_B = 1$, equations (4.12) and (4.13) can be checked by computing $\langle\Delta\omega^2\rangle$ and $\langle\Delta\omega^4\rangle$ with the explicit formulas for the resonance frequencies and relative intensities of the $A_{n_A}B$ systems given in Chapter 6. The calculations for arbitrary n_A are rather tedious, but for $n_A = 1, 2$, it is easily verified that (4.12) and (4.13) are indeed identities.

D. Three-Group Systems

For systems composed of three groups of magnetically equivalent spin-$\frac{1}{2}$ nuclei, the first three moments provide the equations:

$$\begin{aligned} n_A \Delta\omega_A + n_B \Delta\omega_B + n_C \Delta\omega_C &= 0, \\ n_A(\Delta\omega_A)^2 + n_B(\Delta\omega_B)^2 + n_C(\Delta\omega_C)^2 &= N\langle\Delta\omega^2\rangle, \\ n_A(\Delta\omega_A)^3 + n_B(\Delta\omega_B)^3 + n_C(\Delta\omega_C)^3 &= N\langle\Delta\omega^3\rangle. \end{aligned} \tag{4.14}$$

If $\langle\Delta\omega^2\rangle$ and $\langle\Delta\omega^3\rangle$ are determined experimentally, equations (4.14) constitute a set of simultaneous equations for the chemical shifts. If the three coupling constants are desired, the fourth, fifth, and sixth moments are required.

The study of equations (4.14) is facilitated by introducing the dimensionless quantity

$$r = \frac{\Delta\omega_C}{\Delta\omega_B}. \tag{4.15}$$

From (4.14) and (4.15) it follows that

$$\Delta\omega_A = -\frac{n_B + r n_C}{n_A} \Delta\omega_B, \tag{4.16}$$

$$\Delta\omega_B = \frac{n_A^2(n_B + r^2 n_C) + n_A(n_B + r n_C)^2}{n_A^2(n_B + r^3 n_C) - (n_B + r n_C)^3} \frac{\langle\Delta\omega^3\rangle}{\langle\Delta\omega^2\rangle}, \tag{4.17}$$

$$\left(\frac{N}{n_A}\right)^{1/3} \frac{[n_A^2(n_B + r^3 n_C) - (n_B + r n_C)^3]^{2/3}}{n_A(n_B + r^2 n_C) + (n_B + r n_C)^2} = \rho, \tag{4.18}$$

where

$$\rho = \frac{\langle\Delta\omega^3\rangle^{2/3}}{\langle\Delta\omega^2\rangle}. \tag{4.19}$$

Since n_A, n_B, n_C, and N are presumed known, values can be assigned to r ($-\infty \leqslant r \leqslant \infty$) and the corresponding values of ρ computed with (4.18). From these data a graph of r vs. ρ can be prepared. The values of r corresponding to a given experimental value of ρ may then be determined graphically and the chemical shifts determined by equations (4.15) through (4.17).

In general, a given value of ρ will yield more than one value of r. Indeed, a well-known theorem of algebra states that a set of simultaneous algebraic equations of integral degrees $d_1, d_2, \ldots, d_n$ possesses $d_1 \times d_2 \times \cdots \times d_n$ solutions. It follows that the system (4.14) possesses six solutions, so there must be six values of r and, therefore, six sets of chemical shifts. Some of these sets may be discarded by comparison with the experimental spectrum; other sets may require additional information for their elimination.

When $n_A = n_B = n_C = N/3$, equations (4.15) through (4.18) reduce to

$$\Delta\omega_A = -(1 + r)\,\Delta\omega_B\,, \qquad \Delta\omega_C = r\,\Delta\omega_B \tag{4.20}$$

$$\Delta\omega_B = -\frac{2(r^2 + r + 1)}{3r(r + 1)}\frac{\langle\Delta\omega^3\rangle}{\langle\Delta\omega^2\rangle} \tag{4.21}$$

$$\rho = \frac{3[r(r + 1)]^{2/3}}{2[r^2 + r + 1]}\,. \tag{4.22}$$

A graph of ρ vs. r is shown in Fig. 7.12. From the figure it is clear that when $0 < \rho < 2^{-1/3} = 0.794...$, there will be six distinct values of r. The corresponding sets of chemical shifts are essentially equivalent, since equations (4.14) are symmetrical in $\Delta\omega_A$, $\Delta\omega_B$, and $\Delta\omega_C$ when $n_A = n_B = n_C = N/3$. The six values of r correspond to the six possible permutations of the labels A, B, C. This can be verified analytically upon noting that if $r = \lambda$ is a solution of (4.22) which yields the chemical shifts ($\Delta\omega_A$, $\Delta\omega_B$, $\Delta\omega_C$), then

$$\frac{1}{\lambda}, \quad -(\lambda + 1), \quad -\frac{1}{\lambda + 1}, \quad -\frac{1 + \lambda}{\lambda}, \quad -\frac{\lambda}{\lambda + 1},$$

are also solutions of (4.22). From equations (4.20) it can be shown that the chemical shifts corresponding to these solutions are just the six

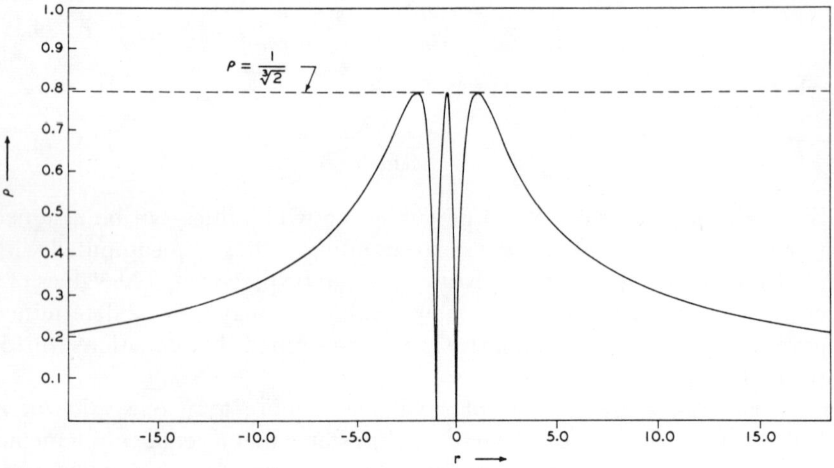

FIG. 7.12. Graph of r vs. ρ for $n_A = n_B = n_C$.

permutations of A, B, C. The relations between the values of r and the corresponding chemical shifts are indicated in the accompanying tabulation and in Fig. 7.13.

r			
λ	$\Delta\omega_A$	$\Delta\omega_B$	$\Delta\omega_C$
$1/\lambda$	$\Delta\omega_A$	$\Delta\omega_C$	$\Delta\omega_B$
$-(\lambda + 1)$	$\Delta\omega_C$	$\Delta\omega_B$	$\Delta\omega_A$
$-1/(\lambda + 1)$	$\Delta\omega_B$	$\Delta\omega_C$	$\Delta\omega_A$
$-(1 + \lambda)/\lambda$	$\Delta\omega_C$	$\Delta\omega_A$	$\Delta\omega_B$
$-\lambda/(1 + \lambda)$	$\Delta\omega_B$	$\Delta\omega_A$	$\Delta\omega_C$

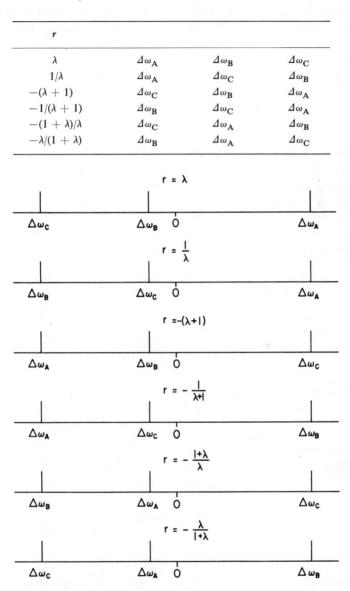

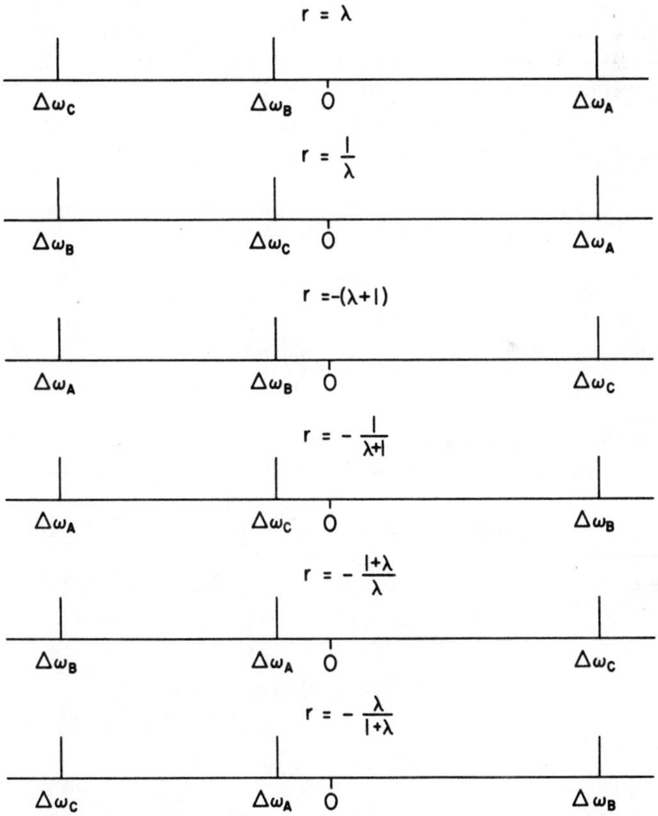

FIG. 7.13. Graphical representation of the six solutions of the first three moment equations when $n_A = n_B = n_C$.

There are two limiting cases for which the solutions of (4.22) may be obtained exactly.

(1) $\rho = 2^{-1/3}$. In this case it may be verified by direct substitution in (4.22) that $r = 1$ is a solution. From the foregoing discussion it follows that $r = 1, -\frac{1}{2}, -2$, are double roots of (4.22). For $r = 1$, $\Delta\omega_B$ and $\Delta\omega_C$ have the same algebraic sign, and $\Delta\omega_A = -2\Delta\omega_B$. There are two possibilities: $\Delta\omega_B, \Delta\omega_C > 0, \Delta\omega_A < 0$; $\Delta\omega_B, \Delta\omega_C < 0, \Delta\omega_A > 0$. Similar remarks apply for $r = -\frac{1}{2}$ and $r = -2$. The results for all six cases are sketched in Fig. 7.14.

(2) $\rho = 0$. When $\rho = 0$, which implies that the third moment vanishes, the solutions of (4.22) are $r = +\infty, -\infty, -1, 0$, the latter two being double roots. The solution $r = \Delta\omega_C/\Delta\omega_B = +\infty$ requires that $\Delta\omega_B = 0$, and that $\Delta\omega_C > 0$. From $\Delta\omega_A + \Delta\omega_B + \Delta\omega_C = 0$, it then follows that $\Delta\omega_A < 0$. The remaining solutions are studied in a similar manner; the results are shown in Fig. 7.15.

An alternative method of solving equations (4.14) commences with the introduction of reduced chemical shifts defined by

$$x = \frac{\Delta\omega_A \cos\alpha}{(\langle\Delta\omega^2\rangle)^{1/2}}, \qquad y = \frac{\Delta\omega_B \cos\beta}{(\langle\Delta\omega^2\rangle)^{1/2}}, \qquad z = \frac{\Delta\omega_C \cos\gamma}{(\langle\Delta\omega^2\rangle)^{1/2}}, \tag{4.23}$$

where

$$\cos\alpha = \left(\frac{n_A}{N}\right)^{1/2}, \qquad \cos\beta = \left(\frac{n_B}{N}\right)^{1/2}, \qquad \cos\gamma = \left(\frac{n_C}{N}\right)^{1/2}. \tag{4.24}$$

Equations (4.24) define a unit vector $\mathbf{n} = (\cos\alpha, \cos\beta, \cos\gamma)$, whose components may also be expressed in terms of the polar angles φ, θ:

$$\cos\alpha = \sin\theta\cos\varphi, \qquad \cos\beta = \sin\theta\sin\varphi, \qquad \cos\gamma = \cos\theta. \tag{4.25}$$

In terms of the reduced chemical shifts, equations (4.14) take the form

$$x\cos\alpha + y\cos\beta + z\cos\gamma = 0, \tag{4.26}$$

$$x^2 + y^2 + z^2 = 1, \tag{4.27}$$

$$\frac{x^3}{\cos\alpha} + \frac{y^3}{\cos\beta} + \frac{z^3}{\cos\gamma} = \rho^{3/2}. \tag{4.28}$$

Equation (4.26) requires the reduced shifts to lie in a plane passing through the origin and perpendicular to $\mathbf{n}$. Equation (4.27) is the equation of the unit sphere about the origin, so that (4.26) and (4.27) together

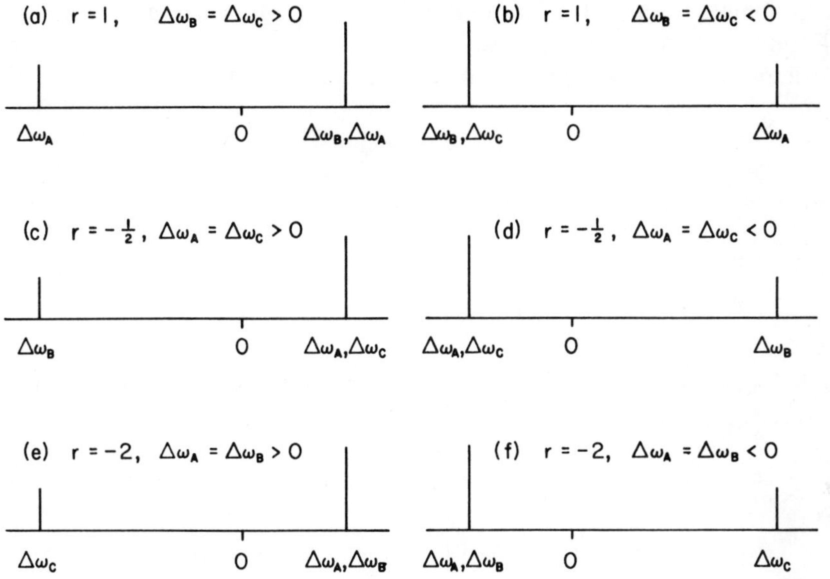

FIG. 7.14. Solutions of the first three moment equations for $n_A = n_B = n_C$, and $\rho = 2^{1/3}$.

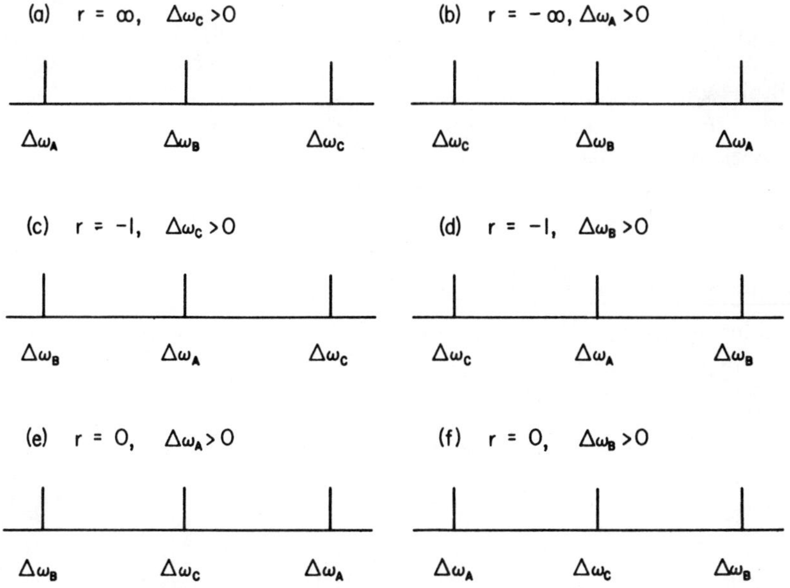

FIG. 7.15. Solutions of the first three moment equations for $n_A = n_B = n_C$, and $\rho = 0$.

state that x, y, and z lie on the unit circle defined by the intersection of the plane (4.26) with the sphere (4.27). The intersection of this circle with the surface (4.28) defines the possible values of the reduced chemical shifts. These geometric considerations suggest the introduction of new variables (u, v, w), defined by the orthogonal transformation:

$$\begin{aligned} x &= u \cos\theta \cos\varphi - v \sin\varphi + w \sin\theta \cos\varphi, \\ y &= u \cos\theta \sin\varphi + v \cos\varphi + w \sin\theta \sin\varphi, \\ z &= -u \sin\theta + w \cos\theta. \end{aligned} \tag{4.29}$$

Substituting (4.29) in (4.26) through (4.28), one finds that u, v, and w satisfy the equations

$$u^2 + v^2 = 1, \tag{4.30}$$

$$2u^3 \cot 2\theta + 3uv^2 \cot\theta + \frac{2v^3 \cot 2\varphi}{\sin\theta} = \rho^{3/2}, \tag{4.31}$$

$$w = 0. \tag{4.32}$$

Equations (4.30) through (4.32) are quite useful in the study of particular three-group systems. Their use will be illustrated by a hypothetical example that also illustrates the existence of nontrivial multiple solutions of (4.14).

Consider a three-group system with $n_A = n_B = 1$, $n_C = 2$, whose chemical shifts relative to $\langle\omega\rangle$ are $\Delta\omega_A = -6$ cps, $\Delta\omega_B = -2$ cps, $\Delta\omega_C = 4$ cps. From these data one finds

$$\langle\Delta\omega^2\rangle = 18\ (\text{cps})^2, \qquad \langle\Delta\omega^3\rangle = -24\ (\text{cps})^3, \qquad \rho^{3/2} = -\frac{2}{9}\sqrt{2}.$$

Consider now the problem of computing $\Delta\omega_A$, $\Delta\omega_B$, and $\Delta\omega_C$, given the above values for $\langle\Delta\omega^2\rangle$, $\langle\Delta\omega^3\rangle$, and $\rho^{3/2}$. Since $\tan\varphi = \tan\theta = 1$, equations (4.30) and (4.31) yield the cubic equation

$$u^3 - u - \frac{2\sqrt{2}}{27} = 0$$

whose roots are

$$u = -\frac{2\sqrt{2}}{3}, \quad \frac{1}{3}(\sqrt{2} + \sqrt{3}), \quad \frac{1}{3}(\sqrt{2} - \sqrt{3}).$$

The corresponding values of v are given by $\pm(1 - u^2)^{1/2}$ ($w = 0$ for all values of u and v). From these results one finds the solutions given in the accompanying tabulation, where $R_\pm = (\sqrt{6} \pm 2)^{1/2}$. Only three

	(1)	(2)	(3)
$\Delta\omega_A$	-6	$2(1 - iR_-\sqrt{2}) + \sqrt{6}$	$2(1 - R_+\sqrt{2}) - \sqrt{6}$
$\Delta\omega_B$	-2	$2(1 + iR_-\sqrt{2}) + \sqrt{6}$	$2(1 + R_+\sqrt{2}) - \sqrt{6}$
$\Delta\omega_C$	4	$-(2 + \sqrt{6})$	$-(2 - \sqrt{6})$

of the six solutions are given in the tabulation; the remaining three solutions are obtained by interchanging $\Delta\omega_A$ and $\Delta\omega_B$ in solutions (1), (2), and (3). It should be verified that these solutions satisfy the equations

$$\Delta\omega_A + \Delta\omega_B + 2\,\Delta\omega_C = 0,$$

$$(\Delta\omega_A)^2 + (\Delta\omega_B)^2 + 2(\Delta\omega_C)^2 = 72,$$

$$(\Delta\omega_A)^3 + (\Delta\omega_B)^3 + 2(\Delta\omega_C)^3 = -96.$$

Geometrically speaking, the existence of two imaginary solutions means that the circle (4.30) intersects the plane curve (4.31) at four points. Errors in the experimental moments could introduce an imaginary component in an otherwise acceptable solution. Hence imaginary solutions should not be summarily dismissed without investigating the possibility that such solutions are imaginary only by virtue of experimental errors in $\langle\Delta\omega^2\rangle$ and $\langle\Delta\omega^3\rangle$.

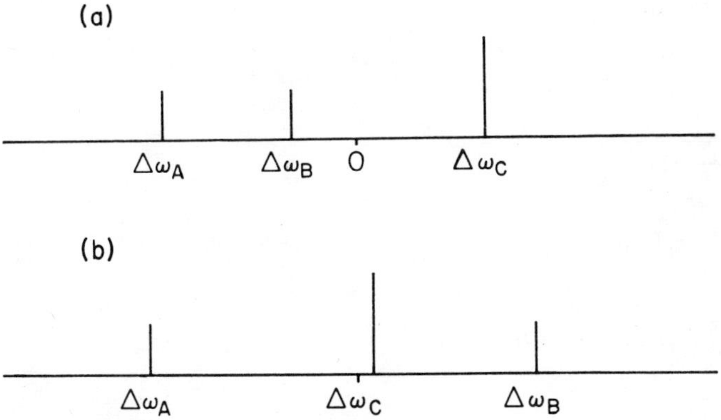

FIG. 7.16. Multiple solutions of the first three moment equations for $n_A = n_B = 1$, $n_C = 2$, $\langle\Delta\omega^2\rangle = 18$ (cps)^2 $\langle\Delta\omega^3\rangle = -24$ (cps)^3. These data also yield complex solutions (see the text).

Solution (3) is a real, acceptable solution whose rejection in favor of solution (1) would require additional information. Solutions (1) and (3) are sketched in Fig. 7.16.

E. Approximate Moment Calculations

The moment method can also be applied to systems of the type described in Section 2. The selection rules for such systems show that one obtains a set of moment equations for each spectral region. Consider, for example, the $A_{n_A}B_{n_B} \cdots X_{n_X}Y_{n_Y} \cdots$ system. Let I denote the common spin quantum number of the $N_{AB\cdots} = n_A + n_B + \cdots$ nuclei forming groups A, B, ..., and let I' and $N_{XY\cdots}$ denote the corresponding quantities for groups X, Y, ... The moment equations of the irreducible $A_{I_A}B_{I_B} \cdots X_{I_X}Y_{I_Y} \cdots$ component for the AB $\cdots$ region are obtained from (4.2), using (2.5) without the negative sign for $\mathscr{H}$, and $I^{\pm}(AB \cdots)$ for $I^{\pm}$. The moments for the AB $\cdots$ region of the complete system may be obtained by a procedure similar to that used for the $A_{n_A}B_{n_B} \cdots$ system. Similar remarks apply to the calculation of the moments for the XY $\cdots$ region of the spectrum. The results for the first three moments of each spectral region are

$$\sum_{G} n_G\, \Delta\omega_G = 0,$$

$$\sum_{G} n_G(\Delta\omega_G)^2 + \tfrac{1}{3}I'(I'+1)\sum_{G}\sum_{S} n_G n_S J_{GS}^2 = N_{AB\cdots}\langle \Delta\omega_{AB\cdots}^2 \rangle, \tag{4.33}$$

$$\sum_{G} n_G(\Delta\omega_G)^3 + \tfrac{1}{3}I'(I'+1)\sum_{G}\sum_{S} n_G n_S\, \Delta\omega_G J_{GS}^2 = N_{AB\cdots}\langle \Delta\omega_{AB\cdots}^3 \rangle;$$

$$\sum_{S} n_S\, \Delta\omega_S = 0,$$

$$\sum_{S} n_S(\Delta\omega_S)^2 + \tfrac{1}{3}I(I+1)\sum_{G}\sum_{S} n_G n_S J_{GS}^2 = N_{XY\cdots}\langle \Delta\omega_{XY\cdots}^2 \rangle, \tag{4.34}$$

$$\sum_{S} n_S(\Delta\omega_S)^3 + \tfrac{1}{3}I(I+1)\sum_{G}\sum_{S} n_G n_S\, \Delta\omega_S J_{GS}^2 = N_{XY\cdots}\langle \Delta\omega_{XY\cdots}^3 \rangle,$$

where G = A, B, ..., S = X, Y, ..., and $\langle \Delta\omega_{AB\cdots}^n \rangle$, $\langle \Delta\omega_{XY\cdots}^n \rangle$ denote the nth moments computed with respect to the mean frequencies of the AB $\cdots$ and XY $\cdots$ regions of the spectrum.

F. Remarks on the Moment Method

The most attractive feature of the moment method is the directness of its approach to the problem of spectral analysis—the parameters of interest appear as unknown quantities in a system of simultaneous algebraic equations. The theoretical moments are exactly calculable, so that one can always set up a number of moment equations equal to the number of chemical shifts and coupling constants. In principle, therefore, the moment method provides a direct, general method for the analysis of complex spectra. In practice, the usefulness of the method is rather limited, owing to some inherent difficulties in the method itself, and in the determination of experimental moments.

Experimental moments are calculated by expressions of the form

$$\frac{\sum A_i(\omega_i)^n}{\sum A_i} \qquad (n = 1, 2, \ldots),$$

where A_i and ω_i denote the integrated intensity and resonance frequency of the *i*th resonance, respectively. Measurements of resonance frequencies are usually more reliable than intensity measurements, and it is fortunate that repeated multiplications of experimental intensities are not required. However, these operations are performed on experimental frequencies, and even small errors in frequency measurements can introduce serious errors in the calculation of higher moments.

Additional errors are introduced when the spectrum contains overlapping signals that require a decomposition into subareas and the assignment of fractional areas to each resonance. Furthermore, unobserved resonances may have large-frequency arms whose contributions to higher moments may be significant. This is an inherent difficulty of the moment method, since the contributions of all resonances are taken into account in the calculation of theoretical moments.

Finally, there are the ambiguities that arise whenever the moment equations possess multiple solutions.

Although the moment method is not suitable for the study of incompletely resolved spectra, the lower moments can often be used to obtain partial analyses of well-resolved spectra. For example, the second and third moments of the proton resonances of 2-bromothiophene (Fig. 7.4) at 60 Mcps are

$$\langle \Delta\omega^2 \rangle = 61.558 \quad (\text{cps})^2, \qquad \langle \Delta\omega^3 \rangle = 253.146 \quad (\text{cps})^3.$$

From these data one finds that $\rho = 0.65$ and, from Fig. 7.12, that $r = -3.54, -1.39, -0.72, 0.29, 0.39, 2.53$. The value $r = -3.54$ yields $\omega_{AB}/2\pi = 13.4$ cps, $\omega_{AC}/2\pi = 18.0$ cps. A somewhat better correspondence with the results of the direct analysis could be obtained by using the properties of the ABC system derived in Section 1 to introduce corrections for the mixed transitions not included in the calculation of $\langle \Delta\omega^2 \rangle$ and $\langle \Delta\omega^3 \rangle$.

REFERENCES

1. W. A. Anderson, *Phys. Rev.* **102**, 151 (1956).
2. L. I. Schiff, "Quantum Mechanics," 2nd ed., Chap. VII. McGraw-Hill, New York, 1955.
3. E. O. Bishop and R. E. Richards, *Mol. Phys.* **3**, 114 (1960).
4. W. Brügel, T. Ankel, and F. Krückeberg, *Z. Electrochem.* **64**, 1121 (1960).
5. S. Castellano and J. S. Waugh, *J. Chem. Phys.* **34**, 295 (1961); **35**, 1900 (1961). See also J. R. Cavanaugh, *ibid.* **39**, 2378 (1963); **40**, 248 (1964).
6. J. R. Cavanaugh, P. S. Landis, and P. L. Corio, Socony Mobil Technical Report (unpublished).
7. G. A. Williams and H. S. Gutowsky, *J. Chem. Phys.* **25**, 1288 (1956)
8. P. L. Corio, *Chem. Rev.* **60**, 363 (1960); *J. Mol. Spectry.* **8**, 193 (1962).
9. (a) P. T. Narasimhan and M. T. Rogers, *J. Chem. Phys.* **31**, 1430 (1959); **34**, 1049 (1961); (b) S. Alexander, *J. Chem. Phys.* **32**, 1700 (1960); (c) J. A. Pople and T. Schaefer, *Mol. Phys.* **3**, 547 (1960); (d) P. Diehl and J. A. Pople, *ibid.*, 557 (1960).
10. (a) H. S. Gutowsky, C. H. Holm, A. Saika, and G. A. Williams, *J. Am. Chem. Soc.* **79**, 4596 (1957); (b) F. S. Mortimer, *J. Mol. Spectry.* **3**, 355 (1959); (c) A. D. Cohen and N. Sheppard, *Proc. Roy. Soc.* (*London*) **A252**, 488 (1959); (d) R. W. Fessenden and J. S. Waugh, *J. Chem. Phys.* **30**, 944 (1959); (e) C. N. Banwell and N. Sheppard, *Proc. Roy. Soc.* (*London*) **A263**, 136 (1961).
11. R. C. Hirst, D. M. Grant, and E. G. Paul, *J. Chem. Phys.* **44**, 4305 (1966).
12. W. A. Anderson and H. M. McConnell, *J. Chem. Phys.* **26**, 1946 (1957). See also H. Primas and H. Gunthard, *Helv. Phys. Acta* **31**, 43 (1955).
13. D. R. Whitman, *J. Mol. Spectry.* **10**, 250 (1963).
14. C. N. Banwell and H. Primas, *Mol. Phys.* **6**, 225 (1963).

CHAPTER 8

The Analysis of Symmetrical Spin Systems

The study of a spin system can be materially simplified whenever the structure of the molecule containing the system admits the introduction of symmetry considerations.[1] For the existence of symmetry in a spin system invariably implies the existence of *symmetry constants of the motion*. These operators satisfy the two conditions required of a physical constant of the motion—they commute with the hamiltonian operator and are not explicit functions of time—but they need not be constants of the motion in the usual physical sense. Symmetry constants of the motion commute with each other and with I_z, so that if the basis vectors are simultaneous eigenvectors of all constants of the motion, optimum factorization of the stationary hamiltonian matrix is automatically achieved. Furthermore, the symmetry constants of the motion commute with the transverse components of the total angular momentum, a circumstance that leads to selection principles of considerable assistance in the determination and classification of transitions.

The symmetry constants of the motion cannot, in general, be deduced by elementary considerations, but instead require a systematic analysis based on the theory of groups and their representations. The following discussion of these concepts is designed to provide the special mathematical techniques required for the systematic study of symmetrical spin systems and some understanding of their theoretical basis. Although this exposition may be considered to be complete insofar as its own limited objectives are concerned, it scarcely does justice to what is undoubtedly one of the most important subjects in the whole of mathematics. For more general discussions of group theory and its application to physical problems, the references listed at the end of this chapter should be consulted (*1–10*).

[1] A precise definition of "symmetry" will be given in Section 1.D.

1. Properties of Finite Groups

A. The Group Concept

A nonempty set $\mathcal{G}$ containing a finite or infinite number of elements, $a, b, c, \ldots$, together with a law of composition, called *multiplication*, is said to be an *abstract group* if the following axioms are satisfied:

(1) To every pair of elements a, b, taken in a definite order (a, b), the law of composition assigns a uniquely determined element of $\mathcal{G}$ called their *product* and denoted ab.

(2) The law of composition is associative; that is, for any three elements a, b, c,

$$(ab)c = a(bc).$$

(3) $\mathcal{G}$ contains an element e, called the *group identity*, such that

$$xe = ex = x,$$

for all x in $\mathcal{G}$.

(4) For every element x there exists an element x^{-1}, called the *inverse* of x, such that

$$xx^{-1} = x^{-1}x = e.$$

The definition of an abstract group makes no reference to the specific nature of the elements in $\mathcal{G}$ or the law of composition. The term "multiplication" could mean numerical multiplication, operator multiplication, numerical addition, etc., depending upon the specific interpretation attached to the elements of $\mathcal{G}$ and the law of composition.

If two group elements x and y are such that $xy = yx$, then x and y are said to commute. The two possible products of a group element with itself are indistinguishable, so that each element of the group commutes with itself, the group identity, and its own inverse. If every element of the group commutes with every other element of the group, so that the law of composition is associative and commutative, the group is said to be *abelian*.

Since there is no ambiguity in the product of a group element with itself, xx is abbreviated to x^2. By the associative law, $xxx = x(xx) = (xx)x = xx^2 = x^2x$, which is defined to be x^3. In general, x^{n+1} is defined as $xx^n = x^nx$. Similarly, $x^{-1}x^{-1}$ can be condensed to x^{-2}, $x^{-1}x^{-1}x^{-1}$ to x^{-3}, etc. It is easy to verify that x^{-n} is the inverse of x^n. More generally, the inverse of a product of any number of group elements is given by the product of the inverses taken in reverse order. For example, the inverse of ab is $b^{-1}a^{-1}$, since $ab(b^{-1}a^{-1}) = a[(bb^{-1})a^{-1}] = a(ea^{-1}) = aa^{-1} = e$, by axioms (2), (3), and (4).

The number of elements contained in a finite group $\mathscr{G}$ is called the *order* of $\mathscr{G}$ and denoted g. Groups containing an infinite number of elements are said to be of infinite order. Following are some examples of groups:

(1) Let $\mathscr{G}$ be the set of all integers, $\mathscr{G} = \{0, \pm 1, \pm 2, \ldots\}$, and let the law of composition be ordinary addition. $\mathscr{G}$ is then an (additive) abelian group of infinite order. The group identity is the number 0 ($a + 0 = 0 + a = a$), and the inverse of any element is its negative [$a + (-a) = (-a) + a = 0$].

(2) Let $\mathscr{G}$ consist of the numbers ± 1, $\pm i$ ($i = \sqrt{-1}$), with ordinary multiplication as the law of composition. $\mathscr{G}$ is then an abelian group of order 4. The group identity is the number 1, and the inverse elements of ± 1 and $\pm i$, are ± 1 and $\mp i$, respectively.

(3) Let $\mathscr{G}$ consist of all nonsingular square matrices of dimension n, and let the law of composition be matrix multiplication. This law of composition is associative but will not, in general, be commutative. Since the product of two nonsingular matrices is also nonsingular, $\mathscr{G}$ contains the matrix AB whenever it contains the matrices A and B. The group identity is the n-dimensional unit matrix, and the inverse of any matrix A in $\mathscr{G}$ is the inverse matrix A^{-1}.

In any group $\mathscr{G}$, the identity element and all inverse elements are unique. To prove the uniqueness of e, suppose that $\mathscr{G}$ contains an element e' which also satisfies $xe' = e'x = x$, for all x in $\mathscr{G}$. In particular, if $x = e$, $ee' = e'e = e$. On the other hand, if x in axiom (3) is taken to be e', one obtains $ee' = e'e = e'$, so that $e = e'$.

The uniqueness of any inverse element is established by assuming the existence of an element y^{-1} for which $xy^{-1} = y^{-1}x = e$. Multiplying $xy^{-1} = e$ from the left with x^{-1} shows that $y^{-1} = x^{-1}$.

The properties of a finite group can be conveniently displayed in a multiplication table exhibiting the g^2 products of the group elements. The group elements label the rows and columns, and the product xy is entered at the intersection of the xth row and the yth column:

	e	a	$\cdots$	x	$\cdots$	y
e	e	a	$\cdots$	x	$\cdots$	y
a	a	a^2	$\cdots$	ax	$\cdots$	ay
$\cdot$	$\cdot$	$\cdot$	$\cdots$	$\cdot$	$\cdots$	$\cdot$
x	x	xa	$\cdots$	x^2	$\cdots$	xy
$\cdot$	$\cdot$	$\cdot$	$\cdots$	$\cdot$	$\cdots$	$\cdot$
y	y	ya	$\cdots$	yx	$\cdots$	y^2

When the law of composition is known, all compound products can be reduced to a single group element. If the group is abelian, the multiplication table will be symmetric with respect to a diagonal line running from the upper left-hand corner to the lower right-hand corner.

The construction of multiplication tables consistent with the group axioms is not difficult for small values of g. For $g = 1$, there is only one possibility, the group consisting of the identity alone. There is one abstract group of order 2, and one of order 3, but $g = 4$ admits two possibilities. Omitting the trivial case $g = 1$, the multiplication tables for these groups are:

	e	*a*
e	*e*	*a*
a	*a*	*e*

(1)

	e	*a*	*b*
e	*e*	*a*	*b*
a	*a*	*b*	*e*
b	*b*	*e*	*a*

(2)

	e	*a*	*b*	*c*
e	*e*	*a*	*b*	*c*
a	*a*	*b*	*c*	*e*
b	*b*	*c*	*e*	*a*
c	*c*	*e*	*a*	*b*

(3)

	e	*a*	*b*	*c*
e	*e*	*a*	*b*	*c*
a	*a*	*e*	*c*	*b*
b	*b*	*c*	*e*	*a*
c	*c*	*b*	*a*	*e*

(4)

The abstract group (4) is called the *four-group*.

The first nonabelian group is of order 6 and has the following multiplication table:

	e	*a*	*b*	*c*	*d*	*f*
e	*e*	*a*	*b*	*c*	*d*	*f*
a	*a*	*b*	*e*	*f*	*c*	*d*
b	*b*	*e*	*a*	*d*	*f*	*c*
c	*c*	*d*	*f*	*e*	*a*	*b*
d	*d*	*f*	*c*	*b*	*e*	*a*
f	*f*	*c*	*d*	*a*	*b*	*e*

(5)

An important property of the group multiplication table is that each element appears once and only once in each row and column. That each element appears once in each row and column follows immediately from the identity law. To prove that each element appears only once in each row and column, suppose first that some element appears twice in the xth row, and that the column entries in each instance are y and z. By assumption, therefore, $xy = xz$, $y \neq z$. Multiplying from the left with x^{-1} yields $y = z$. Since the xth row was arbitrarily chosen, this contradiction establishes the result for all rows of the table. A similar argument can be used to establish the corresponding result for the columns of the multiplication table. An immediate consequence of this property is that the product ax (or xa), for a fixed element a, generates all elements of the group when x is allowed to range over the group elements.

B. Isomorphic and Homomorphic Groups

The abstract group (3) is closely related to the group defined in example (2). These groups have identical multiplication tables if the elements are paired in the following manner:

$$e \leftrightarrow 1, \qquad a \leftrightarrow i, \qquad b \leftrightarrow -1, \qquad c \leftrightarrow -i.$$

A correspondence of this type is called an *isomorphism*. More precisely, two groups $\mathscr{G} = \{a, b, c, ...\}$ and $\mathscr{G}' = \{a', b', c', ...\}$ are said to be *isomorphic* if a one-to-one correspondence $a \leftrightarrow a'$, $b \leftrightarrow b'$, ... can be established between the elements of $\mathscr{G}$ and $\mathscr{G}'$ such that the correspondent of any product ab is equal to the product of the correspondents of a and b:

$$(ab)' = a'b'. \tag{1.1}$$

The essential facts concerning an isomorphism are: (1) the group elements retain their individuality—distinct elements of $\mathscr{G}$ correspond to distinct elements of $\mathscr{G}'$, and (2) the form of group multiplication is preserved—$ab = c$ in $\mathscr{G}$ implies $a'b' = c'$ in $\mathscr{G}'$.

If the one-to-one requirement in the definition of an isomorphism is dropped, the concept of an isomorphism generalizes to that of a *homomorphism*. A homomorphism is a mapping of the elements of a group $\mathscr{G}$ *onto* a group $\mathscr{G}'$ that preserves group multiplication, and is such that every element of $\mathscr{G}'$ is the image of at least one element of $\mathscr{G}$.

Under any homomorphism $\mathscr{G} \to \mathscr{G}'$, the identity of $\mathscr{G}$ is mapped into the identity of $\mathscr{G}'$, and inverses are mapped into inverses. For if b in (1.1) is replaced with e, it follows that $(ae)' = (a)' = a' = a'e'$. Similarly, $(ea)' = a' = e'a'$, so that the image of e is the identity element of $\mathscr{G}'$. The second assertion follows from (1.1) upon putting $b = a^{-1}$ to obtain $(aa^{-1})' = a'(a^{-1})' = e'$.

As an example of a homomorphism, consider the groups

$$\mathscr{G} = \{1, -1, i, -i\} \qquad \text{and} \qquad \mathscr{G}' = \{1, -1\},$$

with ordinary multiplication as the law of composition in each instance. The mapping

$$1 \to 1, \qquad -1 \to 1, \qquad i \to -1, \qquad -i \to -1$$

is a homomorphism of $\mathcal{G}$ onto $\mathcal{G}'$.

C. Subgroups, Cosets, and Classes

Let x be an arbitrary element of a finite group $\mathcal{G}$, and consider the series of group elements obtained by forming the integral powers of x: $x, x^2, x^3, \ldots$. Since $\mathcal{G}$ is of finite order, this sequence cannot generate distinct group elements indefinitely. Hence $x^r = x^s$, for some integer $r > s$. Multiplying this relation from the left with x^{-s} yields $x^{r-s} = e$. The least positive integer n for which $x^n = e$ is called the *order* of x. In the abstract group (5), a and b are of order 3; c, d, and f are of order 2.

The set of elements

$$e, \quad x, \quad x^2, \ldots, x^{n-1} \qquad (x^n = e),$$

called the *period* of x, forms an abelian group of order n. The product of any two powers of x, say x^r and $x^s (1 \leqslant r, s \leqslant n)$, can always be written in the form x^k, where $1 \leqslant k \leqslant n$. This is obviously true if $r + s < n$. If $r + s > n$, one can write $r + s = n + (r + s - n)$, so that $x^{r+s} = x^n x^{(r+s-n)} = e x^{(r+s-n)} = x^{r+s-n}$. Furthermore, the period of x contains the inverse of any element in the period. Indeed, the inverse of x^r is x^{n-r}, since $x^r x^{n-r} = x^{n-r} x^r = x^n = e$.

The abelian group generated by the period of an element x is called a *cyclic group*. If this group does not include all elements of $\mathcal{G}$, the period of x is said to generate a *cyclic subgroup* of $\mathcal{G}$. The abstract groups (1), (2), and (3) are cyclic groups; the elements $\{e, a, a^2 = b\}$ of the abstract group (5) form a cyclic subgroup of (5). More generally, any subset H of $\mathcal{G}$ is said to be a subgroup of $\mathcal{G}$ (not necessarily cyclic) if the elements of H also satisfy the group axioms.

Every group contains two trivial subgroups—$\mathcal{G}$ itself and the group consisting of the identity element alone. These subgroups are said to be *improper subgroups*. A subgroup of order h, $1 < h < g$, is said to be a *proper subgroup*. The abstract group (5) contains four proper subgroups: a cyclic subgroup of order 3, and three subgroups of order 2, $\{e, c\}$, $\{e, d\}$, $\{e, f\}$.

The concept of a subgroup can be used to derive an important theorem concerning the order of any subgroup of a finite group. For this purpose, let $H = \{e, x_1, \ldots, x_{h-1}\}$ be any subgroup of $\mathcal{G}$. If $h = g$, then H must be identical with $\mathcal{G}$, and one can write $\mathcal{G} = H$, where the sign of equality means that the two sets contain the same elements. If $h < g$, let y_1 be any element of $\mathcal{G}$ not included in H and form the set

$$Hy_1 = \{y_1, x_1y_1, ..., x_{h-1}y_1\},$$

called a *right coset* of H. The elements in Hy_1 are all distinct, since $x_ry_1 = x_sy_1$ implies $x_r = x_s$. Moreover, Hy_1 has no elements in common with H. For if it is assumed that Hy_1 contains an element x_ry_1 which is also contained in H, then, for some x_s, $x_s = x_ry_1$, which requires that $y_1 = x_r^{-1}x_s$. But $x_r^{-1}x_s$, being a product of two elements of the subgroup H, must be an element of H. By hypothesis, y_1 is not an element of H, so that H and Hy_1 are disjoint (i.e., H and Hy_1 have no common elements). Thus H and Hy_1 provide $2h$ distinct elements of $\mathcal{G}$. If the elements in H and Hy_1 include all the elements of $\mathcal{G}$, then $\mathcal{G}$ is of order $g = 2h$, and $\mathcal{G} = H + Hy_1$, where the right side of the equation should be read "the elements of H and the elements of Hy_1."

If the order of $\mathcal{G}$ is greater than $2h$, let y_2 be an element of $\mathcal{G}$ not included in H or Hy_1, and form the right coset Hy_2. By the argument given previously, Hy_2 has no elements in common with H. Furthermore, Hy_2 has no elements in common with Hy_1. For if $x_ry_1 = x_sy_2$, then $y_2 = x_s^{-1}x_ry_1$, which implies that y_2 is contained in Hy_1, contrary to assumption. By continuing this process, h new elements of $\mathcal{G}$ are generated at each step. Since $\mathcal{G}$ is of finite order, this process cannot continue indefinitely. It follows that $\mathcal{G}$ admits a decomposition of the form

$$\mathcal{G} = H + Hy_1 + Hy_2 + \cdots + Hy_{k-1}. \tag{1.2}$$

Each term on the right side contains h elements of $\mathcal{G}$, and, since $\mathcal{G}$ is of order g,

$$g = kh, \tag{1.3}$$

where k is a positive integer.

Equation (1.3), which is known as the *theorem of Lagrange*, states that the order of any subgroup of $\mathcal{G}$ is a divisor of the order of $\mathcal{G}$. The theorem may also be derived by decomposing $\mathcal{G}$ into *left cosets* $z_1H = \{z_1, z_1x_1, ..., z_1x_{h-1}\}$, $z_2H = \{z_2, z_2x_1, ..., z_2x_{h-1}\}$, ...

As an illustration of the coset decomposition of a group, consider the abstract group (5), and let H be the cyclic subgroup of order 3: $H = \{e, a, b\}$. Taking y_1 in (1.2) as c, one finds $Hc = \{ec, ac, bc\} = \{c, f, d\}$, so that H and Hc exhaust (5). Similarly, H and Hd, or H and Hf, exhaust (5). Other right-coset decompositions of (5) may be obtained by taking $\{e, c\}$, $\{e, d\}$, or $\{e, f\}$ for H.

The theorem of Lagrange can be used to deduce some important properties of finite groups. For example, since the period of an element of order n generates a subgroup of order n, the order of any group element must be a divisor of the order of $\mathcal{G}$. If the order of $\mathcal{G}$ is a prime number p, the only possible subgroups are of order 1 and p. An element x, other than e, must be of order p, so that the period of x includes all the elements of $\mathcal{G}$. Thus every group of prime order is cyclic. The converse of this theorem is not true, as shown by the abstract cyclic group (3) of order 4.

An important decomposition of a group is based on the concept of *conjugate* elements. An element a is said to be conjugate to an element b if for some element x, not necessarily unique,

$$a = xbx^{-1}. \tag{1.4}$$

The element a is called the *transform* of b, and x is said to be the *transforming* element. Conjugation possesses the following properties:

(1) Every element is conjugate to itself.

(2) If a is conjugate to b, then b is conjugate to a.

(3) If a is conjugate to b, and b is conjugate to c, then a is conjugate to c.

Property (1) follows at once from the identity: $a = aaa^{-1}$. Property (2) follows from (1.4) by solving for b and writing the result in the form $b = (x^{-1})a(x^{-1})^{-1}$. Property (3) may be verified by eliminating b from the equations $a = xbx^{-1}$, $b = ycy^{-1}$, to obtain $a = (xy)c(xy)^{-1}$.

The set of all elements conjugate to a given element a is called the *class of a* and denoted (a). The class of a may be obtained by evaluating xax^{-1}, where x is allowed to range over all of the group elements. For example, the elements of the abstract group (5) may be divided into three distinct classes:

$$(e) = \{e\},$$

$$(a) = (b) = \{a, b\},$$

$$(c) = (d) = (f) = \{c, d, f\}.$$

In any group, the identity e forms a class by itself, since $xex^{-1} = e$, for all x. In an abelian group, each group element forms a class by itself, since $xax^{-1} = xx^{-1}a = a$, for all x. Thus an abelian group of order g contains g classes with one element in each class.

The number of elements in any class of a finite nonabelian group is always less than the order of the group. Moreover, any two classes are either identical or have no elements in common. For if (a) and (b) have a common element, it follows that elements x and y exist such that

$xax^{-1} = yby^{-1}$. This implies that a is conjugate to b and, by property (3), to every element in (b). A similar argument shows that b is conjugate to every element in (a). Hence, if (a) and (b) have a common element, they are identical. It follows that a finite group may be decomposed into a finite number of disjoint classes.

D. Symmetry Groups

A symmetry of a geometric figure is defined to be any linear transformation which sends the figure into itself. Every geometric figure possesses a trivial symmetry, called the *identity transformation*, denoted E, which sends each point of the figure into itself; that is, every point of the figure is its own image under the linear transformation E. For a nontrivial illustration, consider a rotation of a square by $\pi/2$ about an axis perpendicular to the plane of the square and passing through its center. This rotation is a symmetry of the square since it transforms the square into itself. Synonyms for the term "symmetry" are *symmetry operation*, *symmetry transformation*, *symmetry element*, and *isometry*.

The symmetries of any geometric figure can be expressed in terms of rotations, reflections, and translations. The latter are associated with geometric figures of infinite extent, whereas the symmetries of finite figures can be completely described in terms of rotations and reflections.

Axes of rotational symmetry and planes of reflective symmetry, as well as the symmetry operations associated with such axes and planes, are denoted by the symbols C and σ, respectively.[2] In particular, a geometrical figure is said to have an n-fold axis of symmetry if a rotation about the axis by $2\pi/n$ transforms the figure into itself. Since the figure is unaltered by the rotation, a second rotation about the n-fold axis by $2\pi/n$ again transforms the figure into itself, the result of both rotations being a rotation by $2(2\pi/n)$. This process can be repeated $n - 1$ times, so that an n-fold axis of symmetry implies the invariance of the figure with respect to rotations by $1 \cdot (2\pi/n)$, $2 \cdot (2\pi/n)$, ..., $(n - 1)(2\pi/n)$ about the n-fold axis. The symmetry operations corresponding to these rotations are denoted

$$C_n, \quad C_n^2, \ldots, C_n^k, \ldots, C_n^{n-1}, \quad C_n^n = E,$$

where C_n^k is defined as a k-fold repetition of C_n. The equation $C_n^n = E$ means that a rotation by $n(2\pi/n) = 2\pi$ restores all points of the figure

[2] The conventional Schönflies notation will be used for specific symmetry operators. When no particular symmetry group is contemplated, the group elements will be indicated by the notation introduced in Section 1.A.

to their initial positions. The symmetry operations E, C_n, C_n^2, ... form a cyclic group of order n, denoted $\mathscr{C}_n$.

If a symmetrical figure has more than one n-fold axis, these axes are distinguished by primes: C_n, C_n', C_n'', ... An axis of symmetry whose order is greater than that of any other axis of symmetry is called a *principal axis of symmetry*. Axes of symmetry at right angles to the principal axis are called *secondary axes of symmetry*. A square has a fourfold principal axis of symmetry and four twofold secondary axes of symmetry.

Planes of symmetry are denoted σ_h (horizontal plane) or σ_v (vertical plane), accordingly as the plane is perpendicular to or contains the principal axis of symmetry. Two successive reflections in a plane of symmetry return all points to their original positions, so that

$$\sigma_h^2 = \sigma_v^2 = E.$$

The symmetries of many geometric figures can be deduced by inspection. For example, an examination of the equilateral triangle shown in Fig. 8.1 reveals the following symmetries:

(1) The identity transformation: (123) $\rightarrow$ (123).
(2) A rotation through $2\pi/3$ about the z axis: (123) $\rightarrow$ (312).
(3) A rotation through $4\pi/3$ about the z axis: (123) $\rightarrow$ (231).
(4) A rotation by π about C_2 : (123) $\rightarrow$ (132).
(5) A rotation by π about C_2': (123) $\rightarrow$ (321).
(6) A rotation by π about C_2'' : (123) $\rightarrow$ (213).

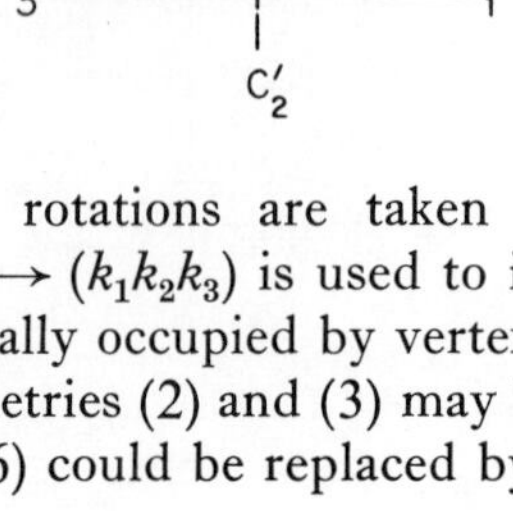

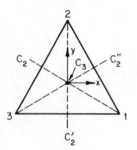

FIG. 8.1. The symmetry operations of an equilateral triangle.

All rotations are taken in the positive sense, and the notation (123) $\rightarrow$ $(k_1k_2k_3)$ is used to indicate that vertex k_j assumes the position originally occupied by vertex j. The principal axis is of order 3, so that symmetries (2) and (3) may be denoted C_3 and C_3^2. Symmetries (4), (5), and (6) could be replaced by reflections σ_v, σ_v', and σ_v'', respectively.

It is easy to demonstrate that there are only six symmetries of the equilateral triangle. For the *final* position occupied by a given vertex, say vertex 1, must be one of the three vertices of the triangle, which admits but three possibilities: $1 \rightarrow 1$, $1 \rightarrow 2$, or $1 \rightarrow 3$. After the final position of vertex 1 has been determined, there are only two symmetries which leave vertex 1 fixed—the identity transformation or the symmetry operation that interchanges the remaining two vertices. Thus there are $3 \times 2 = 6$ symmetries of the equilateral triangle.

The set of six symmetries $\{E, C_3, C_3^2, C_2', C_2''\}$ is called the *symmetry group* of the equilateral triangle and denoted $\mathscr{D}_3$. The multiplication table for $\mathscr{D}_3$ (Table 8.1) shows that $\mathscr{D}_3$ is isomorphic with the abstract group (5).

TABLE 8.1

MULTIPLICATION TABLE FOR THE SYMMETRY GROUP $\mathscr{D}_3$

	E	C_3	C_3^2	C_2	C_2'	C_2''
E	E	C_3	C_3^2	C_2	C_2'	C_2''
C_3	C_3	C_3^2	E	C_2''	C_2	C_2'
C_3^2	C_3^2	E	C_3	C_2'	C_2''	C_2
C_2	C_2	C_2'	C_2''	E	C_3	C_3^2
C_2'	C_2'	C_2''	C_2	C_3^2	E	C_3
C_2''	C_2''	C_2	C_2'	C_3	C_3^2	E

In general, the set of all those linear transformations transforming a geometric figure into itself is called the *symmetry group* of the figure. In particular, the symmetry group of a figure with no symmetry at all consists of the identity transformation alone. This group is denoted $\mathscr{C}_1$.

The symmetry groups of many elementary configurations can be deduced by the method sketched above for the equilateral triangle. It is easy to show, for example, that the symmetry group of the square contains eight symmetries, that of the regular pentagon ten symmetries,..., and that of the regular n-gon $2n$ symmetries. The symmetry group of the regular n-gon is called the *dihedral group* of order $2n$ and denoted $\mathscr{D}_n$. The particular case $n = 3$ corresponds to the symmetry group of the equilateral triangle. The symmetry group of the rectangle (Fig. 8.2 and Table 8.2) contains four symmetry operations. This symmetry group, denoted $\mathscr{D}_2$, is isomorphic to the four-group.

The discussion of symmetry groups will be concluded with brief descriptions of several additional symmetry groups. For further details concerning these groups, the references to this chapter should be consulted (*3–11*).

$\mathscr{C}_{nv}$. This group consists of the n symmetry operations of $\mathscr{C}_n$, together with n planes of reflective symmetry σ_v , σ_v', ..., the angle between successive planes being π/n. $\mathscr{C}_{nv}$ is isomorphic to $\mathscr{D}_n$.

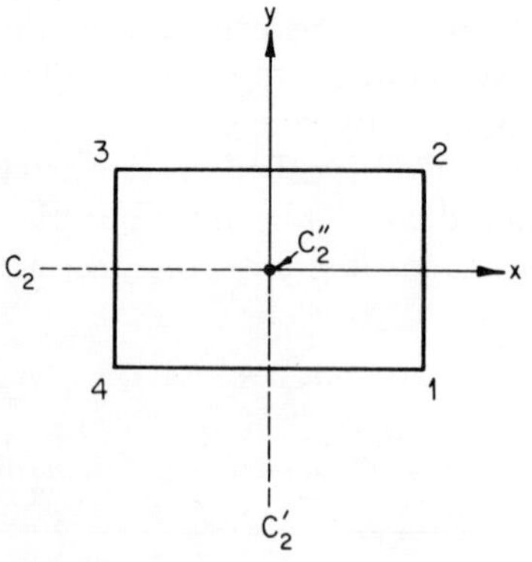

FIG. 8.2. The symmetry operations of a rectangle.

TABLE 8.2

MULTIPLICATION TABLE FOR THE SYMMETRY GROUP $\mathscr{D}_2$

	E	C_2	C_2'	C_2''
E	E	C_2	C_2'	C_2''
C_2	C_2	E	C_2''	C_2'
C_2'	C_2'	C_2''	E	C_2
C_2''	C_2''	C_2'	C_2	E

$\mathscr{C}_{nh}$. The symmetry group of a geometric configuration with an n-fold axis of symmetry and a plane of reflective symmetry σ_h . The order of $\mathscr{C}_{nh}$ is $2n$, since each rotation about the n-fold axis may be followed by the identity transformation or a reflection in σ_h .

$\mathscr{D}_{nh}$. The symmetry group of a geometric configuration with the $2n$ symmetries of $\mathscr{D}_n$ and a plane of reflective symmetry σ_h . The order of $\mathscr{D}_{nh}$ is, therefore, $4n$.

$\mathscr{T}_d$. This symmetry group, called the *full tetrahedral group*, consists of the 24 symmetry operations transforming a regular tetrahedron into itself. The subgroup of 12 proper rotations is called the *tetrahedral group* and denoted $\mathscr{T}$.

$\mathscr{O}_h$. This group, called the *full octahedral group*, is the symmetry group of the cube and of the regular octahedron. $\mathscr{O}_h$ is of order 48. The subgroup of 24 proper rotations is called the *octahedral group* and denoted $\mathscr{O}$.

$\mathscr{O}_3$. This group, called the *three-dimensional rotation group*, is the symmetry group of the sphere—it is of fundamental importance in the general theory of angular momentum (*3, 5, 6, 11*). The elements of $\mathscr{O}_3$

are those improper and proper rotations transforming the sphere into itself. $\mathcal{O}_3$ is of infinite order and contains the following subgroups of infinite order: $\mathcal{O}_3^+$, *the three-dimensional pure rotation group* (i.e., the subgroup of proper three-dimensional rotations); $\mathcal{O}_2$, *the two-dimensional rotation group* (rotations about a fixed axis, together with reflections in any plane containing the axis of rotation); $\mathcal{O}_2^+$, *the two-dimensional pure rotation group* (i.e., proper two-dimensional rotations about a fixed axis). $\mathcal{O}_2$ and $\mathcal{O}_2^+$ are often denoted $\mathscr{C}_{\infty v}$, and $\mathscr{C}_\infty$, respectively. $\mathscr{C}_{\infty v}$ is the symmetry group of linear molecules such as HCl, HC $\equiv$ CD, etc.[3] $\mathcal{O}_3$ also contains subgroups of finite order (e.g., $\mathscr{D}_n$, $\mathscr{T}_d$, $\mathcal{O}_h$).

$\mathscr{D}_{\infty h}$. The symmetry group of a geometric configuration invariant under arbitrary rotations about a fixed axis, reflections in a horizontal plane, and a rotation by π about any axis in σ_h. $\mathscr{D}_{\infty h}$ is the symmetry group of linear molecules such as H_2, HC $\equiv$ CH, etc.[3]

E. Classification of Symmetrical Spin Systems

The symmetry properties of a nuclear spin system are determined by the symmetry properties of the parent molecule. In general, the symmetry group of the spin system will be a proper or improper subgroup of the symmetry group of the parent molecule. Consider, for example, the spin system defined by the protons in water. The symmetry group of the molecule is $\mathscr{C}_{2v} = \{E, C_2, \sigma_v, \sigma_v'\}$, and σ_v will be taken as the plane of the molecule. Insofar as the spin system is concerned, a reflection in σ_v transforms each proton into itself, so that this operation is equivalent to the identity transformation. Thus the symmetry group of the spin system may be taken as $\mathscr{C}_{1v} = \{E, \sigma_v'\}$ or $\mathscr{C}_2 = \{E, C_2\}$. Additional examples are given in Table 8.3.

The last column of Table 8.3 illustrates the notation used for symmetrical spin systems. This notation is based on the following definition. A set of p groups of magnetically equivalent nuclei A, A′, A″, ..., $A^{(p-1)}$, each containing n_A nuclei, is said to be a set of *symmetrically equivalent groups* if these groups transform among themselves, under the operations of the symmetry group of the spin system.[4] (See also footnote 3.) When $n_A = 1$, the definition specializes to a set of *symmetrically equivalent nuclei.* A group of magnetically equivalent nuclei that is transformed into itself under the operations of the symmetry group is called an *invariant group.*

[3] Here the term "symmetry" refers to the symmetry of the molecule in its equilibrium configuration. If the molecule contains groups such as CH_3, CH_2, CF_3, etc., that are assumed to be groups of magnetically equivalent nuclei, the term "symmetry" refers to the symmetry of the time-averaged configuration.

[4] In context, there will be no difficulty in deciding whether the term *group* is used in a mathematical sense or in reference to a group of magnetically equivalent nuclei.

TABLE 8.3

MOLECULAR SYMMETRY GROUPS AND SPIN SYMMETRY GROUPS FOR MOLECULES CONTAINING SPIN-$\frac{1}{2}$ NUCLEI

Molecule	Molecular symmetry	Spin symmetry	Notation
Hydrogen, H_2	$\mathscr{D}_{\infty h}$	$\mathscr{C}_2$	A_2
Acetylene, $HC \equiv CH$	$\mathscr{D}_{\infty h}$	$\mathscr{C}_2$	A_2
Water, H_2O	$\mathscr{C}_{2v}$	$\mathscr{C}_2$	A_2
Chloromethane, CH_3Cl	$\mathscr{C}_{3v}$	$\mathscr{C}_{3v}$	A_3
1, 3, 5-Trichlorobenzene, $C_6H_3Cl_3$	$\mathscr{D}_{3h}$	$\mathscr{D}_3$	A_3
Methane, CH_4	$\mathscr{T}_d$	$\mathscr{T}_d$	A_4
Sulfur hexafluoride, SF_6	$\mathscr{O}_h$	$\mathscr{O}_h$	A_6
Benzene, C_6H_6	$\mathscr{D}_{6h}$	$\mathscr{D}_6$	A_6
1, 2, 3-Trichlorobenzene, $C_6H_3Cl_3$	$\mathscr{C}_{2v}$	$\mathscr{C}_2$	A_2B
Isobutane,[a] $(CH_3)_3CH$	$\mathscr{C}_{3v}$	$\mathscr{C}_{3v}$	A_9B
Propane,[a] $(CH_3)_2CH_2$	$\mathscr{C}_{2v}$	$\mathscr{C}_{2v}$	A_6B_2
m-Dichlorobenzene, $C_6H_4Cl_2$	$\mathscr{C}_{2v}$	$\mathscr{C}_2$	AB_2C
o-Dichlorobenzene, $C_6H_4Cl_2$	$\mathscr{C}_{2v}$	$\mathscr{C}_2$	AA′BB′
Cyclobutanone, C_4H_6O	$\mathscr{C}_{2v}$	$\mathscr{C}_{2v}$	AA′A″A‴BB′
Trans-1, 4-dichloro-2-butene,[b] $ClCH_2CH = CHCH_2Cl$	$\mathscr{C}_{2h}$	$\mathscr{C}_2$	$A_2A_2'BB'$
2, 3-Pentadiene[a]	$\mathscr{C}_2$	$\mathscr{C}_2$	$A_3A_3'BB'$
o-Xylene[a], $(CH_3)_2C_6H_4$	$\mathscr{C}_{2v}$	$\mathscr{C}_2$	$A_3A_3'BB'CC'$
m-Xylene[a], $(CH_3)_2C_6H_4$	$\mathscr{C}_{2v}$	$\mathscr{C}_2$	$A_3A_3'BB'CD$
p-Xylene,[a] $(CH_3)_2C_6H_4$	$\mathscr{D}_{2h}$	$\mathscr{D}_2$	$A_3A_3'BB'B''B'''$
Mesitylene, $(CH_3)_3C_6H_3$	$\mathscr{D}_{3h}$	$\mathscr{D}_3$	$A_3A_3'A_3''BB'B''$
Acetylene-1, 2-C^{13}, $HC^{13} \equiv C^{13}H$	$\mathscr{D}_{\infty h}$	$\mathscr{C}_2$	AA′XX′
Ethylene-1, 2-C^{13}, $H_2C^{13} = C^{13}H_2$	$\mathscr{D}_{2h}$	$\mathscr{D}_2$	AA′A″A‴XX′
p-Difluorobenzene, $C_6H_4F_2$	$\mathscr{D}_{2h}$	$\mathscr{D}_2$	AA′A″A‴XX′
1, 3, 5-Trifluorobenzene, $C_6H_3F_3$	$\mathscr{D}_{3h}$	$\mathscr{D}_3$	AA′A″XX′X″

[a] Methyl-group protons assumed magnetically equivalent.
[b] Methylene-group protons assumed magnetically equivalent.

Sets of symmetrically equivalent groups are denoted $A_{n_A}A'_{n_A}A''_{n_A} \cdots$, $B_{n_B}B'_{n_B}B''_{n_B} \cdots$. The methyl groups in 1, 3, 5-trimethylbenzene constitute a set of symmetrically equivalent groups ($p = n_A = 3$), whereas the protons at positions 2, 4, and 6 form a set of three symmetrically equivalent nuclei. The latter set is chemically shifted from the former set, so that the complete spin system is denoted $A_3A_3'A_3''BB'B''$. If the chemical shift between two symmetrically equivalent sets is large compared to the spin-spin interactions coupling these sets, one of the sets is denoted by a letter at the latter part of the alphabet. Thus the spin system defined by the protons and fluorine nuclei in *p*-difluorobenzene is denoted AA′A″A‴XX′. An example of an invariant group is provided by the methyl group in toluene. The proton *para* to the methyl group is an invariant nucleus.

In symmetrical systems, the Larmor frequencies and coupling constants satisfy auxiliary relations called *symmetry conditions*. Consider, for example, the spin-$\frac{1}{2}$ nuclei in *o*-dichlorobenzene:

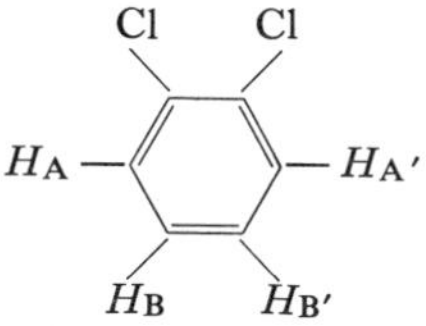

AA′BB′

The symmetry conditions for this system are

$$\begin{aligned} \omega_{\mathrm{A}} &= \omega_{\mathrm{A}'}, & \omega_{\mathrm{B}} &= \omega_{\mathrm{B}'}, \\ J_{\mathrm{AB}} &= J_{\mathrm{A'B'}}, & J_{\mathrm{AB'}} &= J_{\mathrm{A'B}}. \end{aligned} \tag{1.5}$$

In the special case of a system composed of one set of symmetrically equivalent nuclei, the notation $\mathrm{A}_{n_\mathrm{A}}\mathrm{A}'_{n_\mathrm{A}} \cdots \mathrm{A}^{(p-1)}_{n_\mathrm{A}}$ is usually condensed to $\mathrm{A}_{pn_\mathrm{A}}$, since such a set may be considered as a single group of magnetically equivalent nuclei. Neopentane ($p = 4, n_\mathrm{A} = 3$) and methane ($p = 4, n_\mathrm{A} = 1$) are examples. The magnetic equivalence of symmetrically equivalent groups in more general systems will depend upon the symmetry conditions satisfied by the coupling constants. Whenever the symmetry conditions lead to the magnetic equivalence of all sets of symmetrically equivalent groups, the notation for the system will be devoid of accents, and may be studied by the methods described in previous chapters. For example, the symmetry conditions for propane and *m*-dichlorobenzene show that magnetic equivalence is realized for all symmetrically equivalent groups and all symmetrically equivalent nuclei, so that these spin systems are denoted $\mathrm{A}_6\mathrm{B}_2$ and $\mathrm{AB}_2\mathrm{C}$. Symmetrical spin systems for which magnetic equivalence is not realized for all symmetrically equivalent groups must be treated by the methods to be developed in this chapter.

2. Elements of Representation Theory

A. Representations by Linear Operators

Let $\mathscr{G} = \{a, b, c, \ldots\}$ denote an arbitrary group and $T = \{T(a), T(b), \ldots\}$ a set of nonsingular linear operators such that each operator of T is associated with at least one element of $\mathcal{G}$, the operator corresponding to a given element x being denoted $T(x)$. If the operators of T are defined with respect to an n-dimensional vector space, and the correspondence $x \rightarrow T(x)$ is such that

$$T(ab) = T(a)T(b), \tag{2.1}$$

the set $\{T(a), T(b), ...\}$ is said to be an *n-dimensional operator representation* of $\mathcal{G}$. The operators $T(a)$, $T(b)$, ... are said to yield a *faithful* or *unfaithful* representation of $\mathcal{G}$, accordingly as the correspondence $a \rightarrow T(a)$, $b \rightarrow T(b)$, ... is an isomorphism or a homomorphism. In either case, equation (2.1) implies that

$$T(e) = 1, \qquad T(x^{-1}) = T^{-1}(x), \tag{2.2}$$

so that the distinct elements of T form a group.

The concept of a representation by linear operators is illustrated by the correspondence

$$\begin{aligned} &e \leftrightarrow E, \qquad a \leftrightarrow C_3, \qquad b \leftrightarrow C_3^2, \\ &c \leftrightarrow C_2, \qquad d \leftrightarrow C_2', \qquad f \leftrightarrow C_2'', \end{aligned} \tag{2.3}$$

which is a three-dimensional faithful representation of the abstract group (5) by the linear operators of the symmetry group $\mathcal{D}_3$. For examples of unfaithful representations, consider the one-dimensional vector space of ordinary numbers. The operators on this space are also ordinary numbers, and the following correspondences are unfaithful representations of the abstract group (5):

$$e \rightarrow 1, \quad a \rightarrow 1, \quad b \rightarrow 1, \quad c \rightarrow 1, \quad d \rightarrow 1, \quad f \rightarrow 1; \tag{2.4}$$

$$e \rightarrow 1, \quad a \rightarrow 1, \quad b \rightarrow 1, \quad c \rightarrow -1, \quad d \rightarrow -1, \quad f \rightarrow -1. \tag{2.5}$$

The representation (2.4) is a homomorphism onto the group consisting of the number 1 alone, whereas (2.5) is a homomorphism onto the group $\{1, -1\}$. The one-dimensional representation that associates the number 1 with each element of a group is called the *identity representation.*

From a given representation T, one can construct other representations by subjecting each operator of T to a similarity transformation with a (nonsingular) operator S:

$$T' = \{T'(a), T'(b), ...\} = \{ST(a)S^{-1}, ST(b)S^{-1}, ...\}. \tag{2.6}$$

Since

$$\begin{aligned} T'(a)T'(b) &= ST(a)S^{-1}ST(b)S^{-1} \\ &= ST(a)T(b)S^{-1} \\ &= ST(ab)S^{-1} = T'(ab), \end{aligned} \tag{2.7}$$

the operators of T' also generate a representation of $\mathscr{G}$. Representations related by a similarity transformation are said to be *equivalent*.

B. The Symmetry Group of the Hamiltonian Operator

Let $\mathscr{H}$ denote the hamiltonian operator for a physical system and $\mathscr{G}$ the set of all nonsingular linear transformations satisfying

$$R\mathscr{H}R^{-1} = \mathscr{H}. \tag{2.8}$$

The operators of $\mathscr{G}$ form a group called the *symmetry group of the hamiltonian operator*. The proof is straightforward. $\mathscr{G}$ is certainly nonempty, since the identity transformation satisfies (2.8). If $\mathscr{G}$ contains operators other than the identity transformation, these elements obey the associative law, since, by definition, they are linear operators. Furthermore, $\mathscr{G}$ contains R^{-1} whenever it contains R, since (2.8) implies $\mathscr{H} = R^{-1}\mathscr{H}R \equiv R^{-1}\mathscr{H}(R^{-1})^{-1}$. Finally, $\mathscr{G}$ contains RQ whenever it contains R and Q, since

$$(RQ)\mathscr{H}(RQ)^{-1} = RQ\mathscr{H}Q^{-1}R^{-1} = R\mathscr{H}R^{-1} = \mathscr{H}.$$

If the hamiltonian operator is defined with respect to an n-dimensional space, the elements of $\mathscr{G}$ constitute an n-dimensional operator representation of the symmetry group of the physical system. Consider, for example, a coupled nuclear spin system in the absence of an applied field, so that the hamiltonian operator is

$$\mathscr{H} = -V = -\sum_{j<k}\sum J_{jk}\mathbf{I}_j \cdot \mathbf{I}_k .$$

Since the system is isolated, the symmetry group of the physical system is the three-dimensional rotation group. The symmetry group of the hamiltonian operator is an n-dimensional representation of the three-dimensional rotation group, where n is the dimension of the spin space. For the proper rotations of $\mathscr{O}_3$, (2.8) has the specific form

$$e^{i\varphi\mathbf{n}\cdot\mathbf{I}}\mathscr{H}e^{-i\varphi\mathbf{n}\cdot\mathbf{I}} = \mathscr{H},$$

which simply expresses the rotational invariance of V.[5]

If the spin system is subjected to a unidirectional external field whose magnitude may vary with time, the symmetry group of the physical

[5] In this case the nuclear configuration need not be symmetrical, since the rotational invariance of the spin-spin interactions is independent of the relative disposition of the nuclei.

system will be a subgroup of the three-dimensional rotation group—the two-dimensional rotation group. In particular, if the applied field is directed along the z axis, then

$$\mathscr{H} = -\Big\{\sum_j \omega_j I_{zj} + \sum_{j<k}\sum J_{jk}\mathbf{I}_j\cdot\mathbf{I}_k\Big\}, \qquad e^{i\varphi I_z}\mathscr{H}e^{-i\varphi I_z} = \mathscr{H}.$$

When the direction of the applied field changes with time, the physical system will not conform to any symmetry group unless the nuclear configuration is symmetrical. If the physical system possesses the symmetries of a finite symmetry group, the group of the hamiltonian operator will be an n-dimensional representation of this symmetry group. Henceforth, the term symmetry group will always refer to the finite symmetry group of the nuclear configuration or to its n-dimensional representation in spin space.

The elements of the symmetry group of the hamiltonian operator can always be expressed in terms of spin operators. Consider, for example, two spin-$\frac{1}{2}$ nuclei A, A′, with $\mathscr{C}_2$ symmetry. The elements of the symmetry group are $\{E, C_2\}$, and the problem is to find four-dimensional representations of these operators in terms of appropriate spin operators. The identity operator obviously corresponds to the four-dimensional identity operator 1, while the symmetry operator C_2 is represented by the Dirac permutation operator

$$P = \tfrac{1}{2}\{1 + \boldsymbol{\sigma}_{\mathrm{A}}\cdot\boldsymbol{\sigma}_{\mathrm{A}'}\}, \tag{2.9}$$

where $\boldsymbol{\sigma}_{\mathrm{A}}$ and $\boldsymbol{\sigma}_{\mathrm{A}'}$ are the Pauli spin vectors for A and A′. It is easily verified that $P^2 = 1$, in agreement with the equation $C_2{}^2 = E$, and that

$$PI_{\mathrm{A}\lambda}P^{-1} = I_{\mathrm{A}'\lambda} \qquad (\lambda = x, y, z).$$

This equation can be used to show that the hamiltonian operator

$$\mathscr{H}(t) = -\{\gamma(1-\sigma)\mathbf{H}(t)\cdot(\mathbf{I}_{\mathrm{A}} + \mathbf{I}_{\mathrm{A}'}) + J_{\mathrm{AA}'}\mathbf{I}_{\mathrm{A}}\cdot\mathbf{I}_{\mathrm{A}'}\},$$

where σ denotes the shielding constant, satisfies $P\mathscr{H}(t)P^{-1} = \mathscr{H}(t)$.

Although constructions of the type (2.9) can be carried out for any element of the symmetry group of the spin hamiltonian, explicit expressions for the symmetry operators in terms of the spin operators will not be required. The reason is that the symmetry group of the nuclear configuration and that of the hamiltonian operator are two different representations of the same group. If an element of the symmetry group of the nuclear configuration permutes the groups in symmetrically equivalent sets, then a similarity transformation of $\mathscr{H}$ with the representative of this operator in spin space generates a corresponding permutation of the spin operators in the hamiltonian operator. This observation permits the use of fixed symbols for symmetry operators. Thus the permutation operator P may be denoted C_2 without ambiguity, as long as the context clearly defines the dimensionality of the representation.

The preceding results may be summarized as follows. If $\mathscr{G}$ is the symmetry group of the hamiltonian operator, and R is any element of $\mathscr{G}$, then

$$R\mathscr{H}(t)R^{-1} = \mathscr{H}(t), \tag{2.10}$$

$$RI_\lambda R^{-1} = I_\lambda \qquad (\lambda = x, y, z), \tag{2.11}$$

$$R\mathbf{I}_{\mathrm{G}}{}^2R^{-1} = \mathbf{I}_{\mathrm{G}'}^2 , \tag{2.12}$$

where I_x, I_y, and I_z are the cartesian components of the total spin angular momentum operator $\mathbf{I}$, and G and G′ denote symmetrically equivalent groups.

When the symmetry group of the hamiltonian operator is nonabelian, the group elements do not constitute a complete set of commuting operators. It is possible, however, to construct linear combinations of group elements that commute with each other. These operators, being linear combinations of group elements, necessarily commute with $\mathscr{H}(t)$, I_x, I_y, and I_z, so that such linear combinations are symmetry constants of the motion. It should be emphasized that this conclusion must be stated in terms of commutators rather than the invariance relations (2.10) through (2.12). The reason is that of the two conditions demanded of a constant of the motion X,

$$\frac{\partial X}{\partial t} = 0, \qquad [\mathscr{H}(t), X] = 0,$$

the second condition is not equivalent to $X\mathscr{H}(t)X^{-1}$ unless X possesses an inverse. It will be shown later that the symmetry constants of the motion do not, in general, possess inverses.

C. Matrix Representations

The representation of a finite group $\mathscr{G} = \{a, b, ...\}$ by a set of nonsingular linear operators $T = \{T(a), T(b), ...\}$, defined with respect to an n-dimensional vector space, leads at once to the possibility of an n-dimensional *matrix representation* of $\mathscr{G}$. For, upon introducing a basis for the vector space, each operator $T(a)$ can be represented by a nonsingular $n \times n$ matrix $\Gamma[T(a)]$ with matrix components $\Gamma_{ij}[T(a)]$. Since matrices multiply in the same way as the operators they represent, it follows that

$$\Gamma[T(a)]\Gamma[T(b)] = \Gamma[T(ab)],$$

which is simply the matrix transcription of (2.1). Evidently the matrices $\Gamma = \{\Gamma[T(a)], \ldots\}$ form an n-dimensional matrix representation of $\mathscr{G}$, so that it is permissible to abbreviate $\Gamma[T(a)]$ to $\Gamma(a)$. In this simplified notation, the condition that the matrices of Γ constitute a representation of $\mathscr{G}$ is

$$\Gamma(a)\Gamma(b) = \Gamma(ab). \tag{2.13}$$

The number of distinct matrices in the representation Γ will be denoted γ.

The terminology introduced in Section 2.A for the representation of $\mathscr{G}$ by linear operators is also used to describe matrix representations. Thus the matrix representation Γ is said to be *faithful* or *unfaithful*, accordingly as $\gamma = g$ or $\gamma < g$. Furthermore, two matrix representations are said to be *equivalent* if the matrices of one set are related to those of the other by a similarity transformation. Equivalent matrix representations correspond to different choices for the basis of the n-dimensional space. Matrix representations that cannot be related by a similarity transformation are said to be *nonequivalent*.

The only restrictions imposed upon the matrices of a representation Γ are (2.11) and the condition that all matrices in Γ be nonsingular. Henceforth, it will be assumed that all the matrices in any matrix representation are unitary. It can be shown (*3*), that any matrix representation of a finite group can always be transformed into an equivalent matrix representation consisting entirely of unitary matrices. Thus there is no loss of generality in supplementing the matrix transcriptions of (2.2) with the unitary condition:

$$\Gamma(e) = 1, \qquad \Gamma(x^{-1}) = \Gamma^{-1}(x) = \Gamma^{\dagger}(x), \tag{2.14}$$

where x is an arbitrary element of $\mathscr{G}$. In terms of the matrix elements of $\Gamma(x)$, the unitary condition $\Gamma(x)\Gamma^{\dagger}(x) = 1$ is equivalent to

$$\sum_{k=1}^{n} \Gamma_{ik}(x)\Gamma_{jk}^{*}(x) = \delta_{ij} \qquad (i, j = 1, 2, \ldots, n). \tag{2.15}$$

The equivalence of matrix representations related by a similarity transformation lends importance to those properties of matrices which are invariant under a similarity transformation. Two important invariants are the determinant and trace of a matrix. If Γ and Γ' are two equivalent matrix representations,

$$\det \Gamma(x) = \det \Gamma'(x), \qquad \operatorname{tr} \Gamma(x) = \operatorname{tr} \Gamma'(x). \tag{2.16}$$

The trace of $\Gamma(x)$ is called the *character* of x, and denoted

$$\chi(x) = \operatorname{tr} \Gamma(x). \tag{2.17}$$

The distinct characters of a representation Γ are collectively described as a *character system.* For a given representation, elements in the same class have the same character and the same determinant.

The distinctions between operators, matrices, and ordinary numbers vanish for one-dimensional representations, so that (2.4) and (2.5) are also examples of one-dimensional matrix representations of $\mathscr{D}_3$. A three-dimensional matrix representation of $\mathscr{D}_3$ may be derived by inserting the appropriate direction cosines and angles of rotation for each element of $\mathscr{D}_3$ into the general three-dimensional rotation matrix derived in Appendix II. The required parameters are easily deduced from Fig. 8.1; they yield the following faithful representation of $\mathscr{D}_3$:

$$E = \begin{pmatrix} 1 & 0 & 0 \\ 0 & 1 & 0 \\ 0 & 0 & 1 \end{pmatrix}, \qquad C_3 = \begin{pmatrix} -\frac{1}{2} & \frac{1}{2}\sqrt{3} & 0 \\ -\frac{1}{2}\sqrt{3} & -\frac{1}{2} & 0 \\ 0 & 0 & 1 \end{pmatrix},$$

$$C_3^2 = \begin{pmatrix} -\frac{1}{2} & -\frac{1}{2}\sqrt{3} & 0 \\ \frac{1}{2}\sqrt{3} & -\frac{1}{2} & 0 \\ 0 & 0 & 1 \end{pmatrix}, \qquad C_2'' = \begin{pmatrix} \frac{1}{2} & \frac{1}{2}\sqrt{3} & 0 \\ \frac{1}{2}\sqrt{3} & -\frac{1}{2} & 0 \\ 0 & 0 & -1 \end{pmatrix}, \tag{2.18}$$

$$C_2' = \begin{pmatrix} -1 & 0 & 0 \\ 0 & 1 & 0 \\ 0 & 0 & -1 \end{pmatrix}, \qquad C_2 = \begin{pmatrix} \frac{1}{2} & -\frac{1}{2}\sqrt{3} & 0 \\ -\frac{1}{2}\sqrt{3} & -\frac{1}{2} & 0 \\ 0 & 0 & -1 \end{pmatrix}.$$

It is easily verified that the multiplication table for these matrices is identical with that of the symmetry group $\mathscr{D}_3$.

The general three-dimensional rotation matrix may also be used to obtain a three-dimensional faithful representation of $\mathscr{D}_2$:

$$E = \begin{pmatrix} 1 & 0 & 0 \\ 0 & 1 & 0 \\ 0 & 0 & 1 \end{pmatrix}, \qquad C_2 = \begin{pmatrix} 1 & 0 & 0 \\ 0 & -1 & 0 \\ 0 & 0 & -1 \end{pmatrix},$$

$$C_2' = \begin{pmatrix} -1 & 0 & 0 \\ 0 & 1 & 0 \\ 0 & 0 & -1 \end{pmatrix}, \qquad C_2'' = \begin{pmatrix} -1 & 0 & 0 \\ 0 & -1 & 0 \\ 0 & 0 & 1 \end{pmatrix}. \tag{2.19}$$

All these matrices are in diagonal form, a circumstance which is possible only in the case of an abelian group (cf. the theorem on commuting operators, Appendix I). In addition to this three-dimensional representation, one has the identity representation

$$E \to 1, \qquad C_2 \to 1, \qquad C_2' \to 1, \qquad C_2'' \to 1. \tag{2.20}$$

The existence of higher-dimensional matrix representations will be illustrated by exhibiting an eight-dimensional matrix representation of $\mathscr{D}_3$. For this purpose, consider a spin system consisting of three identical spin-$\frac{1}{2}$ nuclei with $\mathscr{D}_3$ symmetry. A physical realization of this system is provided by the protons in 1, 3, 5–trichlorobenzene. The elements of the product basis can be geometrically represented by eight equilateral triangles, with the z components of angular momentum of each nucleus indicated at the vertices of the representing triangles (Fig. 8.3). If one applies a symmetry operator of $\mathscr{D}_3$ to each of these triangles, one induces a transformation of the spin space. It will be assumed that the particles are fixed, and numbered as in Fig. 8.1. The symmetry operations then permute the z components of angular momentum. For example, the operator C_3 rotates each triangle through 120°, so that the basis vector $|+++\rangle$ is transformed into itself, $|++-\rangle$ is transformed into $|-++\rangle$, etc. The transformations are given in Table 8.4, from which one may derive the following faithful eight-dimensional representation of $\mathscr{D}_3$:

$$\begin{aligned} E &= 1 \oplus D_1 \oplus D_1 \oplus 1, & C_3 &= 1 \oplus D_2 \oplus D_3 \oplus 1, \\ C_3^2 &= 1 \oplus D_3 \oplus D_2 \oplus 1, & C_2 &= 1 \oplus D_4 \oplus D_5 \oplus 1, \\ C_2' &= 1 \oplus D_6 \oplus D_6 \oplus 1, & C_2'' &= 1 \oplus D_5 \oplus D_4 \oplus 1, \end{aligned} \tag{2.21}$$

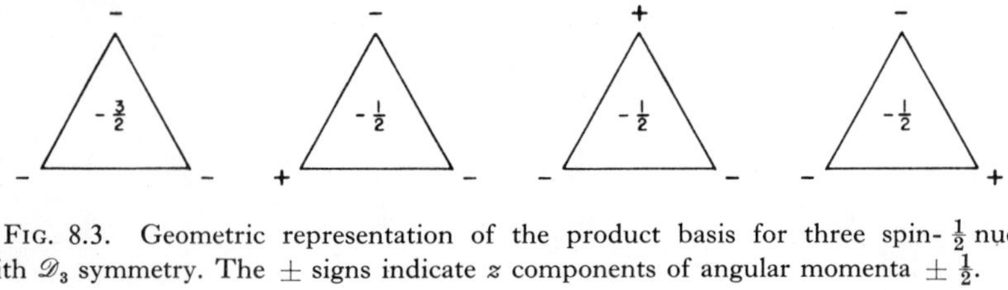

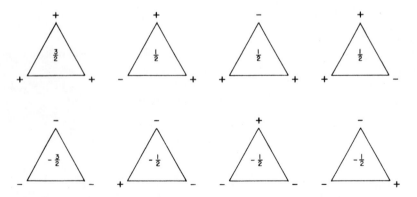

FIG. 8.3. Geometric representation of the product basis for three spin-$\frac{1}{2}$ nuclei with $\mathscr{D}_3$ symmetry. The $\pm$ signs indicate z components of angular momenta $\pm\frac{1}{2}$.

TABLE 8.4

Basis Vector Transforms

	$\|+++\rangle$	$\|++-\rangle$	$\|+-+\rangle$	$\|-++\rangle$	$\|+--\rangle$	$\|-+-\rangle$	$\|--+\rangle$	$\|---\rangle$
E	$\|+++\rangle$	$\|++-\rangle$	$\|+-+\rangle$	$\|-++\rangle$	$\|+--\rangle$	$\|-+-\rangle$	$\|--+\rangle$	$\|---\rangle$
C_3	$\|+++\rangle$	$\|-++\rangle$	$\|++-\rangle$	$\|+-+\rangle$	$\|-+-\rangle$	$\|--+\rangle$	$\|+--\rangle$	$\|---\rangle$
$C_3{}^2$	$\|+++\rangle$	$\|+-+\rangle$	$\|-++\rangle$	$\|++-\rangle$	$\|--+\rangle$	$\|+--\rangle$	$\|-+-\rangle$	$\|---\rangle$
C_2	$\|+++\rangle$	$\|+-+\rangle$	$\|++-\rangle$	$\|-++\rangle$	$\|+--\rangle$	$\|--+\rangle$	$\|-+-\rangle$	$\|---\rangle$
$C_2{}'$	$\|+++\rangle$	$\|-++\rangle$	$\|+-+\rangle$	$\|++-\rangle$	$\|--+\rangle$	$\|-+-\rangle$	$\|+--\rangle$	$\|---\rangle$
C_2''	$\|+++\rangle$	$\|++-\rangle$	$\|-++\rangle$	$\|+-+\rangle$	$\|-+-\rangle$	$\|+--\rangle$	$\|--+\rangle$	$\|---\rangle$

where $\mathit{1}$ denotes the 1×1 unit matrix, $\oplus$ denotes the direct sum[6] of the indicated matrices, and

$$D_1 = \begin{pmatrix} 1 & 0 & 0 \\ 0 & 1 & 0 \\ 0 & 0 & 1 \end{pmatrix}, \quad D_2 = \begin{pmatrix} 0 & 1 & 0 \\ 0 & 0 & 1 \\ 1 & 0 & 0 \end{pmatrix}, \quad D_3 = \begin{pmatrix} 0 & 0 & 1 \\ 1 & 0 & 0 \\ 0 & 1 & 0 \end{pmatrix},$$
$$D_4 = \begin{pmatrix} 0 & 1 & 0 \\ 1 & 0 & 0 \\ 0 & 0 & 1 \end{pmatrix}, \quad D_5 = \begin{pmatrix} 1 & 0 & 0 \\ 0 & 0 & 1 \\ 0 & 1 & 0 \end{pmatrix}, \quad D_6 = \begin{pmatrix} 0 & 0 & 1 \\ 0 & 1 & 0 \\ 1 & 0 & 0 \end{pmatrix}. \tag{2.22}$$

For example, the 8×8 matrix for C_3 is

$$C_3 = \mathit{1} \oplus D_2 \oplus D_3 \oplus \mathit{1} = \begin{pmatrix} 1 & 0 & 0 & 0 & 0 & 0 & 0 & 0 \\ 0 & 0 & 1 & 0 & 0 & 0 & 0 & 0 \\ 0 & 0 & 0 & 1 & 0 & 0 & 0 & 0 \\ 0 & 1 & 0 & 0 & 0 & 0 & 0 & 0 \\ 0 & 0 & 0 & 0 & 0 & 0 & 1 & 0 \\ 0 & 0 & 0 & 0 & 1 & 0 & 0 & 0 \\ 0 & 0 & 0 & 0 & 0 & 1 & 0 & 0 \\ 0 & 0 & 0 & 0 & 0 & 0 & 0 & 1 \end{pmatrix}.$$

D. Reducible and Irreducible Representations

An n-dimensional (unitary) matrix representation $\Gamma = \{\Gamma(a), \Gamma(b), ...\}$ of a finite group $\mathscr{G} = \{a, b, ...\}$ is said to be *reducible* if there exists a nonsingular matrix S such that a similarity transformation of every matrix of Γ with S leads to direct sum decompositions of the form

$$S^{-1}\Gamma(x)S = \Gamma'(x) \oplus \Gamma''(x) \qquad (x = e, a, b, ...),$$

[6] The elementary properties of direct sums of matrices are described in Appendix I.

where dim $\Gamma'(a)$ = dim $\Gamma'(b) = \cdots = n'$, dim $\Gamma''(a)$ = dim $\Gamma''(b) = \cdots = n''$, and $n' + n'' = n$. The significance of this definition is that $\Gamma' = \{\Gamma'(a), \Gamma'(b), ...\}$ and $\Gamma'' = \{\Gamma''(a), \Gamma''(b), ...\}$ are, respectively, n'- and n''-dimensional representations of $\mathscr{G}$. For if $ab = c$, then

$$\begin{aligned} S^{-1}\Gamma(c)S &= \Gamma'(c) \oplus \Gamma''(c) = S^{-1}\Gamma(ab)S \\ &= S^{-1}\Gamma(a)SS^{-1}\Gamma(b)S = \{\Gamma'(a) \oplus \Gamma''(a)\}\{\Gamma'(b) \oplus \Gamma''(b)\} \\ &= \Gamma'(a)\Gamma'(b) \oplus \Gamma''(a)\Gamma''(b), \end{aligned}$$

so that

$$\Gamma'(c) = \Gamma'(a)\Gamma'(b), \qquad \Gamma''(c) = \Gamma''(a)\Gamma''(b).$$

The reduction of Γ into the component representations Γ' and Γ'' is symbolically denoted

$$\Gamma = \Gamma' \oplus \Gamma''.$$

It may happen that one or both of the representations Γ', Γ'' are reducible, and that one or both of their component representations are reducible, and so on. If the several components are denoted $\Gamma^{(i)}$, $i = 1, 2, ..., r$, with dim $\Gamma^{(i)} = n_i$, then

$$\begin{aligned} \Gamma &= \Gamma^{(1)} \oplus \Gamma^{(2)} \oplus \cdots \oplus \Gamma^{(r)}, \\ \Gamma^{(i)} &= \{\Gamma^{(i)}(a), \Gamma^{(i)}(b), ...\}, \\ \Gamma^{(i)}(c) &= \Gamma^{(i)}(a)\Gamma^{(i)}(b) \qquad (\text{if } c = ab), \\ n &= n_1 + n_2 \cdots + n_r . \end{aligned} \tag{2.23}$$

A matrix representation that is not reducible is said to be *irreducible.* Obviously, all one-dimensional representations are irreducible.

Equations (2.23) are illustrated by equations (2.18). This representation of $\mathscr{D}_3$ is already in reduced form. The 2×2 matrices in the upper left-hand corner generate a two-dimensional faithful representation of $\mathscr{D}_3$, while the elements in the third row and third column of each matrix generate a one-dimensional unfaithful representation of $\mathscr{D}_3$ identical to (2.5).

The eight-dimensional representation of $\mathscr{D}_3$ derived above is also in reduced form. The identity representation appears (explicitly) twice, and the 3×3 matrices generate two faithful three-dimensional representations:

	E	C_3	C_3^2	C_2	C_2'	C_2''
Γ	D_1	D_2	D_3	D_4	D_6	D_5
Γ'	D_1	D_3	D_2	D_5	D_6	D_4

These representations are equivalent, since $D_6 = D_6^{-1}$, and

$$D_6D_1D_6 = D_1\,, \qquad D_6D_2D_6 = D_3\,, \qquad D_6D_3D_6 = D_2\,,$$
$$D_6D_4D_6 = D_5\,, \qquad D_6D_6D_6 = D_6\,, \qquad D_6D_5D_6 = D_4\,.$$

It will be shown in Section 2.E that the identity representation is actually contained four times in (2.21).

The repeated reduction of a representation terminates, in the case of an abelian group, when the matrices of the representation are in diagonal form, that is, when the representation is decomposed into one-dimensional representations. In the case of a nonabelian group, the ultimate decomposition of a reducible matrix representation will, in general, include representations with dimensions greater than unity, since the matrices do not form a complete commuting set.

A systematic investigation of the irreducible representations[7] of finite groups (*3, 5, 6, 9*) shows that

(1) The number of nonequivalent irreducible representations of any finite group $\mathscr{G}$ is equal to the number of classes.

(2) The sum of the squares of the dimensions of all nonequivalent irreducible representations is equal to the order of $\mathscr{G}$:

$$\sum_{\mu} n_{\mu}^{2} = g, \tag{2.24}$$

where n_μ is the dimension of the μth irreducible matrix representation $\Gamma^{(\mu)} = \{\Gamma^{(\mu)}(a), \Gamma^{(\mu)}(b), ...\}$.

(3) The matrix elements of the nonequivalent irreducible unitary representations satisfy the orthogonality relations

$$\sum_{x} \Gamma_{ij}^{(\mu)*}(x)\Gamma_{kl}^{(\nu)}(x) = \frac{g}{n_\mu}\,\delta_{\mu\nu}\,\delta_{ik}\,\delta_{jl}\,, \tag{2.25}$$

where the summation is to be taken over all elements of $\mathscr{G}$.

For an abelian group, (1) and (2) assert that there are exactly g nonequivalent irreducible one-dimensional representations. In this case, all matrices consist of a single matrix element—the "one-one" element. Thus the orthogonality relations (2.25) simplify to

$$\sum_{x} \chi^{(\mu)*}(x)\chi^{(\nu)}(x) = g\,\delta_{\mu\nu}\,, \tag{2.26}$$

[7] In molecular spectroscopy, irreducible representations are often called *symmetry species.*

where $\chi^{(\mu)}(x) \equiv \Gamma_{11}^{(\mu)}(x)$ is the character of the 1×1 matrix representing x. If the g numbers $\chi^{(\mu)}(e)$, $\chi^{(\mu)}(a)$, ... are interpreted as the components of a vector in a g-dimensional space, (2.26) states that the g vectors formed from each irreducible representation are orthogonal and of length g, in the hermitian sense.

The irreducible representations (character tables) for several abelian groups are given below. The representations are denoted $\mathcal{A}$ or $\mathcal{B}$, accordingly as the character of a rotation about the principal axis is $+1$ or -1. Higher-dimensional representations occur only for nonabelian groups; two-dimensional representations are denoted $\mathcal{E}$, three-dimensional representations $\mathcal{F}$. For cyclic groups, where the character of the principal axis is, in general, a complex number, the irreducible representations, other than $\mathcal{A}$ and $\mathcal{B}$, are grouped into pairs and labeled as though they were two-dimensional representations.

The generating element of a cyclic group of order g satisfies $x^g = e$. Thus the complex number ϵ representing x satisfies $\epsilon^g = 1$, so that $\epsilon = e^{2\pi i k/g}$, $k = 0, 1, 2, ..., g - 1$. With this result and the relations $x^2 = xx$, $x^3 = x^2x$, ..., it is easy to derive the character table of any cyclic group (see accompanying tabulations).

$\mathcal{C}_1$	E
$\mathcal{A}$	1

$\mathcal{C}_2$	E	C_2
$\mathcal{A}$	1	1
$\mathcal{B}$	1	-1

$\mathcal{C}_3$	E	C_3	C_3^2
$\mathcal{A}$	1	1	1
$\mathcal{E}$	1	ϵ	ϵ^2
	1	ϵ^2	ϵ

($\epsilon = e^{2\pi i/3}$)

$\mathcal{C}_4$	E	C_4	C_4^2	C_4^3
$\mathcal{A}$	1	1	1	1
$\mathcal{B}$	1	-1	1	-1
$\mathcal{E}$	1	i	-1	$-i$
	1	$-i$	-1	i

$\mathcal{C}_{2v}$	E	C_2	σ_v	σ_v
$\mathcal{A}_1$	1	1	1	1
$\mathcal{A}_2$	1	1	-1	-1
$\mathcal{B}_1$	1	-1	1	-1
$\mathcal{B}_2$	1	-1	-1	1

$\mathcal{D}_2$	E	C_2	C_2'	C_2''
$\mathcal{A}_1$	1	1	1	1
$\mathcal{B}_1$	1	1	-1	-1
$\mathcal{B}_2$	1	-1	1	-1
$\mathcal{B}_3$	1	-1	-1	1

The determination of all nonequivalent irreducible matrix representations of an arbitrary nonabelian finite group is a problem of considerable difficulty. No generally applicable method has been discovered, but many particular cases yield to elementary techniques (*8*). For example,

$\mathscr{D}_3$ has six elements in three classes, so that $n_1^2 + n_2^2 + n_3^2 = 6$. The only integer solution of this equation is $n_1 = n_2 = 1$, $n_3 = 2$. The irreducible representations of $\mathscr{D}_3$ have, in fact, already been determined. They are contained in (2.4), (2.5), and (2.18) (see accompanying tabulation). The proof that the two-dimensional representation is irreducible is simple. If this representation were reducible, each matrix could be brought into diagonal form by a similarity transformation with a unitary matrix. But this is not possible, since the six matrices of the representation do not constitute a complete commuting set of matrices.

$\mathscr{D}_3$	E	C_3	C_3^2
$\mathscr{A}_1$	1	1	1
$\mathscr{A}_2$	1	1	1
$\mathscr{E}$	$\begin{pmatrix} 1 & 0 \\ 0 & 1 \end{pmatrix}$	$-\frac{1}{2}\begin{pmatrix} 1 & -\sqrt{3} \\ \sqrt{3} & 1 \end{pmatrix}$	$-\frac{1}{2}\begin{pmatrix} 1 & \sqrt{3} \\ -\sqrt{3} & 1 \end{pmatrix}$
$\mathscr{D}_3$	C_2''	C_2'	C_2
$\mathscr{A}_1$	1	1	1
$\mathscr{A}_2$	-1	-1	-1
$\mathscr{E}$	$\frac{1}{2}\begin{pmatrix} 1 & \sqrt{3} \\ \sqrt{3} & -1 \end{pmatrix}$	$\begin{pmatrix} -1 & 0 \\ 0 & 1 \end{pmatrix}$	$\frac{1}{2}\begin{pmatrix} 1 & -\sqrt{3} \\ -\sqrt{3} & -1 \end{pmatrix}$

In many physical applications of group theory, it is not necessary to have the complete matrices of all nonequivalent irreducible representations of the relevant symmetry group. A table giving the characters of the matrices in each irreducible representation is usually sufficient. The character table for $\mathscr{D}_3$ is shown in the accompanying tabulation.

$\mathscr{D}_3$	E	C_3	C_3^2	C_2	C_2'	C_2''
$\mathscr{A}_1$	1	1	1	1	1	1
$\mathscr{A}_2$	1	1	1	-1	-1	-1
$\mathscr{E}$	2	-1	-1	0	0	0

The character table for $\mathscr{D}_3$ satisfies the same orthogonality relations noted for abelian groups—equations (2.26). This result is generally valid.

For upon setting $i = j$ and $l = k$ in (2.25), and then summing over i and k, one obtains

$$\sum_x \sum_{i=1}^{n_\mu} \sum_{k=1}^{n_\nu} \Gamma_{ii}^{(\mu)*}(x)\Gamma_{kk}^{(\nu)}(x) = \frac{g}{n_\mu} \delta_{\mu\nu} \sum_{i=1}^{n_\mu} \sum_{k=1}^{n_\nu} \delta_{ik}\, \delta_{ik} = g\, \delta_{\mu\nu}\,.$$

But

$$\sum_{i=1}^{n_\mu} \sum_{k=1}^{n_\nu} \Gamma_{ii}^{(\mu)*}(x)\Gamma_{kk}^{(\nu)}(x) = \chi^{(\mu)*}(x)\chi^{(\nu)}(x),$$

so that

$$\sum_x \chi^{(\mu)*}(x)\chi^{(\nu)}(x) = g\, \delta_{\mu\nu} \tag{2.27}$$

for any finite group $\mathscr{G}$.

The construction of character tables is very much simpler than the construction of the matrices for the irreducible representations (*8*). Character tables for the symmetry groups of interest in physical problems are given in most texts on group theory (*6–10*).

E. Reduction of a Representation

One of the most important problems in the application of group theory to physical systems is the reduction of a matrix representation. Consider, for example, the problem of analyzing the spectrum of a symmetrical spin system. The product basis generates a matrix representation of the symmetry group of the system, but as this basis is not chosen with regard to the symmetry properties of the system, the representation will, in general, be reducible. The representation may be reduced by a transformation to a new "symmetrized" basis.

A method for obtaining symmetrized bases will be described in the following section. Here some general properties of reducible and irreducible representations will be derived.

Let $\Gamma = \{\Gamma(a), \Gamma(b), \ldots\}$ be a matrix representation of a finite group $\mathscr{G}$, and $\Gamma^{(\mu)} = \{\Gamma^{(\mu)}(a), \Gamma^{(\mu)}(b), \ldots\}$ the μth irreducible matrix representation of dimension n_μ ($\mu = 1, 2, \ldots$). If Γ is reducible, an appropriate similarity transformation will decompose each matrix of Γ into a direct sum of matrices contained in $\Gamma^{(1)}$, $\Gamma^{(2)}$, etc. It is conceivable that the matrices of $\Gamma^{(\mu)}$ may occur c_μ times in the decomposition. By rearranging the elements of the new basis, the matrix for $\Gamma(x)$, where x is an arbitrary element, can be written

$$\Gamma(x) = \underbrace{\{\Gamma^{(1)}(x) \oplus \Gamma^{(1)}(x) \oplus \cdots \oplus \Gamma^{(1)}\}}_{c_1 \text{ factors}} \oplus \underbrace{\{\Gamma^{(2)}(x) \oplus \Gamma^{(2)}(x) \oplus \cdots \oplus \Gamma^{(2)}(x)\}}_{c_2 \text{ factors}} \oplus \cdots.$$

It is convenient to write

$$\underbrace{\Gamma^{(\mu)}(x) \oplus \Gamma^{(\mu)}(x) \oplus \cdots \oplus \Gamma^{(\mu)}(x)}_{c_\mu \text{ factors}} = c_\mu \Gamma^{(\mu)}(x),$$

so that

$$\Gamma(x) = c_1 \Gamma^{(1)}(x) \oplus c_2 \Gamma^{(2)}(x) \oplus \cdots \oplus c_\mu \Gamma^{(\mu)}(x) \oplus \cdots . \tag{2.28}$$

It must be emphasized that each matrix of Γ may be written in this form, and that the c_μ are nonnegative integers independent of x.

The character of $\Gamma(x)$ is obtained by taking the trace of (2.28):

$$\chi(x) = c_1 \chi^{(1)}(x) + c_2 \chi^{(2)}(x) + \cdots . \tag{2.29}$$

Multiplying this equation by $\chi^{(\mu)*}(x)$, and then summing over all group elements, one obtains, by virtue of (2.27),

$$c_\mu = \frac{1}{g} \sum_x \chi^{(\mu)*}(x) \chi(x). \tag{2.30}$$

If the matrices of Γ are n-dimensional, then

$$n = c_1 n_1 + c_2 n_2 + \cdots . \tag{2.31}$$

The decomposition (2.28) is unique, except for the ordering of the irreducible representations. For if it is assumed that

$$\Gamma(x) = c_1' \Gamma^{(1)}(x) \oplus c_2' \Gamma^{(2)}(x) \oplus \cdots ,$$

then the argument leading to (2.30) shows that $c_\mu = c_\mu'$, for all μ.

A simple criterion for ascertaining whether a given representation is reducible or irreducible may be obtained by forming the absolute square of (2.29) and summing over x:

$$\sum_x |\chi(x)|^2 = \sum_x \sum_\mu \sum_\nu c_\mu c_\nu \chi^{(\mu)*}(x) \chi^{(\nu)}(x).$$

Since the characters of irreducible representations satisfy (2.27), it follows that

$$\sum_x |\chi(x)|^2 = g \sum_\mu c_\mu^2. \tag{2.32}$$

If Γ is irreducible, then all c_μ but one are zero, so that $\sum |\chi(x)|^2 = g$, for an irreducible representation. If Γ is reducible, then $\sum |\chi(x)|^2 > g$.

The preceding results will be illustrated by applying them to the eight-dimensional representation of $\mathscr{D}_3$ given by (2.21). For this representation

$$\operatorname{tr} E = 8, \qquad \operatorname{tr} C_3 = \operatorname{tr} C_3{}^2 = 2,$$
$$\operatorname{tr} C_2 = \operatorname{tr} C_2{}' = \operatorname{tr} C_2'' = 4. \tag{2.33}$$

These results, together with the character table for $\mathscr{D}_3$, show that

$$c_{\mathscr{A}_1} = \tfrac{1}{6}\{8 \cdot 1 + 2 \cdot 1 + 2 \cdot 1 + 4 \cdot 1 + 4 \cdot 1 + 4 \cdot 1\} = 4,$$

$$c_{\mathscr{A}_2} = \tfrac{1}{6}\{8 \cdot 1 + 2 \cdot 1 + 2 \cdot 1 - 4 \cdot 1 - 4 \cdot 1 - 4 \cdot 1\} = 0,$$

$$c_{\mathscr{E}} = \tfrac{1}{6}\{8 \cdot 2 - 2 \cdot 1 - 2 \cdot 1 + 4 \cdot 0 + 4 \cdot 0 + 4 \cdot 0\} = 2.$$

3. Symmetrization of Basis Vectors

A. Projection Operators

A linear operator P is said to be *idempotent* if

$$P^2 = P. \tag{3.1}$$

If P is nonsingular, multiplication from the left or right with P^{-1} shows that P is the identity operator. To exclude this possibility, it will be assumed that

$$\det P = 0. \tag{3.2}$$

The trivial case where P is the zero operator will be eliminated by stipulating that $P \neq 0$.

Let

$$A - \begin{pmatrix} 1 & a \\ 0 & 0 \end{pmatrix}$$

be the matrix representative of a linear operator defined on a two-dimensional vector space. Evidently A is nonzero and satisfies (3.1) and (3.2) for any value of a. If $a = 0$, A is in diagonal form, but A cannot be diagonalized when $a \neq 0$. Henceforth, it will be assumed that the matrix representatives of all nonzero operators satisfying (3.1) and (3.2) can be diagonalized. In fact, it will be assumed that P is hermitian:

$$P = P^{\dagger}. \tag{3.3}$$

A nonzero linear operator that is idempotent, singular, and hermitian is called a *projection operator*, or more precisely, a *perpendicular projection operator* (*12*). The significance of this terminology will be disclosed in the following discussion.

A projection operator P has only two distinct eigenvalues: 1 or 0. For if p is any eigenvalue of P, it must satisfy (3.1), so that $p = 0$ or $p = 1$. The degeneracy of the eigenvalue 1 is called the *rank* of P and denoted $\rho(P)$; the degeneracy of the eigenvalue 0 is called the *nullity* of P and denoted $\nu(P)$. The rank of P is equal to the number of linearly independent rows or columns in any matrix representative of P. If P is defined on an n-dimensional vector space,

$$\rho(P) = \text{tr}\, P, \qquad \nu(P) = n - \rho(P). \tag{3.4}$$

Let S be an n-dimensional vector space, $\{e_1, e_2, ..., e_n\}$ an orthonormal basis for S, and P a projection operator on S. If ξ and $P\xi$ are nonzero, then $P\xi$ and $(1 - P)\xi$ are eigenvectors of P corresponding, respectively, to the eigenvalues 1 and 0. These assertions are immediate consequences of (3.1):

$$P(P\xi) = P^2\xi = P\xi, \qquad P(1 - P)\xi = (P - P^2)\xi = 0.$$

There are $\rho(P)$ linearly independent eigenvectors with the eigenvalue $p = 1$. These eigenvectors may be obtained by

(1) Forming the sequence of n vectors $Pe_1, Pe_2, ..., Pe_n$.

(2) Deleting the zero vector wherever it occurs in the sequence.

(3) deleting any nonzero vector that is a linear combination of vectors preceding it in the sequence.

The eigenvectors thus obtained are $\rho(P)$-fold degenerate, so that any set of $\rho(P)$ linear combinations of these vectors is also a set of eigenvectors with $p = 1$. Similar remarks apply to the $\nu(P)$ eigenvectors of P corresponding to the eigenvalue $p = 0$.

Consider now the set S_1, consisting of *all* vectors in S satisfying $P\eta = \eta$. This set is a subspace of S, since it contains the zero vector and $c_1\eta_1 + c_2\eta_2$, whenever it contains η_1 and η_2. The eigenvectors of P corresponding to the eigenvalue 1 constitute a basis for S_1, so that $\dim S_1 = \rho(P)$. Similarly, the set S_2, consisting of *all* vectors in S satisfying $P\xi = 0$, is a subspace of S. The eigenvectors of P corresponding to the eigenvalue 0 constitute a basis for S_2, so that $\dim S_2 = \nu(P)$. The only vector of S belonging to both S_1 and S_2 is the zero vector. For if ξ is any such vector, $P\xi = \xi = 0$. Furthermore, an arbitrary vector of S can be expressed as the sum of a vector in S_1

and a vector in S_2. The proof follows from the fact that every vector in S may be written in the form

$$\xi = P\xi + (1 - P)\xi. \tag{3.5}$$

Since $P(P\xi) = P\xi$, and $P(1 - P)\xi = 0$, $P\xi$ is in S_1, and $(1 - P)\xi$ is in S_2, as asserted. This decomposition of S is often described by saying that S is the direct sum of S_1 and S_2.

The significance of the term "projection operator" becomes evident upon observing that the effect of P on any ξ in S is to project ξ onto the $\rho(P)$-dimensional subspace S_1. For, by (3.5), $P\xi = P^2\xi + P(1 - P)\xi = P\xi + 0$. Similarly, the effect of $1 - P$ is to project ξ onto the $\nu(P)$-dimensional subspace S_2. The significance of the term "perpendicular projection operator" is revealed by the fact that any vector in S_1 is orthogonal to any vector in S_2. This result is a consequence of the hermitian character of P, and the fact that $P(1 - P) = 0$:

$$(P\xi, [1 - P]\xi) = (\xi, P[1 - P]\xi) = 0. \tag{3.6}$$

To illustrate these results, let S be a real three-dimensional space and

$$e_1 = \begin{pmatrix} 1 \\ 0 \\ 0 \end{pmatrix}, \qquad e_2 = \begin{pmatrix} 0 \\ 1 \\ 0 \end{pmatrix}, \qquad e_3 = \begin{pmatrix} 0 \\ 0 \\ 1 \end{pmatrix},$$

$$P = \frac{1}{2}\begin{pmatrix} 1 & 0 & -1 \\ 0 & 2 & 0 \\ -1 & 0 & 1 \end{pmatrix}, \qquad 1 - P = \frac{1}{2}\begin{pmatrix} 1 & 0 & 1 \\ 0 & 0 & 0 \\ 1 & 0 & 1 \end{pmatrix}.$$

It is easily verified that P is a projection operator of rank 2. Operating on the elements of the basis with P yields

$$Pe_1 = \tfrac{1}{2}(e_1 - e_3), \qquad Pe_2 = e_2, \qquad Pe_3 = -\tfrac{1}{2}(e_1 - e_3).$$

Pe_3 may be discarded, since it is a scalar multiple of Pe_1. Therefore, the (normalized) eigenvectors of P corresponding to $p = 1$ are e_2 and $\tfrac{1}{2}\sqrt{2}(e_1 - e_3)$. In this case, the subspace S_1 is the plane defined by these eigenvectors.

The remaining eigenvector of P may be obtained by applying $(1 - P)$ to e_1, e_2, and e_3:

$$(1 - P)e_1 = \tfrac{1}{2}(e_1 + e_3), \qquad (1 - P)e_2 = 0, \qquad (1 - P)e_3 = \tfrac{1}{2}(e_1 + e_3).$$

Hence $\tfrac{1}{2}\sqrt{2}(e_1 + e_3)$ is a normalized eigenvector with $p = 0$, and S_2 consists of the line defined by this vector. If $\xi = \xi_1 e_1 + \xi_2 e_2 + \xi_3 e_3$ is an arbitrary vector in S, the component of ξ in S_1 (*i.e.*, the projection of ξ on S_1) is $P\xi = \frac{1}{2}(\xi_1 - \xi_3)(e_1 - e_3) + \xi_2 e_2$, and the component of ξ in S_2 is $(1 - P)\xi = \frac{1}{2}(\xi_1 + \xi_3)(e_1 + e_3)$.

The preceding theory can be put into a more symmetrical form upon noting that if P is a projection operator of rank $\rho(P)$, then $1 - P$ is a projection operator of rank $\rho(1 - P) = \text{tr}(1 - P) = \nu(P)$. Since P is a projection on S_1, and $1 - P$ a projection on S_2, the notation can be simplified by writing P_1 for P, and P_2 for $1 - P$. These projection operators satisfy the relations

$$\begin{aligned} &P_1^2 = P_1, \qquad P_2^2 = P_2, \\ &P_1 + P_2 = 1, \\ &P_1 P_2 = P_2 P_1 = 0. \end{aligned}$$

Any operators A, B, such that $AB = BA = 0$, are said to be *mutually orthogonal.* Obviously, mutually orthogonal operators commute.

The theory of projection operators is easily generalized. A set of l $(1 < l \leqslant n)$ projection operators $P_1, P_2, ..., P_l$, satisfying

$$P_i P_j = \delta_{ij} P_j \qquad (i, j = 1, 2, ..., l), \tag{3.7}$$

$$P_1 + P_2 + \cdots + P_l = 1 \tag{3.8}$$

leads to a direct sum decomposition of S into subspaces $S_1, S_2, ..., S_l$. The subspace S_i contains all vectors in S satisfying $P_i\xi = \xi$. The eigenvectors of P_i corresponding to the eigenvalue 1 are a basis for S_i, so that $\dim S_i = \text{tr}\, P_i$. Every vector in S can be expressed as the sum of a vector from each S_i. Indeed (3.8) shows that, for any ξ in S,

$$\xi = P_1\xi + P_2\xi + \cdots + P_l\xi. \tag{3.9}$$

Furthermore, the only vector common to each S_i is the zero vector. For if ξ is contained in each S_i, then $\xi = P_1\xi = P_2\xi = \cdots = P_l\xi$. Combining these equations with (3.9), it follows that $l\xi = \xi$ $(l \neq 1)$, whence $\xi = 0$. Finally, bases for $S_1, S_2, ..., S_l$ may be combined to give a set of n linearly independent vectors that is a basis for the whole space S.

B. Construction of Projection Operators

The preceding results may be combined with the theory of irreducible representations to provide results of fundamental importance in the study of symmetrical systems. Let $\mathscr{G} = \{a, b, ...\}$ denote a finite group of order g, and $\Gamma^{(\mu)} = \{\Gamma^{(\mu)}(a), \Gamma^{(\mu)}(b), ...\}$ the μth irreducible (unitary) matrix representation of dimension n_μ. With the elements of $\mathscr{G}$ and the matrices of $\Gamma^{(\mu)}$, one can construct the following linear combinations of group elements

$$R_{\mu;ij} = \sum_x \Gamma_{ij}^{(\mu)*}(x)x. \tag{3.10}$$

The adjoint of $R_{\mu;ij}$ is

$$R_{\mu;ij}^\dagger = \sum_x \Gamma_{ij}^{(\mu)}(x)x^\dagger = \sum_x \Gamma_{ji}^{(\mu)*}(x^{-1})x^{-1}.$$

Now the correspondence $x \leftrightarrow x^{-1}$ ($x = e, a, ...$) is an isomorphism, so that when x ranges over the elements of $\mathscr{G}$, so does x^{-1}; hence

$$R_{\mu;ij}^\dagger = R_{\mu;ji}\,. \tag{3.11}$$

The product of $R_{\mu;ij}$ with any one of the similar operators constructed from the matrices of the νth irreducible representation may be evaluated with the help of the orthogonality relations. From (3.10) and the analogous equation for $R_{\nu;kl}$,

$$R_{\mu;ij}R_{\nu;kl} = \sum_x \sum_{x'} \Gamma_{ij}^{(\mu)*}(x)\Gamma_{kl}^{(\nu)*}(x')xx'$$

$$= \sum_x \sum_{x^{-1}x''} \Gamma_{ij}^{(\mu)*}(x)\Gamma_{kl}^{(\nu)*}(x^{-1}x'')x'',$$

where $x'' = xx'$. Now

$$\Gamma_{kl}^{(\nu)*}(x^{-1}x'') = \sum_{s=1}^{n_\nu} \Gamma_{ks}^{(\nu)*}(x^{-1})\Gamma_{sl}^{(\nu)*}(x'')$$

$$= \sum_{s=1}^{n_\nu} \Gamma_{sk}^{(\nu)}(x)\Gamma_{sl}^{(\nu)*}(x''),$$

by the rule for matrix multiplication, so that

$$R_{\mu;ij}R_{\nu;kl} = \sum_x \sum_{s=1}^{n_\nu} \Gamma_{ij}^{(\mu)*}(x)\Gamma_{sk}^{(\nu)}(x)R_{\nu;sl}$$

$$= \sum_{s=1}^{n_\nu} \frac{g}{n_\mu}\,\delta_{\mu\nu}\,\delta_{is}\,\delta_{jk}\,R_{\nu;sl}$$

$$= \frac{g}{n_\mu}\,\delta_{\mu\nu}\,\delta_{jk}\,R_{\nu;il}\,. \tag{3.12}$$

Equation (3.12) can be written in a more convenient form by introducing the operator

$$P_{\mu;ij} = \frac{n_\mu}{g} R_{\mu;ij}, \tag{3.13}$$

obtaining

$$P_{\mu;ij} P_{\nu;kl} = \delta_{\mu\nu} \delta_{jk} P_{\nu;il}. \tag{3.14}$$

This equation shows that the operators constructed from different irreducible representations are mutually orthogonal. When $\mu = \nu$, $i = j$, and $k = l$, (3.14) reduces to

$$P_{\mu;ii} P_{\mu;kk} = \delta_{ik} P_{\mu;ik}, \tag{3.15}$$

which shows that all $P_{\mu;ii}$ are idempotent, and orthogonal to all $P_{\mu;kk}$ ($i \neq k$). Moreover, (3.11) and (3.13) show that the $P_{\mu;ii}$ are hermitian.

If $\mathscr{G}$ is the symmetry group of the hamiltonian operator, the perpendicular projection operators, $P_{\mu;ii}$, being linear combinations of group elements, commute with $\mathscr{H}$, I_x, I_y, and I_z. *The $P_{\mu;ii}$ are symmetry constants of the motion.* If the elements of the initial basis are eigenvectors of I_z and of the $P_{\mu;ii}$, the matrix elements of the stationary hamiltonian that connect the eigenvectors of projection operators with $\mu \neq \nu$ vanish. For if $P_{\mu;ii}\Phi$ and $P_{\nu;jj}\Psi$ are nonzero, then, since $P_{\mu;ii}$ and $P_{\nu;jj}$ are mutually orthogonal and hermitian,

$$\begin{aligned}(P_{\mu;ii}\Phi, \mathscr{H} P_{\nu;jj}\Psi) &= (\Phi, P_{\mu;ii} \mathscr{H} P_{\nu;jj}\Psi) \\ &= (\Phi, \mathscr{H} P_{\mu;ii} P_{\nu;jj}\Psi) = 0.\end{aligned}$$

Thus the hamiltonian matrix admits a direct sum decomposition, such that each submatrix in the decomposition is identified with a particular irreducible representation. If the symmetry group of the hamiltonian operator has irreducible representations with dimensions exceeding unity, further direct sum decompositions occur. For example, the submatrix identified with an n_μ-dimensional irreducible representation decomposes into n_μ submatrices, since the projection operators $P_{\mu;ii}$, $i = 1, 2, \ldots, n_\mu$ are mutually orthogonal. Finally, all submatrices of $\mathscr{H}$ admit additional direct sum decompositions by virtue of the fact that $[\mathscr{H}, I_z] = 0$.

The eigenvectors of the hamiltonian will be of the form $P_{\mu;ii}\Psi_m$, where m is the eigenvalue of I_z. An allowed transition (i.e., a single quantum transition) must satisfy the selection rule $\Delta m = -1$. However, since all projection operators commute with I_x and I_y, it follows that

$$(P_{\;;ii}\Psi_m, I^- P_{\nu;jj}\Phi_{m'}) = 0,$$

unless $m' = m + 1$, $\mu = \nu$, and $i = j$. Thus transitions are forbidden between states "belonging to" different irreducible representations, and between states of the same irreducible representation that are eigenvectors of distinct projection operators ($\mu = \nu$, $i \neq j$).

If the symmetry group of a spin system has r irreducible representations, one can, in principle, construct $n_1 + n_2 + \cdots + n_r$ projection operators, where n_μ is the dimension of $\Gamma^{(\mu)}$. However, the only nontrivial projection operators will be those of nonzero rank. The rank of a projection operator in any given problem is

$$\operatorname{tr} P_{\mu;ii} = \frac{n_\mu}{g} \sum_x \Gamma_{ii}^{(\mu)*}(x) \operatorname{tr} x = \frac{n_\mu}{g} \sum_x \Gamma_{ii}^{(\mu)*}(x) \chi(x), \tag{3.16}$$

where the $\chi(x)$ are obtained from the matrices of the representation defined by the initial basis.

The projection operators for $\mathscr{C}_2$, $\mathscr{C}_{2v}$, $\mathscr{D}_2$, and $\mathscr{D}_3$ are

$$\mathscr{C}_2: \quad \begin{aligned} P_{\mathscr{A}} &= \tfrac{1}{2}(E + C_2), \\ P_{\mathscr{B}} &= \tfrac{1}{2}(E - C_2); \end{aligned} \tag{3.17}$$

$$\mathscr{C}_{2v}: \quad \begin{aligned} P_{\mathscr{A}_1} &= \tfrac{1}{4}\{E + C_2 + \sigma_v + \sigma_v'\}, \\ P_{\mathscr{A}_2} &= \tfrac{1}{4}\{E + C_2 - \sigma_v - \sigma_v'\}, \\ P_{\mathscr{B}_1} &= \tfrac{1}{4}\{E - C_2 + \sigma_v - \sigma_v'\}, \\ P_{\mathscr{B}_2} &= \tfrac{1}{4}\{E - C_2 - \sigma_v + \sigma_v'\}; \end{aligned} \tag{3.18}$$

$$\mathscr{D}_2: \quad \begin{aligned} P_{\mathscr{A}} &= \tfrac{1}{4}\{E + C_2 + C_2' + C_2''\}, \\ P_{\mathscr{B}_1} &- \tfrac{1}{4}\{E + C_2 - C_2' - C_2''\}, \\ P_{\mathscr{B}_2} &= \tfrac{1}{4}\{E - C_2 + C_2' - C_2''\}, \\ P_{\mathscr{B}_3} &= \tfrac{1}{4}\{E - C_2 - C_2' + C_2''\}; \end{aligned} \tag{3.19}$$

$$\mathscr{D}_3: \quad \begin{aligned} P_{\mathscr{A}_1} &= \tfrac{1}{6}\{E + C_3 + C_3^2 + C_2 + C_2' + C_2''\}, \\ P_{\mathscr{A}_2} &= \tfrac{1}{6}\{E + C_3 + C_3^2 - C_2 - C_2' - C_2''\}, \\ P_{\mathscr{E}} &= \tfrac{1}{3}\{E - \tfrac{1}{2}(C_3 + C_3^2) + \tfrac{1}{2}(C_2 - 2C_2' + C_2'')\}, \\ P_{\mathscr{E}}' &= \tfrac{1}{3}\{E - \tfrac{1}{2}(C_3 + C_3^2) - \tfrac{1}{2}(C_2 - 2C_2' + C_2'')\}. \end{aligned} \tag{3.20}$$

To simplify the notation, $P_{\mu;ii}$ has been abbreviated to P_μ and primes introduced to distinguish the projection operators of multidimensional representations. It is a simple exercise to verify that each of these sets of projection operators satisfy (3.7) and (3.8).

If the full matrices of the irreducible representations of $\mathscr{G}$ are not available, one can construct useful projection operators with the character table for $\mathscr{G}$. These operators are obtained from (3.13) by setting $j = i$ and summing over i:

$$\mathscr{P}_\mu \equiv \sum_i P_{\mu;ii} = \frac{n_\mu}{g} \sum_x \chi^{(\mu)*}(x)x. \tag{3.21}$$

The mutual orthogonality of $\mathscr{P}_\mu$ and $\mathscr{P}_\nu$ follows from (3.14), on setting $j = i$, $l = k$, and summing over i and k:

$$\mathscr{P}_\mu \mathscr{P}_\nu = \delta_{\mu\nu} \sum_i \sum_k \delta_{ik} P_{\nu;ik} = \delta_{\mu\nu} \mathscr{P}_\nu . \tag{3.22}$$

C. Symmetrized Bases for $AA' \cdots A^{(N-1)}$ Systems

The construction of symmetrized bases will be illustrated first for systems composed of one set of N symmetrically equivalent nuclei. A system of this type is equivalent to an A_N system, whose properties have already been discussed by the method of magnetically equivalent nuclei. However, the symmetrized bases for particular $AA' \cdots A^{(N-1)}$ systems are useful in the study of systems composed of two or more weakly coupled sets of symmetrically equivalent nuclei (cf. Section 5).

The eigenvectors of an $AA' \cdots A^{(N-1)}$ system may be labeled with the eigenvalues of $\mathbf{I}^2$ and I_z, as well as a symbol denoting the symmetry species. The notation $(\mathscr{S})_{I,m}$, where $\mathscr{S}$ denotes the symmetry species, is especially convenient.[8] If the multiplicity of the spin quantum number is greater than unity, the various sets of eigenvectors will be distinguished by primes: $(\mathscr{S})_{I,m}$, $(\mathscr{S}')_{I,m}$, $\cdots$.

The simplest case occurs when only one coupling constant, say $J_{AA'}$, is required to describe the spin-spin interactions. The hamiltonian operator is

$$\begin{aligned}\mathscr{H}(AA' \cdots) &= -\{\omega_A I_z + J_{AA'}(\mathbf{I}_A \cdot \mathbf{I}_{A'} + \mathbf{I}_A \cdot \mathbf{I}_{A''} + \cdots)\} \\ &= -\{\omega_A I_z + \tfrac{1}{2} J_{AA'}(\mathbf{I}^2 - \mathbf{I}_A{}^2 - \mathbf{I}_{A'}^2 - \mathbf{I}_{A''}^2 - \cdots)\},\end{aligned} \tag{3.23}$$

[8] The basis vectors obtained with the use of projection operators will always have the desired symmetry, but there is no guarantee that these vectors will be eigenvectors of $\mathbf{I}^2$. However, one can always form linear combinations of symmetrized vectors that are eigenvectors of $\mathbf{I}^2$.

where $\mathbf{I} = \mathbf{I}_A + \mathbf{I}_{A'} + \cdots$. Now $I_A = I_{A'} = I_{A''} = \cdots$, so that the energy of a state with total spin quantum number I and z component of angular momentum m is

$$\Omega_{I,m} = -\{\omega_A m + \tfrac{1}{2}J_{AA'}[I(I+1) - NI_A(I_A+1)]\}. \tag{3.24}$$

$\mathscr{C}_2$ Symmetry, $N = 2$

$I_A = \frac{1}{2}$, $I = 1, 0$. The product basis for two spin-$\frac{1}{2}$ nuclei generates a four-dimensional representation of $\mathscr{C}_2$. The product kets may be geometrically represented by four line segments with the eigenvalues of I_{Az} and $I_{A'z}$ indicated at the end points (Fig. 8.4). The C_2 axis passes

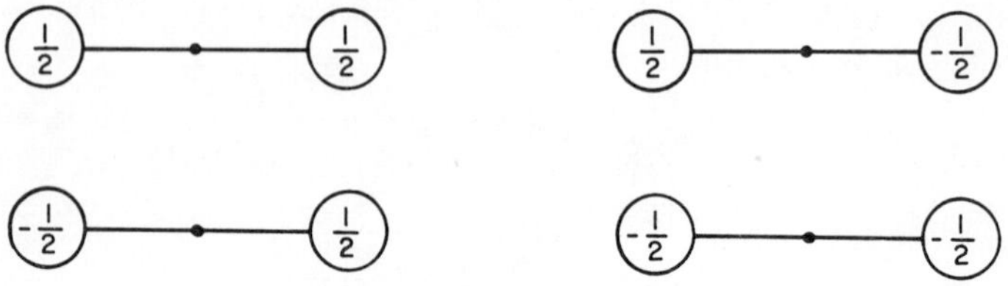

FIG. 8.4. Geometric representation of the product basis for two spin-$\frac{1}{2}$ nuclei with $\mathscr{C}_2$ symmetry.

through the midpoint of each segment and is perpendicular to the line joining the two nuclei.[9] Applying the operations E and C_2 to these figures, one obtains the following results:

	$\|++\rangle$	$\|+-\rangle$	$\|-+\rangle$	$\|--\rangle$
E	$\|++\rangle$	$\|+-\rangle$	$\|-+\rangle$	$\|--\rangle$
C_2	$\|++\rangle$	$\|-+\rangle$	$\|+-\rangle$	$\|--\rangle$

From this table it is easy to construct the matrices for E and C_2:

$$E = \begin{pmatrix} 1 & 0 & 0 & 0 \\ 0 & 1 & 0 & 0 \\ 0 & 0 & 1 & 0 \\ 0 & 0 & 0 & 1 \end{pmatrix}, \qquad C_2 = \begin{pmatrix} 1 & 0 & 0 & 0 \\ 0 & 0 & 1 & 0 \\ 0 & 1 & 0 & 0 \\ 0 & 0 & 0 & 1 \end{pmatrix}.$$

It follows that

$$\operatorname{tr} E = 4, \qquad \operatorname{tr} C_2 = 2, \tag{3.25}$$

[9] The use of geometric figures to represent the product basis is a very useful device; they should be constructed for every problem until the symmetrization technique is mastered.

and, by (2.30), that

$$c_{\mathscr{A}} = \tfrac{1}{2}(4 \cdot 1 + 2 \cdot 1) = 3, \qquad c_{\mathscr{B}} = \tfrac{1}{2}(4 \cdot 1 - 2 \cdot 1) = 1.$$

Thus the four-dimensional representation contains the (one-dimensional) irreducible representation $\mathscr{A}$ three times, and the (one-dimensional) irreducible representation $\mathscr{B}$ once.

The subspace spanned by vectors belonging to the symmetry species $\mathscr{A}$ is three-dimensional. A basis for this subspace is obtained by applying $P_{\mathscr{A}} = \frac{1}{2}(E + C_2)$ to the elements of the product basis:

$$P_{\mathscr{A}}|++\rangle = |++\rangle,$$
$$P_{\mathscr{A}}|+-\rangle = P_{\mathscr{A}}|-+\rangle = \tfrac{1}{2}\{|+-\rangle + |-+\rangle\},$$
$$P_{\mathscr{A}}|--\rangle = |--\rangle.$$

The three vectors projected "out" of the product kets by $P_{\mathscr{A}}$ are linearly independent, and, in this case, eigenvectors of $\mathbf{I}^2$ corresponding to $I = 1$.

The remaining element of the symmetrized basis is obtained by applying $P_{\mathscr{B}}$ to the elements of the product basis:

$$P_{\mathscr{B}}|++\rangle = 0,$$
$$P_{\mathscr{B}}|+-\rangle = \tfrac{1}{2}\{|+-\rangle - |-+\rangle\} = -P_{\mathscr{B}}|-+\rangle,$$
$$P_{\mathscr{B}}|--\rangle = 0.$$

Therefore, the required (unnormalized) eigenvector, which is an eigenvector of $\mathbf{I}^2$ corresponding to $I = 0$, is given by $P_{\mathscr{B}}|+-\rangle$. The symmetrized (normalized) eigenvectors for $I = 1, 0$ are collected in Table 8.5.

TABLE 8.5

SYMMETRIZED BASIS VECTORS FOR TWO SPIN-$\frac{1}{2}$ NUCLEI WITH $\mathscr{C}_2$ SYMMETRY

Basis vector	$(\mathscr{S})_{I,m}$
$\|++\rangle$	$(\mathscr{A})_{1,1}$
$\frac{1}{\sqrt{2}}\{\|+-\rangle + \|-+\rangle\}$	$(\mathscr{A})_{1,0}$
$\|--\rangle$	$(\mathscr{A})_{1,-1}$
$\frac{1}{\sqrt{2}}\{\|+-\rangle - \|-+\rangle\}$	$(\mathscr{B})_{0,0}$

$I_A = 1, I = 2, 1, 0$. The calculations for two spin-1 nuclei with $\mathscr{C}_2$ symmetry are analogous to those for two spin-$\frac{1}{2}$ nuclei. The product basis generates a nine-dimensional representation of $\mathscr{C}_2$, and it is easily verified that

$$\begin{gathered} \operatorname{tr} E = 9, \qquad \operatorname{tr} C_2 = 3, \\ c_{\mathscr{A}} = \tfrac{1}{2}(9 \cdot 1 + 3 \cdot 1) = 6, \qquad c_{\mathscr{B}} = \tfrac{1}{2}(9 \cdot 1 - 3 \cdot 1) = 3. \end{gathered} \tag{3.26}$$

A symmetrized basis may be obtained by applying $P_{\mathscr{A}}$ and $P_{\mathscr{B}}$ to the product basis:

$$P_{\mathscr{A}}|\,1, 1; 1, 1\rangle = |\,1, 1; 1, 1\rangle,$$

$$P_{\mathscr{A}}|\,1, 0; 1, 1\rangle = P_{\mathscr{A}}|\,1, 1; 1, 0\rangle = \tfrac{1}{2}\{|\,1, 0; 1, 1\rangle + |\,1, 1; 1, 0\rangle\},$$

$$P_{\mathscr{A}}|\,1, -1; 1, 1\rangle = P_{\mathscr{A}}|\,1, 1; 1, -1\rangle = \tfrac{1}{2}\{|\,1, -1; 1, 1\rangle + |\,1, 1; 1, -1\rangle\},$$

$$P_{\mathscr{A}}|\,1, 0; 1, -1\rangle = P_{\mathscr{A}}|\,1, -1; 1, 0\rangle = \tfrac{1}{2}\{|\,1, 0; 1, -1\rangle + |\,1, -1; 1, 0\rangle\},$$

$$P_{\mathscr{A}}|\,1, 0; 1, 0\rangle = |\,1, 0; 1, 0\rangle,$$

$$P_{\mathscr{A}}|\,1, -1; 1, -1\rangle = |\,1, -1; 1, -1\rangle;$$

$$P_{\mathscr{B}}|\,1, 1; 1, 1\rangle = P_{\mathscr{B}}|\,1, -1; 1, -1\rangle = P_{\mathscr{B}}|\,1, 0; 1, 0\rangle = 0,$$

$$P_{\mathscr{B}}|\,1, 1; 1, 0\rangle = -P_{\mathscr{B}}|\,1, 0; 1, 1\rangle = \tfrac{1}{2}\{|\,1, 1; 1, 0\rangle - |\,1, 0; 1, 1\rangle\},$$

$$P_{\mathscr{B}}|\,1, 1; 1, -1\rangle = -P_{\mathscr{B}}|\,1, -1; 1, 1\rangle = \tfrac{1}{2}\{|\,1, 1; 1, -1\rangle - |\,1, -1; 1, 1\rangle\},$$

$$P_{\mathscr{B}}|\,1, 0; 1, -1\rangle = -P_{\mathscr{B}}|\,1, -1; 1, 0\rangle = \tfrac{1}{2}\{|\,1, 0; 1, -1\rangle - |\,1, -1; 1, 0\rangle\}.$$

These results give six vectors with $\mathscr{A}$ symmetry and three vectors with $\mathscr{B}$ symmetry, but not all these vectors are eigenvectors of $\mathbf{I}^2$. It is a simple matter, however, to set up and diagonalize the matrix for $\mathbf{I}^2$. The results of this calculation are given in Table 8.6.

$I_A = \frac{3}{2}, I = 3, 2, 1, 0$. The details of the calculation for this case will be omitted. The results are given in Table 8.7.

$\mathscr{D}_3$ *Symmetry*, $N = 3$

$I_A = \frac{1}{2}, I = \frac{3}{2}, \frac{1}{2}$. It was shown in Section 3 that the product basis generates an eight-dimensional representation of $\mathscr{D}_3$ for which $c_{\mathscr{A}_1} = 4$, $c_{\mathscr{A}_2} = 0$, $c_{\mathscr{E}} = 2$. This means that any symmetrized basis will contain four linearly independent vectors with $\mathscr{A}_1$ symmetry, and, since $\dim \mathscr{E} = 2$, four linearly independent vectors with $\mathscr{E}$ symmetry. These results can be verified by using Table 8.4 to compute the traces of the

TABLE 8.6

SYMMETRIZED BASIS VECTORS FOR TWO SPIN-1 NUCLEI WITH $\mathscr{C}_2$ SYMMETRY

Basis vector	$(\mathscr{S})_{I,m}$
$\vert 1, 1; 1, 1\rangle$	$(\mathscr{A})_{2,2}$
$\frac{1}{\sqrt{2}}\{\vert 1, 1; 1, 0\rangle + \vert 1, 0; 1, 1\rangle\}$	$(\mathscr{A})_{2,1}$
$\frac{1}{\sqrt{6}}\{\vert 1, 1; 1, -1\rangle + 2\vert 1, 0; 1, 0\rangle + \vert 1, -1; 1, 1\rangle\}$	$(\mathscr{A})_{2,0}$
$\frac{1}{\sqrt{2}}\{\vert 1, -1; 1, 0\rangle + \vert 1, 0; 1, -1\rangle\}$	$(\mathscr{A})_{2,-1}$
$\vert 1, -1; 1, -1\rangle$	$(\mathscr{A})_{2,-2}$
$\frac{1}{\sqrt{2}}\{\vert 1, 1; 1, 0\rangle - \vert 1, 0; 1, 1\rangle\}$	$(\mathscr{B})_{1,1}$
$\frac{1}{\sqrt{2}}\{\vert 1, 1; 1, -1\rangle - \vert 1, -1; 1, 1\rangle\}$	$(\mathscr{B})_{1,0}$
$\frac{1}{\sqrt{2}}\{\vert 1, 0; 1, -1\rangle - \vert 1, -1; 1, 0\rangle\}$	$(\mathscr{B})_{1,-1}$
$\frac{1}{\sqrt{3}}\{\vert 1, 1; 1, -1\rangle - \vert 1, 0; 1, 0\rangle + \vert 1, -1; 1, 1\rangle\}$	$(\mathscr{A})_{0,0}$

group elements, and then computing the ranks of the projection operators (3.20). One finds that

$$\operatorname{tr} P_{\mathscr{A}_1} = 4, \qquad \operatorname{tr} P_{\mathscr{A}_2} = 0, \qquad \operatorname{tr} P_{\mathscr{E}} = \operatorname{tr} P_{\mathscr{E}}' = 2. \tag{3.27}$$

These relations show that $P_{\mathscr{A}_1}$, $P_{\mathscr{E}}$, and $P_{\mathscr{E}}'$ decompose the eight-dimensional spin space into three disjoint subspaces (the P_i are mutually orthogonal) of dimensions 4, 2, 2.

The symmetrization of the product basis is carried out by applying $P_{\mathscr{A}_1}$, $P_{\mathscr{E}}$, and $P_{\mathscr{E}}'$ to the elements of the product basis. After symmetrizing the basis, it is a relatively easy problem to determine a symmetrized basis whose elements are eigenvectors of $\mathbf{I}^2$ and I_z (Table 8.8).

The procedure sketched above for three spin-$\frac{1}{2}$ nuclei with $\mathscr{D}_3$ symmetry may also be applied to three nuclei with $I_A > \frac{1}{2}$.

$\mathscr{D}_2$ Symmetry, $N = 4$

$I_A = \frac{1}{2}, I = 2, 1, 0$. A model for this system consists of four spin-$\frac{1}{2}$ nuclei at the corners of a rectangle. The product basis generates a 16-dimensional representation of $\mathscr{D}_2$ with

$$\operatorname{tr} E = 16, \qquad \operatorname{tr} C_2 = \operatorname{tr} C_2' = \operatorname{tr} C_2'' = 4, \tag{3.28}$$

TABLE 8.7

SYMMETRIZED BASIS VECTORS FOR TWO SPIN-$\frac{3}{2}$ NUCLEI WITH $\mathscr{C}_2$ SYMMETRY

Basis vectors	$(\mathscr{S})_{I,m}$
$\lvert\tfrac{3}{2},\tfrac{3}{2};\tfrac{3}{2},\tfrac{3}{2}\rangle$	$(\mathscr{A})_{3,3}$
$\frac{1}{\sqrt{2}}\{\lvert\tfrac{3}{2},\tfrac{3}{2};\tfrac{3}{2},\tfrac{1}{2}\rangle+\lvert\tfrac{3}{2},\tfrac{1}{2};\tfrac{3}{2},\tfrac{3}{2}\rangle\}$	$(\mathscr{A})_{3,2}$
$\frac{1}{\sqrt{5}}\{\lvert\tfrac{3}{2},\tfrac{3}{2};\tfrac{3}{2},-\tfrac{1}{2}\rangle+\sqrt{3}\,\lvert\tfrac{3}{2},\tfrac{1}{2};\tfrac{3}{2},\tfrac{1}{2}\rangle+\lvert\tfrac{3}{2},-\tfrac{1}{2};\tfrac{3}{2},\tfrac{3}{2}\rangle\}$	$(\mathscr{A})_{3,1}$
$\frac{1}{2\sqrt{5}}\{\lvert\tfrac{3}{2},\tfrac{3}{2};\tfrac{3}{2},-\tfrac{3}{2}\rangle+3\,\lvert\tfrac{3}{2},\tfrac{1}{2};\tfrac{3}{2},-\tfrac{1}{2}\rangle+3\,\lvert\tfrac{3}{2},-\tfrac{1}{2};\tfrac{3}{2},\tfrac{1}{2}\rangle+\lvert\tfrac{3}{2},-\tfrac{3}{2};\tfrac{3}{2},\tfrac{3}{2}\rangle\}$	$(\mathscr{A})_{3,0}$
$\frac{1}{\sqrt{5}}\{\lvert\tfrac{3}{2},-\tfrac{3}{2};\tfrac{3}{2},\tfrac{1}{2}\rangle+\sqrt{3}\,\lvert\tfrac{3}{2},-\tfrac{1}{2};\tfrac{3}{2},-\tfrac{1}{2}\rangle+\lvert\tfrac{3}{2},\tfrac{1}{2};\tfrac{3}{2},-\tfrac{3}{2}\rangle\}$	$(\mathscr{A})_{3,-1}$
$\frac{1}{\sqrt{2}}\{\lvert\tfrac{3}{2},-\tfrac{3}{2};\tfrac{3}{2},-\tfrac{1}{2}\rangle+\lvert\tfrac{3}{2},-\tfrac{1}{2};\tfrac{3}{2},-\tfrac{3}{2}\rangle\}$	$(\mathscr{A})_{3,-2}$
$\lvert\tfrac{3}{2},-\tfrac{3}{2};\tfrac{3}{2},-\tfrac{3}{2}\rangle$	$(\mathscr{A})_{3,-3}$
$\frac{1}{\sqrt{2}}\{\lvert\tfrac{3}{2},\tfrac{3}{2};\tfrac{3}{2},\tfrac{1}{2}\rangle-\lvert\tfrac{3}{2},\tfrac{1}{2};\tfrac{3}{2},\tfrac{3}{2}\rangle\}$	$(\mathscr{B})_{2,2}$
$\frac{1}{\sqrt{2}}\{\lvert\tfrac{3}{2},\tfrac{3}{2};\tfrac{3}{2},-\tfrac{1}{2}\rangle-\lvert\tfrac{3}{2},-\tfrac{1}{2};\tfrac{3}{2},\tfrac{3}{2}\rangle\}$	$(\mathscr{B})_{2,1}$
$\frac{1}{2}\{\lvert\tfrac{3}{2},\tfrac{1}{2};\tfrac{3}{2},-\tfrac{1}{2}\rangle+\lvert\tfrac{3}{2},\tfrac{3}{2};\tfrac{3}{2},-\tfrac{3}{2}\rangle-\lvert\tfrac{3}{2},-\tfrac{3}{2};\tfrac{3}{2},\tfrac{3}{2}\rangle-\lvert\tfrac{3}{2},-\tfrac{1}{2};\tfrac{3}{2},\tfrac{1}{2}\rangle\}$	$(\mathscr{B})_{2,0}$
$\frac{1}{\sqrt{2}}\{\lvert\tfrac{3}{2},\tfrac{1}{2};\tfrac{3}{2},-\tfrac{3}{2}\rangle-\lvert\tfrac{3}{2},-\tfrac{3}{2};\tfrac{3}{2},\tfrac{1}{2}\rangle\}$	$(\mathscr{B})_{2,-1}$
$\frac{1}{\sqrt{2}}\{\lvert\tfrac{3}{2},-\tfrac{1}{2};\tfrac{3}{2},-\tfrac{3}{2}\rangle-\lvert\tfrac{3}{2},-\tfrac{3}{2};\tfrac{3}{2},-\tfrac{1}{2}\rangle\}$	$(\mathscr{B})_{2,-2}$
$\sqrt{\frac{3}{10}}\{\lvert\tfrac{3}{2},\tfrac{3}{2};\tfrac{3}{2},-\tfrac{1}{2}\rangle-\tfrac{2}{3}\sqrt{3}\,\lvert\tfrac{3}{2},\tfrac{1}{2};\tfrac{3}{2};\tfrac{1}{2}\rangle+\lvert\tfrac{3}{2},-\tfrac{1}{2};\tfrac{3}{2},\tfrac{3}{2}\rangle\}$	$(\mathscr{A})_{1,1}$
$\frac{3}{2\sqrt{5}}\{\lvert\tfrac{3}{2},\tfrac{3}{2};\tfrac{3}{2},-\tfrac{3}{2}\rangle-\tfrac{1}{3}\,\lvert\tfrac{3}{2},\tfrac{1}{2};\tfrac{3}{2},-\tfrac{1}{2}\rangle+\lvert\tfrac{3}{2},-\tfrac{3}{2};\tfrac{3}{2},\tfrac{3}{2}\rangle-\tfrac{1}{3}\,\lvert\tfrac{3}{2},-\tfrac{1}{2};\tfrac{3}{2},\tfrac{1}{2}\rangle\}$	$(\mathscr{A})_{1,0}$
$\sqrt{\frac{3}{10}}\{\lvert\tfrac{3}{2},\tfrac{1}{2};\tfrac{3}{2},-\tfrac{3}{2}\rangle-\tfrac{2}{3}\sqrt{3}\,\lvert\tfrac{3}{2},-\tfrac{1}{2};\tfrac{3}{2},-\tfrac{1}{2}\rangle+\lvert\tfrac{3}{2},-\tfrac{3}{2};\tfrac{3}{2},\tfrac{1}{2}\rangle\}$	$(\mathscr{A})_{1,-1}$
$\frac{1}{2}\{\lvert\tfrac{3}{2},\tfrac{1}{2};\tfrac{3}{2},-\tfrac{1}{2}\rangle-\lvert\tfrac{3}{2},-\tfrac{1}{2};\tfrac{3}{2},\tfrac{1}{2}\rangle-\lvert\tfrac{3}{2},\tfrac{3}{2};\tfrac{3}{2},-\tfrac{3}{2}\rangle+\lvert\tfrac{3}{2},-\tfrac{3}{2};\tfrac{3}{2},\tfrac{3}{2}\rangle\}$	$(\mathscr{B})_{0,0}$

TABLE 8.8

SYMMETRIZED BASIS VECTORS FOR THREE SPIN-$\frac{1}{2}$ NUCLEI WITH $\mathscr{D}_3$ SYMMETRY

Basis vector	$(\mathscr{S})_{I,m}$
$\vert +++\rangle$	$(\mathscr{A}_1)_{3/2,3/2}$
$\frac{1}{\sqrt{3}}\{\vert ++-\rangle + \vert +-+\rangle + \vert -++\rangle\}$	$(\mathscr{A}_1)_{3/2,1/2}$
$\frac{1}{\sqrt{3}}\{\vert --+\rangle + \vert -+-\rangle + \vert +--\rangle\}$	$(\mathscr{A}_1)_{3/2,-1/2}$
$\vert ---\rangle$	$(\mathscr{A}_1)_{3/2,-3/2}$
$\frac{1}{\sqrt{2}}\{\vert ++-\rangle - \vert -++\rangle\}$	$(\mathscr{E})_{1/2,1/2}$
$\frac{1}{\sqrt{2}}\{\vert +--\rangle - \vert --+\rangle\}$	$(\mathscr{E})_{1/2,-1/2}$
$\frac{1}{\sqrt{6}}\{\vert ++-\rangle + \vert -++\rangle - 2\vert +-+\rangle\}$	$(\mathscr{E}')_{1/2,1/2}$
$\frac{1}{\sqrt{6}}\{2\vert -+-\rangle - \vert --+\rangle - \vert +--\rangle\}$	$(\mathscr{E}')_{1/2,-1/2}$

so that $c_{\mathscr{A}} = 7$, $c_{\mathscr{B}_1} = c_{\mathscr{B}_2} = c_{\mathscr{B}_3} = 3$. Table 8.9 gives a symmetrized basis whose elements are also eigenvectors of $\mathbf{I}^2$ and I_z. However, not all these vectors are eigenvectors of the hamiltonian operator

$$\begin{aligned}\mathscr{H}(\mathrm{AA'A''A'''}) = -\{&\omega_A I_z + J_{AA'}(\mathbf{I}_A \cdot \mathbf{I}_{A'} + \mathbf{I}_{A''} \cdot \mathbf{I}_{A'''}) \\ &+ J_{AA''}(\mathbf{I}_A \cdot \mathbf{I}_{A''} + \mathbf{I}_{A'} \cdot \mathbf{I}_{A'''}) \\ &+ J_{AA'''}(\mathbf{I}_A \cdot \mathbf{I}_{A'''} + \mathbf{I}_{A'} \cdot \mathbf{I}_{A''})\}. \end{aligned} \tag{3.29}$$

The first 14 entries of Table 8.9 are eigenvectors of $\mathscr{H}$ with the eigenvalues

$$\begin{aligned}
(\mathscr{A})_{2,m}: &\quad \Omega_{2,m} = -\{m\omega_A + \tfrac{1}{2}(J_{AA'} + J_{AA''} + J_{AA'''})\},\\
(\mathscr{B}_1)_{1,m}: &\quad \Omega_{1,m} = -\{m\omega_A - \tfrac{1}{2}(J_{AA'} - J_{AA''} + J_{AA'''})\},\\
(\mathscr{B}_2)_{1,m}: &\quad \Omega_{1,m} = -\{m\omega_A - \tfrac{1}{2}(J_{AA'} + J_{AA''} - J_{AA'''})\},\\
(\mathscr{B}_3)_{1,m}: &\quad \Omega_{1,m} = -\{m\omega_A + \tfrac{1}{2}(J_{AA'} - J_{AA''} - J_{AA'''})\},
\end{aligned} \tag{3.30}$$

where $m = 0, \pm 1, \pm 2$ for $\Omega_{2,m}$, and $m = 0, \pm 1$ for all $\Omega_{1,m}$. The last two entries in the table are mixed by the spin-spin interactions. The

TABLE 8.9

SYMMETRIZED BASIS VECTORS FOR FOUR SPIN-$\frac{1}{2}$ NUCLEI WITH $\mathscr{D}_2$ SYMMETRY

Basis vector	$(\mathscr{S})_{I,m}$
$\|++++\rangle$	$(\mathscr{A})_{2,2}$
$\frac{1}{2}\{\|+++-\rangle+\|++-+\rangle+\|+-++\rangle+\|-+++\rangle\}$	$(\mathscr{A})_{2,1}$
$\frac{1}{\sqrt{6}}\{\|++--\rangle+\|+--+\rangle+\|+-+-\rangle+\|-++-\rangle$ $+\|--++\rangle+\|-+-+\rangle\}$	$(\mathscr{A})_{2,0}$
$\frac{1}{2}\{\|---+\rangle+\|--+-\rangle+\|-+--\rangle+\|+---\rangle\}$	$(\mathscr{A})_{2,-1}$
$\|----\rangle$	$(\mathscr{A})_{2,-2}$
$\frac{1}{2}\{\|+++-\rangle-\|++-+\rangle-\|-+++\rangle+\|+-++\rangle\}$	$(\mathscr{B}_1)_{1,1}$
$\frac{1}{\sqrt{2}}\{\|+-+-\rangle-\|-+-+\rangle\}$	$(\mathscr{B}_1)_{1,0}$
$\frac{1}{2}\{\|+---\rangle-\|-+--\rangle+\|--+-\rangle-\|---+\rangle\}$	$(\mathscr{B}_1)_{1,-1}$
$\frac{1}{2}\{\|+++-\rangle-\|++-+\rangle+\|-+++\rangle-\|+-++\rangle\}$	$(\mathscr{B}_2)_{1,1}$
$\frac{1}{\sqrt{2}}\{\|-++-\rangle-\|+--+\rangle\}$	$(\mathscr{B}_2)_{1,0}$
$\frac{1}{2}\{\|-+--\rangle-\|+---\rangle+\|--+-\rangle-\|---+\rangle\}$	$(\mathscr{B}_2)_{1,-1}$
$\frac{1}{2}\{\|+++-\rangle+\|++-+\rangle-\|-+++\rangle-\|+-++\rangle\}$	$(\mathscr{B}_3)_{1,1}$
$\frac{1}{\sqrt{2}}\{\|++--\rangle-\|--++\rangle\}$	$(\mathscr{B}_3)_{1,0}$
$\frac{1}{2}\{\|-+--\rangle+\|+---\rangle-\|--+-\rangle-\|---+\rangle\}$	$(\mathscr{B}_3)_{1,-1}$
$\frac{1}{2}\{\|++--\rangle+\|--++\rangle-\|+-+-\rangle-\|-+-+\rangle\}$	$(\mathscr{A})_{0,0}$
$\frac{1}{2\sqrt{3}}\{\|++--\rangle+\|--++\rangle+\|+-+-\rangle+\|-+-+\rangle$ $-2\|-++-\rangle-2\|+--+\rangle\}$	$(\mathscr{A}')_{0,0}$

eigenvalues and eigenvectors of $\mathscr{H}$ may be determined by diagonalizing the 2×2 submatrix of $\mathscr{H}$ generated by these vectors. The results are

$$(\mathscr{A})_{0,0;1} = \frac{1}{(1+Q^2)^{1/2}}\{(\mathscr{A})_{0,0} - Q(\mathscr{A}')_{0,0}\},$$
$$(\mathscr{A})_{0,0;2} = \frac{1}{(1+Q^2)^{1/2}}\{Q(\mathscr{A})_{0,0} + (\mathscr{A}')_{0,0}\}, \tag{3.31}$$

$$\Omega_{0,0;1} = \tfrac{1}{2}\{J_{\mathrm{AA}'} + J_{\mathrm{AA}''} + J_{\mathrm{AA}'''} + R\},$$
$$\Omega_{0,0;2} = \tfrac{1}{2}\{J_{\mathrm{AA}'} + J_{\mathrm{AA}''} + J_{\mathrm{AA}'''} - R\}, \tag{3.32}$$

where

$$R = [(J_{\mathrm{AA}'} + J_{\mathrm{AA}''} - 2J_{\mathrm{AA}'''})^2 + 3(J_{\mathrm{AA}'} - J_{\mathrm{AA}''})^2]^{1/2},$$
$$Q = \frac{\sqrt{3}(J_{\mathrm{AA}'} - J_{\mathrm{AA}''})}{J_{\mathrm{AA}'} + J_{\mathrm{AA}''} - 2J_{\mathrm{AA}'''} + R}. \tag{3.33}$$

D. Symmetrized Bases for AA′ ··· BB′ ··· CC′ ··· Systems

There are two methods for constructing symmetrized bases for systems of the form AA′ ··· BB′ ··· CC′ ··· *(13–15)*. The first method considers the spin system as a single entity, and generates a symmetrized basis by forming the product basis and applying the appropriate projection operators to its elements. Since the square of the total angular momentum is not conserved, it is not necessary to construct a symmetrized basis whose elements are eigenvectors of $\mathbf{I}^2$.

To illustrate the method, consider an AA′BB′ system (i.e., four spin-$\frac{1}{2}$ nuclei with $\mathscr{C}_2$ symmetry, none of the nuclei being on the C_2 axis). The product basis generates a 16-dimensional representation of $\mathscr{C}_2$, and the matrix for C_2 may be obtained by observing that, for any product ket,

$$C_2 \mid m_{\mathrm{A}} m_{\mathrm{A}'} m_{\mathrm{B}} m_{\mathrm{B}'}\rangle = \mid m_{\mathrm{A}'} m_{\mathrm{A}} m_{\mathrm{B}'} m_{\mathrm{B}}\rangle. \tag{3.34}$$

For example, $C_2|+-+-\rangle = |-+-+\rangle$, $C_2|+++-\rangle = |++-+\rangle$, etc. The only product kets invariant under C_2 are $|++++\rangle$, $|++--\rangle$, $|--++\rangle$, and $|----\rangle$, so that $\mathrm{tr}\, C_2 = 4$. Since $\mathrm{tr}\, E = 16$, it follows that $c_{\mathscr{A}} = 10$, $c_{\mathscr{B}} = 6$. A symmetrized basis for the system is obtained by applying $P_{\mathscr{A}}$ and $P_{\mathscr{B}}$ to the elements of the product basis, and selecting the appropriate number of nonzero, linearly independent vectors for each symmetry species. The results are given in Table 8.10, where basis vectors corresponding to the same eigenvalue of I_z are distinguished by writing $n(\mathscr{S})_m$, $n = 1, 2, \ldots$.

TABLE 8.10

SYMMETRIZED BASIS VECTORS FOR THE AA′BB′ SYSTEM ($\mathscr{C}_2$ SYMMETRY)

Basis vector	$(\mathscr{S})_m$	Basis vector	$(\mathscr{S})_m$
$\lvert ++++\rangle$	$(\mathscr{A})_2$	$\lvert ----\rangle$	$(\mathscr{A})_{-2}$
$\frac{1}{\sqrt{2}}\{\lvert +++-\rangle + \lvert ++-+\rangle\}$	$1(\mathscr{A})_1$	$\frac{1}{\sqrt{2}}\{\lvert +++-\rangle - \lvert ++-+\rangle\}$	$1(\mathscr{B})_1$
$\frac{1}{\sqrt{2}}\{\lvert +-++\rangle + \lvert -+++\rangle\}$	$2(\mathscr{A})_1$	$\frac{1}{\sqrt{2}}\{\lvert +-++\rangle - \lvert -+++\rangle\}$	$2(\mathscr{B})_1$
$\lvert ++--\rangle$	$1(\mathscr{A})_0$	$\frac{1}{\sqrt{2}}\{\lvert +-+-\rangle - \lvert -+-+\rangle\}$	$1(\mathscr{B})_0$
$\lvert --++\rangle$	$2(\mathscr{A})_0$	$\frac{1}{\sqrt{2}}\{\lvert +--+\rangle - \lvert -++-\rangle\}$	$2(\mathscr{B})_0$
$\frac{1}{\sqrt{2}}\{\lvert +-+-\rangle + \lvert -+-+\rangle\}$	$3(\mathscr{A})_0$	$\frac{1}{\sqrt{2}}\{\lvert +---\rangle - \lvert -+--\rangle\}$	$1(\mathscr{B})_{-1}$
$\frac{1}{\sqrt{2}}\{\lvert +--+\rangle + \lvert -++-\rangle\}$	$4(\mathscr{A})_0$	$\frac{1}{\sqrt{2}}\{\lvert --+-\rangle - \lvert ---+\rangle\}$	$2(\mathscr{B})_{-1}$
$\frac{1}{\sqrt{2}}\{\lvert +---\rangle + \lvert -+--\rangle\}$	$1(\mathscr{A})_{-1}$		
$\frac{1}{\sqrt{2}}\{\lvert --+-\rangle + \lvert ---+\rangle\}$	$2(\mathscr{A})_{-1}$		

The second method, to be discussed at greater length in Section 5, considers the complete system to be built up from subsystems. These subsystems are usually composed of symmetrically equivalent nuclei, but it is occasionally necessary to consider a set of symmetrically equivalent nuclei together with invariant nuclei as the subsystem. In any case, each subsystem conforms to a particular symmetry group, and the projection operators for this group are used to obtain a symmetrized basis for the subsystem. A basis for the complete system is obtained by forming the set of all possible products of the symmetrized bases of the several subsystems.

To illustrate the second method, consider again the AA′BB′ system. There are two subsystems: the AA′ nuclei and the BB′ nuclei. Both subsystems have $\mathscr{C}_2$ symmetry, and a symmetrized basis for either subsystem is given by the vectors in Table 8.5. The 16 products of the basis vectors for both subsystems yield a basis for the AA′BB′ system (Table 8.11). The symmetry species of these products are determined by the rules for representation multiplication (Section 5), which, in the present instance, are given by $\mathscr{A} \otimes \mathscr{A} = \mathscr{A}$, $\mathscr{A} \otimes \mathscr{B} = \mathscr{B} \otimes \mathscr{A} = \mathscr{B}$, $\mathscr{B} \otimes \mathscr{B} = \mathscr{A}$. These rules state that the symmetry species of any product is $\mathscr{A}$ or $\mathscr{B}$, accordingly as both factors in the product are taken from the same or different symmetry species.

TABLE 8.11

SYMMETRIZED BASIS VECTORS FOR THE AA′BB′ SYSTEM ($\mathscr{C}_2$ SYMMETRY)

Basis vector	$m_{AA'}$	$m_{XX'}$	$(\mathscr{S})_m$
$\vert ++++\rangle$	1	1	$(\mathscr{A})_2$
$\frac{1}{\sqrt{2}}\{\vert +++-\rangle + \vert ++-+\rangle\}$	1	0	$1(\mathscr{A})_1$
$\frac{1}{\sqrt{2}}\{\vert +-++\rangle + \vert -+++\rangle\}$	0	1	$2(\mathscr{A})_1$
$\vert ++--\rangle$	1	−1	$1(\mathscr{A})_0$
$\vert --++\rangle$	−1	1	$2(\mathscr{A})_0$
$\frac{1}{2}\{\vert +-+-\rangle + \vert +--+\rangle + \vert -+-+\rangle + \vert -++-\rangle\}$	0	0	$3(\mathscr{A})_0$
$\frac{1}{2}\{\vert +-+-\rangle - \vert +--+\rangle - \vert -++-\rangle + \vert -++-\rangle\}$	0	0	$4(\mathscr{A})_0$
$\frac{1}{\sqrt{2}}\{\vert +---\rangle + \vert -+--\rangle\}$	0	−1	$1(\mathscr{A})_{-1}$
$\frac{1}{\sqrt{2}}\{\vert --+-\rangle + \vert ---+\rangle\}$	−1	0	$2(\mathscr{A})_{-1}$
$\vert ----\rangle$	−1	−1	$(\mathscr{A})_{-2}$
$\frac{1}{\sqrt{2}}\{\vert +++-\rangle - \vert ++-+\rangle\}$	1	0	$1(\mathscr{B})_1$
$\frac{1}{\sqrt{2}}\{\vert +-++\rangle - \vert -+++\rangle\}$	0	1	$2(\mathscr{B})_1$
$\frac{1}{2}\{\vert +-+-\rangle - \vert +--+\rangle - \quad -+-+\rangle + \vert -++-\rangle\}$	0	0	$1(\mathscr{B})_0$
$\frac{1}{2}\{\vert +-+-\rangle + \vert +--+\rangle - \vert -+-+\rangle - \vert -++-\rangle\}$	0	0	$2(\mathscr{B})_0$
$\frac{1}{\sqrt{2}}\{\vert +---\rangle - \vert -+--\rangle\}$	0	−1	$1(\mathscr{B})_{-1}$
$\frac{1}{\sqrt{2}}\{\vert --+-\rangle - \vert ---+\rangle\}$	−1	0	$2(\mathscr{B})_{-1}$

It should be recognized that both methods are quite general and can be used to construct symmetrized bases for systems of the form $A_{I_A}A'_{I_A} \cdots B_{I_B}B'_{I_B} \cdots$. The first method is preferable when no assumptions are made concerning the spin-spin interactions. Its main advantage is the rapidity with which the symmetry species of the basis vectors are determined. It has the disadvantage that the decomposition of the hamiltonian matrix in the weak-coupling approximation is not readily inferred.

The second method is preferable in the weak-coupling limit. For then, the several factors in a product spin function can be labeled with their z components of angular momenta, and these labels determine the additional decompositions of the hamiltonian matrix in the weak-coupling approximation. The disadvantage of the method is that it may be necessary to carry out a resymmetrization of the product functions to determine their symmetry species (cf. Section 5).

An especially simple case occurs with spin systems containing invariant nuclei. If a symmetrized set of basis vectors for the noninvariant nuclei is given, a symmetrized basis for the complete system is obtained by forming the products of the given set with the kets for the invariant nuclei. The symmetry species of any such product is given by the symmetry species of the noninvariant factor. For example, in the case of a monosubstituted benzene, the protons *ortho* and *meta* to the substituent, which is presumed to have no influence on the magnetic resonance spectrum, may be initially considered as an AA′BB′ system, and the *para* proton an invariant nucleus. A symmetrized basis for the entire system is given by the 64 products of $|+\rangle$ and $|-\rangle$, with the vectors of Table 8.10 (or Table 8.11). The symmetry species of these products are given by the rules $(\mathscr{A})_m| \pm\rangle = (\mathscr{A})_{m\pm1/2}$, $(\mathscr{B})_m| \pm\rangle = (\mathscr{B})_{m\pm1/2}$.

E. The AA′BB′ System

The reduction of the determinantal equation for a symmetrical spin system will be explicitly illustrated for the AA′BB′ system (*16–18*). The stationary hamiltonian operator is

$$\mathscr{H} = -\{\omega_A(I_{Az} + I_{A'z}) + \omega_B(I_{Bz} + I_{B'z}) + J_{AA'}\mathbf{I}_A \cdot \mathbf{I}_{A'} + J_{BB'}\mathbf{I}_B \cdot \mathbf{I}_{B'} + J_{AB}(\mathbf{I}_A \cdot \mathbf{I}_B + \mathbf{I}_{A'} \cdot \mathbf{I}_{B'}) + J_{AB'}(\mathbf{I}_A \cdot \mathbf{I}_{B'} + \mathbf{I}_{A'} \cdot \mathbf{I}_B)\}, \qquad (3.35)$$

and is defined with respect to a 16-dimensional spin space. According to the discussion of Section 3.B, (3.35) admits I_z, $P_{\mathscr{A}} = \frac{1}{2}(E + C_2)$, and $P_{\mathscr{B}} = \frac{1}{2}(E - C_2)$ as constants of the motion. These operators decompose the spin space into disjoint subspaces, and the hamiltonian matrix into a direct sum of lower dimensional submatrices.

The direct sum decomposition of the hamiltonian matrix is automatically accomplished by choosing the vectors of the initial basis to be eigenvectors of I_z, $P_{\mathscr{A}}$, and $P_{\mathscr{B}}$. For this purpose, one may use the vectors of Table 8.10 or Table 8.11 as a basis. To facilitate the subsequent discussion of the AA′XX′ system, the vectors of Table 8.11 will be used as an initial basis. Relative to this basis, the hamiltonian matrix is the direct sum of a 10×10 matrix, generated by basis vectors with $\mathscr{A}$ symmetry, and a 6 × 6 matrix, generated by basis vectors with $\mathscr{B}$ symmetry (Fig. 8.5). Each of these submatrices decomposes into smaller submatrices whose dimensions are determined by the degeneracies of the I_z eigenvalues. Thus the 10 × 10 matrix is the direct sum of five submatrices of dimensions 1, 2, 4, 2, 1, and the 6 × 6 matrix is the direct sum of three two-dimensional matrices (Fig. 8.5). Therefore, the analysis of the eigenvalue problem requires the solution of algebraic equations of the first, second, and fourth degrees.

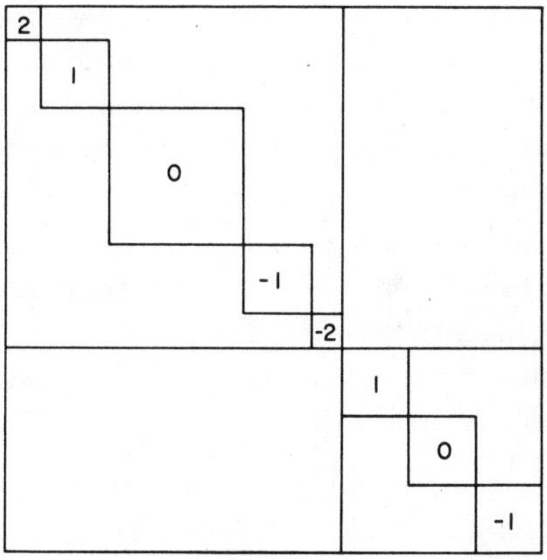

FIG. 8.5. Factorization of the secular determinant for the AA′BB′ system.

The 4 × 4 matrix generated by the basis vectors $n(\mathscr{A})_0$ $(n = 1, 2, 3, 4)$, is

$$\mathscr{H}(0) = \begin{pmatrix} -\delta - \frac{1}{4}K_+ + \frac{1}{2}L_+ & 0 & -\frac{1}{2}L_+ & -\frac{1}{2}L_- \\ 0 & \delta - \frac{1}{4}K_+ + \frac{1}{2}L_+ & -\frac{1}{2}L_+ & -\frac{1}{2}L_- \\ -\frac{1}{2}L_+ & -\frac{1}{2}L_+ & -\frac{1}{4}K_+ & \frac{1}{2}L_- \\ -\frac{1}{2}L_- & -\frac{1}{2}L_- & \frac{1}{2}L_- & \frac{3}{4}K_+ \end{pmatrix}, \tag{3.36}$$

where

$$K_\pm = J_{AA'} \pm J_{BB'}, \qquad L_\pm = J_{AB} \pm J_{AB'}. \tag{3.37}$$

The eigenvalues of (3.36) will be denoted Ω_i, $i = 1, 2, 3, 4$, where

$$\Omega_1 \to -\delta - \tfrac{1}{4}K_+ + \tfrac{1}{2}L_+, \qquad \Omega_2 \to \delta - \tfrac{1}{4}K_+ + \tfrac{1}{2}L_+,$$
$$\Omega_3 \to -\tfrac{1}{4}K_+, \qquad \Omega_4 \to \tfrac{3}{4}K_+,$$

as the off-diagonal elements of (3.36) tend to zero. The matrix that diagonalizes (3.36) will be denoted (a_{ij}). Since (3.36) is a real, symmetric matrix, there is no essential loss of generality in assuming that (a_{ij}) is orthogonal.

The quartic equation $\det[\mathscr{H}(0) - \lambda I] = 0$ can be solved by radicals (cf. Reference *1*, Chapter 5), but the expressions are quite cumbersome, and of limited practical value. In practice, the eigenvalues and eigenvectors of $\mathscr{H}(0)$ are obtained numerically, using a set of trial parameters. There are, however, three properties of the eigenvalues and eigenvectors of (3.36) that can be deduced by inspection.

(1) The eigenvalues and eigenvectors of (3.36) are independent of K_-.

(2) The replacement of δ with $-\delta$ is equivalent to interchanging Ω_1 and Ω_2, and the corresponding eigenvectors. This property follows from an interchange of the first and second rows of $\det[\mathscr{H}(0) - \lambda I]$, and an interchange of the first and second columns in the resulting determinant.

(3) The eigenvalues and eigenvectors of (3.36) are unaltered if L_- is replaced by $-L_-$. For a change in the sign of L_- is equivalent to removing a factor of -1 from the fourth row and the fourth column of $\det[\mathscr{H}(0) - \lambda I]$. The removal of these factors simply multiplies the determinant by $(-1)(-1) = +1$.

It should be noted that the eigenvalues and eigenvectors of (3.36) are altered if K_+ is replaced by $-K_+$, or if L_+ is replaced by $-L_+$ (unless $K_+ = 0$, or $L_+ = 0$).

The solutions of the linear and quadratic equations for the remaining eigenvalues and eigenvectors are given in Table 8.12, where

$$R_1 = [(\delta + K_-)^2 + L_-^2]^{1/2}, \qquad R_2 = [K_-^2 + L_-^2]^{1/2},$$

$$R_3 = [(\delta - K_-)^2 + L_-^2]^{1/2}, \qquad R_4 = [\delta^2 + L_+^2]^{1/2},$$

$$Q_1 = -\frac{L_-}{\delta + K_- + R_1}, \qquad Q_2 = -\frac{L_-}{K_- + R_2},$$

$$Q_3 = -\frac{L_-}{\delta - K_- + R_3}, \qquad Q_4 = \frac{L_+}{\delta + R_4},$$

$$\delta = \omega_A - \omega_B .$$

With this table, and the selection rules derived in Section 3.B, one obtains the resonance frequencies and relative intensities given in Table 8.13. It turns out that the spectrum is symmetrical with respect to the mean resonance frequency, so that only half of the 28 allowed transitions are tabulated.

Detailed descriptions of the types of AA′BB′ spectra predicted by Table 8.13 for various values of the internal chemical shifts and spin-

TABLE 8.12

EIGENVALUES AND EIGENVECTORS OF THE AA′BB′ SYSTEM

Eigenvector	Eigenvalue
$(\mathscr{A})_2$	$-\{\omega_A + \omega_B + \frac{1}{4}K_+ + \frac{1}{2}L_+\}$
$\frac{1}{(1+Q_4^2)^{1/2}}\{[1(\mathscr{A})_1] + Q_4[2(\mathscr{A})_1]\}$	$-\frac{1}{2}\{\omega_A + \omega_B + \frac{1}{2}K_+ + R_4\}$
$\frac{1}{(1+Q_4^2)^{1/2}}\{Q_4[1(\mathscr{A})_1] - [2(\mathscr{A})_1]\}$	$-\frac{1}{2}\{\omega_A + \omega_B + \frac{1}{2}K_+ - R_4\}$
$a_{11}[1(\mathscr{A})_0] + a_{12}[2(\mathscr{A})_0] + a_{13}[3(\mathscr{A})_0] + a_{14}[4(\mathscr{A})_0]$	Ω_1
$a_{21}[1(\mathscr{A})_0] + a_{22}[2(\mathscr{A})_0] + a_{23}[3(\mathscr{A})_0] + a_{24}[4(\mathscr{A})_0]$	Ω_2
$a_{31}[1(\mathscr{A})_0] + a_{32}[2(\mathscr{A})_0] + a_{33}[3(\mathscr{A})_0] + a_{34}[4(\mathscr{A})_0]$	Ω_3
$a_{41}[1(\mathscr{A})_0] + a_{42}[2(\mathscr{A})_0] + a_{43}[3(\mathscr{A})_0] + a_{44}(4(\mathscr{A})_0]$	Ω_4
$\frac{1}{(1+Q_4^2)^{1/2}}\{[1(\mathscr{A})_{-1}] + Q_4[2(\mathscr{A})_{-1}]\}$	$\frac{1}{2}\{\omega_A + \omega_B - \frac{1}{2}K_+ - R_4\}$
$\frac{1}{(1+Q_4^2)^{1/2}}\{Q_4[1(\mathscr{A})_{-1}] - [2(\mathscr{A})_{-1}]\}$	$\frac{1}{2}\{\omega_A + \omega_B - \frac{1}{2}K_+ + R_4\}$
$(\mathscr{A})_{-2}$	$\omega_A + \omega_B - \frac{1}{4}K_+ - \frac{1}{2}L_+$
$\frac{1}{(1+Q_1^2)^{1/2}}\{[1(\mathscr{B})_1] + Q_1[2(\mathscr{B})_1]\}$	$-\frac{1}{2}\{\omega_A + \omega_B - \frac{1}{2}K_+ + R_1\}$
$\frac{1}{(1+Q_1^2)^{1/2}}\{Q_1[1(\mathscr{B})_1] - [2(\mathscr{B})_1]\}$	$-\frac{1}{2}\{\omega_A + \omega_B - \frac{1}{2}K_+ - R_1\}$
$\frac{1}{(1+Q_2^2)^{1/2}}\{[1(\mathscr{B})_0] + Q_2[2(\mathscr{B})_0]\}$	$\frac{1}{2}\{\frac{1}{2}K_+ - R_2\}$
$\frac{1}{(1+Q_2^2)^{1/2}}\{Q_2[1(\mathscr{B})_0] - [2(\mathscr{B})_0]\}$	$\frac{1}{2}\{\frac{1}{2}K_+ + R_2\}$
$\frac{1}{(1+Q_3^2)^{1/2}}\{[1(\mathscr{B})_{-1}] + Q_3[2(\mathscr{B})_{-1}]\}$	$\frac{1}{2}\{\omega_A + \omega_B + \frac{1}{2}K_+ - R_3\}$
$\frac{1}{(1+Q_3^2)^{1/2}}\{Q_3[1(\mathscr{B})_{-1}] - [2(\mathscr{B})_{-1}]\}$	$\frac{1}{2}\{\omega_A + \omega_B + \frac{1}{2}K_+ + R_3\}$

spin coupling constants have been given in the literature (*17–19*) and will not be repeated here. The following discussion will note some general properties of such spectra and some special cases of interest.

From Table 8.13, and the properties of the $(\mathscr{A})_0$ states mentioned above, it is easy to show that the appearance of an AA′BB′ spectrum is unchanged under any of the following transformations: (1) $\delta \to -\delta$;

TABLE 8.13.

RESONANCE FREQUENCIES AND RELATIVE INTENSITIES FOR THE AA′BB′ SYSTEM

Transition[a]	Intensity	Frequency
	𝒜 Transitions	
1. $1(\mathscr{A})_{-1} \to (\mathscr{A})_{-2}$	$2\left(1 + \frac{L_+}{R_4}\right)$	$\frac{1}{2}(\omega_A + \omega_B - L_+ + R_4)$
2. $(\mathscr{A})_2 \to 2(\mathscr{A})_1$	$2\left(1 - \frac{L_+}{R_4}\right)$	$\frac{1}{2}(\omega_A + \omega_B + L_+ + R_4)$
3. $1(\mathscr{A})_0 \to 1(\mathscr{A})_{-1}$	$\frac{2}{1+Q_4^2}[a_{11} + (1+Q_4)a_{31} + Q_4 a_{21}]^2$	$\frac{1}{2}(\omega_A + \omega_B - \frac{1}{2}K_+ - R_4 - 2\Omega_1)$
4. $1(\mathscr{A})_1 \to 2(\mathscr{A})_0$	$\frac{2}{1+Q_4^2}[a_{12} + (1+Q_4)a_{32} + Q_4 a_{22}]^2$	$\frac{1}{2}(\omega_A + \omega_B + \frac{1}{2}K_+ + R_4 + 2\Omega_2)$
5. $1(\mathscr{A})_1 \to 3(\mathscr{A})_0$	$\frac{2}{1+Q_4^2}[a_{13} + (1+Q_4)a_{33} + Q_4 a_{23}]^2$	$\frac{1}{2}(\omega_A + \omega_B + \frac{1}{2}K_+ + R_4 + 2\Omega_3)$
6. $1(\mathscr{A})_1 \to 4(\mathscr{A})_0$	$\frac{2}{1+Q_4^2}[a_{14} + (1+Q_4)a_{34} + Q_4 a_{24}]^2$	$\frac{1}{2}(\omega_A + \omega_B + \frac{1}{2}K_+ + R_4 + 2\Omega_4)$
7. $1(\mathscr{A})_0 \to 2(\mathscr{A})_{-1}$	$\frac{2}{1+Q_4^2}[Q_4 a_{11} + (Q_4-1)a_{31} - a_{21}]^2$	$\frac{1}{2}(\omega_A + \omega_B - \frac{1}{2}K_+ + R_4 - 2\Omega_1)$
8. $2(\mathscr{A})_1 \to 2(\mathscr{A})_0$	$\frac{2}{1+Q_4^2}[Q_4 a_{12} + (Q_4-1)a_{32} - a_{22}]^2$	$\frac{1}{2}(\omega_A + \omega_B + \frac{1}{2}K_+ - R_4 + 2\Omega_2)$
9. $3(\mathscr{A})_0 \to 2(\mathscr{A})_{-1}$	$\frac{2}{1+Q_4^2}[Q_4 a_{13} + (Q_4-1)a_{33} - a_{23}]^2$	$\frac{1}{2}(\omega_A + \omega_B - \frac{1}{2}K_+ + R_4 - 2\Omega_3)$
10. $4(\mathscr{A})_0 \to 2(\mathscr{A})_{-1}$	$\frac{2}{1+Q_4^2}[Q_4 a_{14} + (Q_4-1)a_{34} - a_{24}]^2$	$\frac{1}{2}(\omega_A + \omega_B - \frac{1}{2}K_+ + R_4 - 2\Omega_4)$
	ℬ Transitions	
11. $1(\mathscr{B})_1 \to 1(\mathscr{B})_0$	$\frac{2(1+Q_1Q_2)^2}{(1+Q_1^2)(1+Q_2^2)}$	$\frac{1}{2}\{\omega_A + \omega_B + R_1 - R_2\}$
12. $1(\mathscr{B})_1 \to 2(\mathscr{B})_0$	$\frac{2(Q_2-Q_1)^2}{(1+Q_1^2)(1+Q_3^2)}$	$\frac{1}{2}\{\omega_A + \omega_B + R_1 + R_2\}$
13. $1(\mathscr{B})_0 \to 2(\mathscr{B})_{-1}$	$\frac{2(1-Q_2Q_3)^2}{(1+Q_2^2)(1+Q_3^2)}$	$\frac{1}{2}\{\omega_A + \omega_B + R_2 + R_3\}$
14. $2(\mathscr{B})_0 \to 2(\mathscr{B})_{-1}$	$\frac{2(Q_2+Q_3)^2}{(1+Q_2^2)(1+Q_3^2)}$	$\frac{1}{2}\{\omega_A + \omega_B - R_2 + R_3\}$

[a] In the limit as all $J_{ij} \to 0$.

(2) $L_- \to -L_-$; (3) $K_- \to -K_-$. Therefore, a given experimental spectrum will, at best, yield $|\delta|$, $|K_\pm|$, $|L_\pm|$, and the sign of K_+ relative to L_+. From this information, one can deduce the magnitudes of the coupling constants and their relative signs. It is not possible, however, to distinguish $J_{AA'}$ from $J_{BB'}$, or $J_{AB'}$ from $J_{A'B'}$. The assignment of these parameters to particular pairs of nuclei in the molecule, and the determination of the sign of δ, requires supplementary information.

The frequencies of the transitions recorded in Table 8.13 have the property that, as all $J_{ij} \to 0$, transitions 4 and 7 approach $3\delta/2$, while the remaining frequencies approach $\delta/2$. Thus the frequencies of all transitions in the table are greater than or less than $\frac{1}{2}(\omega_A + \omega_B)$, accordingly, as $\omega_A > \omega_B$ or $\omega_A < \omega_B$. It should not be concluded, however, that this property persists for nonvanishing values of the coupling constants. In fact, it is not uncommon for "crossovers" to occur.

The assignment of transitions in an observed AA′BB′ spectrum normally commences with the attempt to assign those transitions whose frequencies and intensities are given explicitly in terms of the spectral parameters. The assignment of transitions 1 and 2, together with their images 1′ and 2′, is particularly important. These transitions form an AB type of quartet, except that J is replaced by $J + J'$, so that their assignment yields $|\delta|$ and $|J + J'|$. The assignment may not be obvious, since there will usually be several sets of four resonance frequencies that resemble an AB spectrum. A simple check on the assignment is provided by the relation

$$\text{Int } 1 + \text{Int } 2 = 4.$$

Since the frequency separation of transitions 1 and 2 is independent of the applied field, the assignment may also be checked by experiments at different polarizing field strengths.

The next step in the analysis is the assignment of the $\mathscr{B}$ transitions, from which one obtains $|K_-|$ and $|L_-|$. The assignment of these transitions may be checked by the relations

$$\text{Int } 11 + \text{Int } 12 = 2, \qquad \text{Int } 13 + \text{Int } 14 = 2.$$

The determination of $|K_+|$ and the sign of K_+ relative to L_+ requires an investigation of the transitions involving the $(\mathscr{A})_0$ states. This investigation is usually carried out by "trial-and-error" techniques, using numerical diagonalizations of (3.36). The assignment of these transitions may be checked with the help of the relations

$$\text{Int } 3 + \text{Int } 4 + \text{Int } 5 + \text{Int } 6 = 4(1 + L_+/2R_4),$$
$$\text{Int } 7 + \text{Int } 8 + \text{Int } 9 + \text{Int } 10 = 4(1 - L_+/2R_4).$$

which follow from Table 8.13 by expanding the squares of transitions 3 to 10, and using the orthogonality relations satisfied by the a_{ij}.

The protons in *o*-dichlorobenzene (*17*) provide a good illustration of a well-resolved AA′BB′ spectrum (Fig. 8.6). Only four transitions are unresolved: 4, 4′, 7, 7′. The sign of δ and the assignment of coupling constants were inferred from observed results of related systems (*17*).

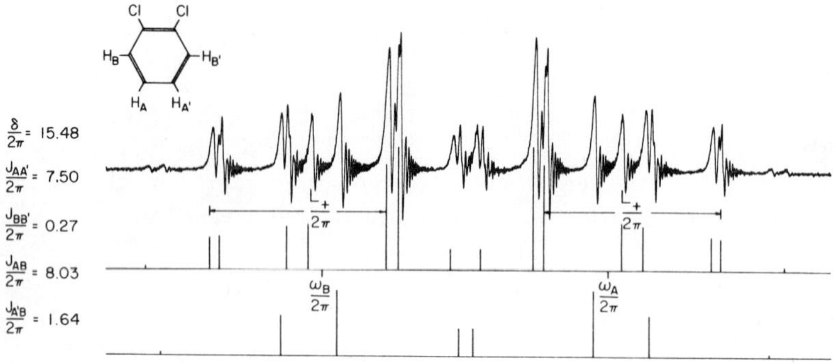

FIG. 8.6. Experimental and theoretical proton magnetic resonance spectra for pure *o*-dichlorobenzene at 60 Mcps.

The discussion of the AA′BB′ system will be concluded with brief descriptions of five special cases for which the eigenvalues and eigenvectors of $\mathscr{H}(0)$ can be readily calculated.

(1) $\delta = 0$. The simplest limiting case occurs when $\delta = 0$. The system is then equivalent to an A_4 system, so that the spectrum consists of a single line at $\omega_A = \omega_B$. The verification that Table 8.13 also yields this result may be easily carried out, upon noting that the secular equation $\det[\mathscr{H}(0) - \lambda I] = 0$ is equivalent to a pair of linear equations and a quadratic equation. On solving these equations, one need only solve linear equations to obtain the a_{ij}. With these results one may apply perturbation theory to calculate the spectrum of the AA′BB′ system in the strong coupling limit ($|J_{AA'}|, |J_{BB'}|, |J_{AB}|, |J_{A'B}| \gg |\delta|$).

(2) $J_{AB} = J_{AB'} = 0$. In this case the eigenvalues of $\mathscr{H}(0)$ are given by the diagonal elements of (3.36), so that $(a_{ij}) = (\delta_{ij})$. The spectrum consists of two lines of equal intensity, one at ω_A, the other at ω_B.

(3) $J_{AA'} = J_{BB'} = J_{A'B} = 0$. In this case, the eigenvalues of (3.36) are $\pm \frac{1}{2}J_{AB}$, $\frac{1}{2}J_{AB} \pm (\delta^2 + J_{AB}^2)^{1/2}$. With these eigenvalues one can determine the eigenvectors of $\mathscr{H}(0)$, and obtain an explicit reduction of Table 8.13. It is much simpler, however, to note that the hamiltonian operator is the sum of the hamiltonian operators for two independent,

but otherwise identical, AB systems. The spectrum will thus have the appearance of an AB quartet.

(4) $J_{AB} = J_{AB'} \neq 0$. When $J_{AB} = J_{AB'}$, $L_- = Q_1 = Q_2 = Q_3 = 0$. Furthermore, $\Omega_4 = \frac{3}{4} K_+$, so that $a_{i4} = a_{4i} = \delta_{i4}$, $i = 1, 2, 3, 4$. From these results it can be shown that the intensities of transitions 6, 10, 12, and 14 vanish, and that Table 8.13 correctly reduces to the A_2B_2 system. Note that transitions 4 and 7 are mixed transitions, and that transitions 11 and 13 have the common resonance frequency $\frac{1}{2}(\omega_A + \omega_B + \delta)$. It will be recalled that the spectrum of an A_2B_2 system depends only upon the absolute magnitudes of J_{AB} and δ.

(5) $|\delta| \to \infty$. An important special case of the AA′BB′ system occurs when $|\delta| \to \infty$, but all coupling constants remain finite (*13*). In this limit,[10] AA′BB′ → AA′XX′, and the proper reduction of Table 8.13 is obtained by replacing B, B′ with X, X′, and allowing $|\delta| \to \infty$. The only $(\mathcal{O})_0$ states mixed by the spin-spin interactions are $3(\mathcal{O})_0$ and $4(\mathcal{O})_0$, so that

$$\Omega_1 = -\omega_A + \omega_X - \tfrac{1}{4}K_+ + \tfrac{1}{2}L_+,$$
$$\Omega_2 = \omega_A - \omega_X - \tfrac{1}{4}K_+ + \tfrac{1}{2}L_+,$$
$$\Omega_3 = \tfrac{1}{4}L_+ - \tfrac{1}{2}R_5,$$
$$\Omega_4 = \tfrac{1}{4}L_+ + \tfrac{1}{2}R_5,$$

where

$$R_5 = (K_+^2 + L_-^2)^{1/2}.$$

The corresponding eigenvectors are

$$1(\mathcal{O})_0, \qquad \frac{1}{(1 + Q_5^2)^{1/2}}\{[3(\mathcal{O})_0] + Q_5[4(\mathcal{O})_0]\},$$

$$2(\mathcal{O})_0, \qquad \frac{1}{(1 + Q_5^2)^{1/2}}\{Q_5[3(\mathcal{O})_0] - [4(\mathcal{O})_0]\},$$

where

$$Q_5 = -\frac{L_-}{K_+ + R_5}.$$

Using these results, one obtains the frequencies and intensities given in Table 8.14. The table shows that the AA′ region of the spectrum generally consists of a symmetrical 10-line spectrum, with ω_A at the center of symmetry. If all 10 lines are resolved, the frequency separation

[10] A more systematic procedure for arriving at the weak-coupling limit in symmetrical systems is described in Section 5.

of transitions 1 and 2, which will be the most intense lines of the spectrum, yields $|L_+| = |J_{AX} + J_{A'X}|$.

If the sign of $J_{XX'}$ is reversed, $K_\pm \to K_\mp$, $Q_5 \to Q_2$, $Q_2 \to Q_5$, $R_5 \to R_2$, and $R_2 \to R_5$. On the other hand, $K_\pm \to K_\mp$, $Q_5 \to -1/Q_2$, $Q_2 \to -1/Q_5$, $R_5 \to R_2$, and $R_2 \to R_5$, if the sign of $J_{AA'}$ is reversed. In either case the spectrum is transformed into itself, so that the remaining lines of the spectrum will, at best, yield $|J_{AA}'|$, $|J_{XX'}|$, and $|L_-| = |J_{AX} - J_{AX'}|$. A comparison of $|L_+|$ and $|L_-|$ then gives the sign of J_{AX} relative to $J_{AX'}$.

In the special case where $L_- = 0$, Table 8.14 correctly reduces to the 1 : 2 : 1 triplet expected for the A region of an A_2X_2 system.

TABLE 8.14

RESONANCE FREQUENCIES AND RELATIVE INTENSITIES FOR THE AA'XX' SYSTEM

Transition[a]	Intensity	Frequency
	$\mathcal{A}$ Transitions	
1. $1(\mathcal{A})_{-1} \to (\mathcal{A})_{-2}$ $1(\mathcal{A})_0 \to 1(\mathcal{A})_{-1}$	4	$\omega_A - \frac{1}{2}L_+$
2. $(\mathcal{A})_2 \to 2(\mathcal{A})_1$ $2(\mathcal{A})_1 \to 2(\mathcal{A})_0$	4	$\omega_A + \frac{1}{2}L_+$
3. $1(\mathcal{A})_1 \to 3(\mathcal{A})_0$	$\frac{2}{1+Q_5^2}$	$\frac{1}{2}\{2\omega_A + K_+ - R_5\}$
4. $1(\mathcal{A})_1 \to 4(\mathcal{A})_0$	$\frac{2Q_5^2}{1+Q_5^2}$	$\frac{1}{2}\{2\omega_A + K_+ + R_5\}$
5. $3(\mathcal{A})_0 \to 2(\mathcal{A})_{-1}$	$\frac{2}{1+Q_5^2}$	$\frac{1}{2}\{2\omega_A - K_+ + R_5\}$
6. $4(\mathcal{A})_0 \to 2(\mathcal{A})_{-1}$	$\frac{2Q_5^2}{1+Q_5^2}$	$\frac{1}{2}\{2\omega_A - K_+ - R_5\}$
7. $1(\mathcal{A})_0 \to 2(\mathcal{A})_{-1}$	0	$\frac{1}{2}\{4\omega_A - 2\omega_X - L_+\}$
8. $1(\mathcal{A})_1 \to 2(\mathcal{A})_0$	0	$\frac{1}{2}\{4\omega_A - 2\omega_X + L_+\}$
	$\mathcal{B}$ Transitions	
9. $1(\mathcal{B})_1 \to 1(\mathcal{B})_0$	$\frac{2}{1+Q_2^2}$	$\frac{1}{2}\{2\omega_A + K_- - R_2\}$
10. $1(\mathcal{B})_1 \to 3(\mathcal{B})_0$	$\frac{2Q_2^2}{1+Q_2^2}$	$\frac{1}{2}\{2\omega_A + K_- + R_2\}$
11. $1(\mathcal{B})_0 \to 2(\mathcal{B})_{-1}$	$\frac{2}{1+Q_2^2}$	$\frac{1}{2}\{2\omega_A - K_- + R_2\}$
12. $2(\mathcal{B})_0 \to 2(\mathcal{B})_{-1}$	$\frac{2Q_2^2}{1+Q_2^2}$	$\frac{1}{2}\{2\omega_A - K_- - R_2\}$

[a] In the limit as all $J_{ij} \to 0$.

4. Systems Containing Symmetrically Equivalent Groups

A. Reduction into Irreducible Components

The theory developed in the preceding sections is strictly applicable only to systems composed of sets of symmetrically equivalent nuclei. However, the extension of the theory to systems containing sets of symmetrically equivalent groups is quite simple.

The first step in the analysis is the decomposition of the system into its irreducible components. The procedure is analogous to that employed in Chapters 5 through 7. Consider, for example, the $A_3A_3'BB'$ system ($\mathscr{C}_2$ symmetry). The irreducible components of this system are $A_{3/2}A'_{3/2}B_{1/2}B'_{1/2}$, $A_{3/2}A'_{1/2}B_{1/2}B'_{1/2}$, $A_{1/2}A'_{3/2}B_{1/2}B'_{1/2}$, $A_{1/2}A'_{1/2}B_{1/2}B'_{1/2}$. These components are schematically indicated in Figure 8.7(a), where the larger circles refer to groups A, A′, the smaller circles to groups B, B′. The numbers within the circles are the total spin quantum numbers; the number within each diagram is the product of the spin multiplicities $g_{I_A}g_{I_A'}g_{I_B}g_{I_B'}$, that is, the number of times each irreducible component appears in the reduction of the system. Diagrams of this type will be called *spin diagrams.*

At this point, the study of the $A_3A_3'BB'$ system is reduced to the study of its four irreducible components. The spectrum of each irreducible component is computed independently of the others, and the results, with appropriately weighted intensities, superposed to give the spectrum of the complete system (cf. Section 4.E, Chapter 5). However, a further simplification results upon noting that, except for notation, the irreducible

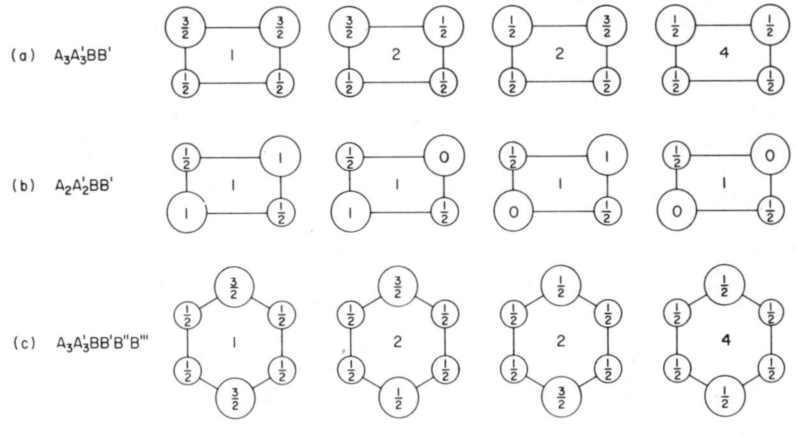

FIG. 8.7. Spin diagrams for (a) the $A_3A_3'BB'$ system; (b) the $A_2A_2'BB'$ system; (c) the $A_3A_3'BB'B''B'''$ system.

components $A_{3/2}A'_{1/2}B_{1/2}B'_{1/2}$ and $A_{1/2}A'_{3/2}B_{1/2}B'_{1/2}$ are equivalent. Indeed, the spin diagrams for these components can be superimposed. The spectra of these irreducible components must be identical, so that only one of these components need be analyzed, provided that an additional factor of 2 is introduced in the intensities. Thus the decomposition of the $A_3A_3'BB'$ system into its nonequivalent irreducible components is given by

$$A_3A_3'BB' = A_{3/2}A'_{3/2}B_{1/2}B'_{1/2} + 4A_{3/2}A'_{1/2}B_{1/2}B'_{1/2} + 4A_{1/2}A'_{1/2}B_{1/2}B'_{1/2} . \quad (4.1)$$

The spin diagrams of the $A_2A_2'BB'$ and $A_3A_3'BB'B''B'''$ systems are also shown in Fig. 8.7. From these diagrams, one obtains the following reductions into nonequivalent irreducible components:

$$A_2A_2'BB' = A_1A_1'B_{1/2}B'_{1/2} + 2A_1A_0'B_{1/2}B'_{1/2} + A_0A_0'B_{1/2}B'_{1/2} , \quad (4.2)$$

$$A_3A_3'BB'B''B''' = A_{3/2}A'_{3/2}B_{1/2}B'_{1/2}B''_{1/2}B'''_{1/2} + 4A_{3/2}A'_{1/2}B_{1/2}B'_{1/2}B''_{1/2}B'''_{1/2}$$
$$+ 4A_{1/2}A'_{1/2}B_{1/2}B'_{1/2}B''_{1/2}B'''_{1/2} . \quad (4.3)$$

The same procedure is used in the reduction of other multispin systems. Thus the reduction of the $A_3A_3'A_3''BB'B''$ system ($\mathscr{D}_3$ symmetry) into its nonequivalent irreducible components is (Fig. 8.8)

$$A_3A_3'A_3''BB'B'' = A_{3/2}A'_{3/2}A''_{3/2}B_{1/2}B'_{1/2}B''_{1/2} + 6A_{3/2}A'_{3/2}A''_{1/2}B_{1/2}B'_{1/2}B''_{1/2}$$
$$+ 12A_{3/2}A'_{1/2}A''_{1/2}B_{1/2}B'_{1/2}B''_{1/2} + 8A_{1/2}A'_{1/2}A''_{1/2}B_{1/2}B'_{1/2}B''_{1/2} . \quad (4.4)$$

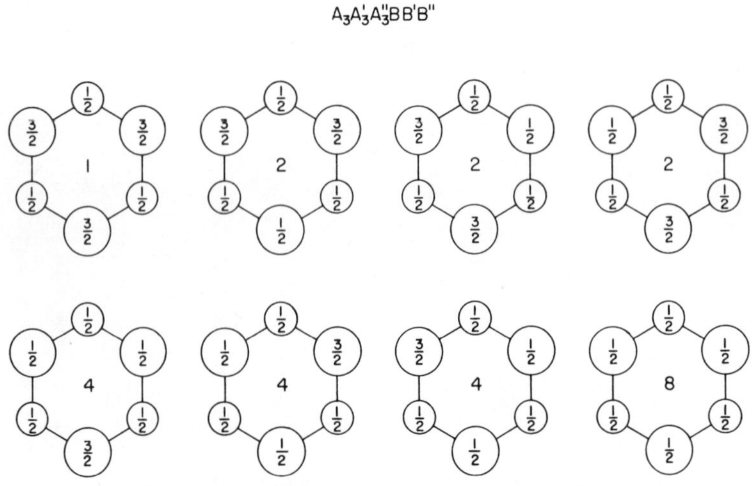

FIG. 8.8. Spin diagrams for the $A_3A_3'A_3''BB'B''$ system.

The intensities of irreducible components may be determined from the general formula derived in Chapter 5 [equation (4.22)]. These intensities may be used to confirm the assignment of experimental resonances to a particular irreducible component, and to calculate the contribution of a given irreducible component to the total intensity. For example, the intensities of the nonequivalent irreducible components of the $A_3A_3'BB'$ system are

$$\text{Int } A_{3/2}A'_{3/2}B_{1/2}B'_{1/2} = 3 \cdot 2^7,$$

$$\text{Int } A_{3/2}A'_{1/2}B_{1/2}B'_{1/2} = 2^7,$$

$$\text{Int } A_{1/2}A'_{1/2}B_{1/2}B'_{1/2} = 2^5.$$

Multiplying each of these intensities by the weighting factors given in (4.1), one obtains

$$\text{Int } A_3A_3'BB' = 3 \cdot 2^7 + 4 \cdot 2^7 + 4 \cdot 2^5 = 2^{10},$$

in agreement with the total-intensity formula [equation (4.26), Chapter 5] for a system of eight spin -$\frac{1}{2}$nuclei. It follows that the fractional contributions of $A_{3/2}A'_{3/2}B_{1/2}B'_{1/2}$, $A_{3/2}A'_{1/2}B_{1/2}B'_{1/2}$, and $A_{1/2}A'_{1/2}B_{1/2}B'_{1/2}$ to the total intensity are $\frac{3}{8}$, $\frac{1}{2}$, and $\frac{1}{8}$, respectively.

B. Symmetry Groups of Irreducible Components

In the reduction of a system containing symmetrically equivalent groups, the relative disposition of the groups in the molecule is unchanged—only the total spin quantum numbers are changed. It follows that the symmetry group of any irreducible component must be a proper or improper subgroup of the symmetry group of the spin system. The symmetry groups for the irreducible components of the systems illustrated in Figs. 8.7 and 8.8 are given in Table 8.15.

To illustrate the procedure to be followed in the study of systems containing symmetrically equivalent groups, consider again the $A_3A_3'BB'$ system. The $A_{3/2}A'_{3/2}B_{1/2}B'_{1/2}$ component has $\mathscr{C}_2$ symmetry, and the product basis generates a 64-dimensional representation of $\mathscr{C}_2$. A symmetrized basis for this irreducible component may be obtained by applying $P_{\mathscr{A}}$ and $P_{\mathscr{B}}$ to the elements of the product basis, or by forming the 64 products of vectors in Table 8.5 and 8.7, using the rules given in Section 3.D to determine the symmetry species of the products. By either method, one finds that the symmetrized basis contains 36 vectors with $\mathscr{A}$ symmetry, and 28 vectors with $\mathscr{B}$ symmetry. The $\mathscr{A}$ block of the hamiltonian matrix breaks up into nine submatrices of dimensions

TABLE 8.15

SYMMETRY GROUPS OF THE IRREDUCIBLE COMPONENTS OF SOME MULTISPIN SYSTEMS

Spin system	Symmetry groups of nonequivalent irreducible components
$A_2A_2'BB'$	$\mathscr{C}_2(A_1A_1'B_{1/2}B'_{1/2}, A_0A_0'B_{1/2}B'_{1/2})$; $\mathscr{C}_1(A_1A_0'B_{1/2}B'_{1/2})$
$A_3A_3'BB'$	$\mathscr{C}_2(A_{3/2}A'_{3/2}B_{1/2}B'_{1/2}, A_{1/2}A'_{1/2}B_{1/2}B'_{1/2})$; $\mathscr{C}_1(A_{3/2}A'_{1/2}B_{1/2}B'_{1/2})$
$A_3A_3'BB'B''B'''$	$\mathscr{D}_2(A_{3/2}A'_{3/2}B_{1/2}B'_{1/2}B''_{1/2}B'''_{1/2}, A_{1/2}A'_{1/2}B_{1/2}B'_{1/2}B''_{1/2}B'''_{1/2})$; $\mathscr{C}_2(A_{3/2}A'_{1/2}B_{1/2}B'_{1/2}B''_{1/2}B'''_{1/2})$
$A_3A_3'A_3''BB'B''$	$\mathscr{D}_3(A_{3/2}A'_{3/2}A''_{3/2}B_{1/2}B'_{1/2}B''_{1/2}, A_{1/2}A'_{1/2}A''_{1/2}B_{1/2}B'_{1/2}B''_{1/2})$; $\mathscr{C}_2(A_{3/2}A'_{1/2}A''_{1/2}B_{1/2}B'_{1/2}B''_{1/2}, A_{3/2}A'_{3/2}A''_{1/2}B_{1/2}B'_{1/2}B''_{1/2})$

1, 2, 5, 6, 8, 5, 6, 2, 1, corresponding to $m = 4, 3, 2, 1, 0, -1, -2, -3, -4$. The $\mathscr{B}$ block of $\mathscr{H}$ decomposes into seven submatrices of dimensions 2, 3, 6, 6, 6, 3, 2, corresponding to $m = 3, 2, 1, 0, -1, -2, -3$.

The $A_{3/2}A'_{1/2}B_{1/2}B'_{1/2}$ component has $\mathscr{C}_1$ symmetry, that is, the symmetry group of this component consists of the identity alone. For this reason, there is no need to symmetrize the initial basis; the product basis is quite acceptable. The hamiltonian matrix for this irreducible component decomposes into seven submatrices of dimensions, 1, 4, 7, 8, 7, 4, 1, corresponding to $m = 3, 2, 1, 0, -1, -2, -3$. Of course, in setting up the hamiltonian matrix for the $A_{3/2}A'_{1/2}B_{1/2}B'_{1/2}$ component, one employs the symmetry conditions $\omega_A = \omega_{A'}$, $\omega_B = \omega_{B'}$, etc.

The $A_{1/2}A'_{1/2}B_{1/2}B'_{1/2}$ component ($\mathscr{C}_2$ symmetry) is equivalent to the AA'BB' system, which has already been discussed.

5. The X Approximation for Symmetrical Systems

A. Zero-Order Bases

The weak-coupling or X approximation discussed in Section 2 of Chapter 7 is frequently applicable to symmetrical spin systems. It will be recalled that the significance of this approximation is that it leads to additional (approximate) constants of the motion—specifically the z components of the angular momenta of certain collections of nuclei.

This implies that the interactions coupling any two of these collections may be treated by first-order perturbation theory.

The simplest procedure for taking advantage of the additional constants of the motion is to decompose the spin system into symmetrical subsystems defined by inequalities analogous to (2.4) of Chapter 7. The *zero-order* hamiltonian operator for the composite system is obtained by adding the hamiltonian operators of the several subsystems. Consider, for example, the hydrogen and fluorine nuclei in 1,1-difluoroethylene (*13*), 1, 3, 5-trifluorobenzene (*14*, *19*), and *p*-difluorobenzene (*20*):

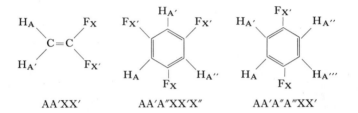

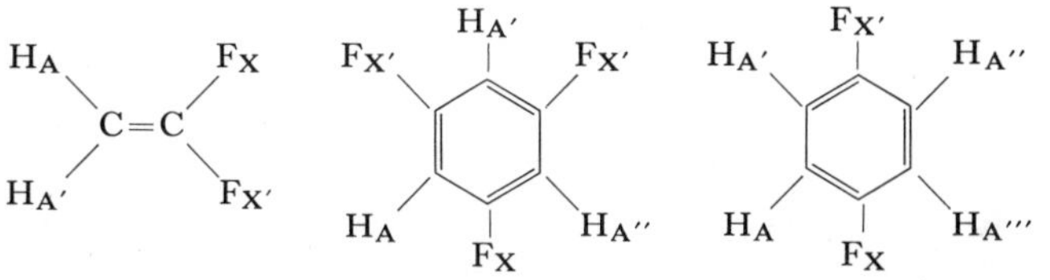

AA′XX′ AA′A″XX′X″ AA′A″A‴XX′

Each of these systems contains two subsystems, the AA′ ··· nuclei and the XX′ ··· nuclei. The hamiltonian operators for the AA′ ··· subsystems are

$$\mathscr{H}(\mathrm{AA'}) = -\{\omega_\mathrm{A}(I_{\mathrm{A}z} + I_{\mathrm{A'}z}) + J_{\mathrm{AA'}}\mathbf{I}_\mathrm{A} \cdot \mathbf{I}_{\mathrm{A'}}\}, \tag{5.1}$$

$$\begin{aligned}\mathscr{H}(\mathrm{AA'A''}) = -\{&\omega_\mathrm{A}(I_{\mathrm{A}z} + I_{\mathrm{A'}z} + I_{\mathrm{A''}z}) \\ &+ J_{\mathrm{AA'}}(\mathbf{I}_\mathrm{A} \cdot \mathbf{I}_{\mathrm{A'}} + \mathbf{I}_\mathrm{A} \cdot \mathbf{I}_{\mathrm{A''}} + \mathbf{I}_{\mathrm{A'}} \cdot \mathbf{I}_{\mathrm{A''}})\},\end{aligned} \tag{5.2}$$

$$\begin{aligned}\mathscr{H}(\mathrm{AA'A''A'''}) = -\{&\omega_\mathrm{A}(I_{\mathrm{A}z} + I_{\mathrm{A'}z} + I_{\mathrm{A''}z} + I_{\mathrm{A'''}z}) \\ &+ J_{\mathrm{AA'}}(\mathbf{I}_\mathrm{A} \cdot \mathbf{I}_{\mathrm{A'}} + \mathbf{I}_{\mathrm{A''}} \cdot \mathbf{I}_{\mathrm{A'''}}) + J_{\mathrm{AA''}}(\mathbf{I}_\mathrm{A} \cdot \mathbf{I}_{\mathrm{A''}} + \mathbf{I}_{\mathrm{A'}} \cdot \mathbf{I}_{\mathrm{A'''}}) \\ &+ J_{\mathrm{AA'''}}(\mathbf{I}_\mathrm{A} \cdot \mathbf{I}_{\mathrm{A'''}} + \mathbf{I}_{\mathrm{A'}} \cdot \mathbf{I}_{\mathrm{A''}})\}.\end{aligned} \tag{5.3}$$

These operators, together with the operators obtained from (5.1) and (5.2) by trivial literal substitutions, yield the following zero-order hamiltonian operators of the composite spin systems:

$$\mathscr{H}^{(0)}(\mathrm{AA'XX'}) = \mathscr{H}(\mathrm{AA'}) + \mathscr{H}(\mathrm{XX'}), \tag{5.4}$$

$$\mathscr{H}^{(0)}(\mathrm{AA'A''XX'X''}) = \mathscr{H}(\mathrm{AA'A''}) + \mathscr{H}(\mathrm{XX'X''}), \tag{5.5}$$

$$\mathscr{H}^{(0)}(\mathrm{AA'A''A'''XX'}) = \mathscr{H}(\mathrm{AA'A''A'''}) + \mathscr{H}(\mathrm{XX'}). \tag{5.6}$$

The complete hamiltonian operators are obtained by adding the appropriate first-order interactions to the right-hand members:

$$V^{(1)}(\mathrm{AA'XX'}) = -\{J_{\mathrm{AX}}(I_{\mathrm{A}z}I_{\mathrm{X}z} + I_{\mathrm{A}'z}I_{\mathrm{X}'z}) + J_{\mathrm{AX}'}(I_{\mathrm{A}z}I_{\mathrm{X}'z} + I_{\mathrm{A}'z}I_{\mathrm{X}z})\}, \tag{5.7}$$

$$\begin{aligned} V^{(1)}(\mathrm{AA'A''XX'X''}) = -\{&J_{\mathrm{AX}}[I_{\mathrm{A}z}(I_{\mathrm{X}z} + I_{\mathrm{X}'z}) + I_{\mathrm{A}'z}(I_{\mathrm{X}'z} + I_{\mathrm{X}''z}) \\ &+ I_{\mathrm{A}''z}(I_{\mathrm{X}z} + I_{\mathrm{X}''z})] + J_{\mathrm{A'X}}(I_{\mathrm{A}'z}I_{\mathrm{X}z} + I_{\mathrm{A}''z}I_{\mathrm{X}'z} \\ &+ I_{\mathrm{A}z}I_{\mathrm{X}''z})\}, \end{aligned} \tag{5.8}$$

$$\begin{aligned} V^{(1)}(\mathrm{AA'A''A'''XX'}) = -\{&J_{\mathrm{AX}}[I_{\mathrm{X}z}(I_{\mathrm{A}z} + I_{\mathrm{A}'''z}) + I_{\mathrm{X}'z}(I_{\mathrm{A}'z} + I_{\mathrm{A}''z})] \\ &+ J_{\mathrm{AX}'}[I_{\mathrm{X}z}(I_{\mathrm{A}'z} + I_{\mathrm{A}''z}) + I_{\mathrm{X}'z}(I_{\mathrm{A}z} + I_{\mathrm{A}'''z})]\}. \end{aligned} \tag{5.9}$$

In the preceding examples, the spin systems contained two subsystems with $n_{\mathrm{A}} = n_{\mathrm{X}} = 1$. If the spin system contains subsystems with $n_{\mathrm{A}}, n_{\mathrm{X}} > 1$, one first carries out a decomposition of the complete system into its irreducible components, and then a subsequent decomposition of the hamiltonian operator for each irreducible component into zero- and first-order terms, as indicated above. The following discussion will be limited to AA′ ··· XX′ ··· systems, but may be extended to include the irreducible components of more complex systems. To facilitate the discussion, it will be convenient to introduce an abbreviated notation.

The AA′ ··· subsystem is a symmetrical system, equivalent to an A_N system. Therefore, any element of a symmetrized basis for this subsystem may be labeled with the total spin quantum number $I(\mathrm{AA}' \cdots)$, the z component of angular momentum $m_{\mathrm{AA}'\cdots}$, the eigenvalue of $\mathscr{H}(\mathrm{AA}' \cdots)$, the symmetry species $\mathscr{S}$, and any additional labels required to distinguish linearly independent basis vectors. The use of all such labels to denote a generic basis vector would result in a very cumbersome notation. For this reason an arbitrary basis vector will be denoted $|\,\mathrm{A}\rangle$, if the symmetry species need not be specified, or $|\,\mathscr{S}\rangle$, if it becomes necessary to specify the symmetry species explicitly. All other labels will be omitted. Similar conventions will be adopted for the XX′ ··· nuclei. Furthermore, the notation for the hamiltonian operators of the two subsystems will be condensed to $\mathscr{H}_{\mathrm{A}}$ and $\mathscr{H}_{\mathrm{X}}$. The zero-order hamiltonian for the composite system and the first-order interactions coupling the subsystems will be denoted $\mathscr{H}^{(0)}$ and $V^{(1)}$, respectively, so that

$$\mathscr{H}^{(0)} = \mathscr{H}_{\mathrm{A}} + \mathscr{H}_{\mathrm{X}}, \tag{5.10}$$

$$\mathscr{H} = \mathscr{H}^{(0)} + V^{(1)}, \tag{5.11}$$

where $\mathscr{H}$ is the stationary hamiltonian for the composite system in the weak-coupling limit.

A zero-order basis for the AA′ ··· XX′ ··· system is easily constructed: it consists of the set of all products $\{| A\rangle | X\rangle\}$. Although the vectors $| A\rangle$ and $| X\rangle$ are, in general, linear combinations of product kets, the set $\{| A\rangle | X\rangle\}$ will be called the *product basis*. The elements of the product basis for the AA′XX′ system are given in Table 8.11. Tables 8.5, 8.8, and 8.9 may be used to construct product bases for the AA′A″A‴XX′ and AA′A″XX′X″ systems.

The advantage of the product basis is that the new constants of the motion are systematically taken into account. Every element of the product basis is an eigenvector of I_z(AA′ ···) and I_z(XX′ ···). However, three group-theoretical questions remain: (1) What is the symmetry group of the zero-order hamiltonian? (2) What realization of the symmetry group of the complete hamiltonian operator is consistent with the preceding formulation of the weak-coupling approximation? (3) What are the symmetry species of the products[11] $| \mathscr{S}\rangle | \mathscr{S}'\rangle$? These questions will be investigated in Sections 5.B and 5.C.

In the special case of a system containing invariant groups, the symmetry species of any element of the product basis is determined by the symmetry species of those vectors not contained in invariant groups. The AA′BB′X_{n_X} system provides an illustration of this point. The basis vectors for the AA′BB′ system (Table 8.10) have $\mathscr{A}$ or $\mathscr{B}$ symmetry. Since the X group is invariant, the symmetry species of the product $| \text{AA'BB'}\rangle | I_X, m_X\rangle$ is given by the symmetry species of $| \text{AA'BB'}\rangle$. This observation, together with the results already derived for the AA′BB′ system, may be used to deduce the spectrum of the AA′BB′X_{n_X} system in a form similar to that of Table 8.13. The concept of effective chemical shifts (Section 2, Chapter 5) is applicable to AA′BB′X_{n_X} systems, and may be helpful in the analysis of experimental spectra. The treatment of systems such as AA′XX′P_{n_P}, where the symmetry species of $| A\rangle | X\rangle | I_P, m_P\rangle$ depends upon the first two factors, can be inferred from the results of the following sections.

B. Direct Product Groups

Let $\mathscr{G} = \{a, b, c, ...\}$ be a finite group of order g, $\mathscr{G}' = \{a', b', c', ...\}$ a finite group of order g', and consider the set of Kronecker products

[11] Note that the lexicographical ordering of the elements of the product basis precludes any ambiguities in products of the form $| \mathscr{S}\rangle | \mathscr{S}'\rangle$.

(cf. Chapter 4) $\mathscr{G} \otimes \mathscr{G}' = \{a \otimes a',\ a \otimes b',\ \ldots,\ b \otimes a',\ b \otimes b', \ldots\}$. If multiplication of the elements in $\mathscr{G} \otimes \mathscr{G}'$ is defined by

$$(x \otimes x')(y \otimes y') = xy \otimes x'y', \tag{5.12}$$

then $\mathscr{G} \otimes \mathscr{G}'$ is a group of order gg' called the *direct product* of $\mathscr{G}$ and $\mathscr{G}'$. The proof of this statement requires a verification of the group axioms.

(1) Since xy and $x'y'$ are elements of $\mathscr{G}$ and $\mathscr{G}'$, respectively, $xy \otimes x'y'$ is, by definition, an element of $\mathscr{G} \otimes \mathscr{G}'$. Thus $\mathscr{G} \otimes \mathscr{G}'$ contains the product of $(x \otimes x')$ and $(y \otimes y')$, whenever it contains $x \otimes x'$ and $y \otimes y'$.

(2) Multiplication of the elements in $\mathscr{G} \otimes \mathscr{G}'$ is associative, since, by (5.12),

$$[(x \otimes x')(y \otimes y')](z \otimes z') = (xy \otimes x'y')(z \otimes z') = (xy)z \otimes (x'y')z',$$

$$(x \otimes x')[(y \otimes y')(z \otimes z')] = (x \otimes x')(yz \otimes y'z') = x(yz) \otimes x'(y'z').$$

These expansions are equal, since the elements of $\mathscr{G}$ and $\mathscr{G}'$ obey the associative law of multiplication:

$$x(yz) = (xy)z, \qquad x'(y'z') = (x'y')z'.$$

(3) The identity of $\mathscr{G} \otimes \mathscr{G}'$ is $e \otimes e'$, the Kronecker product of the identities of $\mathscr{G}$ and $\mathscr{G}'$. For if $x \otimes x'$ is any element in $\mathscr{G} \otimes \mathscr{G}'$, then

$$(e \otimes e')(x \otimes x') = (ex \otimes e'x') = x \otimes x',$$

$$(x \otimes x')(e \otimes e') = xe \otimes x'e' = x \otimes x'.$$

(4) If $x \otimes x'$ is any element of $\mathscr{G} \otimes \mathscr{G}'$, the inverse element is also in $\mathscr{G} \otimes \mathscr{G}'$. Indeed, the inverse element is $(x \otimes x')^{-1} = x^{-1} \otimes x'^{-1}$, since

$$(x \otimes x')(x^{-1} \otimes x'^{-1}) = xx^{-1} \otimes x'x'^{-1} = e \otimes e',$$

$$(x^{-1} \otimes x'^{-1})(x \otimes x') = x^{-1}x \otimes x'^{-1}x' = e \otimes e'.$$

The direct product of two groups is often denoted $\mathscr{G} \times \mathscr{G}'$, rather than $\mathscr{G} \otimes \mathscr{G}'$. The latter notation has been used here, since the multiplication rule (5.12) is formally identical to the operator product of two Kronecker products, defined in Chapter 2. The ordering conventions adopted for Kronecker products will also be used here. Thus, in any product $a \otimes a'$, the first factor will be an element of the first group, the second factor an element of the second group.

If $\mathscr{G} \otimes \mathscr{G}'$ is the direct product of $\mathscr{G}$ and $\mathscr{G}'$, the set of all elements of the form $\{a \otimes e', b \otimes e', \ldots\}$ is a subgroup of order g. The one-to-one correspondence $a \leftrightarrow a \otimes e'$, $b \leftrightarrow b \otimes e'$, ..., shows that $\{a \otimes e', b \otimes e', ...\}$ is isomorphic to $\mathscr{G}$. Similarly, the set of all elements of the form $\{e \otimes a', e \otimes b', ...\}$ is a subgroup of $\mathscr{G} \otimes \mathscr{G}'$ isomorphic to $\mathscr{G}'$. If $\mathscr{G} = \mathscr{G}'$, the set of elements $\{a \otimes a, b \otimes b, ...\}$ provides another subgroup isomorphic to $\mathscr{G}$.

The significance of direct product groups in the study of systems conforming to the weak-coupling approximation is that the symmetry group of the zero-order hamiltonian (5.10) is the direct product of the symmetry groups of $\mathscr{H}_{\mathrm{A}}$ and $\mathscr{H}_{\mathrm{X}}$. To prove this theorem, it must be recalled that the right-hand members of (5.10) are abbreviations for $\mathscr{H}_{\mathrm{A}} \otimes 1_{\mathrm{X}}$ and $1_{\mathrm{A}} \otimes \mathscr{H}_{\mathrm{X}}$, where 1_{A} and 1_{X} are identity operators for the AA′ ⋯ and XX′ ⋯ subsystems. Now let $\mathscr{G}$ and $\mathscr{G}'$ denote the symmetry groups of $\mathscr{H}_{\mathrm{A}}$ and $\mathscr{H}_{\mathrm{X}}$, $\mathscr{G} \otimes \mathscr{G}'$ their direct product. If Q is in $\mathscr{G}$, and R is in $\mathscr{G}'$, then $Q \otimes R$ is in $\mathscr{G} \otimes \mathscr{G}'$, so that

$$Q \otimes R\mathscr{H}^{(0)}Q^{-1} \otimes R^{-1} = Q\mathscr{H}_{\mathrm{A}}Q^{-1} \otimes R1_{\mathrm{X}}R^{-1} + Q1_{\mathrm{A}}Q^{-1} \otimes R\mathscr{H}_{\mathrm{X}}R^{-1}$$
$$= \mathscr{H}_{\mathrm{A}} \otimes 1_{\mathrm{X}} + 1_{\mathrm{A}} \otimes \mathscr{H}_{\mathrm{X}} = \mathscr{H}^{(0)},$$

since $Q\mathscr{H}_{\mathrm{A}}Q^{-1} = \mathscr{H}_{\mathrm{A}}$, $R\mathscr{H}_{\mathrm{X}}R^{-1} = \mathscr{H}_{\mathrm{X}}$. This proves that $\mathscr{H}^{(0)}$ is invariant under a similarity transformation with any element of $\mathscr{G} \otimes \mathscr{G}'$. In other words, every element in $\mathscr{G} \otimes \mathscr{G}'$ is contained in the symmetry group of $\mathscr{H}^{(0)}$.

Consider now a generic element in the symmetry group of $\mathscr{H}^{(0)}$. This element, by virtue of the manner in which $\mathscr{H}^{(0)}$ was constructed, can be written in the form $S \otimes T$, where $\dim S = \dim \mathscr{H}_{\mathrm{A}}$ and $\dim T = \dim \mathscr{H}_{\mathrm{X}}$. Note that S and T are not required to be elements of $\mathscr{G}$ and $\mathscr{G}'$, respectively. By definition,

$$S \otimes T\mathscr{H}^{(0)}S^{-1} \otimes T^{-1} = \mathscr{H}^{(0)} = S\mathscr{H}_{\mathrm{A}}S^{-1} \otimes 1_{\mathrm{X}} + 1_{\mathrm{A}} \otimes T\mathscr{H}_{\mathrm{X}}T^{-1}.$$

Subtracting this result from (5.10), one obtains

$$[S\mathscr{H}_{\mathrm{A}}S^{-1} - \mathscr{H}_{\mathrm{A}}] \otimes 1_{\mathrm{X}} + 1_{\mathrm{A}} \otimes [T\mathscr{H}_{\mathrm{X}}T^{-1} - \mathscr{H}_{\mathrm{X}}] = 0,$$

so that $S\mathscr{H}_{\mathrm{A}}S^{-1} = \mathscr{H}_{\mathrm{A}}$ and $T\mathscr{H}_{\mathrm{X}}T^{-1} = \mathscr{H}_{\mathrm{X}}$. It follows that S is in $\mathscr{G}$, and T is in $\mathscr{G}'$, so that $S \otimes T$ is in $\mathscr{G} \otimes \mathscr{G}'$. This shows that every element in the symmetry group of $\mathscr{H}^{(0)}$ is in $\mathscr{G} \otimes \mathscr{G}'$, and completes the proof.

The preceding theorem shows that the symmetry groups of (5.4), (5.5), and (5.6) are $\mathscr{C}_2 \otimes \mathscr{C}_2$, $\mathscr{D}_2 \otimes \mathscr{C}_2$, and $\mathscr{D}_3 \otimes \mathscr{D}_3$, respectively. It must not be concluded, however, that these groups are the symmetry groups of the complete hamiltonian operators. If $\mathscr{G} \otimes \mathscr{G}'$ is the symmetry group of $\mathscr{H}^{(0)}$, the symmetry group of $\mathscr{H}$ consists of those elements $R \otimes S$ in $\mathscr{G} \otimes \mathscr{G}'$ for which

$$Q \otimes RV^{(1)}Q^{-1} \otimes R^{-1} = V^{(1)}. \tag{5.13}$$

Therefore, the symmetry group of the complete hamiltonian is a subgroup of $\mathscr{G} \otimes \mathscr{G}'$.

To illustrate this result, consider the AA′XX′ system. The symmetry group of the zero-order hamiltonian is $\mathscr{C}_2 \otimes \mathscr{C}_2 = \{E \otimes E, E \otimes C_2, C_2 \otimes E, C_2 \otimes C_2\}$, where the first factor in each element of $\mathscr{C}_2 \otimes \mathscr{C}_2$ refers to the AA′ nuclei, the second factor to the XX′ nuclei. It is easily verified that, with $V^{(1)}$ given by (5.7), the only elements of $\mathscr{C}_2 \otimes \mathscr{C}_2$ satisfying (5.13) are $E \otimes E$ and $C_2 \otimes C_2$. These elements form a subgroup of $\mathscr{C}_2 \otimes \mathscr{C}_2$, which is an isomorphic image of $\mathscr{C}_2 = \{E, C_2\}$, the symmetry group of the composite spin system. The isomorphism is given by

$$E \leftrightarrow E \otimes E, \qquad C_2 \leftrightarrow C_2 \otimes C_2 . \tag{5.14}$$

In general, the symmetry group of the complete hamiltonian will be an isomorphic image of the symmetry group of the nuclear configuration, realized as a subgroup of the direct product of the symmetry groups of the component subsystems. Care must be taken, however, to verify that the elements of the subgroup satisfy (5.13), since the requirement that the correct subgroup be an isomorphic image of the symmetry group of $\mathscr{H}$ is only a necessary condition. For example, the subgroups $\{E \otimes E, E \otimes C_2\}$ and $\{E \otimes E, C_2 \otimes E\}$ are isomorphic to $\mathscr{C}_2$, but neither $E \otimes C_2$ nor $C_2 \otimes E$ satisfy (5.13) in the case of an AA′XX′ system.

From the foregoing remarks, it is not difficult to show that, for the AA′A″A‴XX′ and AA′A″XX′X″ systems, the correct realizations of $\mathscr{D}_2$ and $\mathscr{D}_3$ as subgroups of $\mathscr{D}_2 \otimes \mathscr{C}_2$ and $\mathscr{D}_3 \otimes \mathscr{D}_3$ are

$$\mathscr{D}_2 = \{E \otimes E, C_2 \otimes C_2, C_2' \otimes E, C_2'' \otimes C_2\},$$

$$\mathscr{D}_3 = \{E \otimes E, C_3 \otimes C_3, C_3^2 \otimes C_3, C_2 \otimes C_2, C_2' \otimes C_2', C_2'' \otimes C_2\}.$$

The isomorphisms between the elements of these groups and those of Tables 8.1 and 8.2 are explicitly given by

$$\mathscr{D}_2: \quad E \leftrightarrow E \otimes E, \quad C_2 \leftrightarrow C_2 \otimes C_2, \quad C_2' \leftrightarrow C_2' \otimes E, \quad C_2'' \leftrightarrow C_2'' \otimes C_2, \tag{5.15}$$

$$\begin{aligned}\mathscr{D}_3: \quad & E \leftrightarrow E \otimes E, \quad C_3 \leftrightarrow C_3 \otimes C_3, \quad C_3^2 \leftrightarrow C_3^2 \otimes C_3^2, \\ & C_2 \leftrightarrow C_2 \otimes C_2, \quad C_2' \leftrightarrow C_2' \otimes C_2', \quad C_2'' \leftrightarrow C_2'' \otimes C_2'' .\end{aligned} \tag{5.16}$$

In general, if $\mathscr{G} = \mathscr{G}'$, the symmetry group of the hamiltonian operator will consist of all elements of the form $E \otimes E$, $R \otimes R$, $S \otimes S$, ...

C. Decomposition of the Hamiltonian Matrix

From the theory developed in Section 3, and the isomorphisms (5.14) through (5.16), it follows that the symmetry constants of the motion (projection operators) for the AA′XX′, AA′A″A‴XX′, and AA′A″XX′X″ systems are[12]

$$\mathscr{C}_2: \quad \begin{aligned} P_{\mathscr{A}}(\otimes) &= \tfrac{1}{2}\{E \otimes E + C_2 \otimes C_2\}, \\ P_{\mathscr{B}}(\otimes) &= \tfrac{1}{2}\{E \otimes E - C_2 \otimes C_2\}; \end{aligned} \tag{5.17}$$

$$\mathscr{D}_2: \quad \begin{aligned} P_{\mathscr{A}_1}(\otimes) &= \tfrac{1}{4}\{E \otimes E + C_2 \otimes C_2 + C_2' \otimes E + C_2'' \otimes C_2\}, \\ P_{\mathscr{B}_1}(\otimes) &= \tfrac{1}{4}\{E \otimes E + C_2 \otimes C_2 - C_2' \otimes E - C_2'' \otimes C_2\}, \\ P_{\mathscr{B}_2}(\otimes) &= \tfrac{1}{4}\{E \otimes E - C_2 \otimes C_2 + C_2' \otimes E - C_2'' \otimes C_2\}, \\ P_{\mathscr{B}_3}(\otimes) &= \tfrac{1}{4}\{E \otimes E - C_2 \otimes C_2 - C_2' \otimes E + C_2'' \otimes C_2\}; \end{aligned} \tag{5.18}$$

$$\mathscr{D}_3: \quad \begin{aligned} P_{\mathscr{A}_1}(\otimes) &= \tfrac{1}{6}\{E \otimes E + C_3 \otimes C_3 + C_3^2 \otimes C_3^2 \\ &\qquad + C_2 \otimes C_2 + C_2' \otimes C_2' + C_2'' \otimes C_2''\}, \\ P_{\mathscr{A}_2}(\otimes) &= \tfrac{1}{6}\{E \otimes E + C_3 \otimes C_3 + C_3^2 \otimes C_3^2 \\ &\qquad - C_2 \otimes C_2 - C_2' \otimes C_2' - C_2'' \otimes C_2''\}, \\ P_{\mathscr{E}}(\otimes) &= \tfrac{1}{3}\{E \otimes E - \tfrac{1}{2}(C_3 \otimes C_3 + C_3^2 \otimes C_3^2) \\ &\qquad + \tfrac{1}{2}(C_2 \otimes C_2 - 2C_2' \otimes C_2' + C_2'' \otimes C_2'')\}, \\ P_{\mathscr{E}}'(\otimes) &= \tfrac{1}{3}\{E \otimes E - \tfrac{1}{2}(C_3 \otimes C_3 + C_3^2 \otimes C_3^2) \\ &\qquad - \tfrac{1}{2}(C_2 \otimes C_2 - 2C_2' \otimes C_2' + C_2'' \otimes C_2'')\}. \end{aligned} \tag{5.19}$$

Although these operators were constructed with the AA′XX′, AA′A″A‴XX′, and AA′A″XX′X″ systems as models, they apply also to irreducible components such as $A_{I_A}A'_{I_A}X_{I_X}X'_{I_X}$.

[12] The symbol $\otimes$ has been introduced into the left-hand members of these equations to indicate that the projection operators are constructed from realizations of the appropriate symmetry groups as subgroups of direct product groups.

The projection operators for a given system decompose the spin space into disjoint subspaces. This decomposition is independent of any assumptions concerning the spin-spin interactions, so that the description of the direct sum decomposition of the hamiltonian matrix given in Section 3 also applies to the present discussion. In the weak-coupling approximation $I_z(AA' \cdots)$ and $I_z(XX' \cdots)$, more precisely $I_z(AA' \cdots) \otimes 1_X$ and $1_A \otimes I_z(XX' \cdots)$, commute with each other and $\mathscr{H}$. Furthermore, the structure of (5.17) through (5.19) shows that $I_z(AA' \cdots)$, $I_z(XX' \cdots)$, and $\mathscr{H}$ also commute with the projection operators derived from the appropriate symmetry groups. This reveals the particular advantage of the preceding formulation of the weak-coupling approximation for symmetrical systems—all nontrivial constants of the motion are explicitly taken into account.

The construction of symmetrized bases for AA′ ⋯ XX′ ⋯ systems may be carried out according to the general prescription described in Section 3. However, the calculations can often be expedited by the rules for representation multiplication, and will be illustrated for some particular AA′ ⋯ XX′ ⋯ systems.

1. *The* AA′XX′ *System*. Table 8.5 gives a set of symmetrized vectors that constitute a basis for the space of the AA′ subsystem. In the construction of this basis, it was shown that tr $E = 4$, tr $C_2 = 2$. Since the trace is a matrix invariant, these relations also hold for the matrices of E and C_2 defined by the vectors of Table 8.5.

The vectors of Table 8.5 may also be used as a symmetrized basis for the XX′ nuclei, so that tr $E = 4$, tr $C_2 = 2$, when E and C_2 refer to the XX′ nuclei. From these results one can calculate the ranks of $P_{\mathscr{A}}(\otimes)$ and $P_{\mathscr{B}}(\otimes)$ relative to the product basis $\{|A\rangle|X\rangle\}$:

$$\text{tr}\, P_{\mathscr{A}}(\otimes) = \tfrac{1}{2}\{4 \cdot 4 + 2 \cdot 2\} = 10, \qquad \text{tr}\, P_{\mathscr{B}}(\otimes) = \tfrac{1}{2}\{4 \cdot 4 - 2 \cdot 2\} = 6,$$

since $\text{tr}\, R \otimes S = \text{tr}\, R\, \text{tr}\, S$. It follows that $P_{\mathscr{A}}(\otimes)$ and $P_{\mathscr{B}}(\otimes)$ will decompose the 16-dimensional spin space into disjoint subspaces of dimensions 10 and 6, in agreement with the results previously obtained for the AA′BB′ system.

The only remaining problem is the determination of the symmetry species of the products $|A\rangle|X\rangle$. One can formally construct 10 linearly independent vectors with $\mathscr{A}$ symmetry, and six linearly independent vectors with $\mathscr{B}$ symmetry by applying $P_{\mathscr{A}}(\otimes)$ and $P_{\mathscr{B}}(\otimes)$ to all elements of $\{|A\rangle|X\rangle\}$. In the present case, the following procedure is preferable.

The elements of $\{|A\rangle\}$ are all of the form $P_{\mathscr{A}}\Phi$, $P_{\mathscr{B}}\Phi'$, where $P_{\mathscr{A}}$ and $P_{\mathscr{B}}$ are given by (3.17) and Φ, Φ' are appropriate product kets. Similarly, the elements of $\{|\,\mathrm{X}\rangle\}$ are of the form $P_{\mathcal{A}}\Psi$, $P_{\mathcal{B}}\Psi'$. Thus there are four types of products in the basis $\{|\,\mathrm{A}\rangle|\,\mathrm{X}\rangle\}$:

$$\begin{aligned}
P_{\mathcal{A}}\Phi P_{\mathcal{A}}\Psi &\equiv P_{\mathcal{A}}\Phi \otimes P_{\mathcal{A}}\Psi = P_{\mathcal{A}} \otimes P_{\mathcal{A}}(\Phi \otimes \Psi),\\
P_{\mathcal{A}}\Phi P_{\mathcal{B}}\Psi' &\equiv P_{\mathcal{A}}\Phi \otimes P_{\mathcal{B}}\Psi' = P_{\mathcal{A}} \otimes P_{\mathcal{B}}(\Phi \otimes \Psi'),\\
P_{\mathcal{B}}\Phi' P_{\mathcal{A}}\Psi &\equiv P_{\mathcal{B}}\Phi' \otimes P_{\mathcal{A}}\Psi = P_{\mathcal{B}} \otimes P_{\mathcal{A}}(\Phi' \otimes \Psi),\\
P_{\mathcal{B}}\Phi' P_{\mathcal{B}}\Psi' &\equiv P_{\mathcal{B}}\Phi' \otimes P_{\mathcal{B}}\Psi' = P_{\mathcal{B}} \otimes P_{\mathcal{B}}(\Phi' \otimes \Psi').
\end{aligned}$$

These results, which follow from the theory of Kronecker products developed in Chapter 4, show that the application of $P_{\mathcal{A}}(\otimes)$ or $P_{\mathcal{B}}(\otimes)$ to $P_{\mathcal{S}}\Phi P_{\mathcal{S}'}\Psi$ is equivalent to applying $P_{\mathcal{A}}(\otimes)P_{\mathcal{S}} \otimes P_{\mathcal{S}'}$ or $P_{\mathcal{B}}(\otimes)P_{\mathcal{S}} \otimes P_{\mathcal{S}'}$ to the vector $\Phi \otimes \Psi$. This suggests an examination of the operator products $P_{\mathcal{A}}(\otimes)P_{\mathcal{A}} \otimes P_{\mathcal{A}}$, etc. Now

$$\begin{aligned}
P_{\mathcal{A}} \otimes P_{\mathcal{A}} &= \tfrac{1}{4}\{E \otimes E + E \otimes C_2 + C_2 \otimes E + C_2 \otimes C_2\},\\
P_{\mathcal{A}} \otimes P_{\mathcal{B}} &= \tfrac{1}{4}\{E \otimes E - E \otimes C_2 + C_2 \otimes E - C_2 \otimes C_2\},\\
P_{\mathcal{B}} \otimes P_{\mathcal{A}} &= \tfrac{1}{4}\{E \otimes E + E \otimes C_2 - C_2 \otimes E - C_2 \otimes C_2\},\\
P_{\mathcal{B}} \otimes P_{\mathcal{B}} &= \tfrac{1}{4}\{E \otimes E - E \otimes C_2 - C_2 \otimes E + C_2 \otimes C_2\},
\end{aligned} \tag{5.20}$$

by (3.17). Applying $P_{\mathcal{A}}(\otimes)$ and $P_{\mathcal{B}}(\otimes)$ to these equations, one finds, by the rule for multiplying Kronecker products and the $\mathscr{C}_2$ multiplication table,

$$\begin{aligned}
P_{\mathcal{A}}(\otimes)P_{\mathcal{A}} \otimes P_{\mathcal{A}} &= P_{\mathcal{A}} \otimes P_{\mathcal{A}},\\
P_{\mathcal{A}}(\otimes)P_{\mathcal{A}} \otimes P_{\mathcal{B}} &= P_{\mathcal{A}}(\otimes)P_{\mathcal{B}} \otimes P_{\mathcal{A}} = 0,\\
P_{\mathcal{A}}(\otimes)P_{\mathcal{B}} \otimes P_{\mathcal{B}} &= P_{\mathcal{B}} \otimes P_{\mathcal{B}};
\end{aligned} \tag{5.21}$$

$$\begin{aligned}
P_{\mathcal{B}}(\otimes)P_{\mathcal{A}} \otimes P_{\mathcal{A}} &= P_{\mathcal{B}}(\otimes)P_{\mathcal{B}} \otimes P_{\mathcal{B}} = 0,\\
P_{\mathcal{B}}(\otimes)P_{\mathcal{A}} \otimes P_{\mathcal{B}} &= P_{\mathcal{A}} \otimes P_{\mathcal{B}},\\
P_{\mathcal{B}}(\otimes)P_{\mathcal{B}} \otimes P_{\mathcal{A}} &= P_{\mathcal{B}} \otimes P_{\mathcal{A}}.
\end{aligned} \tag{5.22}$$

Equations (5.21) show that all products of the form $P_{\mathcal{A}}\Phi \otimes P_{\mathcal{A}}\Psi$ or $P_{\mathcal{B}}\Phi \otimes P_{\mathcal{B}}\Psi$ are eigenvectors of $P_{\mathcal{A}}(\otimes)$ corresponding to the eigenvalue 1, so that such products belong to the symmetry species $\mathcal{A}$.

Equations (5.21) also show that the application of $P_{\mathcal{A}}(\otimes)$ to products of the form $P_{\mathcal{A}}\Phi \otimes P_{\mathcal{B}}\Psi$ or $P_{\mathcal{B}}\Phi \otimes P_{\mathcal{A}}\Psi$ yields the zero vector, so that such products do not belong to the $\mathcal{A}$ representation. On the other hand, equations (5.22) show that these products are eigenvectors of $P_{\mathcal{B}}(\otimes)$ corresponding to the eigenvalue 1.

The basis $\{|\,\mathrm{A}\rangle|\,\mathrm{X}\rangle\}$ is given in Table 8.11, from which one may readily infer the factorization of the secular determinant. In general, mixing occurs only between those products of a given symmetry species with the same eigenvalue of I_z and the same eigenvalues of $I_z(\mathrm{AA}' \cdots)$ and $I_z(\mathrm{XX}' \cdots)$. In the present case, the only $\mathcal{A}$ states mixed by $V^{(1)}$ are $3(\mathcal{A})_0$ and $4(\mathcal{A})_0$; the only $\mathcal{B}$ states mixed by $V^{(1)}$ are $1(\mathcal{B})_0$ and $2(\mathcal{B})_0$. Hence the hamiltonian matrix is the direct sum of twelve 1×1 submatrices and two 2×2 submatrices (Fig. 8.9). All diagonal elements of $\mathcal{H}$ are of the form $\Omega_{I,m_{\mathrm{AA}'}} + \Omega_{I,m_{\mathrm{XX}'}}$, and may be obtained directly from (3.24). For example, one obtains $\Omega_{I,m_{\mathrm{AA}'}}$ by setting $N = 2, I_{\mathrm{A}} = \frac{1}{2}, m = m_{\mathrm{AA}'}$; the value of I is 1 or 0, accordingly as $|\,\mathrm{A}\rangle = |\,\mathcal{A}\rangle$ or $|\,\mathcal{B}\rangle$.

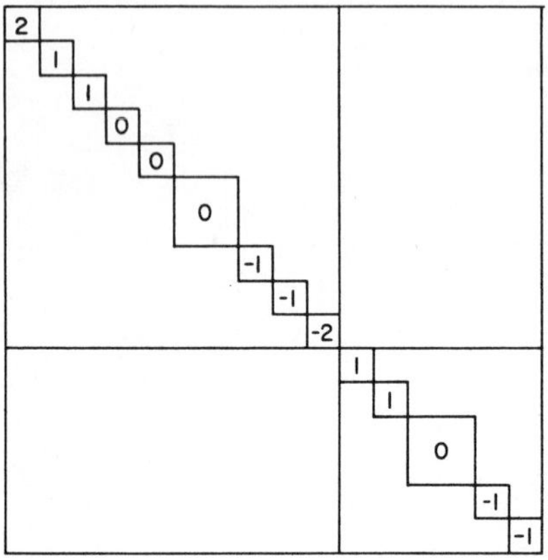

FIG. 8.9. Factorization of the secular determinant for the AA′XX′ system.

2. *The* AA′A″A‴XX′ *System.* A basis for the AA′A″A‴ subsystem is given by the first 14 entries of Table 8.9, and the vectors $1(\mathcal{A})_{0,0}$, $2(\mathcal{A})_{0,0}$, given in Section 3.C. It was noted in Section 3.A that, relative to the spin space of the AA′A″A‴ system, tr $E = 16$, tr $C_2 =$ tr $C_2' =$ tr $C_2'' = 4$. For the XX′ subsystem, one uses Table 8.5 and the trace relations tr $E = 4$, tr $C_2 = 2$. With these results, equations (5.18) yield

$$\mathrm{tr}\, P_{\mathcal{A}}(\otimes) = \tfrac{1}{4}\{16 \cdot 4 + 4 \cdot 2 + 4 \cdot 4 + 4 \cdot 2\} = 24,$$

$$\mathrm{tr}\, P_{\mathcal{B}_1}(\otimes) = \tfrac{1}{4}\{16 \cdot 4 + 4 \cdot 2 - 4 \cdot 4 - 4 \cdot 2\} = 12,$$

$$\mathrm{tr}\, P_{\mathcal{B}_2}(\otimes) = \tfrac{1}{4}\{16 \cdot 4 - 4 \cdot 2 + 4 \cdot 4 - 4 \cdot 2\} = 16,$$

$$\mathrm{tr}\, P_{\mathcal{B}_3}(\otimes) = \tfrac{1}{4}\{16 \cdot 4 - 4 \cdot 2 - 4 \cdot 4 + 4 \cdot 2\} = 12.$$

The product basis contains eight types of products: $|\,\mathcal{A}\rangle|\,\mathcal{A}\rangle$, $|\,\mathcal{B}_1\rangle|\,\mathcal{A}\rangle$, ..., $|\,\mathcal{B}_3\rangle|\,\mathcal{B}\rangle$. These products may be considered to be generated by the application of $P_{\mathcal{A}} \otimes P_{\mathcal{A}}$, $P_{\mathcal{B}_1} \otimes P_{\mathcal{A}}$, ..., $P_{\mathcal{B}_3} \otimes P_{\mathcal{B}}$, which can be obtained from (3.17) and (3.19), to appropriate product kets. It is not difficult to show that

$$\begin{aligned} P_{\mathcal{A}}(\otimes) &= P_{\mathcal{A}} \otimes P_{\mathcal{A}} + P_{\mathcal{B}_2} \otimes P_{\mathcal{B}}\,, \\ P_{\mathcal{B}_1}(\otimes) &= P_{\mathcal{B}_1} \otimes P_{\mathcal{A}} + P_{\mathcal{B}_2} \otimes P_{\mathcal{B}}\,, \\ P_{\mathcal{B}_2}(\otimes) &= P_{\mathcal{B}_2} \otimes P_{\mathcal{A}} + P_{\mathcal{A}} \otimes P_{\mathcal{B}}\,, \\ P_{\mathcal{B}_3}(\otimes) &= P_{\mathcal{B}_3} \otimes P_{\mathcal{A}} + P_{\mathcal{B}_1} \otimes P_{\mathcal{B}}\,. \end{aligned} \tag{5.23}$$

From these results it follows that the symmetry species of the products $|\,\mathcal{S}\rangle|\,\mathcal{S}'\rangle$ are given by the rules

$$\begin{aligned} |\,\mathcal{A}\rangle|\,\mathcal{A}\rangle &= |\,\mathcal{B}_2\rangle|\,\mathcal{B}\rangle = |\,\mathcal{A}\rangle, \\ |\,\mathcal{B}_1\rangle|\,\mathcal{A}\rangle &= |\,\mathcal{B}_3\rangle|\,\mathcal{B}\rangle = |\,\mathcal{B}_1\rangle, \\ |\,\mathcal{B}_2\rangle|\,\mathcal{A}\rangle &= |\,\mathcal{A}\rangle|\,\mathcal{B}\rangle = |\,\mathcal{B}_2\rangle, \\ |\,\mathcal{B}_3\rangle|\,\mathcal{A}\rangle &= |\,\mathcal{B}_1\rangle|\,\mathcal{B}\rangle = |\,\mathcal{B}_3\rangle. \end{aligned} \tag{5.24}$$

The proof of these rules makes use of the mutual orthogonality and idempotence of projection operators. For example, to prove that $|\,\mathcal{A}\rangle|\,\mathcal{A}\rangle = |\,\mathcal{A}\rangle$, one multiplies the first of equations (5.23) from the right with $P_{\mathcal{A}} \otimes P_{\mathcal{A}}$ to obtain

$$\begin{aligned} P_{\mathcal{A}}(\otimes)P_{\mathcal{A}} \otimes P_{\mathcal{A}} &= (P_{\mathcal{A}} \otimes P_{\mathcal{A}})(P_{\mathcal{A}} \otimes P_{\mathcal{A}}) + (P_{\mathcal{B}_2} \otimes P_{\mathcal{B}})(P_{\mathcal{A}} \otimes P_{\mathcal{A}}) \\ &= P_{\mathcal{A}}^2 \otimes P_{\mathcal{A}}^2 + P_{\mathcal{B}_2}P_{\mathcal{A}} \otimes P_{\mathcal{B}}P_{\mathcal{A}} \\ &= P_{\mathcal{A}} \otimes P_{\mathcal{A}}\,, \end{aligned}$$

since $P_{\mathcal{A}}^2 = P_{\mathcal{A}}$, and $P_{\mathcal{B}_2}P_{\mathcal{A}} = P_{\mathcal{B}}P_{\mathcal{A}} = 0$. Similar calculations establish the symmetry species of other types of products. From these results, it is easy to show that the hamiltonian matrix decomposes according to the scheme given in Table 8.16.

3. *The* AA′A″XX′X″ *System.* The product basis for this system is obtained by first identifying the vectors of Table 8.8 with the AA′A″ nuclei, then the XX′X″ nuclei, and then forming the 64 products $\{|\,\mathrm{A}\rangle|\,\mathrm{X}\rangle\}$. Since $\mathcal{G} = \mathcal{G}' = \mathcal{D}_3$, equations (2.33) may be used to compute the ranks of the projection operators (5.19):

$$\begin{aligned} \operatorname{tr} P_{\mathcal{A}_1}(\otimes) &= \tfrac{1}{6}\{8 \cdot 8 + 2 \cdot 2 + 2 \cdot 2 + 4 \cdot 4 + 4 \cdot 4 + 4 \cdot 4\} = 20, \\ \operatorname{tr} P_{\mathcal{A}_2}(\otimes) &= \tfrac{1}{6}\{8 \cdot 8 + 2 \cdot 2 + 2 \cdot 2 - (4 \cdot 4 + 4 \cdot 4 + 4 \cdot 4)\} = 4, \\ \operatorname{tr} P_{\mathcal{E}}(\otimes) &= \tfrac{1}{3}\{8 \cdot 8 - \tfrac{1}{2}(2 \cdot 2 + 2 \cdot 2) + \tfrac{1}{2}(4 \cdot 4 - 2 \cdot 4 \cdot 4 + 4 \cdot 4)\} = 20, \\ \operatorname{tr} P_{\mathcal{E}}'(\otimes) &= \tfrac{1}{3}\{8 \cdot 8 - \tfrac{1}{2}(2 \cdot 2 + 2 \cdot 2) - \tfrac{1}{2}(4 \cdot 4 - 2 \cdot 4 \cdot 4 + 4 \cdot 4)\} = 20. \end{aligned}$$

TABLE 8.16

DECOMPOSITION OF THE HAMILTONIAN MATRIX FOR THE AA′A″A‴XX′ SYSTEM

m	$\mathscr{A}$	$\mathscr{B}_1$
3	1×1	
2	$1 \times 1, 1 \times 1$	1×1
1	$1 \times 1, 2 \times 2, 3 \times 3$	$1 \times 1, 2 \times 2$
0	$1 \times 1, 1 \times 1, 4 \times 4$	$1 \times 1, 1 \times 1, 2 \times 2$
−1	$1 \times 1, 2 \times 2, 3 \times 3$	$1 \times 1, 2 \times 2$
−2	$1 \times 1, 1 \times 1$	1×1
−3	1×1	
m	$\mathscr{B}_2$	$\mathscr{B}_3$
3		
2	$1 \times 1, 1 \times 1$	1×1
1	$1 \times 1, 2 \times 2$	$1 \times 1, 2 \times 2$
0	$1 \times 1, 1 \times 1, 4 \times 4$	$1 \times 1, 1 \times 1, 2 \times 2$
−1	$1 \times 1, 2 \times 2$	$1 \times 1, 2 \times 2$
−2	$1 \times 1, 1 \times 1$	1×1
−3		

Hence a symmetrized basis for the AA′A″XX′X″ system contains 20 vectors with $\mathscr{A}_1$ symmetry, four vectors with $\mathscr{A}_2$ symmetry, and 40 vectors with $\mathscr{E}$ symmetry.

The analysis of the symmetry species of the products $|\,\mathscr{S}\rangle|\,\mathscr{S}'\rangle$ will be carried out for product bases that include products of the form $|\,\mathscr{A}_2\rangle|\,\mathscr{S}\rangle$, $|\,\mathscr{S}\rangle|\,\mathscr{A}_2\rangle$. These products do not occur in the AA′A″XX′X″ system, since Table 8.8 does not contain any vectors with $\mathscr{A}_2$ symmetry.

In a general basis, there will be 16 types of products $|\,\mathscr{S}\rangle|\,\mathscr{S}'\rangle = P_{\mathscr{S}}\Phi \otimes P_{\mathscr{S}'}\Psi = P_{\mathscr{S}} \otimes P_{\mathscr{S}'}(\Phi \otimes \Psi)$, where Φ and Ψ are product kets. By expanding the Kronecker products $P_{\mathscr{S}} \otimes P_{\mathscr{S}'}$, one can show that

$$P_{\mathscr{A}_1}(\otimes) + P_{\mathscr{E}}'(\otimes) = P_{\mathscr{A}_1} \otimes P_{\mathscr{A}_1} + P_{\mathscr{A}_2} \otimes P_{\mathscr{A}_2} + P_{\mathscr{E}}' \otimes P_{\mathscr{A}_1} + P_{\mathscr{A}_1} \otimes P_{\mathscr{E}}' + P_{\mathscr{A}_2} \otimes P_{\mathscr{E}} + P_{\mathscr{E}} \otimes P_{\mathscr{A}_2} + P_{\mathscr{E}} \otimes P_{\mathscr{E}} + P_{\mathscr{E}}' \otimes P_{\mathscr{E}}', \quad (5.25)$$

$$P_{\mathcal{A}_2}(\otimes) + P_{\mathcal{E}}(\otimes) = P_{\mathcal{A}_1} \otimes P_{\mathcal{A}_2} + P_{\mathcal{A}_2} \otimes P_{\mathcal{A}_1} + P_{\mathcal{A}_1} \otimes P_{\mathcal{E}} + P_{\mathcal{E}} \otimes P_{\mathcal{A}_1}$$
$$+ P_{\mathcal{A}_2} \otimes P_{\mathcal{E}}' + P_{\mathcal{E}}' \otimes P_{\mathcal{A}_2} + P_{\mathcal{E}} \otimes P_{\mathcal{E}}' + P_{\mathcal{E}}' \otimes P_{\mathcal{E}} . \tag{5.26}$$

The interpretation of these equations is simple. Equation (5.25) states that all elements of the product basis that are eigenvectors of the projection operators on the right side contribute to the $\mathcal{A}_1$ and $\mathcal{E}'$ species of a symmetrized basis. This result can be sharpened for particular elements of the product basis. If S is any element in $\mathcal{D}_3$, then $SP_{\mathcal{A}_1} = P_{\mathcal{A}_1}$, so that

$$P_{\mathcal{A}_1}(\otimes)P_{\mathcal{A}_1} \otimes P_{\mathcal{A}_1} = \tfrac{1}{6}\sum_S (S \otimes S)P_{\mathcal{A}_1} \otimes P_{\mathcal{A}_1}$$
$$= \tfrac{1}{6}\sum_S SP_{\mathcal{A}_1} \otimes SP_{\mathcal{A}_1} = P_{\mathcal{A}_1} \otimes P_{\mathcal{A}_1} .$$

Therefore, any product of the form $|\mathcal{A}_1\rangle|\mathcal{A}_1\rangle$ belongs to the symmetry species $\mathcal{A}_1$. Furthermore, $EP_{\mathcal{A}_2} = C_3P_{\mathcal{A}_2} = C_3{}^2P_{\mathcal{A}_2} = P_{\mathcal{A}_2}$, whereas $C_2P_{\mathcal{A}_2} = C_2'P_{\mathcal{A}_2} = C_2''P_{\mathcal{A}_2} = -P_{\mathcal{A}_2}$, so that

$$P_{\mathcal{A}_1}(\otimes)P_{\mathcal{A}_2} \otimes P_{\mathcal{A}_2} = \tfrac{1}{6}\sum_S (S \otimes S)P_{\mathcal{A}_2} \otimes P_{\mathcal{A}_2} = P_{\mathcal{A}_2} \otimes P_{\mathcal{A}_2} .$$

Hence any basis element of the form $|\mathcal{A}_2\rangle|\mathcal{A}_2\rangle$ belongs to the symmetry species $|\mathcal{A}_1\rangle$. Products such as $|\mathcal{S}\rangle|\mathcal{E}\rangle$, $|\mathcal{S}\rangle|\mathcal{E}'\rangle$, $|\mathcal{E}\rangle|\mathcal{S}\rangle$, $|\mathcal{E}'\rangle|\mathcal{S}\rangle$, where $\mathcal{S} = \mathcal{A}_1$ or $\mathcal{A}_2$, belong to $\mathcal{E}'$. This may be proved by showing that such products do not belong to $\mathcal{A}_1$. For example, the application of $P_{\mathcal{A}_1}(\otimes)$ to $P_{\mathcal{E}}' \otimes P_{\mathcal{A}_1}$ gives

$$P_{\mathcal{A}_1}(\otimes)P_{\mathcal{E}}' \otimes P_{\mathcal{A}_1} = \tfrac{1}{6}\sum_S SP_{\mathcal{E}}' \otimes SP_{\mathcal{A}_1} = \tfrac{1}{6}\sum_S SP_{\mathcal{E}}' \otimes P_{\mathcal{A}_1}$$
$$= \tfrac{1}{6}\left\{\left(\sum_S S\right) P_{\mathcal{E}}'\right\} \otimes P_{\mathcal{A}_1} = P_{\mathcal{A}_1}P_{\mathcal{E}}' \otimes P_{\mathcal{A}_1} = 0,$$

since $P_{\mathcal{A}_1}$ and $P_{\mathcal{E}}'$ are mutually orthogonal. Hence, by (5.25), any product of the form $P_{\mathcal{E}}'\Phi \otimes P_{\mathcal{A}_1}\Psi$ belongs to $\mathcal{E}'$. One has, therefore, the following rules:

$$|\mathcal{A}_1\rangle|\mathcal{A}_1\rangle = |\mathcal{A}_2\rangle|\mathcal{A}_2\rangle = |\mathcal{A}_1\rangle, \tag{5.27}$$

$$|\mathcal{A}_1\rangle|\mathcal{E}'\rangle = |\mathcal{E}'\rangle|\mathcal{A}_1\rangle = |\mathcal{A}_2\rangle|\mathcal{E}\rangle = |\mathcal{E}\rangle|\mathcal{A}_2\rangle = |\mathcal{E}'\rangle. \tag{5.28}$$

Products of the form $|\mathcal{E}\rangle|\mathcal{E}\rangle$ and $|\mathcal{E}'\rangle|\mathcal{E}'\rangle$ contain the symmetry species $\mathcal{A}_1$ and $\mathcal{E}'$, so that all products of this form must be resym-

TABLE 8.17

RESYMMETRIZED BASIS VECTORS FOR THE AA′A″XX′X″ SYSTEM

Basis vector	$(\mathscr{S})_m$
$\frac{1}{\sqrt{2}}\{(\mathscr{E})_{1/2}(\mathscr{E})_{1/2} + (\mathscr{E}')_{1/2}(\mathscr{E}')_{1/2}\}$	$(\mathscr{A}_1)_1$
$\frac{1}{\sqrt{2}}\{(\mathscr{E})_{1/2}(\mathscr{E})_{-1/2} + (\mathscr{E}')_{1/2}(\mathscr{E}')_{-1/2}\}$	$(\mathscr{A}_1)_0$
$\frac{1}{\sqrt{2}}\{(\mathscr{E})_{-1/2}(\mathscr{E})_{1/2} + (\mathscr{E}')_{-1/2}(\mathscr{E}')_{1/2}\}$	$(\mathscr{A}_1)_0$
$\frac{1}{\sqrt{2}}\{(\mathscr{E})_{-1/2}(\mathscr{E})_{-1/2} + (\mathscr{E}')_{-1/2}(\mathscr{E}')_{-1/2}\}$	$(\mathscr{A}_1)_{-1}$
$\frac{1}{\sqrt{2}}\{(\mathscr{E})_{1/2}(\mathscr{E}')_{1/2} - (\mathscr{E}')_{1/2}(\mathscr{E})_{1/2}\}$	$(\mathscr{A}_2)_1$
$\frac{1}{\sqrt{2}}\{(\mathscr{E})_{1/2}(\mathscr{E}')_{-1/2} - (\mathscr{E}')_{1/2}(\mathscr{E})_{-1/2}\}$	$(\mathscr{A}_2)_0$
$\frac{1}{\sqrt{2}}\{(\mathscr{E}')_{-1/2}(\mathscr{E})_{1/2} - (\mathscr{E})_{-1/2}(\mathscr{E}')_{1/2}\}$	$(\mathscr{A}_2)_0$
$\frac{1}{\sqrt{2}}\{(\mathscr{E})_{-1/2}(\mathscr{E}')_{-1/2} - (\mathscr{E}')_{-1/2}(\mathscr{E})_{-1/2}\}$	$(\mathscr{A}_2)_{-1}$
$\frac{1}{\sqrt{2}}\{(\mathscr{E})_{1/2}(\mathscr{E}')_{1/2} + (\mathscr{E}')_{1/2}(\mathscr{E})_{1/2}\}$	$(\mathscr{E})_1$
$\frac{1}{\sqrt{2}}\{(\mathscr{E})_{1/2}(\mathscr{E}')_{-1/2} + (\mathscr{E}')_{1/2}(\mathscr{E})_{-1/2}\}$	$(\mathscr{E})_0$
$\frac{1}{\sqrt{2}}\{(\mathscr{E}')_{-1/2}(\mathscr{E})_{1/2} + (\mathscr{E})_{-1/2}(\mathscr{E}')_{1/2}\}$	$(\mathscr{E})_0$
$\frac{1}{\sqrt{2}}\{(\mathscr{E})_{-1/2}(\mathscr{E}')_{-1/2} + (\mathscr{E}')_{-1/2}(\mathscr{E})_{-1/2}\}$	$(\mathscr{E})_{-1}$
$\frac{1}{\sqrt{2}}\{(\mathscr{E})_{1/2}(\mathscr{E})_{1/2} - (\mathscr{E}')_{1/2}(\mathscr{E}')_{1/2}\}$	$(\mathscr{E}')_1$
$\frac{1}{\sqrt{2}}\{(\mathscr{E})_{1/2}(\mathscr{E})_{-1/2} - (\mathscr{E}')_{1/2}(\mathscr{E}')_{-1/2}\}$	$(\mathscr{E}')_0$
$\frac{1}{\sqrt{2}}\{(\mathscr{E})_{-1/2}(\mathscr{E})_{1/2} - (\mathscr{E}')_{-1/2}(\mathscr{E}')_{1/2}\}$	$(\mathscr{E}')_0$
$\frac{1}{\sqrt{2}}\{(\mathscr{E})_{-1/2}(\mathscr{E})_{-1/2} - (\mathscr{E}')_{-1/2}(\mathscr{E}')_{-1/2}\}$	$(\mathscr{E}')_{-1}$

metrized. For this purpose, one applies $P_{\mathcal{A}_1}(\otimes)$ and $P_{\mathcal{E}}'(\otimes)$ to these products, and obtains basis vectors of $\mathcal{A}_1$ and $\mathcal{E}'$ symmetry in the usual manner.

A similar analysis of the projection operators on the right side of (5.26) shows that

$$|\mathcal{A}_1\rangle|\mathcal{A}_2\rangle = |\mathcal{A}_2\rangle|\mathcal{A}_1\rangle = |\mathcal{A}_2\rangle, \tag{5.29}$$

$$|\mathcal{A}_1\rangle|\mathcal{E}\rangle = |\mathcal{E}\rangle|\mathcal{A}_1\rangle = |\mathcal{A}_2\rangle|\mathcal{E}'\rangle = |\mathcal{E}'\rangle|\mathcal{A}_2\rangle = |\mathcal{E}\rangle. \tag{5.30}$$

Products of the form $|\mathcal{E}\rangle|\mathcal{E}'\rangle$ and $|\mathcal{E}'\rangle|\mathcal{E}\rangle$ contain the symmetry species $\mathcal{A}_2$ and $\mathcal{E}$, so that all such products must be resymmetrized with $P_{\mathcal{A}_2}(\otimes)$ and $P_{\mathcal{E}}(\otimes)$.

The application of the preceding results to the AA′A″XX′X″ system shows that it is necessary to resymmetrize $|\mathcal{E}\rangle|\mathcal{E}\rangle$, $|\mathcal{E}\rangle|\mathcal{E}'\rangle$, $|\mathcal{E}'\rangle|\mathcal{E}\rangle$, $|\mathcal{E}'\rangle|\mathcal{E}'\rangle$, to obtain a symmetrized basis for the composite system. The resymmetrized vectors are given in Table 8.17. For notational simplicity $(\mathcal{E})_{1/2,\pm1/2}$ and $(\mathcal{E}')_{1/2,\pm1/2}$ have been written $(\mathcal{E})_{\pm1/2}$, $(\mathcal{E}')_{\pm1/2}$. The symmetry species of all other products are given by (5.27), (5.28), and (5.30). From these results one may deduce the decomposition of the hamiltonian matrix given in Table 8.18.

TABLE 8.18

DECOMPOSITION OF THE HAMILTONIAN MATRIX FOR THE AA′A″XX′X″ SYSTEM

m	$\mathcal{A}_1$	$\mathcal{A}_2$	$\mathcal{E}$, $\mathcal{E}'$
3	1×1		
2	1×1, 1×1		1×1, 1×1
1	1×1, 1×1, 2×2	1×1	1×1, 1×1, 3×3
0	1×1, 1×1, 2×2, 2×2	1×1, 1×1	3×3, 3×3
−1	1×1, 1×1, 2×2	1×1	1×1, 1×1, 3×3
−2	1×1, 1×1		1×1, 1×1
−3	1×1		

D. Remarks on the Theory of Symmetrical Systems

The discussion of this chapter has been principally concerned with the theory of finite groups, their representations, and the application of these concepts to the study of symmetrical spin systems. However, some further remarks concerning the three-dimensional rotation group $\mathcal{O}_3$ are appropriate at this point. It has already been mentioned that $\mathcal{O}_3$ is of fundamental importance in the quantum mechanical theory of angular momentum. In fact, one can say that the theory of $\mathcal{O}_3$ and its irreducible representations is the theory of angular momentum.

$\mathcal{O}_3$ has a denumerably infinite number of irreducible representations. There is exactly one irreducible representation for every dimension from 1 to infinity. To translate these results into more familiar terms, consider a particle of spin I, and the associated basis $\{|I, m\rangle\}$, whose elements are eigenvectors of $\mathbf{I}^2$ and I_z. In group-theoretical language, the vectors $\{|I, m\rangle\}$ constitute a basis for an irreducible representation of $\mathcal{O}_3$ of dimension $2I + 1$. The spin quantum number labels the irreducible representation, the dimension of the spin space specifies the dimension of the irreducible representation, and the eigenvalues of I_z label the basis vectors.

The addition of two angular momenta $\mathbf{I}_1$ and $\mathbf{I}_2$, to obtain their resultant $\mathbf{I}$, is equivalent to reducing the product basis $\{|I_1, m_1\rangle|I_2, m_2\rangle\}$, which generates a $(2I_1 + 1)(2I_2 + 1)$-dimensional representation of $\mathcal{O}_3$, into its nonequivalent irreducible components. The latter are labeled by the total spin quantum numbers $I = I_1 + I_2, I_1 + I_2 - 1, \ldots, |I_1 - I_2|$, each occurring exactly once in the decomposition. The coefficients expressing the eigenvectors of $\mathbf{I}^2$ and I_z in terms of the product bases are called the *Clebsch-Gordan coefficients.* In general, the spin multiplicity g_I gives the number of times the irreducible representation labeled by the quantum number I occurs in the reduction. Of course, all $g_I = 1$ for the addition of two angular momenta. These remarks indicate the motivation behind the term "irreducible component" introduced in Chapter 5 to describe systems of the form $A_{I_A}B_{I_B}C_{I_C}\cdots$. The reduction of a given spin system into its irreducible components is nothing more than a recognition, in physical terms, of the irreducible representations of $\mathcal{O}_3$.

Finally, two contingencies of the weak-coupling approximation will be noted. Occasionally, certain subblocks of the hamiltonian matrix reveal additional decompositions that are not predicted by the theory given above. These decompositions depend upon the particular system under study, and cannot be anticipated. The reason is that the additional decompositions do not occur throughout the complete hamiltonian matrix, so that they cannot be attributed to an unrecognized constant of the motion.

A useful occurrence in the spectra of weakly coupled symmetrical systems is the appearance of certain sets of lines that can be made to correspond with the spectra of other systems (*19*, *21*). For example, some of the resonances observed in the spectrum of 1, 3, 5-trifluorobenzene can be interpreted as an ABC spectrum (*19*). The recognition of such patterns can materially simplify the analysis. However, to establish such correlations it is necessary to compare the matrix elements in certain subblocks of the hamiltonian matrix with those appearing in the hamiltonian matrix of the correlated system. This detailed examination of matrix elements precludes the existence of general rules for determining such correlations—each spin system must be separately examined for any existing correlations. This situation should be contrasted with the theory of the irreducible components of multispin systems. One can determine, in advance, which irreducible components will appear in the spectrum of a given system, and their relative weights—without calculating a single matrix element.

REFERENCES

1. G. Birkhoff and S. MacLane, "A Survey of Modern Algebra," rev. ed., Chap VI. Macmillan, New York, 1953.
2. W. Ledermann, "Introduction to The Theory of Finite Groups." Wiley (Interscience), New York, 1953.
3. E. P. Wigner, "Group Theory and Its Application to the Quantum Mechanics of Atomic Spectra." Academic Press, New York, 1959.
4. H. Weyl, "The Theory of Groups and Quantum Mechanics." Dover, New York, 1949.
5. F. D. Murnaghan, "The Theory of Group Representations." Dover, New York, 1963.
6. M. Hamermesh, "Group Theory and Its Application to Physical Problems." Addison-Wesley, Reading, Massachusetts, 1962.
7. L. D. Landau and E. M. Lifshitz, "Quantum Mechanics—Non-Relativistic Theory." Chap. XII. Addison-Wesley, Reading, Massachusetts, 1958.
8. J. S. Lomont, "Applications of Finite Groups." Academic Press, New York, 1959.
9. M. Tinkham, "Group Theory and Quantum Mechanics." McGraw-Hill, New York, 1964.
10. E. B. Wilson, Jr., J. C. Decius, and P. C. Cross, "Molecular Vibrations." McGraw-Hill, New York, 1955.
11. I. M. Gel'fand, R. A. Minlos, and Z. Ya. Shapiro, "Representations of the Rotation and Lorentz Groups and their Applications." Pergamon Press, New York, 1963.
12. P. R. Halmos, "Finite-Dimensional Vector Spaces," 2nd ed., Chap. II. Van Nostrand, Princeton, New Jersey, 1958.
13. H. M. McConnell, A. D. McLean, and C. A. Reilly, *J. Chem. Phys.* **23**, 1152 (1955).
14. E. B. Wilson, Jr., *J. Chem. Phys.* **27**, 60 (1957).
15. P. L. Corio, *Chem. Rev.* **60**, 363 (1960).
16. J. A. Pople, W. G. Schneider, and H. J. Bernstein, "High-Resolution Nuclear Magnetic Resonance," Chap. 6. McGraw-Hill, New York, 1959.
17. D. M. Grant, R. C. Hirst, and H. S. Gutowsky, *J. Chem. Phys.* **38**, 470 (1963).
18. B. Dischler and G. Englert, *Z. Naturforsch.* **16a**, 1180 (1961).
19. R. G. Jones, R. C. Hirst, and H. J. Bernstein, *Can. J. Chem.* **43**, 683 (1965).
20. W. G. Patterson and E. J. Wells, *J. Mol. Spectry.* **14**, 101 (1964).
21. P. Diehl, *Helv. Chim. Acta* **48**, 567 (1965).

CHAPTER 9

Multiple Quantum Transitions, Double Resonance and Spin Echo Experiments

The preceding chapters have been almost exclusively concerned with the theory of single quantum transitions induced by a linearly polarized rf field. This chapter will be concerned with introductory accounts of the multiple quantum transitions observed at increased amplitudes of a single rf field (*1–8*), the simultaneous application of two rf fields (*9–22*), and a single rf field applied in the form of a coherent pulse train (*23–27*). It will be assumed throughout that the amplitudes of the applied rf fields are much smaller than the steady z field, so that only the appropriately sensed circularly polarized components need be retained in the hamiltonian operators. The discussion will be simplified further by ignoring the interactions coupling a representative spin system to its molecular surroundings. Although this limitation precludes a complete theoretical discussion, it is nevertheless possible to obtain useful results with the theory developed in earlier chapters.

1. Multiple Quantum Transitions

A. Introduction

An *n-tuple* or *multiple quantum transition* may be described as a transition involving the exchange of n rf quanta between the rf field and the nuclear spin system. A multiple quantum transition is said to be *absorptive* or *emissive*, accordingly as the exchange of quanta increases or decreases the energy of the spin system. In an absorptive transition, the number of rf quanta transferred from the rf field to the spin system is equal to minus the change in the z component of angular momentum. For example, if the z components of angular momenta of the initial and final states are m and m', respectively, then, since $m' < m$, $n = -(m' - m)$. In an emissive transition, $m' > m$, so that $n = +(m' - m)$.

Multiple quantum transitions were mentioned briefly in Section 3.C of Chapter 1 for the case of a single nucleus with $I > \frac{1}{2}$, and in Chapter 3 it was shown that the transition probabilities corresponding to $n = 0, 1, 2, ..., 2I$ are given by the Majorana formula [equation (3.14), Chapter 3]. In Section 5.4 it was shown that multiple quantum transitions also occur in the more general A_N system. The analysis of this system showed that the transition probabilities are independent of the spin-spin interactions, and are, in fact, still given by the Majorana formula. Because of the importance of the Majorana formula in many problems, its physical significance will be restated.

Consider a single nucleus of spin I, or an irreducible component of an A_N system, in a steady z field $\mathbf{H}_0$. It will be assumed that $\gamma > 0$, that the angular momentum is quantized along the z axis, and that the system is initially in the eigenstate $|I, m\rangle$. If the system is subjected to a circularly polarized rf field at $t = 0$, the Majorana formula gives the probability that the system is in the eigenstate $|I, m'\rangle$ at time t. For an alternative interpretation, and for later reference, suppose that at $t = 0$ the system is suddenly subjected to a constant field $\mathbf{H} \neq \mathbf{H}_0$. The Majorana formula, in the form [cf. Section 2.3, equations (3.45) and (3.48)]

$$P^{(I)}_{m\to m'}(\varphi) = [D^{(I)}_{m'm}(\varphi)]^2 = (I+m)!(I-m)!(I+m')!(I-m')!\left(\cos\frac{\varphi}{2}\right)^{4I} \times \left\{\sum_k \frac{(-1)^k[\tan(\varphi/2)]^{m-m'+2k}}{(I-m-k)!(m-m'+k)!(I+m'-k)!k!}\right\}^2, \qquad (1.1)$$

where φ is the angle between the positive z axis and $\mathbf{H}$, gives the probability that an angular momentum determination will yield the eigenvalue m' for the component of $\mathbf{I}$ along $\mathbf{H}$. This interpretation of the Majorana formula will be used in the discussion of double resonance experiments.

The essential point concerning multiple quantum transitions between the energy levels of a nucleus with spin $I > \frac{1}{2}$, or an irreducible component of an A_N system, is that, in either case, the levels are equally spaced. Although the rf field supplies monoenergetic quanta only at frequency ω, an n-tuple quantum transition can occur through the absorption of n equienergetic rf quanta via intermediate states connecting the initial and final states. The importance of the intermediate states in the calculation of the transition probability is explicitly indicated by the summation in the Majorana formula.

The frequency of an absorptive n-tuple quantum transition is easily calculated. Let m and $\hbar\Omega_m$ denote the z component of angular momentum and energy of the initial state, and m', $\hbar\Omega_{m'}$ the corresponding quantities for the final state. The energy given up by the rf field must be (approximately) equal to the energy absorbed by the spin system. It follows that $n\hbar\omega = \hbar(\Omega_{m'} - \Omega_m)$; hence the (angular) frequency of an n-tuple quantum transition is

$$\omega = \frac{1}{n}(\Omega_{m'} - \Omega_m). \tag{1.2}$$

For a single nucleus with spin I, $\Omega_{m'} - \Omega_m = (m' - m)\gamma H_0 = n\omega_0$, while $\Omega_{m'} - \Omega_m = n(1 - \sigma)\omega_0$, for an irreducible component of an A_N system. Equation (1.2) shows that, in either case, the resonance frequencies of all multiple quantum transitions ($n = 1, 2, ..., 2I$) are equal—specifically $\omega = \omega_0$, for a single nucleus, and $\omega = (1 - \sigma)\omega_0$ for an irreducible component of an A_N system.

Multiple quantum transitions can also occur in coupled nuclear spin systems with nonvanishing internal chemical shifts (*2, 3*). For the changes in the zero-order energies resulting from internal chemical shifts and spin-spin coupling constants are usually small compared to nuclear Larmor frequencies, so that normally only small deviations from the equal-spacing condition occur. For example, in the AB system (Table 6.1) the energy levels corresponding to $m = 0$ can be expected to be approximately halfway between the levels with $m = 1$ and $m = -1$. The only multiple quantum transition possible in an AB system is a double quantum transition (*2*). The frequency of the double quantum transition is, by (1.2) and Tables 6.1 and 6.2,

$$\tfrac{1}{2}(\Omega_{-1} - \Omega_1) = \tfrac{1}{2}(\omega_A + \omega_B) = \tfrac{1}{2}(A_1 + B_1) = \tfrac{1}{2}(A_2 + B_2),$$

which shows that the frequency of the double quantum transition is midway between the frequencies of the single quantum transitions A_1, B_1 and A_2, B_2. In general,

$$\tfrac{1}{2}(\Omega_{m-2} - \Omega_m) = \tfrac{1}{2}(\Omega_{m-2} - \Omega_{m-1}) + \tfrac{1}{2}(\Omega_{m-1} - \Omega_m),$$

an identity that provides a simple relation between the frequencies of single and double quantum transitions. Similar rules are easily derived for $n = 3, 4, ...$.

One obvious application of multiple quantum transitions is the determination of frequency separations that cannot be obtained from single quantum transitions, provided, of course, that the multiple quantum transitions can be detected.

The intensities of n-tuple transitions can be calculated by extending the time-dependent perturbation calculation developed in Section 5.3 to higher orders in the amplitude of the rf field. Before carrying out this program, a simple consequence of (1.2) will be noted. If it is assumed that the uncertainties of all energy levels are comparable, then, all other considerations aside, (1.2) shows that the width of an n-tuple quantum transition should be n times smaller than the width of a single quantum transition. This conclusion is confirmed by the general theory of multiple quantum transitions in coupled spin systems (*4*).

B. Theory of Multiple Quantum Transitions

Consider a coupled spin system in a stationary z field, and let $| m)$ denote an eigenstate of energy Ω_m and z component of angular momentum m. If the system is subjected to a circularly polarized (transverse) rf field at $t = 0$, the probability amplitude for the state $| m')$ at time t is given, to the second order in H_1, by (3.17) of Chapter 5. In the discussion of that equation, it was pointed out that the second-order term includes contributions from intermediate states. The second-order term is

$$(\gamma H_1)^2 \sum_{m''} \frac{(m' \mid I_x \mid m'')(m'' \mid I_x \mid m)}{W_m - W_{m''}} \left\{ \frac{e^{iW_{m'}t} - e^{iW_m t}}{W_{m'} - W_m} - \frac{e^{iW_{m''}t} - e^{iW_m t}}{W_{m''} - W_m} \right\},$$

where $W_m = -(\Omega_m + m\omega)$.

The study of the preceding expression is facilitated by replacing I_x with $\frac{1}{2}(I^+ + I^-)$, so that the product of the matrix elements in I_x becomes

$$\begin{aligned}(m' \mid I_x \mid m'')(m'' \mid I_x \mid m) = \tfrac{1}{4}[&(m' \mid I^- \mid m'')(m'' \mid I^- \mid m) \\ &+ (m' \mid I^- \mid m'')(m'' \mid I^+ \mid m) \\ &+ (m' \mid I^+ \mid m'')(m'' \mid I^- \mid m) \\ &+ (m' \mid I^+ \mid m'')(m'' \mid I^+ \mid m)].\end{aligned}$$

Now $(m' | I^{\pm} | m) = 0$, unless $m' = m \pm 1$, so that the first term within the square bracket vanishes, unless $m' = m - 2$. Terms of this form yield a contribution to the probability amplitude of an absorptive double quantum transition.

The second and third terms in the square bracket vanish, unless $m' = m$, so that terms of this form yield a second-order correction to the probability that the system is still in the initial state $| m)$ at time t. It will be assumed, as in Section 5.3, that the time interval t is short enough to ensure that $P_{mm}(t) \approx 1$, so that higher-order corrections to $P_{mm}(t)$

can be neglected. It will also be assumed that t is long enough to permit a subsequent integration over a range of energies to obtain the transition probability per unit time (Section 3.B, Chapter 5).

The remaining term in the square bracket vanishes, unless $m' = m + 2$. Terms of this form yield a contribution to the probability amplitude of an emissive double quantum transition.

The perturbation expansion may be carried out to higher orders, and an examination of these terms [Section 2, Appendix III] shows that the fourth-order terms also contribute to the probability amplitude of $| m - 2)$ at time t. This contribution, and the contributions of all higher-order terms, will be neglected. Therefore, the second-order probability amplitude for $| m - 2)$ at time t is

$$\left(\frac{\gamma H_1}{2}\right)^2 \sum_{m''} \frac{(m' \mid I^- \mid m'')(m'' \mid I^- \mid m)}{W_m - W_{m''}} \left\{\frac{e^{iW_{m'}t} - e^{iW_m t}}{W_{m'} - W_m} - \frac{e^{iW_{m''}t} - e^{iW_m t}}{W_{m''} - W_m}\right\},$$

where $m' = m - 2$, $m'' = m - 1$, and the summation is to be taken over all states with $m'' = m - 1$. The absolute square of this quantity gives the probability of the double quantum transition $| m) \to | m - 2)$. A simplification results upon noting that only the first term within the brackets gives an appreciable contribution to the transition probability when $\omega \approx \frac{1}{2}(\Omega_{m-2} - \Omega_m)$. Therefore,

$$P_{m\to m-2}(t) = \left(\frac{\gamma H_1}{2}\right)^4 \left(\frac{\sin \frac{1}{2}(\Omega_{m-2} - \Omega_m - 2\omega)t}{\frac{1}{2}(\Omega_{m-2} - \Omega_m - 2\omega)}\right)^2 \times \left| \sum_{m''} \frac{(m - 2 \mid I^- \mid m'')(m'' \mid I^- \mid m)}{\Omega_{m''} - \Omega_m + (m'' - m)\omega} \right|^2. \tag{1.3}$$

The preceding argument can be extended to multiple quantum transitions with $n > 2$. With the same restrictions on the time interval t, the probability that the system is in the state $| m - n)$ at time t is

$$P_{m\to m-n}(t) = \left(\frac{\gamma H_1}{2}\right)^{2n} \left(\frac{\sin \frac{1}{2}(\Omega_{m-n} - \Omega_m - n\omega)t}{\frac{1}{2}(\Omega_{m-n} - \Omega_m - n\omega)}\right)^2 | K_n |^2. \tag{1.4}$$

The quantity K_n is defined by

$$K_n = \sum{}' \left\{\frac{\prod_{r=0}^{n-1} (m - n + r \mid I^- \mid m - n + r + 1)}{\prod_{r=1}^{n-1} (\Omega_{m-r} - \Omega_m - \omega)}\right\}, \tag{1.5}$$

where the prime on the summation sign indicates multiple summations over all intermediate states connecting $| m)$ and $| m - n)$. For $n = 2$, (1.4) reduces to (1.3).

Equation (1.4) shows that the transition probability of an n-tuple quantum transition is proportional to the $2n$th power of the rf-field amplitude. Moveover, $P_{m\to m-n}(t)$, considered as a function of ω, has an absolute maximum at

$$\omega = \frac{1}{n}(\Omega_{m-n} - \Omega_m). \tag{1.6}$$

When the intensity of an n-tuple quantum transition is calculated, the value of ω given by (1.6) is to be inserted in the denominator of (1.5). It should also be noted that the absolute square of $(m - n + r|\, I^- \,|m - n + r + 1)$, which appears in the numerator of (1.5), is the relative intensity of the single quantum transition $|\, m - n + r + 1) \to |\, m - n + r)$. Now the coefficients in the expressions that define the eigenvectors of $\mathscr{H}$ as linear combinations of basis vectors can be chosen to be real numbers, so that one can assume that

$$(m - n + r \mid I^- \mid m - n + r + 1) = (\mathrm{Int})^{1/2}_{m-n+r+1\to m-n+r}\,. \tag{1.7}$$

The intensity of an n-tuple quantum transition may be obtained by using (1.4) to determine the transition probability per unit time, defined by

$$w_{m\to m-n} = \int dw_{m\to m-n} = \int_{-\infty}^{\infty} \lim_{t\to\infty} \left\{\frac{1}{t} P_{m\to m-n}(t)\right\} d(\Omega_{m-n} - \Omega_m - n\omega).$$

Once $w_{m\to m-n}$ has been evaluated, the intensity of the transition may be determined by a procedure analogous to that used in Section 3.E of Chapter 5. The result is

$$(\mathrm{Int})_{m\to m-n} = \frac{2\pi N_0 \gamma^{2n} H_1^{2n-1} \hbar^2 (\Omega_{m-n} - \Omega_m)^2 \mid K_n \mid^2}{2^{2n} kT \dim S}, \tag{1.8}$$

where dim S is the dimension of the spin space, and the usual approximations have been introduced in the Boltzmann distribution.

Equation (1.8) shows that the integrated intensity of an n-tuple quantum transition is proportional to H_1^{2n-1}. The increase of the signal intensity with H_1 may be used to distinguish multiple quantum transitions corresponding to different values of n. Indeed, (1.8) shows that the graph of $\log(\mathrm{Int})_{m\to m-n}$ vs. $\log H_1$ will have slope $2n - 1$.

Equations (1.6) and (1.8) are strictly applicable only in the region where the rf-field amplitude is sufficiently small to avoid saturation of the multiple quantum transition. Unfortunately, it is often difficult to avoid some degree of saturation. In such instances it is then necessary to resort to the general theory of multiple quantum transitions for intensity and frequency calculations (*4*). In particular, the general theory shows that there is a shift in the resonance frequency proportional to H_1^2. This shift is given by

$$d = (\gamma H_1)^2 \sum{}' \frac{|(m \mid I_x \mid m')|^2 - |(m' \mid I_x \mid m-n)|^2}{\Omega_{m'} - \Omega_{m-n}}. \tag{1.9}$$

The resonance frequency is now given by

$$\omega = \frac{1}{n}(\Omega_{m-n} - \Omega_m + d). \tag{1.10}$$

In the region where the transition is unsaturated, the frequency shift can be neglected. However, it should be included if accurate frequency differences are required.

C. Elementary Applications

The preceding results will be illustrated for the AB, A_2B, and the ABX systems.

1. *The* AB *System.* For the AB system, only a double quantum transition is possible: $| m = +1) \rightarrow | m' = -1)$. The intermediate states are $| 0; r)$, where $r = 1, 2$, so that (1.5) reduces to

$$K_2 = \frac{(-1 \mid I^- \mid 0; 1)(0; 1 \mid I^- \mid 1)}{[\Omega_{0;1} - \Omega_1 - \frac{1}{2}(\Omega_{-1} - \Omega_1)]} + \frac{(-1 \mid I^- \mid 0; 2)(0; 2 \mid I^- \mid 1)}{[\Omega_{0;2} - \Omega_1 - \frac{1}{2}(\Omega_{-1} - \Omega_1)]}.$$

The matrix elements and energy differences may be obtained from the work of Section 6.1:

$$(-1 \mid I^- \mid 0; 1)(0; 1 \mid I^- \mid 1) = 1 - \frac{J}{(J^2 + \delta^2)^{1/2}},$$

$$(-1 \mid I^- \mid 0; 2)(0; 2 \mid I^- \mid 1) = 1 + \frac{J}{(J^2 + \delta^2)^{1/2}},$$

$$\Omega_{0;1} - \Omega_1 - \tfrac{1}{2}(\Omega_{-1} - \Omega_1) = \tfrac{1}{2}[J + (J^2 + \delta^2)^{1/2}],$$

$$\Omega_{0;2} - \Omega_1 - \tfrac{1}{2}(\Omega_{-1} - \Omega_1) = \tfrac{1}{2}[J - (J^2 + \delta^2)^{1/2}].$$

From these results one finds $| K_2 |^2 = 64J^2/\delta^4$, so that

$$(\text{Int})_{1\rightarrow -1} = \frac{2\pi N_0 \gamma^4 H_1^3 \hbar^2 \langle\omega\rangle^2}{kT}\left(\frac{J^2}{\delta^4}\right),$$

where $\langle\omega\rangle = \frac{1}{2}(\omega_A + \omega_B)$. This shows that the intensity of the double quantum transition tends to zero as $J \rightarrow 0$, or $\delta \rightarrow \infty$.

The integrated intensities of the single quantum transitions may be calculated with (3.39) of Chapter 5. Neglecting corrections of the order of J and δ in the term $(\Omega_{m-1} - \Omega_m)^2$, one obtains

$$(\text{Int})_{1\to 0;1} = (\text{Int})_{0;1\to -1} = \frac{\gamma^2 N_0 \pi H_1 \hbar^2 \langle\omega\rangle^2}{8kT}\left\{1 - \frac{J}{(J^2+\delta^2)^{1/2}}\right\},$$

$$(\text{Int})_{1\to 0;2} = (\text{Int})_{0;2\to -1} = \frac{\gamma^2 N_0 \pi H_1 \hbar^2 \langle\omega\rangle^2}{8kT}\left\{1 + \frac{J}{(J^2+\delta^2)^{1/2}}\right\}.$$

Hence

$$\frac{(\text{Int})_{1\to -1}}{(\text{Int})_{1\to 0;1}} = \left(\frac{4\gamma H_1 J}{\delta^2}\right)^2 \left\{1 - \frac{J}{(J^2+\delta^2)^{1/2}}\right\}^{-1},$$

$$\frac{(\text{Int})_{1\to -1}}{(\text{Int})_{1\to 0;2}} = \left(\frac{4\gamma H_1 J}{\delta^2}\right)^2 \left\{1 + \frac{J}{(J^2+\delta^2)^{1/2}}\right\}^{-1}.$$

The single quantum transitions in the proton magnetic resonance spectrum of 2-bromo-5-chlorothiophene are shown in Fig. 9.1(a); Fig. 9.1(b) shows the double quantum transition (*2*) at $\frac{1}{2}(\omega_A + \omega_B)$.

2. *The* A_2B *System.* In the A_2B system, multiple quantum transitions can occur only between states of the irreducible $A_1B_{1/2}$ component. The eigenvectors of the $A_1B_{1/2}$ system are given in Table 6.4, and will be denoted $|\pm\frac{3}{2})$, $|\pm\frac{1}{2}; r)$, where $r = 1, 2$.

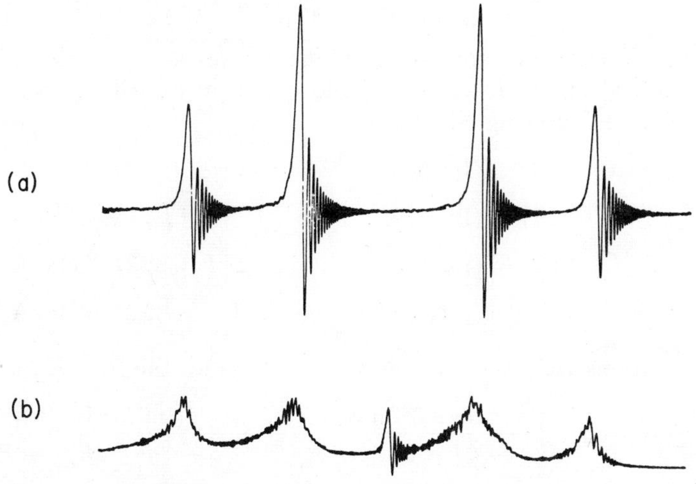

FIG. 9.1. Proton magnetic resonance spectra of pure 2-bromo-5-chlorothiophene at 60 Mcps: (a) single quantum transitions; (b) the double quantum transition at $\frac{1}{2}(\omega_A + \omega_B)$.

There are four double quantum transitions:

$$\begin{aligned} D_1: &\quad |\tfrac{3}{2}) \to |-\tfrac{1}{2}; 1), \\ D_2: &\quad |\tfrac{3}{2}) \to |-\tfrac{1}{2}; 2), \\ D_3: &\quad |\tfrac{1}{2}; 1) \to |-\tfrac{3}{2}), \\ D_4: &\quad |\tfrac{1}{2}; 2) \to |-\tfrac{3}{2}). \end{aligned}$$

The corresponding resonance frequencies are, by (1.2) and Table 6.4,

$$\begin{aligned} D_1: &\quad \tfrac{1}{4}(3\omega_A + \omega_B + \tfrac{3}{2}J + R_{1,-1}) = \tfrac{1}{2}(A_1 + A_2), \\ D_2: &\quad \tfrac{1}{4}(3\omega_A + \omega_B + \tfrac{3}{2}J - R_{1,-1}) = \tfrac{1}{2}(A_1 + B_2), \\ D_3: &\quad \tfrac{1}{4}(3\omega_A + \omega_B - \tfrac{3}{2}J - R_{1,0}) = \tfrac{1}{2}(A_4 + B_2), \\ D_4: &\quad \tfrac{1}{4}(3\omega_A + \omega_B - \tfrac{3}{2}J + R_{1,0}) = \tfrac{1}{2}(A_3 + A_4), \end{aligned}$$

where the A_i and B_i denote the frequencies of the single quantum transitions given in Table 6.5.

The intensities of the double quantum transitions require the evaluation of the four K_2's defined by (1.5) with $n = 2$. For example, K_2 for D_1 is

$$D_1: \quad K_2 = \frac{(-\tfrac{1}{2}; 1 | I^- | \tfrac{1}{2}; 1)(\tfrac{1}{2}; 1 | I^- | \tfrac{3}{2})}{\Omega_{1/2;1} - \Omega_{3/2} - \tfrac{1}{2}(\Omega_{-1/2;1} - \Omega_{3/2})} + \frac{(-\tfrac{1}{2}; 1 | I^- | \tfrac{1}{2}; 2)(\tfrac{1}{2}; 2 | I^- | \tfrac{3}{2})}{\Omega_{1/2;2} - \Omega_{3/2} - \tfrac{1}{2}(\Omega_{-1/2;1} - \Omega_{3/2})}.$$

The matrix elements appearing in the expressions for the K_2's are related to the intensities of the single quantum transitions of the A_2B system by the following equations:

$$\begin{aligned} (\tfrac{1}{2}; 1 | I^- | \tfrac{3}{2}) &= (\text{Int } A_1)^{1/2}, & (\tfrac{1}{2}; 2 | I^- | \tfrac{3}{2}) &= (\text{Int } B_1)^{1/2}, \\ (-\tfrac{1}{2}; 1 | I^- | \tfrac{1}{2}; 1) &= (\text{Int } A_2)^{1/2}, & (-\tfrac{1}{2}; 2 | I^- | \tfrac{1}{2}; 1) &= (\text{Int } B_2)^{1/2}, \\ (-\tfrac{1}{2}; 1 | I^- | \tfrac{1}{2}; 2) &= (\text{Int } M)^{1/2}, & (-\tfrac{1}{2}; 2 | I^- | \tfrac{1}{2}; 2) &= (\text{Int } A_3)^{1/2}, \\ (-\tfrac{3}{2} | I^- | -\tfrac{1}{2}; 1) &= (\text{Int } B_3)^{1/2}, & (-\tfrac{3}{2} | I^- | -\tfrac{1}{2}; 2) &= (\text{Int } A_4)^{1/2}. \end{aligned}$$

These relations yield the following expressions for the four K_2's:

$$D_1: \quad K_2 = -4 \left\{ \frac{[(\text{Int } A_2)(\text{Int } A_1)]^{1/2}}{\delta - \tfrac{3}{2}J - 2R_{1,0} + R_{1,-1}} + \frac{[(\text{Int } M)(\text{Int } B_1)]^{1/2}}{\delta - \tfrac{3}{2}J + 2R_{1,0} + R_{1,-1}} \right\},$$

$$D_2: \quad K_2 = -4 \left\{ \frac{[(\text{Int } B_2)(\text{Int } A_1)]^{1/2}}{\delta - \tfrac{3}{2}J - 2R_{1,0} - R_{1,-1}} + \frac{[(\text{Int } A_2)(\text{Int } B_1)]^{1/2}}{\delta - \tfrac{3}{2}J + 2R_{1,0} - R_{1,-1}} \right\},$$

$$D_3: \quad K_2 = 4\left\{\frac{[(\text{Int B}_3)(\text{Int A}_2)]^{1/2}}{\delta + \frac{3}{2}J + 2R_{1,-1} - R_{1,0}} + \frac{[(\text{Int A}_4)(\text{Int B}_2)]^{1/2}}{\delta + \frac{3}{2}J - 2R_{1,-1} - R_{1,0}}\right\},$$

$$D_4: \quad K_2 = 4\left\{\frac{[(\text{Int B}_3)(\text{Int M})]^{1/2}}{\delta + \frac{3}{2}J + 2R_{1,-1} + R_{1,0}} + \frac{[(\text{Int A}_4)(\text{Int A}_3)]^{1/2}}{\delta + \frac{3}{2}J - 2R_{1,-1} + R_{1,0}}\right\}.$$

The ratios of the absolute squares of these quantities may be taken as measures of the ratios of the integrated intensities of the double quantum transitions.

Figure 9.2(a) shows the single quantum transitions observed in the

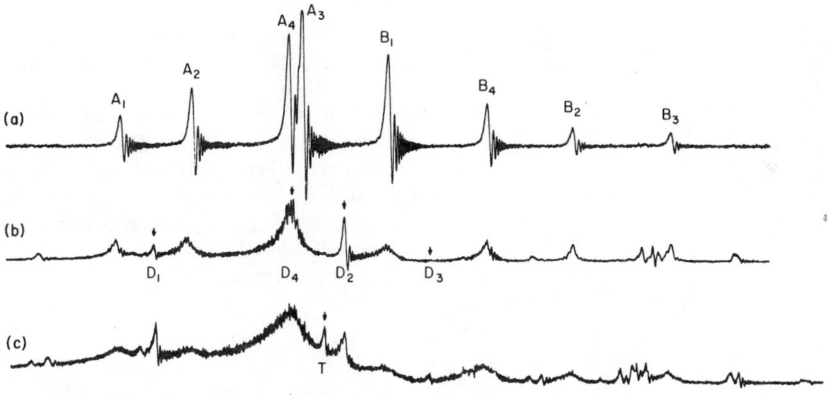

FIG. 9.2. Proton magnetic resonance spectra of 1, 2, 3-trichlorobenzene at 60 Mcps: (a) single quantum transitions of groups A and B; (b) double quantum transitions; (c) the triple quantum transition at $\frac{1}{2}(2\omega_A + \omega_B)$. The extraneous lines are attributed to spinning sidebands.

proton magnetic resonance spectrum of 1, 2, 3-trichlorobenzene in carbon disulfide. An analysis of this spectrum yields[1] $|\delta|/2\pi = 12.89$ cps, $|J|/2\pi = 8.08$ cps. With these values one finds that

$$\text{Int } D_1 : \text{Int } D_2 : \text{Int } D_3 : \text{Int } D_4 = 2 : 13 : \tfrac{1}{100} : 751.$$

The double quantum transitions are shown in Fig. 9.2(b). Transition D_4, which is calculated to be 58 times as intense as D_2, is unobserved. The reason is that D_4, which saturates at a lower power level than D_2, is saturated in Fig. 9.2(b). This is illustrated in Fig. 9.3, which shows an

[1] The value of $\delta/2\pi$ given here differs from that cited in Section 6.2 by 1.08 cps. The concentration of the 1, 2, 3-trichlorobenzene sample used to obtain the spectrum of Fig. 9.2(a) differed from that of the sample used to obtain the spectrum of Fig. 6.9, so that the difference is attributed to a solvent shift.

expanded trace of the single quantum transitions A_3, A_4, B_1, and the double quantum transitions D_4 and D_2, at successively larger amplitudes of the rf field.

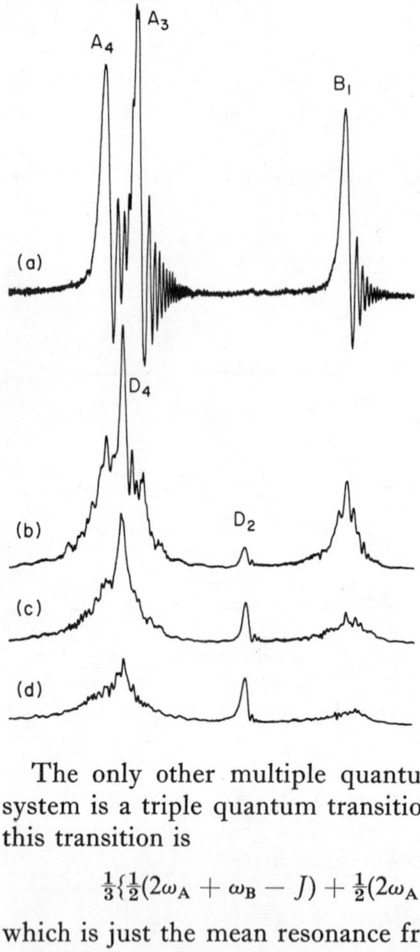

FIG. 9.3. Proton magnetic resonance spectra of 1, 2, 3-trichlorobenzene at 60 Mcps: (a) the single quantum transitions A_3, A_4, B_1; (b) the double quantum transitions D_4 and D_2. The spectra shown in parts (c) and (d) were obtained at successively higher rf amplitudes, and show that D_4 saturates at a lower power level than D_2.

The only other multiple quantum transition possible in an $A_1B_{1/2}$ system is a triple quantum transition: $|\,\frac{3}{2}) \to |-\frac{3}{2})$. The frequency of this transition is

$$\tfrac{1}{3}\{\tfrac{1}{2}(2\omega_A + \omega_B - J) + \tfrac{1}{2}(2\omega_A + \omega_B + J)\} = \tfrac{1}{3}(2\omega_A + \omega_B),$$

which is just the mean resonance frequency of the A_2B system. This is a special case of the following general result. The irreducible $A_{I_A}B_{I_B}C_{I_C}\cdots$ component of an $A_{n_A}B_{n_B}C_{n_C}\cdots$ system, for which all I_G have their maximum values, yields an N-tuple quantum transition ($N = n_A + n_B + \cdots$), whose resonance frequency is just the mean resonance frequency of the $A_{n_A}B_{n_B}C_{n_C}\cdots$ system. To prove this remark, it need only be noted that the eigenvalues for the states with $m = \pm(I_A + I_B + I_C + \cdots)$ are

$$\Big\{\mp \sum_{G} \omega_G I_G - \sum_{G<G'}\sum J_{GG'} I_G I_{G'}\Big\}.$$

Hence the frequency of the $2(I_A + I_B + \cdots)$-tuple quantum transition $|I_A + I_B + \cdots) \to |-I_A - I_B - \cdots)$ is

$$\left\{\sum_G I_G\right\}^{-1} \sum_G \omega_G I_G .$$

If all I_G have their maximum values, that is, $I_G = \frac{1}{2}n_G$, the resonance frequency is $N^{-1} \sum n_G\omega_G = \langle\omega\rangle$.

The triple quantum transition in the proton magnetic resonance spectrum of 1, 2, 3-trichlorobenzene is shown in Fig. 9.2(c).

3. *The* ABX *System.* As a final application, consider the double quantum transitions appearing in the AB region of an ABX system. In Section 7.2 it is shown that the AB region consists of two pseudo AB quartets, so that double quantum transitions should occur at the centers of these quartets. This result can often be used to pick out the pseudo AB quartets in spectra where overlapping occurs.

Figure 9.4(a) shows the single quantum transitions of the proton magnetic resonance spectra of 2-fluoro-4,6-dichlorophenol. Although the decomposition into a pair of pseudo AB quartets is discernible, the decomposition becomes patently apparent with the assistance of the double quantum transitions [Fig. 9.4(b)]. The frequency separation of the double quantum transitions is $(2\pi)^{-1}|(J_{AX} + J_{BX})| = 8.2$ cps, in agreement with the result obtained in Section 7.3. If approximate values

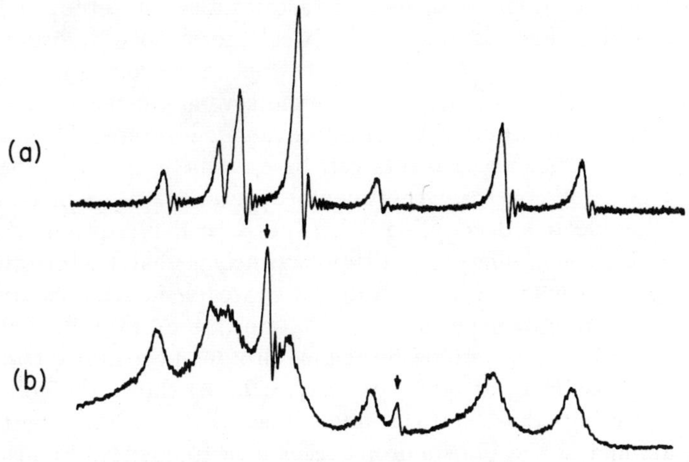

FIG. 9.4. Proton magnetic resonance spectra of 2-fluoro-4,6-dichlorophenol at 60 Mcps: (a) single quantum transitions in the AB region; (b) double quantum transitions at the mean frequencies of the pseudo AB quartets.

of $(2\pi)^{-1}| J_{AX} |$, $(2\pi)^{-1}| J_{BX} |$ are estimated (e.g., by first-order perturbation theory), the sign of J_{AX} relative to J_{BX} can be determined. This idea was used to determine the relative signs of the coupling constants in 1, 2-dibromopropionic acid (*6*).

Multiple quantum transitions have not, as yet, been extensively used in the analysis of high-resolution spectra. It seems likely, however, that the technique will enjoy greater popularity in the future. Recently, double quantum transitions have been used in conjunction with double resonance experiments to assign transitions in complex spectra (*7*).

2. Double Resonance Experiments

A. Introduction

In a nuclear double resonance experiment, the spin system is subjected to a stationary z field $\mathbf{H}_0$, and two linearly polarized rf fields directed along the z axis:

$$\mathbf{H}(t) = (2H_1 \cos \omega_1 t + 2H_2 \cos \omega_2 t, 0, H_0). \tag{2.1}$$

The rf field with maximum amplitude $2H_1$ is called the *stimulating field*; it is "weak" in the sense that it may be treated by first-order time-dependent perturbation theory. The stimulating field is used to observe the resonances of a particular group of nuclei; the second rf field, called the *perturbing* field, simultaneously irradiates a second group of nuclei. The perturbing field is said to be weak or strong, accordingly, as $| \gamma H_2 | \ll | J |$ or $| \gamma H_2 | \gg | J |$, where γ is the gyromagnetic ratio of the nuclei subjected to $\mathbf{H}_2(t)$, and J is the coupling constant describing the spin-spin interactions between the irradiated groups.

Double resonance experiments can be extremely useful in the study of high-resolution spectra. Experimental spectra can often be simplified through the selective decoupling (*12, 13*) of a particular group of spin-$\frac{1}{2}$ nuclei, or by decoupling a quadrupolar nucleus that would otherwise broaden the resonance lines of interest. Two elementary examples of these "decoupling" experiments are shown in Figs. 9.5 and 9.6. Figure 9.5(a) shows the single resonance proton spectrum of trimethylphosphite [$P(OCH_3)_3$] at 60 Mcps. Figure 9.5(b) shows the collapse of the methyl-group doublet to a single line when a strong perturbing field is applied at the phosphorous resonance frequency. Figure 9.6(a) shows the single resonance proton spectrum of formamide (H_2NCHO) at 60 Mcps. Figure 9.6(b) shows the sharpened proton resonances of formamide when a strong perturbing field is applied at the nitrogen

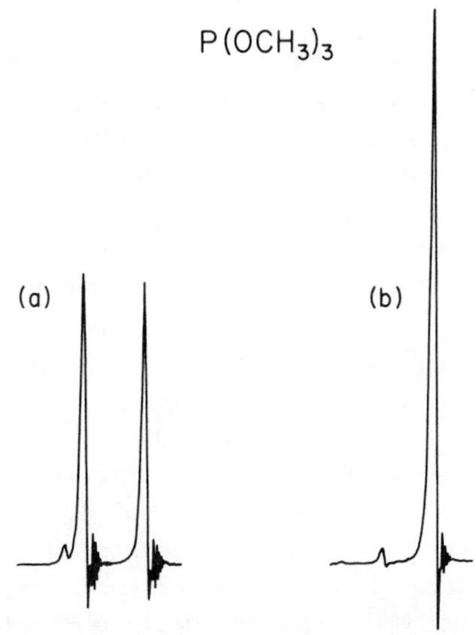

FIG. 9.5. Proton magnetic resonance spectra of trimethylphosphite: (a) single resonance spectrum at 60 Mcps; (b) double resonance spectrum at 60 Mcps with the phosphorus nucleus simultaneously irradiated at 24.28 Mcps (NMR Specialties).

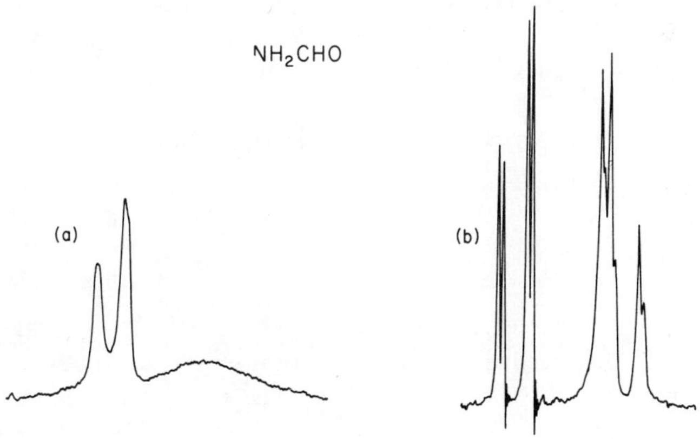

FIG. 9.6. Proton magnetic resonance spectra of formamide: (a) single resonance spectrum at 60 Mcps; (b) double resonance spectrum at 60 Mcps with the nitrogen nucleus simultaneously irradiated at 4.33 Mcps (NMR Specialties).

resonance frequency. The quantum mechanical reason for the collapse of spin-spin multiplets in double irradiation experiments will be given in Section 2.C.

Double resonance experiments can also be used to determine relative signs of spin-spin coupling constants (*14, 15*). It can be shown, through use of a generalized spin inversion operator (*16*), that a double resonance spectrum is independent of the absolute signs of the coupling constants.

A useful application is the determination of "hidden chemical shifts" (i.e., the chemical shifts of nuclei whose resonances are obscured by other resonance lines), provided that the "hidden" nuclei are coupled to other nuclei whose resonances are unobscured (*17*).

Finally, the so-called "tickling experiments" (*22*), where the stimulating and perturbing fields are both weak, provide a method for determining the relative signs of coupling constants, and information that can be used to sketch energy-level diagrams.

An extensive review of double resonance experiments, their generalizations, triple resonance, quadruple resonance, etc. (*28–31*), and their application to the study of high-resolution spectra, will not be attempted here.[2] The discussion will be limited to the elementary physical theory of double resonance for two-group systems conforming to the X approximation (*18–20*), and will be simplified by ignoring relaxation effects and deviations from a Boltzmann distribution that occur for sufficiently large amplitudes of the perturbing field (*9b*).

B. The Hamiltonian Operator

The magnetic field (2.1) may be written

$$\mathbf{H}(t) = \mathbf{H}_+(t) + \mathbf{H}_-(t) + \mathbf{H}_0 . \tag{2.2}$$

where

$$\mathbf{H}_\pm(t) = (H_1 \cos \omega_1 t + H_2 \cos \omega_2 t, \pm H_1 \sin \omega_1 t \pm H_2 \sin \omega_2 t, 0). \tag{2.3}$$

The effective transverse field for a group of magnetically equivalent nuclei is $\mathbf{H}_+(t)$ or $\mathbf{H}_-(t)$, accordingly as the common gyromagnetic ratio of the nuclei is negative or positive. In the special case of a system composed

[2] The reader interested in an extensive discussion of the subject should consult the references to this chapter; references (*19*) and (*20*) are especially recommended. The discussion in this section is based on the work of Anderson and Freeman (*19*).

entirely of magnetically equivalent groups with positive gyromagnetic ratios, the time-dependent double resonance hamiltonian is

$$\mathscr{H}(t) = -\Big\{\sum_{\mathrm{G}} \omega_{\mathrm{G}} I_{\mathrm{G}z} + \sum_{\mathrm{G}<\mathrm{G}'}\sum J_{\mathrm{GG}'} \mathbf{I}_{\mathrm{G}} \cdot \mathbf{I}_{\mathrm{G}'} + (H_1 \cos \omega_1 t + H_2 \cos \omega_2 t)$$
$$\times \sum_{\mathrm{G}} \gamma_{\mathrm{G}} I_{\mathrm{G}x} - (H_1 \sin \omega_1 t + H_2 \sin \omega_2 t) \sum_{\mathrm{G}} \gamma_{\mathrm{G}} I_{\mathrm{G}y}\Big\}. \tag{2.4}$$

It will be assumed that γ_{G} denotes $1 - \sigma_{\mathrm{G}}$ times the common gyromagnetic ratio of the unshielded nuclei in group G, so that $\omega_{\mathrm{G}} = |\gamma_{\mathrm{G}}| H_0$.

If the weak-coupling approximation is valid for some of the groups, which will usually be the case if the groups possess different gyromagnetic ratios, one may use the notation introduced in Section 7.2 to indicate qualitatively large differences of the Larmor frequencies. More important, however, is the fact that the x and y terms may be omitted from the bilinear interactions coupling groups that conform to the weak-coupling approximation.

The stationary terms of (2.4) collectively describe the stationary hamiltonian for a coupled spin system. The stationary hamiltonian admits I_z and all $\mathbf{I}_{\mathrm{G}}^2$ as constants of the motion. However, aside from the possible existence of symmetry constants of the motion, only the $\mathbf{I}_{\mathrm{G}}^2$ are conserved with respect to the time-dependent hamiltonian (2.4).

The conservation of all $\mathbf{I}_{\mathrm{G}}^2$ is an important simplification, as it allows the discussion to be restricted to a particular irreducible component defined by a fixed set of total spin quantum numbers. All results established for a generic irreducible component may be adapted to the complete system by introducing the appropriate spin multiplicities and applying the superposition principle.

The state vector of a spin system described by the hamiltonian (2.4) satisfies

$$i \frac{\partial}{\partial t} \Psi(t) = \mathscr{H}(t) \Psi(t). \tag{2.5}$$

The time-dependent terms in (2.4) represent the interaction of the nuclei with two circularly polarized rf fields, rotating in the negative sense about the z axis with frequencies ω_1 and ω_2. This suggests a transformation of the form

$$\Psi(t) = e^{i\omega t I_z} \Phi(t), \tag{2.6}$$

which is equivalent to describing the problem from a coordinate system rotating in the negative sense about the z axis with frequency ω. The transformation (2.6) will remove the time dependence of the stimulating field or the perturbing field, accordingly as $\omega = \omega_1$ or $\omega = \omega_2$. Taking $\omega = \omega_2$, equations (2.4) through (2.6) yield

$$i \frac{\partial}{\partial t} \Phi(t) = \mathscr{H}_r(t)\Phi(t), \tag{2.7}$$

where

$$\mathscr{H}_r(t) = -\Big\{\sum_{\mathrm{G}} (\omega_{\mathrm{G}} - \omega_2) I_{\mathrm{G}z} + \sum_{\mathrm{G}<\mathrm{G}'}\sum J_{\mathrm{GG}'} \mathbf{I}_{\mathrm{G}} \cdot \mathbf{I}_{\mathrm{G}'} + H_2 \sum_{\mathrm{G}} \gamma_{\mathrm{G}} I_{\mathrm{G}x}$$
$$+ H_1 \sum_{\mathrm{G}} \gamma_{\mathrm{G}}(I_{\mathrm{G}x} \cos \omega_{12} t - I_{\mathrm{G}y} \sin \omega_{12} t)\Big\}, \tag{2.8}$$

$$\omega_{12} = \omega_1 - \omega_2 . \tag{2.9}$$

Equation (2.8) shows that a similarity transformation of $\mathscr{H}(t)$ with $e^{-i\omega_2 t I_z}$ not only removes the time dependence of the perturbing field but also preserves the form of the stationary hamiltonian. However, these remarks do not apply if the system contains groups characterized by gyromagnetic ratios with different algebraic signs. For simplicity, consider two groups A and X, with $\gamma_{\mathrm{A}} > 0$, $\gamma_{\mathrm{X}} < 0$. The time-dependent hamiltonian is

$$\begin{aligned}\mathscr{H}(t) = -\{&\omega_{\mathrm{A}} I_{\mathrm{A}z} + \omega_{\mathrm{X}} I_{\mathrm{X}z} + J_{\mathrm{AX}} \mathbf{I}_{\mathrm{A}} \cdot \mathbf{I}_{\mathrm{X}} \\ &+ (H_1 \cos \omega_1 t + H_2 \cos \omega_2 t)(\gamma_{\mathrm{A}} I_{\mathrm{A}x} + \gamma_{\mathrm{X}} I_{\mathrm{X}x}) \\ &+ (H_1 \sin \omega_1 t + H_2 \sin \omega_2 t)(\gamma_{\mathrm{X}} I_{\mathrm{X}y} - \gamma_{\mathrm{A}} I_{\mathrm{A}y})\}.\end{aligned} \tag{2.10}$$

A similarity transformation with $e^{-i\omega_2 t I_z}$ will preserve the form of the stationary terms but will not remove the time dependence of the perturbing field, since $\mathscr{H}(t)$ includes the interactions of A and X with both circularly polarized components of $(2H_2 \cos \omega_2 t)\mathbf{e}_x$. However, the time dependence of the perturbing field can be removed by a similarity transformation with

$$\exp[-i\omega_2 t(I_{\mathrm{A}z} - I_{\mathrm{X}z})] = \exp(-i\omega_2 t I_{\mathrm{A}z}) \exp(i\omega_2 t I_{\mathrm{X}z}). \tag{2.11}$$

In fact,

$$\begin{aligned}&\exp[-i\omega_2 t(I_{\mathrm{A}z} - I_{\mathrm{X}z})]\mathscr{H}(t)\exp[i\omega_2 t(I_{\mathrm{A}z} - I_{\mathrm{X}z})] \\ &= -\{\omega_{\mathrm{A}} I_{\mathrm{A}z} + \omega_{\mathrm{X}} I_{\mathrm{X}z} + J_{\mathrm{AX}}[(\mathbf{I}_{\mathrm{A}} \cdot \mathbf{I}_{\mathrm{X}} - I_{\mathrm{A}z} I_{\mathrm{X}z}) \cos 2\omega_2 t \\ &\quad - (\mathbf{I}_{\mathrm{A}} \times \mathbf{I}_{\mathrm{X}})_z \sin 2\omega_2 t + I_{\mathrm{A}z} I_{\mathrm{X}z}] + H_1[(\gamma_{\mathrm{A}} I_{\mathrm{A}x} + \gamma_{\mathrm{X}} I_{\mathrm{X}x}) \cos \omega_{12} t \\ &\quad + (\gamma_{\mathrm{X}} I_{\mathrm{X}y} - \gamma_{\mathrm{A}} I_{\mathrm{A}y}) \sin \omega_{12} t] + H_2[\gamma_{\mathrm{A}} I_{\mathrm{A}x} + \gamma_{\mathrm{X}} I_{\mathrm{X}x}]\}.\end{aligned}$$

This equation shows that a similarity transformation of (2.10) with (2.11) removes the time dependence of the perturbing field, but introduces an explicit time dependence into the x and y components of the bilinear interaction $\mathbf{I}_A \cdot \mathbf{I}_X$. The reason is that the bilinear interaction is rotationally invariant, but (2.11) is not a rotation operator. An operator representing a rotation φ about a direction $\mathbf{n}$ is of the form $e^{i\varphi\mathbf{n}\cdot\mathbf{I}}$, where $\mathbf{I}$ is the *total* angular momentum in units of $\hbar$. Although it is in principle impossible to remove the difficulty, the situation is not hopeless. For, by assumption, γ_A and γ_X are of opposite sign, so that $\gamma_A \neq \gamma_X$. Hence, to a normally excellent approximation, $J_{AX}\mathbf{I}_A \cdot \mathbf{I}_X$ may be replaced by $J_{AX}I_{Az}I_{Xz}$, which is invariant under a similarity transformation with (2.11). Because of this result, there is no essential loss of generality in restricting the subsequent discussion to systems for which all $\gamma_G > 0$.

The external parameters in a nuclear double resonance experiment are H_1, H_2, ω_1, ω_2, and H_0. In a given experiment it is customary to fix H_1 and H_2 at predetermined values, and to vary one of the remaining three parameters. An experiment in which ω_1 and ω_2 are fixed, while H_0 is varied, is called a "field sweep" experiment. Experiments in which ω_1 or ω_2 is varied are called "frequency sweep" experiments. The calculation of theoretical double resonance spectra will be carried out for the frequency sweep experiment in which ω_2 and H_0 are fixed, while ω_1 is varied through the A resonances of the $A_{n_A}X_{n_X}$ system. A procedure for obtaining theoretical spectra in the field sweep experiment will be described in Section 2.D.

C. The Irreducible $A_{I_A}X_{I_X}$ System

In the special case of two groups, (2.8) reduces to

$$\begin{aligned}\mathscr{H}_r(t) = -\{&(\omega_A - \omega_2)I_{Az} + (\omega_B - \omega_2)I_{Bz} + J\mathbf{I}_A \cdot \mathbf{I}_B + H_2(\gamma_A I_{Ax} + \gamma_B I_{Bx})\\ &+ H_1[\gamma_A(I_{Ax}\cos\omega_{12}t - I_{Ay}\sin\omega_{12}t)\\ &+ \gamma_B(I_{Bx}\cos\omega_{12}t - I_{By}\sin\omega_{12}t)]\}. \end{aligned} \tag{2.12}$$

If the gyromagnetic ratios for groups A and B are not equal, B is to be replaced by X, and $\mathbf{I}_A \cdot \mathbf{I}_B$ by $I_{Az}I_{Xz}$.

Since the double resonance spectrum does not depend upon the sign of J, it will be arbitrarily assumed that $J > 0$. It will also be assumed that

$$\begin{gathered} |\omega_A - \omega_X| \gg J,\ \gamma_A H_2, \\ \omega_1 \approx \omega_A, \qquad \omega_2 \approx \omega_X. \end{gathered} \tag{2.13}$$

Under these conditions, (2.12) simplifies to

$$\mathscr{H}_r(t) = -\{(\omega_A - \omega_2)I_{Az} + (\omega_X - \omega_2)I_{Xz} + JI_{Az}I_{Xz} + \gamma_X H_2 I_{Xx} + \gamma_A H_1(I_{Ax}\cos\omega_{12}t - I_{Ay}\sin\omega_{12}t)\}. \tag{2.14}$$

The term $\gamma_A H_2 I_{Ax}$ is omitted from (2.14) since, by (2.13), $\gamma_A H_2/|\omega_{AX}| \ll 1$; the time-dependent terms containing I_{Xx} and I_{Xy} are omitted, since $|\omega_{12}|$ is off resonance for X transitions in the rotating frame:

$$|\omega_X - \omega_2 - \omega_{12}| = |\omega_X - \omega_1| \approx |\omega_{AX}|.$$

Equation (2.14) may be studied by the procedure used in Section 5.3. In particular, the time dependence of $\mathscr{H}_r(t)$ can be removed by transforming the state vector with $e^{i\omega_{12}tI_{Az}}$. The details of the analysis will not be repeated here. It need only be recalled that the time-dependent terms in (2.14) induce transitions between the energy levels of

$$\mathscr{H}_r = -\{(\omega_A - \omega_2)I_{Az} + (\omega_X - \omega_2)I_{Xz} + JI_{Az}I_{Xz} + \gamma_X H_2 I_{Xx}\}. \tag{2.15}$$

Now I_{Xz} does not commute with (2.15), but

$$[\mathscr{H}_r, I_{Az}] = 0, \tag{2.16}$$

so that the selection rules for A transitions are

$$\begin{aligned} \Delta I_A &= \Delta I_X = 0, \\ \Delta m_A &= -1, \\ \Delta m_X &= 0, \quad \pm 1, \quad \pm 2, \ldots, \pm 2I_X. \end{aligned} \tag{2.17}$$

The intensities associated with these transitions are proportional to the absolute squares of the matrix elements of I_A^-, all matrix elements being evaluated with respect to the eigenvectors of (2.15).

An initial basis for the eigenvalue problem defined by (2.15) is provided by the $(2I_A + 1)(2I_X + 1)$ product kets $\{|I_A, m_A\rangle|I_X, m_X\rangle\}$. The commutation relation (2.16) implies that the hamiltonian matrix is the direct sum of $2I_A + 1$ $(2I_X + 1)$-dimensional submatrices, each submatrix being characterized by a fixed value of m_A. The operator $\mathscr{H}_r(m_A)$ defining a generic submatrix may be obtained from (2.15) by replacing I_{Az} with m_A:

$$\mathscr{H}_r(m_A) = -\{(\omega_A - \omega_2)m_A + [(\omega_X - \omega_2) + Jm_A]I_{Xz} + \gamma_X H_2 I_{Xx}\}. \tag{2.18}$$

The mathematical significance of this device is worth emphasizing. The operator I_{Az} is more precisely written as the Kronecker product

$I_{Az} \otimes 1_X$, where 1_X is the $(2I_X + 1)$-dimensional identity operator for the spin space of X. In the subspace defined by a fixed value of m_A, the submatrix of the complete matrix for $I_{Az} \otimes 1_X$ is simply m_A times an identity matrix of dimension $(2I_X + 1)$. Therefore, the first term within the curly bracket of (2.18) actually denotes $(\omega_A - \omega_2)m_A$ times a $(2I_X + 1)$-dimensional identity operator; hence this term is just an additive constant tacked on to the diagonal elements. The remaining terms in (2.18) show that when the system is in an eigenstate characterized by the eigenvalue m_A, group X experiences an effective field (Fig. 9.7)

$$\mathbf{H}_r(\mathrm{X}, m_A) = \gamma_X^{-1} R(m_A)[\mathbf{e}_{x'} \sin\theta(m_A) + \mathbf{e}_{z'} \cos\theta(m_A)], \tag{2.19}$$

where

$$R(m_A) = \{[\omega_X - \omega_2 + Jm_A]^2 + \gamma_X^2 H_2^2\}^{1/2}, \tag{2.20}$$

$$\tan\theta(m_A) = \frac{\gamma_X H_2}{\omega_X - \omega_2 + Jm_A}. \tag{2.21}$$

The preceding remarks suggest a similarity transformation of $\mathcal{H}_r(m_A)$ with $\exp[i\theta(m_A)I_{Xy}]$:

$$\exp[i\theta(m_A)I_{Xy}]\mathcal{H}_r(m_A)\exp[-i\theta(m_A)I_{Xy}] = -\{(\omega_A - \omega_2)m_A + R(m_A)I_{Xz}\}, \tag{2.22}$$

by equations (3.10) of Chapter 2. Operating on $| I_X, m_X\rangle$ with (2.22), one obtains

$$\exp[i\theta(m_A)I_{Xy}]\mathcal{H}_r(m_A)\exp[-i\theta(m_A)I_{Xy}]| I_X, m_X\rangle = \Omega(m_A, m_X)| I_X, m_X\rangle, \tag{2.23}$$

where

$$\Omega(m_A, m_X) = -\{(\omega_A - \omega_2)m_A + m_X R(m_A)\}. \tag{2.24}$$

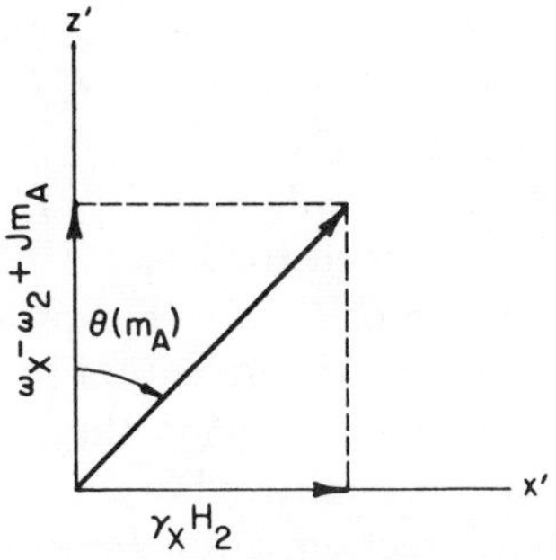

FIG. 9.7. Effective field (in equivalent frequency units) experienced by group X in the rotating frame when the z component of angular momentum for group A is m_A.

The eigenvalue problem for the $\mathscr{H}_r(m_A)$ is now solved by multiplying (2.23) from the left with $\exp[-i\theta(m_A)I_{Xy}]$:

$$\mathscr{H}_r(m_A)\exp[-i\theta(m_A)I_{Xy}]|\,I_X\,,m_X\rangle = \Omega(m_A\,,m_X)\exp[-i\theta(m_A)I_{Xy}]|\,I_X\,,m_X\rangle. \tag{2.25}$$

Thus the eigenvectors of $\mathscr{H}_r(m_A)$ are

$$|\,I_A\,,I_X\,,m_A\,;m_X) = |\,I_A\,,m_A\rangle\exp[-i\theta(m_A)I_{Xy}]|\,I_X\,,m_X\rangle, \tag{2.26}$$

where $m_X = I_X\,, I_X - 1, ..., -I_X$. The corresponding eigenvalues are given by (2.24). The eigenvalues and eigenvectors for the complete hamiltonian matrix are obtained from (2.24) and (2.26) by putting $m_A = I_A\,, I_A - 1, ..., -I_A$.

In the rotating system, transitions occur when ω_{12} is equal to the difference of two energy levels satisfying (2.17). In particular, the resonance frequency and relative intensity of the transition $|\,I_A\,,I_X\,,m_A\,;m_X) \to |\,I_A\,,I_X\,,m_A - 1;m_X')$ are given by

$$\begin{aligned}\omega_1 - \omega_2 &= \Omega(m_A - 1, m_X') - \Omega(m_A\,,m_X)\\ &= \omega_A - \omega_2 + m_X R(m_A) - m_X' R(m_A - 1),\end{aligned} \tag{2.27}$$

$$\begin{aligned}&|(I_A\,,I_X\,,m_A - 1;m_X'\,|\,I_A^-\,|\,I_A\,,I_X\,,m_A\,,m_X)|^2\\ &\quad= (I_A + m_A)(I_A - m_A + 1)|\langle I_X\,,m_X'\,|\exp[i\phi(m_A)I_{Xy}]|\,I_X\,,m_X\rangle|^2,\end{aligned} \tag{2.28}$$

where

$$\phi(m_A) = \theta(m_A - 1) - \theta(m_A), \tag{2.29}$$

$$\tan\phi(m_A) = \frac{\gamma_X H_2 J}{[\omega_X - \omega_2 + Jm_A][\omega_X - \omega_2 + J(m_A - 1)] + \gamma_X{}^2 H_2{}^2}\,. \tag{2.30}$$

The energy levels and resonance frequencies are not explicit functions of I_A and I_X, but their numbers are delimited by I_A and I_X. There are $(2I_A + 1)(2I_X + 1)$ energy levels and $2I_A(2I_X + 1)^2$ resonance frequencies.

The last factor on the right side of (2.28) is just the square of $D^{(I_X)}_{m_X' m_X}(\phi)$, which may be obtained from (1.1). This observation leads to a simple physical interpretation of (2.28). The product of the first two factors gives the relative probability of a transition in which m_A decreases by one unit $m_A \to m_A - 1$. The last factor on the right side of (2.28) gives the probability that group X is quantized in the direction $\mathbf{H}_r(\mathrm{X}, m_A - 1)$, at an angle ϕ to the initial direction, after the transition.

The transformation of (2.27) and (2.28) to the laboratory coordinate system is quite simple. In the laboratory system, transitions occur when

ω_1 is equal to the difference of two energy levels, so that (2.27) is transformed to the laboratory system by canceling ω_2 from the first and third members:

$$\omega_1 = \omega_A + m_X R(m_A) - m_X' R(m_A - 1). \tag{2.31}$$

The relative intensities in the laboratory system are given by

$$|(I_A, I_X, m_A - 1; m_X' \mid e^{-i\omega_2 t I_z} I_A^- e^{i\omega_2 t I_z} \mid I_A, I_X, m_A; m_X)|^2. \tag{2.32}$$

But

$$e^{-i\omega_2 t I_z} I_A^- e^{i\omega_2 t I_z} = e^{i\omega_2 t} I_A^-$$

by (3.5) of Chapter 2. It follows that (2.32) is independent of t, and equal to (2.28).

The resonance frequencies and relative intensities for $I_X = \frac{1}{2}, 1, \frac{3}{2}$ (I_A arbitrary) are given in Tables 9.1, 9.2, and 9.3. [The intensity calculations can be expedited through use of equations (3.47) of Chapter 2.] From Tables 9.1 through 9.3, one can obtain the full spectrum for the irreducible $A_{I_A}X_{1/2}$, $A_{I_A}X_1$, $A_{I_A}X_{3/2}$ systems by inserting the appropriate values of m_A. Note that, except for the last line of Table 9.2, each line of these tables yields two transitions.

Before discussing the implications of these calculations, two special cases will be noted.

1. $H_2 = 0$. When $H_2 = 0$, $\tan\theta(m_A) = 0$, by (2.21), so that $\theta(m_A) = \phi(m_A) = 0$, for any m_A. The exponential operator in (2.28) reduces to the identity operator, so that the relative intensities are

$$(\mathrm{Int})_{m_A \to m_A - 1} = (I_A + m_A)(I_A - m_A + 1)\, \delta_{m_X' m_X}.$$

It follows that when $H_2 = 0$, the only A transitions with nonvanishing intensities satisfy the selection rules $m_A' = m_A - 1$, $m_X' = m_X$, in agreement with the selection rules for transitions in the A region of an $A_{I_A}X_{I_X}$ system for single resonance experiments.

The resonance frequencies for $H_2 = 0$ are obtained from (2.31) by replacing $R(m_A)$ with $\omega_X - \omega_2 + J m_A$, and setting $m_X' = m_X$:

$$\omega_1 = \omega_A + J m_X, \qquad m_X = I_X, I_X - 1, ..., -I_X.$$

Thus the above calculations for double resonance experiments correctly reduce to the familiar results obtained by first-order perturbation theory for the $A_{I_A}X_{I_X}$ system.

2. $\omega_2 = \omega_X$, $\gamma_X H_2 \gg |J m_A|$. In this case, (2.30) shows that $\phi(m_A) \approx 0$. Furthermore, $R(m_A)$ may be approximated by $\gamma_X H_2$, for

TABLE 9.1

DOUBLE RESONANCE FREQUENCIES AND INTENSITIES FOR THE $A_{I_A}X_{1/2}$ SYSTEM

Transition[a]	Frequency[b]	Intensity[c]
$\pm\frac{1}{2} \rightarrow \pm\frac{1}{2}$	$\pm\frac{1}{2}[R(m_A) - R(m_A - 1)]$	$\frac{1}{2}[1 + \cos\phi(m_A)]$
$\pm\frac{1}{2} \rightarrow \mp\frac{1}{2}$	$\pm\frac{1}{2}[R(m_A) + R(m_A - 1)]$	$\frac{1}{2}[1 - \cos\phi(m_A)]$

[a] The transitions are labeled by the change in $m_X : m_X \rightarrow m_X'$.
[b] Relative to ω_A.
[c] In units of $(I_A + m_A)(I_A - m_A + 1)$.

TABLE 9.2

DOUBLE RESONANCE FREQUENCIES AND INTENSITIES FOR THE $A_{I_A}X_1$ SYSTEM

Transition[a]	Frequency[b]	Intensity[c]
$\pm 1 \rightarrow \pm 1$	$\pm [R(m_A) - R(m_A - 1)]$	$\frac{1}{4}[1 + \cos\phi(m_A)]^2$
$\pm 1 \rightarrow \mp 1$	$\pm [R(m_A) + R(m_A - 1)]$	$\frac{1}{4}[1 - \cos\phi(m_A)]^2$
$\pm 1 \rightarrow 0$	$\pm R(m_A)$	$\frac{1}{2}\sin^2\phi(m_A)$
$0 \rightarrow \pm 1$	$\mp R(m_A - 1)$	$\frac{1}{2}\sin^2\phi(m_A)$
$0 \rightarrow 0$	0	$\cos^2\phi(m_A)$

[a] The transitions are labeled by the change in $m_X : m_X \rightarrow m_X'$.
[b] Relative to ω_A.
[c] In units of $(I_A + m_A)(I_A - m_A + 1)$.

TABLE 9.3

DOUBLE RESONANCE FREQUENCIES AND INTENSITIES FOR THE $A_{I_A}X_{3/2}$ SYSTEM

Transition[a]	Frequency[b]	Intensity[c]
$\pm\frac{3}{2} \rightarrow \pm\frac{3}{2}$	$\pm\frac{3}{2}[R(m_A) - R(m_A - 1)]$	$\frac{1}{8}[1 + \cos\phi(m_A)]^3$
$\pm\frac{1}{2} \rightarrow \pm\frac{1}{2}$	$\pm\frac{1}{2}[R(m_A) - R(m_A - 1)]$	$\frac{1}{8}[1 + \cos\phi(m_A)][3\cos\phi(m_A) - 1]^2$
$\pm\frac{3}{2} \rightarrow \pm\frac{1}{2}$	$\pm\frac{3}{2}R(m_A) \mp \frac{1}{2}R(m_A - 1)$	$\frac{3}{8}\sin^2\phi(m_A)[1 + \cos\phi(m_A)]$
$\pm\frac{3}{2} \rightarrow \mp\frac{1}{2}$	$\pm\frac{3}{2}R(m_A) \pm \frac{1}{2}R(m_A - 1)$	$\frac{3}{8}\sin^2\phi(m_A)[1 - \cos\phi(m_A)]$
$\pm\frac{3}{2} \rightarrow \mp\frac{3}{2}$	$\pm\frac{3}{2}[R(m_A) - R(m_A - 1)]$	$\frac{1}{8}[1 - \cos\phi(m_A)]^3$
$\pm\frac{1}{2} \rightarrow \mp\frac{1}{2}$	$\pm\frac{1}{2}[R(m_A) \pm R(m_A - 1)]$	$\frac{1}{8}[1 - \cos\phi(m_A)][3\cos\phi(m_A) + 1]^2$
$\pm\frac{1}{2} \rightarrow \pm\frac{3}{2}$	$\pm\frac{1}{2}R(m_A) \mp \frac{3}{2}R(m_A - 1)$	$\frac{3}{8}\sin^2\phi(m_A)[1 + \cos\phi(m_A)]$
$\pm\frac{1}{2} \rightarrow \mp\frac{3}{2}$	$\pm\frac{1}{2}R(m_A) \pm \frac{3}{2}R(m_A - 1)$	$\frac{3}{8}\sin^2\phi(m_A)[1 - \cos\phi(m_A)]$

[a] The transitions are labeled by the change in $m_X : m_X \rightarrow m_X'$.
[b] Relative to ω_A.
[c] In units of $(I_A + m_A)(I_A - m_A + 1)$.

any value of m_A. The condition $\phi(m_A) \approx 0$ shows, as in case (1), that $m_X' = m_X$. Therefore, the A resonance consists of a single line at $\omega_1 = \omega_A$. This is the decoupling effect alluded to in the introduction.

The quantum mechanical interpretation of the decoupling effect is simple. Since $\phi(m_A) \approx 0$, (2.21) shows that $\theta(m_A) = \theta(m_A - 1) = \pm\pi/2$; hence A and X are quantized along axes at right angles to each other (the z and x axes, respectively) before and after a transition. When A is quantized along the z axis, and X is quantized along the x axis, the diagonal matrix elements of $J\mathbf{I}_A \cdot \mathbf{I}_X$ vanish, so that the spin-spin couplings do not yield a first-order correction to the resonance frequencies. However, second-order perturbation theory, with $J/\gamma_X H_2$ as the perturbation parameter, shows (*19*) that there is a residual splitting of $J^2(m_A - \frac{1}{2})/\gamma_X H_2$. It can also be shown (*19*) that optimum decoupling of the A multiplet is not obtained for $\omega_2 = \omega_X$, but for

$$\omega_2 = \omega_X + \frac{(\gamma_X H_2)^2}{\omega_A - \omega_X}.$$

The reason is that a strong perturbing field causes a shift in the resonance frequency. In a field sweep experiment, optimum decoupling occurs when (*19*)

$$\omega_1 - \omega_2 \approx \omega_A - \omega_X - \frac{(\gamma_X H_2)^2}{2(\omega_A - \omega_X)}.$$

D. The AX System

The theoretical double resonance spectrum for an AX system, obtained from Table 9.1 by setting $m_A = \frac{1}{2}$, is given in Table 9.4, where

$$R_\pm = [(\omega_X - \omega_2 \pm \tfrac{1}{2}J)^2 + \gamma_X^2 H_2^2]^{1/2}, \qquad \phi \equiv \phi(\tfrac{1}{2}) = \theta(-\tfrac{1}{2}) - \theta(\tfrac{1}{2}),$$

$$\tan\theta(\pm\tfrac{1}{2}) = \frac{\gamma_X H_2}{\omega_X - \omega_2 \pm \frac{1}{2}J}, \qquad \tan\phi = \frac{J\gamma_X H_2}{(\omega_X - \omega_2)^2 + \gamma_X^2 H_2^2 - \frac{1}{4}J^2}.$$

TABLE 9.4

DOUBLE RESONANCE FREQUENCIES AND INTENSITIES FOR THE AX SYSTEM

Transition	Frequency	Intensity
1. $\frac{1}{2} \to \frac{1}{2}$	$\frac{1}{2}(R_+ - R_-)$	$\cos^2 \frac{1}{2}\phi$
2. $-\frac{1}{2} \to -\frac{1}{2}$	$-\frac{1}{2}(R_+ - R_-)$	$\cos^2 \frac{1}{2}\phi$
2. $\frac{1}{2} \to -\frac{1}{2}$	$\frac{1}{2}(R_+ + R_-)$	$\sin^2 \frac{1}{2}\phi$
4. $-\frac{1}{2} \to \frac{1}{2}$	$-\frac{1}{2}(R_+ + R_-)$	$\sin^2 \frac{1}{2}\phi$

Evidently, the theoretical frequency sweep spectrum of the A resonances of an AX system is always symmetrical.

Theoretical double resonance spectra for the AX system are sketched in Fig. 9.8 for $\omega_X = \omega_2$, and several values of the dimensionless ratio $\lambda = \gamma_X H_2/J$. Table 9.4 shows that when $\omega_X = \omega_2$, the resonance frequencies of transitions 1 and 2 coincide at the frequency origin (i.e., ω_A). Figure 9.8(a) shows the 1 : 1 doublet predicted by first-order perturbation theory for $H_2 = 0$. As H_2 increases, the coincident lines increase in intensity, whereas transitions 3 and 4 decrease in intensity. As $H_2 \to \infty$, the frequencies of transitions 3 and 4 diverge to $\pm\infty$, where their intensities vanish [Fig. 9.8(h)].

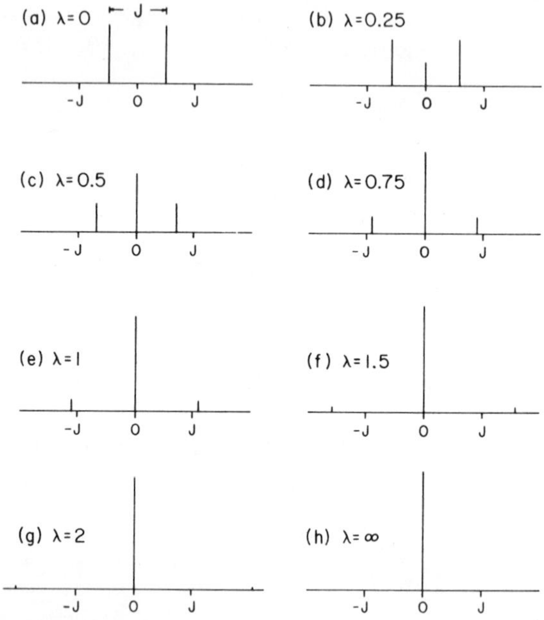

FIG. 9.8. Theoretical double resonance spectra of an AX system for $\omega_2 = \omega_X$ and several values of $\lambda = \gamma_X H_2/J$.

Because of the square roots and trigonometric functions in Tables 9.1 through 9.3, it is a great convenience to prepare graphs of the resonance frequencies and relative intensities (*18*, *19*). For this purpose, one introduces the dimensionless parameters

$$\Delta = \frac{\omega_2 - \omega_X}{J}, \qquad \Omega = \frac{\omega_1 - \omega_A}{J}. \tag{2.33}$$

Graphs of the double resonance frequencies and intensities of the AX system for $\gamma_X H_2 = 2J$ are given in Fig. 9.9. Graphs for other $A_{n_A}X_{n_X}$ systems may be found in the literature (*19*).

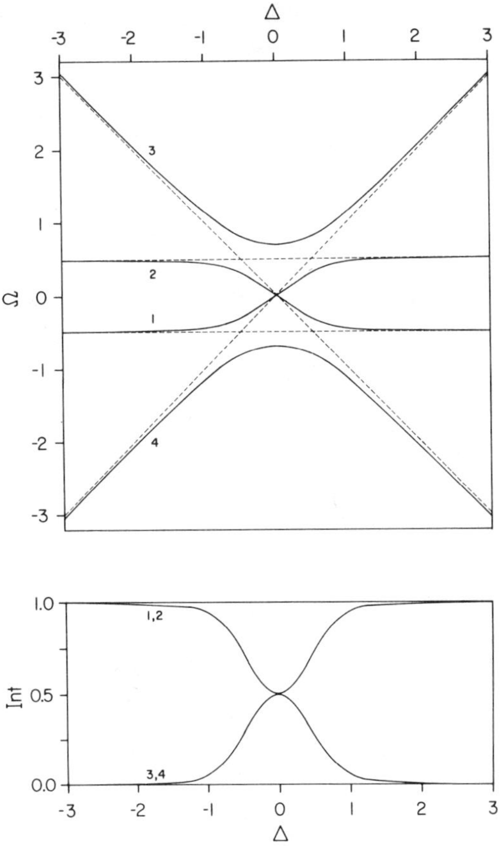

FIG. 9.9. Graphical representations of the resonance frequencies and relative intensities as a function of $\Delta = (\omega_2 - \omega_X)/J$, for $\gamma_X H_2 = 2J$. The dashed lines in the frequency plots denote asymptotes with slopes 0, $\pm$ 1.

The graphs for frequency sweep experiments can also be used for the interpretation of field sweep experiments. The procedure will be illustrated for the AX system. In the expressions for the resonance frequencies of the AX system, one replaces H_0 with $H_0 + \Delta H$, where ΔH denotes the resonant field relative to H_0. From (2.31) and Table 9.4, one obtains

$$(1, 2): \quad \omega_1 - \gamma_A H_0 - \gamma_A \Delta H = \pm\tfrac{1}{2}\{R_+(\Delta H) - R_-(\Delta H)\},$$

$$(3, 4): \quad \omega_1 - \gamma_A H_0 - \gamma_A \Delta H = \pm\tfrac{1}{2}\{R_+(\Delta H) + R_-(\Delta H)\},$$

where

$$R_{\pm}(\Delta H) = [(\omega_X - \omega_2 + \gamma_X \Delta H \pm \tfrac{1}{2}J)^2 + \gamma_X{}^2 H_2{}^2]^{1/2}. \qquad (2.34)$$

To take advantage of the graphs derived for the frequency sweep experiment it is necessary to measure ΔH in equivalent frequency units. This is accomplished by defining

$$h = \gamma_A \Delta H. \qquad (2.35)$$

In a field sweep experiment, ω_1 is fixed at $\gamma_A H_0$, so that the resonant fields, in equivalent frequency units, are given by

$$\begin{aligned} h_1 &= -\tfrac{1}{2}(R_+^{(1)} - R_-^{(1)}), \\ h_2 &= +\tfrac{1}{2}(R_+^{(2)} - R_-^{(2)}), \\ h_3 &= -\tfrac{1}{2}(R_+^{(3)} + R_-^{(3)}), \\ h_4 &= +\tfrac{1}{2}(R_+^{(4)} + R_-^{(4)}), \end{aligned} \qquad (2.36)$$

where

$$R_{\pm}^{(i)} = \left\{[\omega_X - \omega_2 + \left(\frac{\gamma_X}{\gamma_A}\right) h_i \pm \tfrac{1}{2}J]^2 + \gamma_X{}^2 H_2{}^2\right\}^{1/2}. \qquad (2.37)$$

Equations (2.36) define the h_i implicitly in terms of ω_X, ω_2, J, γ_X, and γ_X/γ_A. It should be noted, however, that the h_i have the same form as the resonance frequencies in Table 9.4, except that in $R_{\pm}^{(i)}$, $\omega_X - \omega_2$ is replaced by

$$\omega_X - \omega_2 + \frac{\gamma_X}{\gamma_A} h_i .$$

Since this expression is linear in h_i, it follows that the h_i, in units of J, are given by the points at which the frequency curves of Fig. 9.9 intersect the line

$$h = \frac{\gamma_A}{\gamma_X} \Delta + \Delta'. \qquad (2.38)$$

The intensity corresponding to the transition at h_i is given by the point at which a vertical line through h_i intersects the appropriate intensity curve in Fig. 9.9.

On the frequency curves of Fig. 9.9, (2.38) represents a line of slope γ_A/γ_X, with intercept Δ' on the vertical axis. The dimensionless parameter Δ' represents the deviation of ω_X from ω_2, in units of J, when $\omega_1 = \gamma_A H_0$. It should be noted that the widths of the lines observed in field or frequency sweep experiments will depend upon the angle at which the line (2.38) or the vertical line $\Omega = \Delta$ intersects the curve of interest. Roughly speaking, the line will be broader, the smaller the angle of intersection.

For protons, the slope of (2.38) is very close to unity (shielding corrections introduce a small deviation from unit slope). Hence, one expects, in a field sweep experiment with $\Delta \neq 0$, that line 3 or line 4 will be unobserved.

Examples of field and frequency sweep experiments on dichloroacetaldehyde are shown in Fig. 9.10. The numbers enclosed within each frame denote $J\Delta'$ (field sweep spectra) and $J\Delta$ (frequency sweep spectra). The theoretical field sweep spectra may be obtained from the given values of Δ' and the curves of Fig. 9.9.

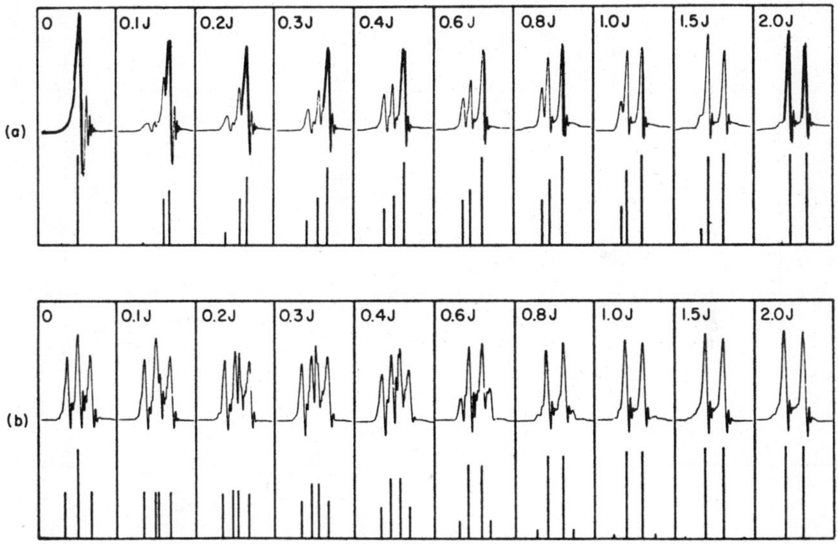

FIG. 9.10. Experimental and theoretical double resonance spectra of the A proton in dichloroacetaldehyde at 60 Mcps: (a) the field sweep method; (b) the frequency sweep method. [Freeman and Whiffen (*18*).]

The method for obtaining field sweep spectra for the AX system may also be applied to other $A_{n_A}X_{n_X}$ systems (*19*). Figures 9.11 and 9.12 illustrate the results of field and frequency sweep experiments with acetaldehyde (*19*).

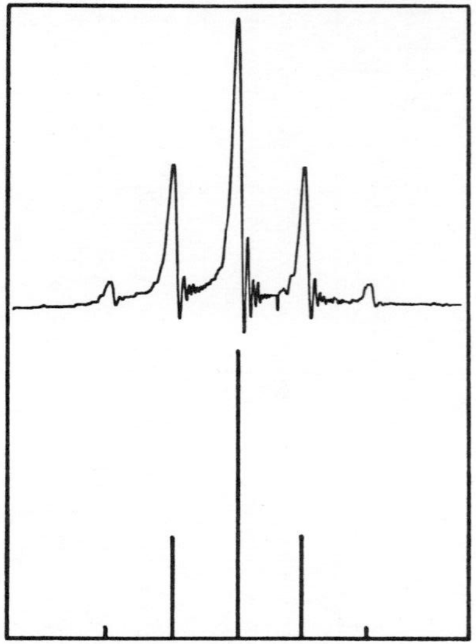

FIG. 9.11 (Above). Experimental and theoretical double resonance frequency sweep spectra of the aldehyde proton in acetaldehyde at 60 Mcps, with $\Delta = 0$, and $\gamma_X H_2 = J$. [Anderson and Freeman (*19*).]

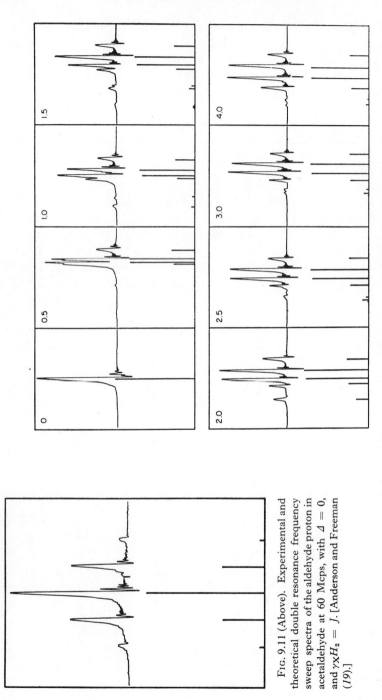

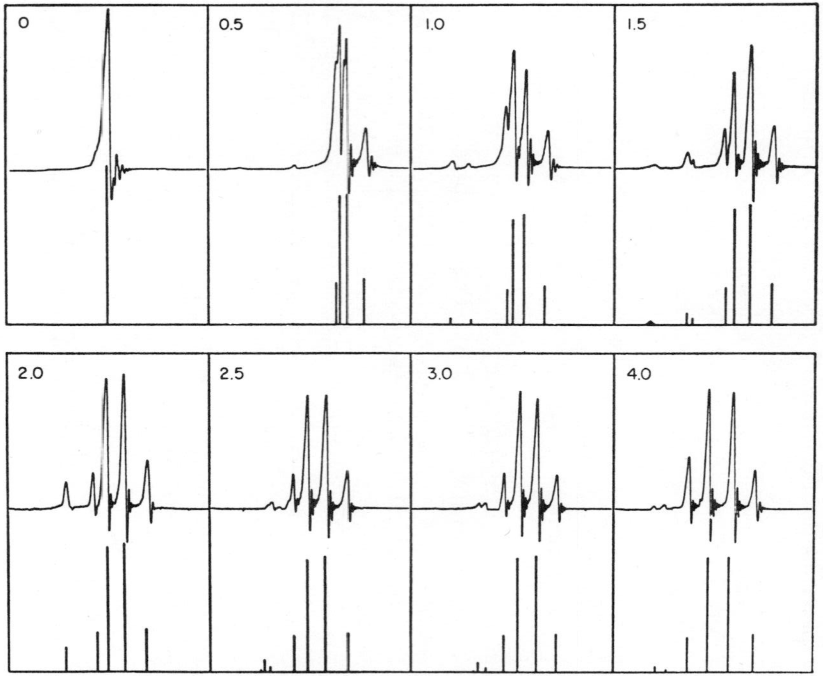

FIG. 9.12 (Right). Experimental and theoretical double resonance field sweep spectra of the aldehyde proton in acetaldehyde at 60 Mcps. The half-amplitude of the perturbing field is fixed at $H_2 = 2J/\gamma_X$, and Δ' has the values indicated. Resonances expected to be abnormally broad have been arbitrarily assigned a triangular line shape. [Anderson and Freeman (*19*).]

E. Tickling Experiments

An interesting consequence of the theory described in Section 2.C occurs when $\gamma_X H_2 \ll J$, and the frequency of the (now weak) perturbing field is adjusted to one of the X lines of the $A_{I_A}X_{I_X}$ system:

$$\omega_2 = \omega_X + Jm_A. \tag{2.39}$$

In this case, the frequencies (2.31) reduce to

$$\begin{aligned} \omega_1 &= \omega_A + m_X\gamma_X H_2 - m_X'(J^2 + \gamma_X{}^2 H_2{}^2)^{1/2} \\ &\approx \omega_A + m_X\gamma_X H_2 - Jm_X', \end{aligned} \tag{2.40}$$

since $\gamma_X H_2 \ll J$. When $H_2 = 0$, the A region of the irreducible $A_{I_A}X_{I_X}$ system consists of $2I_X + 1$ lines, the frequency separation of adjacent lines being J. Equation (2.40) shows that when $H_2 \neq 0$, and $\gamma_X H_2 \ll J$, each line of the original multiplet is split into a submultiplet of $2I_X + 1$ lines, with adjacent lines of the submultiplet separated by $\gamma_X H_2$. Aside from intensity considerations, it is clear that $\gamma_X H_2$ must exceed the line widths of the A resonances in order for the lines of the submultiplet to be observable.

The intensities of the submultiplet components are given by (1.1) and (2.28). The angle $\phi(m_A) \approx \pi/2$, by (2.30) and (2.39), so that (1.1) reduces to

$$P^{(I)}_{m\to m'}\left(\frac{\pi}{2}\right) = \left(\frac{1}{2}\right)^{2I} \frac{(I+m')!(I-m')!}{(I+m)!(I-m)!} \left\{\sum_k (-1)^{m-m'+k} \binom{I+m}{I+m'-k}\binom{I-m}{k}\right\}^2. \tag{2.41}$$

To illustrate these results, consider the A resonances of the AX system. It will be useful to keep in mind the energy-level diagram of the AX system and the corresponding single resonance spectrum (Fig. 9.13). When $\omega_2 = \omega_X - \frac{1}{2}J$, $\phi \approx \pi/2$, and Table 9.4 yields four lines of equal

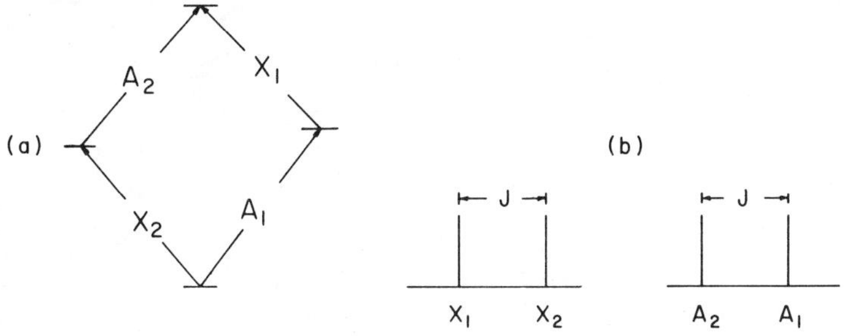

FIG. 9.13. Schematic energy-level diagram for the AX system, and the corresponding single resonance spectrum.

intensity at $\pm \frac{1}{2}(J - \frac{1}{2}\gamma_X H_2)$, $\pm \frac{1}{2}(J + \frac{3}{2}\gamma_X H_2)$, relative to ω_A. Figure 9.14 shows the splitting of each component of the "normal" A doublet into a pair of submultiplets when X_1 is irradiated with a weak perturbing field at the resonance frequency of X_1. A similar spectrum for the A region is obtained when X_2 is irradiated at $\omega_2 = \omega_X + \frac{1}{2}J$.

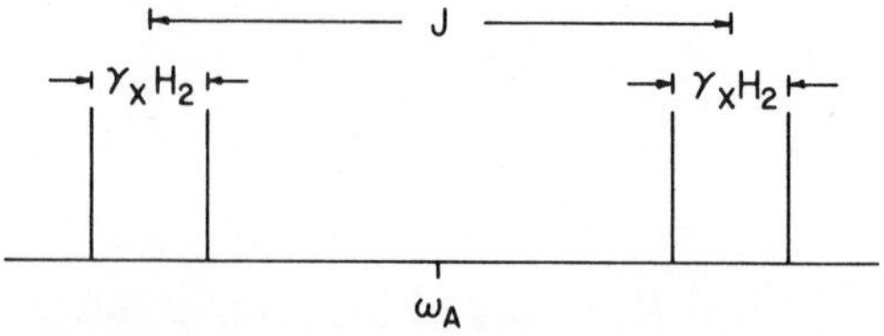

FIG. 9.14. The splitting of the A resonances of an AX system when X_1 or X_2 is irradiated with a weak perturbing field at the resonance frequency of X_1 or X_2.

These results can be stated somewhat differently by noting the relation of X_1, X_2, A_1, and A_2 in the energy-level diagram of Fig. 9.13(a). When X_1 or X_2 is irradiated, A_1 and A_2 are split into doublets. The splitting arises because A_1 and A_2 have an energy level in common with the transition being irradiated (*19*, *22*). Two transitions having a common energy level are called *connected transitions*. With this terminology, one can state that an A transition will be split into a submultiplet if it is connected with the irradiated X transition.

Connected transitions are further classified as *regressive* or *progressive*, accordingly as two of the three energy levels have the same eigenvalues of I_z, or eigenvalues of I_z that differ by two units. For example, in Fig. 9.13(a), A_2 and X_1 are regressive, X_1 and A_1 are progressive.

The theory of the tickling experiment can be readily extended to systems that do not conform to the weak-coupling approximation (*22*), provided that $\mathbf{H}_2$ appreciably perturbs only one transition in a given experiment. In this case, only the two states subjected to the perturbing field are mixed, so that one need only solve a 2×2 matrix to obtain the perturbed eigenvalues and eigenvectors. The development of the theory (*22*) shows that

(1) If a nondegenerate transition is subjected to a weak perturbing field, all connected transitions will be split into doublets.

(2) If the line widths are determined by the inhomogeneity of the z field, regressive transitions are split into well-resolved doublets, and progressive transitions are split into broadened doublets.

(3) The doublet splitting is proportional to H_2 and the square root of the intensity of the irradiated line.

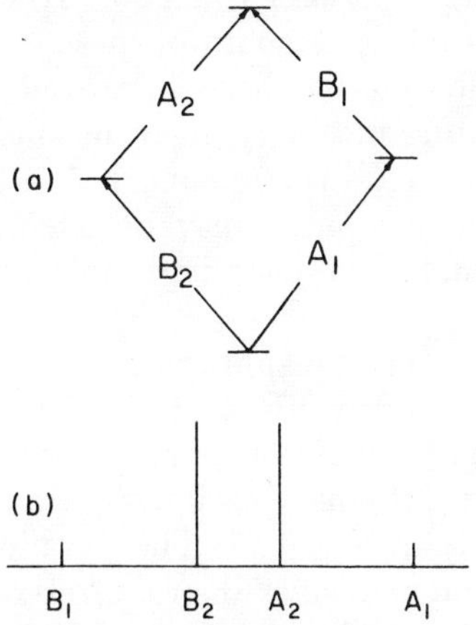

FIG. 9.15 (Above). Schematic energy-level diagram for the AB system, and the corresponding single resonance spectrum.

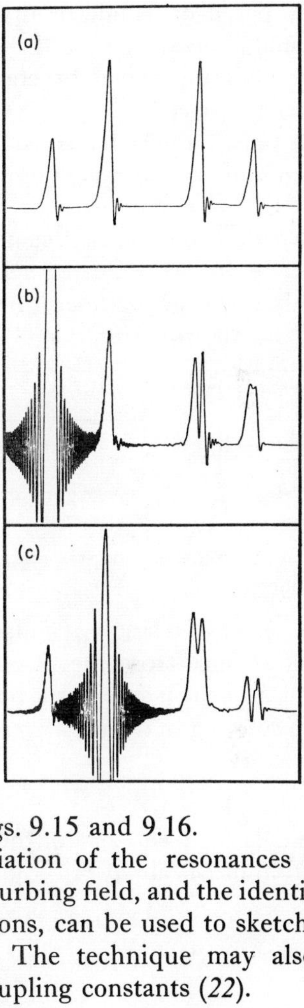

FIG. 9.16 (Right). Proton magnetic resonance spectrum of 2-bromo-5-chlorothiophene (frequency sweep): (a) single resonance spectrum; (b) with the frequency of the perturbing field at the resonance frequency of B_1; (c) with ω_2 at the resonance frequency of B_2. The beat frequencies in (b) and (c) arise during the passage of ω_1 through ω_2. [Freeman and Anderson (*22*).]

Rules (1) and (2) are illustrated by Figs. 9.15 and 9.16.

It is evident that the systematic irradiation of the resonances of a high-resolution spectrum with a weak perturbing field, and the identification of progressive and regressive transitions, can be used to sketch out an energy-level diagram for the system. The technique may also be used to determine the relative signs of coupling constants (*22*).

3. Spin Echo Experiments

A. Introduction

The first exact determinations of internal chemical shifts and spin-spin coupling constants were obtained from analyses of the so-called *spin echo* or *pulsed nuclear magnetic resonance experiments* (*23*, *24*). It seems appropriate, therefore, to conclude with a brief account of these experiments. Although the experimental technique has been improved (*25*), current determinations of chemical shifts and coupling constants are usually based on single or double resonance experiments. It has been suggested, however, that the spin echo technique may be useful for precise determinations of chemical shifts and coupling constants in particular cases (*26*).

In a pulsed nuclear resonance experiment, the spin system, assumed to be initially at thermal equilibrium in a steady z field $\mathbf{H}_0$, is subjected to one or more rf pulses. In the original experiments the pulses were directed along the x axis. A sequence of two rf pulses, each with maximum amplitude H_1, is indicated schematically in Fig. 9.17. The duration of the pulses will be assumed to be very much smaller than the relaxation times and the time interval τ between successive pulses.

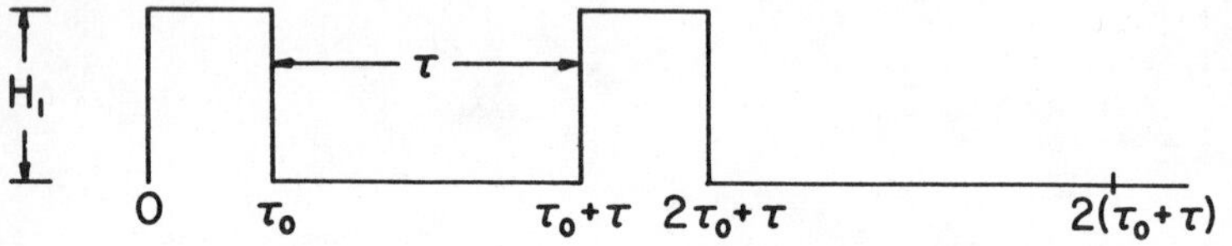

FIG. 9.17. Schematic representation of two rf pulses. In the usual experimental arrangement, $\tau_0 \ll \tau$.

The effect of a single rf pulse on an initial magnetization $\mathbf{M}_0 = M_0\mathbf{e}_z$ follows at once from the discussion in Section 1.3. It will be assumed that the rf field is circularly polarized, and that $\gamma > 0$. In a coordinate system rotating in the negative sense about the z axis, the effective field is

$$\mathbf{H}_e = \left(H_1, 0, H_0 - \frac{\omega}{\gamma}\right),$$

where ω is the frequency of the rf field. A pulse of duration τ_0 generates a rotation of $\mathbf{M}_0$ about $\mathbf{H}_e$, the angle of rotation being

$$|\gamma\mathbf{H}_e|\,\tau_0 = \tau_0[(\gamma H_1)^2 + (\omega_0 - \omega)^2]^{1/2},$$

where $\omega_0 = \gamma H_0$. When $\omega = \omega_0$, the angle of rotation is

$$\varphi = \gamma H_1 \tau_0 \qquad (\omega = \omega_0). \tag{3.1}$$

An rf pulse satisfying (3.1) is called a "φ pulse." In particular, one speaks of a 90° or 180° pulse, accordingly as $\varphi = \pi/2$ or π (Fig. 9.18).

It is evident that after a single φ pulse, relaxation processes will eventually restore the initial magnetization $\mathbf{M}_0$. The signals induced by the precessing magnetization during the return to thermal equilibrium are called *free induction decays*. If a second "refocusing" pulse is applied,

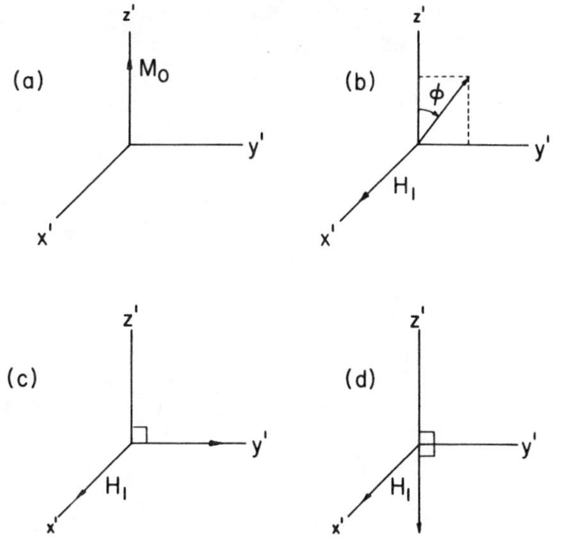

FIG. 9.18. Rotation of the initial magnetization $M_0\mathbf{e}_z$ (a), following a φ pulse (b), a 90° pulse (c), and a 180° pulse (d).

as in Fig. 9.17, a signal, called the *spin echo*, appears at $t = 2(\tau + \tau_0) \approx 2\tau$. In the special case of a system conforming to Bloch's phenomenological theory, the echo amplitude at $t = 2\tau$ may be obtained by solving the Bloch equations for each region of Figure 9.17, assuming continuity of the nuclear magnetization at the boundaries. The calculation shows that the echo amplitude, regarded as a function of τ, decays monotonically with τ. On the other hand, spin systems with $J, \delta \neq 0$, exhibit a modulation of the echo envelope (i.e., the graph of the echo amplitude versus τ). The Bloch equations do not include the perturbations arising from chemical shifts and spin-spin interactions, so that a quantum mechanical analysis is required. The quantity to be calculated is the expectation value of the nuclear magnetization in the xy plane at $t = 2\tau$. Since the system is at thermal equilibrium when $t = 0$, it is necessary to take a statistical average over an initial Boltzmann distribution.

B. The Boltzmann Distribution Matrix

The quantum mechanical expectation value of an operator X at time t is [cf. equations (1.21) and (1.22) in Chapter 3]

$$\langle \mathrm{X} \rangle_t = \Psi^\dagger(t)\mathrm{X}\Psi(t) = \sum_j \sum_k c_j(t) c_k^*(t) \mathrm{X}_{kj}\,, \qquad (3.2)$$

where $\Psi(t)$ is the state vector at time t and the $c_j(t)$ its expansion coefficients relative to a suitable initial basis. The state vector $\Psi(t)$ can be related to $\Psi(0)$ by a unitary operator $U(t)$,

$$\Psi(t) = U(t)\Psi(0), \tag{3.3}$$

so that

$$\langle \mathrm{X} \rangle_t = \Psi^\dagger(0)U^\dagger(t)\mathrm{X}U(t)\Psi(0) = \sum_j \sum_k c_j(0)c_k{}^*(0)[U^\dagger(t)\mathrm{X}U(t)]_{kj}\,. \tag{3.4}$$

This equation can be written

$$\langle \mathrm{X} \rangle_t = \mathrm{tr}\; C(0)U^\dagger(t)\mathrm{X}U(t), \tag{3.5}$$

where

$$C_{ij}(0) = c_j(0)c_i{}^*(0). \tag{3.6}$$

The statistical average of (3.5) is

$$\langle \bar{\mathrm{X}} \rangle_t = \mathrm{tr}\; \rho U^\dagger(t)\mathrm{X}U(t), \tag{3.7}$$

where ρ denotes the statistical average of $C(0)$. By assumption, the system is initially at thermal equilibrium, so that

$$\rho_{ij} = 0, \qquad \text{for} \quad i \neq j,$$

$$\frac{\rho_{ii}}{\rho_{jj}} = \frac{N_i}{N_j} = \exp[-\hbar(\Omega_i - \Omega_j)/kT],$$

where N_i is the occupation number of the ith eigenstate with energy $\hbar\Omega_i$. If the trace of ρ is normalized to the number of systems contained in a macroscopic unit of volume, ρ can be written in operator form as

$$\rho = \frac{N_0 \exp[-\hbar\mathscr{H}_0/kT]}{\mathrm{tr}\exp[-\hbar\mathscr{H}_0/kT]}, \tag{3.8}$$

where $\mathscr{H}_0$ is the stationary hamiltonian prevailing at $t = 0$. In the following discussion, the conditions $|\hbar\Omega_i| \ll kT$, $\mathrm{tr}\,\mathscr{H}_0 = 0$, will be satisfied, so that (3.8) simplifies to

$$\rho = \frac{N_0}{\dim S}\left(1 - \frac{\hbar\mathscr{H}_0}{kT}\right), \tag{3.9}$$

where dim S is the dimension of the spin space.

To illustrate the use of (3.9), consider a single nucleus with spin I in a stationary z field $\mathbf{H}_0$. In this case, $\mathscr{H}_0 = -\gamma H_0 I_z$, and dim $S = 2I + 1$; hence

$$\rho = \frac{N_0}{2I + 1}\left(1 + \frac{\gamma\hbar H_0}{kT} I_z\right). \tag{3.10}$$

The statistical average of I_z at $t = 0$ is, by (3.7),

$$\overline{\langle I_z \rangle}_0 = \text{tr}\, \rho I_z = \frac{N_0}{2I+1} \left\{ \text{tr}\, I_z + \frac{\gamma \hbar H_0}{kT} \text{tr}\, I_z^2 \right\}$$

$$= \frac{N_0 \gamma \hbar H_0 I(I+1)}{3kT}.$$

The steady nuclear polarization is

$$\gamma \hbar \overline{\langle I_z \rangle}_0 = M_0 = \frac{N_0 H_0 \mu^2}{3kT} \left(\frac{I+1}{I} \right),$$

in agreement with the result derived in Chapter 1. Similar calculations show that $\overline{\langle I_x \rangle}_0 = \overline{\langle I_y \rangle}_0 = 0$.

As a second application of (3.10), the magnetization in the xy plane following a single φ pulse will be calculated. The time-dependent hamiltonian is

$$\mathscr{H}(t) = -\{\omega_0 I_z + \gamma H_1 (I_x \cos \omega t - I_y \sin \omega t)\}, \tag{3.11}$$

where $\omega_0 = \gamma H_0$. Introducing the transformation (2.6), one finds that

$$i \frac{\partial \Phi}{\partial t} = -\{\Delta I_z + \gamma H_1 I_x\} \Phi, \tag{3.12}$$

where $\Delta = \omega_0 - \omega$. The solution of (3.12) is

$$\Phi(t) = \exp[i(t - t_0)(\Delta I_z + \gamma H_1 I_x)] \Phi(0). \tag{3.13}$$

If the rf pulse is applied from $t_0 = 0$ to $t = \tau_0$, and the rf frequency is so close to ω_0 that $\Delta \tau_0 \ll 1$, $\tau_0 \Delta I_z$ can be dropped from the exponential argument, and (3.13) simplifies to

$$\Phi(\tau_0) = e^{i\varphi I_x} \Phi(0). \tag{3.14}$$

For $t > \tau_0$, the solution of (3.12) is

$$\Phi(t) = e^{i\Delta t I_z} \Phi(\tau_0), \tag{3.15}$$

since $H_1 = 0$ for $t > \tau_0$. Combining (3.14), (3.15), and (2.6), one obtains

$$\Psi(t) = e^{i\omega t I_z} e^{i\Delta t I_z} e^{i\varphi I_x} \Psi(0)$$

$$= e^{i\omega_0 t I_z} e^{i\varphi I_x} \Psi(0), \tag{3.16}$$

which is of the form (3.3), with $U = e^{i\omega_0 t I_z} e^{i\varphi I_x}$. From (3.7) and (3.16), the x and y components of the nuclear magnetization are given by

$$\begin{aligned}\gamma\hbar\langle\overline{I^\pm}\rangle_t &= M_x \pm iM_y \\ &= \frac{N_0}{2I+1}\,\mathrm{tr}\left\{\left(1 + \frac{\hbar\omega_0}{kT} I_z\right) e^{-i\varphi I_x} e^{-i\omega_0 t I_z} I^\pm e^{i\omega_0 t I_z} e^{i\varphi I_x}\right\} \\ &= \frac{N_0 e^{\mp i\omega_0 t}}{2I+1}\left(\frac{\hbar\omega_0}{kT}\right)\mathrm{tr}\, I_z e^{-i\varphi I_x} I^\pm e^{i\varphi I_x},\end{aligned}$$

since

$$e^{-i\omega_0 t I_z} I^\pm e^{i\omega_0 t I_z} = e^{\mp i\omega_0 t} I^\pm$$

and

$$\mathrm{tr}\, e^{-i\varphi I_x} I^\pm e^{i\varphi I_x} = \mathrm{tr}\, I^\pm = 0.$$

Now

$$\begin{aligned}\mathrm{tr}\, I_z\, e^{-i\varphi I_x} I^\pm e^{i\varphi I_x} &= \mathrm{tr}\, I^\pm\, e^{i\varphi I_x} I_z e^{-i\varphi I_x} \\ &= \mathrm{tr}\{(I_y \sin\varphi + I_z \cos\varphi) I^\pm\} \\ &= \pm\frac{i}{3} I(I+1)(2I+1)\sin\varphi,\end{aligned}$$

so that

$$M_\pm(t) = \pm iM_0\, e^{\mp i\omega_0 t}\sin\varphi,$$

or

$$M_x(t) = M_0 \sin\varphi \sin\omega_0 t, \qquad M_y(t) = M_0 \sin\varphi\cos\omega_0 t.$$

These results are exactly what would be predicted on the basis of classical arguments. The φ pulse turns the z magnetization through an angle φ about the x axis as in Fig. 9.18(b). The y magnetization immediately following the pulse is $M_0 \sin\varphi$, and, after the pulse is turned off, this component precesses in the negative sense about $H_0\mathbf{e}_z$.

C. Modulation of the Echo Envelope

The modulation of the echo amplitude following a pair of 90° pulses will be calculated for the AB system (*23, 24*). To simplify the discussion, nuclear magnetic relaxation, molecular diffusion, and the inhomogeneity of $\mathbf{H}_0$ will be neglected (*23, 24*).

The stationary hamiltonian for the system will be written

$$\mathscr{H}_0 = -\{\tfrac{1}{2}(\omega_A + \omega_B) I_z + \tfrac{1}{2}\delta(I_{Az} - I_{Bz}) + J\mathbf{I}_A\cdot\mathbf{I}_B\}, \tag{3.17}$$

where $\delta = \omega_A - \omega_B$. Since $|\hbar\delta| \ll kT$, $|\hbar J| \ll kT$, and dim $S = 4$, (3.9) becomes

$$\rho = \frac{N_0}{4}\left\{1 + \frac{\hbar(\omega_A + \omega_B)}{2kT} I_z\right\}. \tag{3.18}$$

The time-dependent hamiltonian during a pulse is

$$\mathscr{H}(t) = -\{\omega_A I_{Az} + \omega_B I_{Bz} + J\mathbf{I}_A \cdot \mathbf{I}_B + \gamma H_1(I_x \cos \omega t - I_y \sin \omega t)\}. \quad (3.19)$$

Introducing the transformation (2.6), one finds that the Schrödinger equation in the rotating coordinate system is

$$i\frac{\partial \Phi}{\partial t} = \mathscr{H}_r \Phi, \quad (3.20)$$

where

$$\mathscr{H}_r = -\{(\omega_A - \omega)I_{Az} + (\omega_B - \omega)I_{Bz} + J\mathbf{I}_A \cdot \mathbf{I}_B + \gamma H_1 I_x\}. \quad (3.21)$$

It will now be assumed that ω_A, ω_B, ω, J, and τ_0 satisfy the conditions

$$|\,\omega_A - \omega\,|\,\tau_0\,,\ |\,\omega_B - \omega\,|\,\tau_0\,,\ |\,J\,|\,\tau_0 \ll 1. \quad (3.22)$$

Under these conditions, only $\gamma H_1 I_x$ need be retained in (3.21) during a pulse. Therefore,

$$\Phi(\tau_0) = e^{i\varphi I_x}\Phi(0),$$

$$\Phi(\tau + 2\tau_0) = e^{i\varphi I_x}\Phi(\tau + \tau_0).$$

When $H_1 = 0$, the hamiltonian in the rotating system is $\mathscr{H}_0 + \omega I_z = \mathscr{H}_0'$, so that

$$\Phi(\tau + \tau_0) = \exp(-\tau\mathscr{H}_0')\Phi(\tau_0),$$

$$\Phi(t) = \exp[-i(t - \tau - 2\tau_0)\mathscr{H}_0']\Phi(2\tau_0 + \tau) \qquad (t > \tau + 2\tau_0).$$

Combining the preceding equations, and returning to the laboratory coordinate system, one obtains

$$\Psi(t) = \exp(i\omega t I_z) \exp[-i(t - \tau)\mathscr{H}_0'] \exp(i\varphi I_x) \exp(-i\tau\mathscr{H}_0') \exp(i\varphi I_x)\Psi(0), \quad (3.23)$$

where use has been made of the fact that $2\tau_0 \ll \tau$.

The nuclear magnetization in the xy plane is equal to the statistical average of $\gamma\hbar\langle I^+\rangle_t$ or $\gamma\hbar\langle I^-\rangle_t$. From (3.23),

$$\langle I^+\rangle_t = e^{-i\omega t}\Psi^\dagger(0)U^\dagger(t)I^+U(t)\Psi(0), \quad (3.24)$$

where

$$U = \exp[-i(t - \tau)\mathscr{H}_0'] \exp(i\varphi I_x) \exp(-i\tau\mathscr{H}_0') \exp(i\varphi I_x). \quad (3.25)$$

The statistical average of (3.24) is, therefore,

$$\overline{\langle I^+\rangle}_t = \frac{N_0(\omega_A + \omega_B)e^{-i\omega t}}{8kT}\{\mathrm{tr}\, I_z U^\dagger(t) I^+ U(t)\}. \quad (3.26)$$

The contribution from the identity operator of (3.18) vanishes, since $\operatorname{tr} U^\dagger(t)I^+U(t) = 0$.

In the special case where $\varphi = \pi/2$, the trace in (3.26) simplifies to

$$\operatorname{tr} I_z U^\dagger(t)I^+U(t) = \operatorname{tr} \exp(-i\tau\mathscr{H}_0')I_y \exp(i\tau\mathscr{H}_0') \exp\left(-i\frac{\pi}{2}I_x\right)$$
$$\times \exp[i(t-\tau)\mathscr{H}_0']I^+ \exp[-i(t-\tau)\mathscr{H}_0'] \exp\left(i\frac{\pi}{2}I_x\right). \quad (3.27)$$

The remaining trace is most conveniently evaluated relative to the basis that diagonalizes $\mathscr{H}_0'$. The eigenvectors and eigenvalues of $\mathscr{H}_0'$ are

$$u_1 = |++\rangle, \qquad u_2 = c|+-\rangle + s|-+\rangle,$$
$$u_3 = -s|+-\rangle + c|-+\rangle, \qquad u_4 = |--\rangle,$$
$$\Omega_1 = -\tfrac{1}{2}\{\omega_A + \omega_B - 2\omega + \tfrac{1}{2}J\}, \qquad \Omega_2 = \tfrac{1}{2}(\tfrac{1}{2}J - R),$$
$$\Omega_3 = \tfrac{1}{2}(\tfrac{1}{2}J + R), \qquad \Omega_4 = \tfrac{1}{2}\{\omega_A + \omega_B - 2\omega - \tfrac{1}{2}J\},$$

where

$$c = \frac{1}{(1+Q^2)^{1/2}}, \qquad s = \frac{Q}{(1+Q^2)^{1/2}}, \qquad Q = \frac{J}{\delta + R}, \qquad R = (J^2 + \delta^2)^{1/2}.$$

Relative to this basis, the matrices for I^+ and I_y are

$$I^+ = \begin{pmatrix} 0 & c+s & c-s & 0 \\ 0 & 0 & 0 & c+s \\ 0 & 0 & 0 & c-s \\ 0 & 0 & 0 & 0 \end{pmatrix},$$

$$I_y = \frac{1}{2}i \begin{pmatrix} 0 & -(c+s) & -(c-s) & 0 \\ c+s & 0 & 0 & -(c+s) \\ c-s & 0 & 0 & -(c-s) \\ 0 & c+s & c-s & 0 \end{pmatrix}.$$

The matrices for $\exp(-i\tau\mathscr{H}_0')I_y\exp(i\tau\mathscr{H}_0')$ and $\exp[i(t-\tau)\mathscr{H}_0']I^+ \exp[-i(t-\tau)\mathscr{H}_0']$ may now be computed by equation (1.27) of Chapter 3. The matrix for $e^{i(\pi/2)I_x}$ is, by Table 4.1 and equation (3.17) of Chapter 2,

$$e^{i(\pi/2)I_x} = \frac{1}{2} \begin{pmatrix} 1 & i(c+s) & i(c-s) & -1 \\ i(c+s) & 1-2cs & -(c^2-s^2) & i(c+s) \\ i(c-s) & -(c^2-s^2) & 1+2cs & i(c-s) \\ -1 & i(c+s) & i(c-s) & 1 \end{pmatrix}.$$

The trace calculation is straightforward, but very tedious. The echo amplitude at $t = 2\tau$ is obtained by collecting the coefficients of $\exp[-(i/2)(\omega_A + \omega_B - 2\omega)(t - 2\tau)]$. One finds that the absolute value of the echo amplitude is given by

$$\frac{\delta^2}{2R^2}\left| 1 + \frac{J^2}{2\delta^2} - 2\sin^2 \tfrac{1}{2}J\tau \sin^2 \tfrac{1}{2}R\tau \right|. \tag{3.28}$$

For $|J| \ll |\delta|$, this reduces to

$$\tfrac{1}{2}\,|\,1 - 2\sin^2 \tfrac{1}{2}J\tau \sin^2 \tfrac{1}{2}\delta\tau\,|. \tag{3.29}$$

Figure 9.19 shows the observed echo envelope for the protons in 2-bromo-5-chlorothiophene. The modulation of the envelope is in good agreement with (3.28), and the values of J and δ are in good agreement with the results obtained from steady-state experiments (cf. Chapter 6).

The method of calculation used for two 90° pulses may also be used to calculate the signals observed with more complicated pulse sequences (*27*).

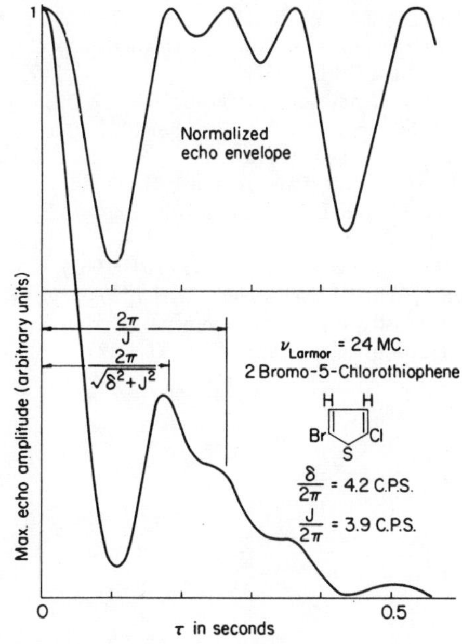

FIG. 9.19. Observed echo envelope for the protons in 2-bromo-5-chlorothiophene. The lower plot of the observed envelope is normalized to unity in the upper plot to correct for the damping effects of nuclear relaxation and diffusion. [Hahn and Maxwell (*23*).]

REFERENCES

1. V. W. Hughes and J. S. Geiger, *Phys. Rev.* **99**, 1842 (1955).
2. W. A. Anderson, *Phys. Rev.* **104**, 850 (1956).
3. J. I. Kaplan and S. Meiboom, *Phys. Rev.* **106**, 499 (1957).
4. S. Yatsiv, *Phys. Rev.* **113**, 1522 (1959).
5. B. Dischler and G. Englert, *Z. Naturforsch.* **16a**, 1180 (1961).
6. K. A. McLauchlan and D. H. Whiffen, *Proc. Chem. Soc.* **1962**, 144.
7. W. A. Anderson , R. Freeman, and C.A. Reilly, *J. Chem. Phys.* **39**, 1518 (1963).
8. J. I. Musher, *J. Chem. Phys.* **40**, 983 (1964).
9. F. Bloch, (a) *Phys. Rev.* **93**, 944 (1954); (b) *ibid.* **102**, 104 (1956).
10. A. L. Bloom and J. N. Shoolery, *Phys. Rev.* **97**, 1261 (1955).
11. W. A. Anderson, *Phys. Rev.* **102**, 151 (1956).
12. R. Kaiser, *Rev. Sci. Instr.* **31**, 963 (1960).
13. R. Freeman, *J. Mol. Phys.* **3**, 435 (1960).
14. J. P. Maher and D. F. Evans, *Proc. Chem. Soc.* **1961**, 208.
15. R. Freeman and D. H. Whiffen, *J. Mol. Phys.* **4**, 321 (1961).
16. (a) R. L. Fulton and J. D. Baldeschwieler, *J. Chem. Phys.* **34**, 1075 (1961); (b) J. M. Anderson and J. D. Baldeschwieler, *ibid.* **37**, 39 (1962).
17. (a) J. A. Elvidge and L. M. Jackman, *J. Chem. Soc.* **1961**, 859; (b) D. W. Turner, *J. Chem. Soc.* **1962**, 847.
18. R. Freeman and D. H. Whiffen, *Proc. Phys. Soc.* (*London*) **79**, 794 (1962).
19. W. A. Anderson and R. Freeman, *J. Chem. Phys.* **37**, 85 (1962).
20. J. D. Baldeschwieler and E. W. Randall, *Chem. Rev.* **63**, 81 (1963).
21. A. Abragam, "The Principles of Nuclear Magnetism," Chap. XII. Oxford Univ. Press, London and New York, 1961.
22. R. Freeman and W. A. Anderson, *J. Chem. Phys.* **37**, 2053 (1962).
23. E. L. Hahn and D. E. Maxwell, *Phys. Rev.* **88**, 1070 (1952).
24. T. P. Das, A. K. Saha, and D. K. Roy, *Proc. Roy. Soc.* (*London*) **A277** 407 (1954).
25. H. Y. Carr and E. M. Purcell, *Phys. Rev.* **88**, 415 (1952).
26. J. G. Powles and A. Hartland, *Proc. Phys. Soc.* (*London*) **77**, 273 (1961).
27. Reference 21, Chap. XI.
28. J. N. Shoolery, *Discussions Faraday Soc.* **34**, 104 (1962).
29. B. D. N. Rao and J. D. Baldeschwieler, *J. Mol. Spectry.* **11**, 440 (1963).
30. R. A. Hoffman, B. Gestblom, and S. Gonowitz, *J. Mol. Spectry.* **11**, 440 (1963).
31. M. Shimizu and H. Shimizu, *J. Chem. Phys.* **41**, 2329 (1964).

APPENDIX I

Some Definitions and Theorems of Linear Algebra

This appendix presents some fundamental definitions and theorems of linear algebra with particular reference to finite-dimensional vector spaces. The subject of linear algebra is quite extensive, and the brief discussion given here is by no means complete. Further details may be found in mathematical texts devoted to the subject; especially recommended are:

1. P. R. Halmos, "Finite-Dimensional Vector Spaces," 2nd ed. Van Nostrand, Princeton, New Jersey, 1958.
2. G. D. Birkhoff and S. MacLane, "A Survey of Modern Algebra," rev. ed. Macmillan, New York, 1953.

1. Mathematical Notation

The mathematical symbols most frequently used in the text are given below, where $M = (M_{ij})$ denotes an $n \times n$ matrix.

$*$	complex conjugation of a number or matrix
$\tilde{}$	transpose of a matrix: $\tilde{M} = (M_{ji})$
$\dagger$	complex conjugation and transposition: $M^\dagger = (M_{ji}^*)$
det M	determinant of M
tr M	trace of M
dim V	dimension of the vector space V
dim M	number of rows or columns in the (square) matrix M
$[A, B]$	commutator of operators or matrices A, B: $[A, B] = AB - BA$
δ_{ij}	Kronecker delta: $\delta_{ij} = 1$, for $i = j$, $\delta_{ij} = 0$, for $i \neq j$

1	identity operator or identity matrix: $1_{ij} \equiv \delta_{ij}$
E	identity operator of a symmetry group
e	identity operator of an abstract group
$A \oplus B$	direct sum of matrices A, B
$A \otimes B$	Kronecker product of operators or matrices A, B
$x^\dagger$	dual of the vector x
(x, y)	hermitian scalar product of the vectors x and y
$\langle x \mid y \rangle$	hermitian scalar product of x and y in the Dirac notation
M^{-1}	inverse matrix of M: $MM^{-1} = M^{-1}M = 1$
$\binom{n}{k}$	binomial coefficient: $\binom{n}{k} \equiv \frac{n!}{(n-k)!k!}$, $0! \equiv 1$

The following nomenclature is used to describe certain types of matrices or operators:

Matrix	*Defining condition*
Symmetric	$M = \tilde{M}$
Skew-symmetric	$M = -\tilde{M}$
Orthogonal	$M^{-1} = \tilde{M}$
Hermitian	$M = M^\dagger$
Skew-hermitian	$M = -M^\dagger$
Unitary	$M^{-1} = M^\dagger$
Singular	$\det M = 0$
Nonsingular	$\det M \neq 0$

2. Vector Spaces

Definition. A vector space over the complex numbers is a set of elements V, called *vectors*, together with two laws of composition, called *vector addition* and *scalar multiplication* defined as follows.

Vector Addition

To every pair of vectors x, y there is associated a unique element of V called the sum of x and y, and denoted $x + y$. Vector addition satisfies the following axioms:

(A1) $x + y = y + x$

(A2) $x + (y + z) = (x + y) + z$

(A3) V contains a unique vector 0, called the *zero vector*, such that for every x in V,
$x + 0 = x$

(A4) For every vector x there exists a unique vector $-x$ such that $x + (-x) = 0$

Scalar Multiplication

To every vector x and every complex number c there corresponds a vector of V called a *scalar multiple* of x, and denoted cx. Scalar multiplication satisfies the following axioms:

(A5) $c(c'x) = (cc')x$

(A6) $1x = x$

(A7) $c(x + y) = cx + cy$

(A8) $(c + c')x = cx + c'x$

Axioms (A1) through (A4) assert that V is an additive abelian group.[1] The zero vector is the additive identity, and $(-x)$ the additive inverse.

The complex numbers are explicitly introduced in the remaining axioms. Axiom (A5) expresses the associativity of scalar multiplication, (A6) displays $1 + 0 \cdot i$ as the scalar identity; (A7) and (A8) express the distributivity of scalar multiplication with respect to vector and scalar addition.

It is worth emphasizing that both laws of composition preserve the vector character of the elements of V and are closed operations; that is, if x and y are in V, then $x + y$ and cx are also in V. Furthermore, the symbol 0 has been used to denote the zero vector and the complex number $0 + 0 \cdot i$, so that some care must be exercised in reading equations. The context will always indicate whether 0 means the zero vector or the scalar zero.

An important illustration of a vector space is provided by the set of all n-dimensional column vectors (i.e., $n \times 1$ matrices) with complex entries:

$$x = \begin{pmatrix} \xi_1 \\ \xi_2 \\ \vdots \\ \xi_n \end{pmatrix}, \qquad y = \begin{pmatrix} \eta_1 \\ \eta_2 \\ \vdots \\ \eta_n \end{pmatrix}, \ldots.$$

Addition and scalar multiplication of column vectors are defined by

$$x + y = \begin{pmatrix} \xi_1 + \eta_1 \\ \xi_2 + \eta_2 \\ \vdots \\ \xi_n + \eta_n \end{pmatrix}, \qquad cx = \begin{pmatrix} c\xi_1 \\ c\xi_2 \\ \vdots \\ c\xi_n \end{pmatrix},$$

[1] Cf. Chapter 8.

with

$$0 = \begin{pmatrix} 0 \\ 0 \\ \vdots \\ 0 \end{pmatrix}, \qquad -x = \begin{pmatrix} -\xi_1 \\ -\xi_2 \\ \vdots \\ -\xi_n \end{pmatrix}.$$

The set of all $n \times 1$ column vectors is said to be a representation of an abstract n-dimensional vector space over the complex numbers.

Henceforth, column vectors ($n \times 1$ matrices) will be written as n-tuples

$$x = (\xi_1, \xi_2, ..., \xi_n) \equiv \begin{pmatrix} \xi_1 \\ \xi_2 \\ \vdots \\ \xi_n \end{pmatrix}.$$

Linear Combinations

Suppose that V contains the r vectors $x_1, x_2, ..., x_r$. From the definition of a vector space, it follows that V also contains c_1x_1, c_2x_2, and $c_1x_1 + c_2x_2$, where c_1 and c_2 are arbitrary complex numbers. But if V contains $c_1x_1 + c_2x_2$, it must also contain $(c_1x_1 + c_2x_2) + c_3x_3 = c_1x_1 + (c_2x_2 + c_3x_3)$. The parentheses in the last equation can be omitted, since the commutative and associative laws for vector addition show that the sum is independent of the ordering of the vectors or the manner in which the vectors are grouped. By induction, V also contains

$$x = c_1x_1 + c_2x_2 + \cdots + c_rx_r = \sum_{k=1}^{r} c_kx_k .$$

A vector x expressible in this form is said to be a *linear combination* of the r vectors $x_1, x_2, ..., x_r \equiv \{x_r\}$.

Subspaces

A subspace S of a vector space V is a nonempty[2] subset of V which is itself a vector space. For example, in the real three-dimensional vector space of analytic geometry, a line through the origin represents a one-dimensional subspace, a plane through the origin a two-dimensional subspace. The subspaces defined by lines and planes must pass through the origin—the origin represents the zero vector and every subspace must contain the zero vector.

[2] A nonempty set is a set containing at least one element.

Any subset of V is a subspace if it contains $cx + c'y$ whenever it contains x and y. The zero vector alone[3] and V itself are subspaces of V.

Theorem. The set of all linear combinations of an *arbitrary* collection of vectors $\{x_i\}$ of V is a subspace of V.

Proof. If $x = \sum_i c_i x_i$, and $x' = \sum_i c_i' x_i$, then

$$cx + c'x' = \sum_i cc_i x_i + \sum_i c'c_i' x_i = \sum_i (cc_i + c'c_i')x_i$$

is also a linear combination of the x_i.

The subspace generated by all linear combinations of the x_i is said to be *spanned* by the set $\{x_i\}$. Note that the given set of vectors is not required to be a subspace, and that every vector in the subspace spanned by $\{x_i\}$ is a linear combination of the x_i.

Linear Independence

The m vectors $x_1, x_2, \ldots, x_m$ are said to be *linearly independent* if the only scalars for which $c_1x_1 + c_2x_2 + \cdots + c_mx_m = 0$ are $c_1 = c_2 = \cdots = c_m = 0$. If the m scalars c_i are not all zero, the given vectors are said to be *linearly dependent.*

For example, the vectors $(-1, -1, -1)$, $(1, 0, 0)$, $(0, 1, 0)$, $(0, 0, 1)$, are linearly dependent, since their sum is the zero vector. On the other hand, the vectors $(-2, 1, 0)$ and $(1, 3, 2)$ are linearly independent. For if it is assumed that these vectors are linearly dependent, then

$$c_1(-2, 1, 0) + c_2(1, 3, 2) = (0, 0, 0).$$

This vector equation may be expanded to give

$$-2c_1 + c_2 = 0, \qquad c_1 + 3c_2 = 0, \qquad 2c_2 = 0,$$

whose solution is $c_1 = c_2 = 0$. This establishes the independence of the given vectors.

Theorem. The nonzero vectors $x_1, x_2, \ldots, x_m$ are linearly dependent if and only if one of these vectors is a linear combination of the preceding vectors.

[3] If an element is selected from a given set, the set is not considered as having been depleted of that element; all elements are available as often as desired.

Proof. Suppose that one of the vectors, say x_k $(k \neq 1)$, is a linear combination of the preceding vectors,

$$x_k = \sum_{i=1}^{k-1} c_i x_i .$$

If $k = m$, then

$$(-1)x_m + c_{m-1}x_{m-1} + \cdots + c_1 x_1 = 0.$$

If $1 < k < m$, one can write

$$0 \cdot x_m + 0 \cdot x_{m-1} + \cdots + (-1)x_k + c_{k-1}x_{k-1} + \cdots + c_1 x_1 = 0.$$

In either case not all c_i are zero, so that the vectors are linearly dependent.

Conversely, if the vectors are linearly dependent, at least one $c_i \neq 0$, say c_k, so that

$$x_k = (c_k^{-1} c_{k-1}) x_{k-1} + \cdots + (c_k^{-1} c_1) x_1 .$$

Hence x_k is a linear combination of the preceding vectors.

Basis and Dimension

A basis of a vector space V is a linearly independent subset of V which spans the whole space. If the number of vectors in the basis is finite, V is said to be a *finite-dimensional vector space.* The number of vectors in a basis for a finite-dimensional vector space V is called the *dimension* of V and denoted dim V.

These definitions are illustrated by the n vectors

$$e_1 = (1, 0, ..., 0), \quad e_2 = (0, 1, ..., 0), ..., e_n = (0, 0, ..., 1),$$

which provide a basis for the n-dimensional vector space of n-tuples. The e_i span the whole space, since an arbitrary n-tuple $x = (\xi_1, \xi_2, ..., \xi_n)$ may be expressed as

$$x = \xi_1 e_1 + \xi_2 e_2 + \cdots + \xi_n e_n .$$

Moreover, the e_i are linearly independent, since

$$c_1 e_1 + c_2 e_2 + \cdots + c_n e_n = 0$$

implies that

$$(c_1, c_2, ..., c_n) = (0, 0, ..., 0),$$

which is equivalent to $c_1 = c_2 = \cdots = c_n = 0$. Thus the vector space of n-tuples is n-dimensional.

It can be shown[4] that if dim $V = n$, (1) any basis for V contains exactly n elements, (2) any set containing more than n vectors is a linearly dependent set.

Theorem. If $\{x_i\}$ is a basis for an n-dimensional vector space V, then every vector x in V can be uniquely expressed as

$$x = \sum_{i=1}^{n} \xi_i x_i .$$

Proof. The $n + 1$ vectors $\{x_1, x_2, ..., x_n, x\}$ are linearly dependent, so that the given expression is just the dependence relation solved for x. Uniqueness follows from the independence of the x_i. For if $x = \sum \xi_i' x_i$, then $x - x = 0 = \sum (\xi_i - \xi_i')x_i$. The independence of the x_i demands that $\xi_i - \xi_i' = 0$, for all i.

The ξ_i are called the *components* of x relative to the basis $\{x_i\}$. In general, the components of a given vector are different relative to different bases. To illustrate the point, consider the vector $x = (\xi_1, \xi_2, \xi_3)$. Relative to the basis $\{(1, 0, 0), (0, 1, 0), (0, 0, 1)\}$, the components of x are ξ_1, ξ_2, and ξ_3. If the basis is $\{(1, 0, 0), (1, 1, 0), (1, 1, 1)\}$, the components of x are $\xi_1' = \xi_1 - \xi_2$, $\xi_2' = \xi_2 - \xi_3$, and $\xi_3' = \xi_3$.

Dual Spaces

Let

$$x = \begin{pmatrix} \xi_1 \\ \xi_2 \\ \vdots \\ \xi_n \end{pmatrix}$$

denote a vector in an n-dimensional vector space V, and $x^\dagger$ the vector obtained from x by taking the complex conjugate of every component of x and then applying the rule for the transposition of matrices:

$$x^\dagger = (\xi_1^* \quad \xi_2^* \quad \cdots \quad \xi_n^*).$$

Evidently, $x^\dagger$ is a $1 \times n$ matrix or row vector, distinguishable from the n-tuple notation for $n \times 1$ matrices through the omission of commas. The vector $x^\dagger$ is of an entirely different nature than the vector x from which it was generated. For although $x^\dagger$ has n components, it cannot be

[4] Reference 1, p. 13.

added to x. However, one can add $x^{\dagger}$ to a row vector $y^{\dagger}$ generated from an element y in V. The vectors $x^{\dagger}$ and $y^{\dagger}$ are elements in an n-dimensional vector space $V^{\dagger}$ called the *dual* of V; $x^{\dagger}$ and $y^{\dagger}$ are called the *vectors dual to x and y*. Note that if $z = c_1x + c_2y$, $z^{\dagger} = c_1{}^*x^{\dagger} + c_2{}^*y^{\dagger}$, so that the relation[5] between V and $V^{\dagger}$ is not linear but antilinear. However, since $(x^{\dagger})^{\dagger} = x$, $(V^{\dagger})^{\dagger} = V$.

Let $\{x_i\}$ be a basis for V containing n elements. Any vector in V may be expressed in the form

$$x = \sum_{i=1}^{n} c_i x_i .$$

Since x is arbitrary, so is $x^{\dagger}$, and the last equation yields

$$x^{\dagger} = \sum_{i=1}^{n} c_i{}^* x_i{}^{\dagger}.$$

Thus the vectors $\{x_i{}^{\dagger}\}$ span $V^{\dagger}$. If $x = 0$, then $x^{\dagger} = 0^{\dagger} = (0 \;\; 0 \;\; 0 \;\; \cdots \;\; 0)$, and

$$\sum_{i=1}^{n} c_i x_i = 0, \qquad \sum_{i=1}^{n} c_i{}^* x_i{}^{\dagger} = 0^{\dagger}.$$

Now the x_i are linearly independent, so that all $c_i = 0$. But this implies that all $c_i{}^* = 0$, so that the $x_i{}^{\mid}$ are also linearly independent. Thus if $\{x_i\}$ is a basis for V, then $\{x_i{}^{\dagger}\}$ is a basis for $V^{\dagger}$ and $\dim V = \dim V^{\dagger}$.

Scalar Products

In a real three-dimensional space, the scalar or inner product of two vectors $\mathbf{a}$ and $\mathbf{b}$ is defined by

$$(\mathbf{a}, \mathbf{b}) = \mathbf{a} \cdot \mathbf{b} = |\,\mathbf{a}\,|\,|\,\mathbf{b}\,| \cos \theta.$$

This scalar is proportional to the lengths of the two vectors and to the cosine of the angle between the vectors. In particular, if $|\,\mathbf{a}\,|$, $|\,\mathbf{b}\,|$ are nonzero, then $\mathbf{a} \cdot \mathbf{b} = 0$ implies that the vectors are orthogonal. If $\mathbf{a} = \mathbf{b}$, then $\theta = 0$, and $\mathbf{a} \cdot \mathbf{b} = |\,\mathbf{a}\,|^2$ is the square of the length of $\mathbf{a}$. However, this definition of the scalar product of vectors is inadequate for complex vector spaces. Consider, for example, the vector $x = (1, i)$. In the complex plane x is represented by a line segment of length $\sqrt{2}$

[5] For a more precise description of the relations between V, $V^{\dagger}$, and $(V^{\dagger})^{\dagger}$, see Reference 1, p. 24.

whose polar angle is $\pi/4$. The above formula for the scalar product gives $(x, x) = 1 \cdot 1 + i \cdot i = 0$. On the other hand, if one defines the *hermitian* scalar product of

$$x = \begin{pmatrix} \xi_1 \\ \xi_2 \end{pmatrix} \quad \text{and} \quad y = \begin{pmatrix} \eta_1 \\ \eta_2 \end{pmatrix},$$

by $(x, y) = \xi_1{}^*\eta_1 + \xi_2{}^*\eta_2$, one obtains $(x, x) = 1^* \cdot 1 + i^* \cdot i = 2$, and $| x | \equiv (x, x)^{1/2} = \sqrt{2}$.

The preceding geometric considerations lead to the following definition of the scalar product of two n-dimensional vectors with complex components:

$$(x, y) = \xi_1{}^*\eta_1 + \xi_2{}^*\eta_2 + \cdots + \xi_n{}^*\eta_n .$$

It follows that

$$\begin{aligned} (x, y) &= (y, x)^*, \\ (x, cy + c'y') &= c(x, y) + c'(x, y'), \\ (cx + c'x', y) &= c^*(x, y) + c'^*(x', y), \\ (x, x) &\geqslant 0. \end{aligned}$$

The definition shows that (x, x) is a real number, and that $(x, x) = 0$ if and only if $x = 0$. These properties make the interpretation of $| x | = (x, x)^{1/2}$ as the (generalized) length of a complex vector plausible. If $(x, y) = 0$, x and y are said to be *orthogonal.*

A vector space over the complex numbers together with the above definition of the hermitian scalar product is called a *unitary space.* A basis $\{x_i\}$ for a unitary space is said to constitute an *orthonormal basis* if

$$(x_i , x_j) = \delta_{ij} ,$$

where

$$\delta_{ij} = \begin{cases} 1 & \text{if} \quad i = j, \\ 0 & \text{if} \quad i \neq j. \end{cases}$$

If the vectors of a given basis do not have unit length, they can be scaled to unit length through division by $| x |$. Moreover, an arbitrary basis can always be converted to an orthonormal basis by the Gram-Schmidt orthogonalization process.[6] The following discussion will be restricted to orthonormal bases.

The scalar product can be connected with the dual space of V by noting that

$$x^\dagger y = (\xi_1{}^* \quad \xi_2{}^* \quad \cdots \quad \xi_n{}^*) \begin{pmatrix} \eta_1 \\ \eta_2 \\ \vdots \\ \eta_n \end{pmatrix} = \sum_{i=1}^{n} \xi_i{}^*\eta_i = (x, y),$$

[6] Reference 1, p. 128; Reference 2, p. 192.

where the row and column matrices are multiplied according to the rule for matrix multiplication. Thus the scalar product may be interpreted as a scalar-valued function[7] of a vector in V and a vector in $V^{\dagger}$.

3. Linear Transformations

Definition. A linear transformation[8] T of a vector space into itself is a law of correspondence which assigns to every vector x in V a vector Tx in V, called the *image* or *transform* of x, in such a way that the image of $cx + c'y$ is

$$T(cx + c'y) = cTx + c'Ty,$$

for all vectors x and y and all scalars c and c'. This definition is intrinsic, in the sense that no reference is made to a particular basis of V.

A linear transformation is defined when its effect on every element of V is known.

Examples

1. Let 0 be the transformation which transforms every element of V into the zero vector:

$$0x = 0, \qquad \text{for all } x.$$

2. Let 1 be the transformation defined by

$$1x = x, \qquad \text{for all } x.$$

3. Let K be the operator which multiplies every vector in V by a fixed scalar k:

$$Kx = kx, \qquad \text{for all } x.$$

In each case the operator is unambiguously defined for every vector in V. The operator 1 is called the *identity operator*, since every vector is its own image; 0 is called the *zero operator*, and K is called a *scalar operator*.

A very important law of composition is defined by the equation

$$(AB)x = A(Bx), \qquad \text{for all } x,$$

where A and B are arbitrary linear transformations. The operator AB is called the *product* of A and B.

---

[7] Reference 1, pp. 130–133.

[8] A linear transformation is often called an *operator*, or, more precisely, a *linear operator*.

The difference of the two possible products of A and B is called the *commutator* of A and B, and denoted $[A, B]$:

$$[A, B] = AB - BA.$$

If $[A, B] = 0$, A and B are said to *commute.* Any two of the operators 0, 1, and K commute. In fact, these operators commute with every operator A.

When working with multiple products of noncommuting operators, it is necessary to preserve the order in which the operators appear. On the other hand, since $[A, A] = 0$, multiple products of a single operator can be manipulated like ordinary numbers. Such products are unambiguous and it is customary to write

$$A = A^1, \quad A^2 = AA, \quad AAA = A^3, \dots .$$

The zeroth power of an operator is defined as $A^0 = 1$.

An important class of linear transformations consists of the so-called *nonsingular* transformations. A linear transformation T is said to be *nonsingular* if:

(1) Every vector y is the image of at least one pre-image x; that is, given any vector y, a vector x exists for which

$$y = Tx.$$

(2) If x and x' are distinct vectors, then Tx and Tx' are also distinct or, equivalently,

$$Tx = Tx' \quad \text{implies that} \quad x = x'.$$

When these conditions are satisfied, there exists a linear operator T^{-1}, called the *inverse of* T, with the properties

$$TT^{-1} = T^{-1}T = 1.$$

If a transformation does not meet requirements (1) and (2), it is said to be *singular*.

The operator $K = k1$ possesses an inverse $K^{-1} = k^{-1}1$, provided that $k \neq 0$. The zero operator is singular since it violates (1) and (2).

The inverse of the inverse operator is the original operator

$$(T^{-1})^{-1} = T;$$

the inverse of a product of nonsingular operators is equal to the product of the inverses taken in reversed order:

$$(A_1 A_2 \dots A_n)^{-1} = A_n^{-1} A_{n-1}^{-1} \dots A_1^{-1}.$$

Matrix Representation of a Linear Transformation

Let T denote a linear transformation of a finite-dimensional vector space V into itself and $\{x_1, ..., x_n\}$ a basis for V. An arbitrary vector x may be expressed as

$$x = \sum_j \xi_j x_j ,$$

where the ξ_j are the components of x relative to $\{x_j\}$. The transform of x is

$$x' = Tx = \sum_j \xi_j T x_j ,$$

and Tx will be determined when the transforms of the basis vectors are known. But the Tx_j are vectors in V, so that

$$Tx_j = \sum_k T_{kj} x_k \qquad (j = 1, 2, ..., n).$$

The T_{kj} are equal to the n^2 scalar products

$$(x_k , Tx_j) = \sum_l T_{lj}(x_k , x_l) = \sum_l T_{lj}\, \delta_{kl} = T_{kj} ,$$

which can be compounded into an $n \times n$ matrix

$$(T_{kj}) = \begin{pmatrix} T_{11} & \cdots & T_{1n} \\ \vdots & & \vdots \\ T_{n1} & \cdots & T_{nn} \end{pmatrix},$$

whose jth column is made up of the components of Tx_j. This matrix is said to *represent* T relative to the basis $\{x_i\}$. If a different basis is chosen for V, the matrix of T in the new basis will, in general, be different from the matrix given above.

The operators 0, I, and K have very simple matrix representations. By the definition of K, it follows that

$$Kx_j = kx_j = 0 \cdot x_1 + 0 \cdot x_2 + \cdots + kx_j + \cdots + 0 \cdot x_n ,$$

so that

$$(K_{jk}) = k(\delta_{jk}) = \begin{pmatrix} k & 0 & 0 & \cdots & 0 \\ 0 & k & 0 & \cdots & 0 \\ 0 & 0 & k & \cdots & 0 \\ \vdots & \vdots & \vdots & & \vdots \\ 0 & 0 & 0 & \cdots & k \end{pmatrix}.$$

The matrices for the zero operator and the identity operator are obtained from (K_{ij}) by setting $k = 0$ and $k = 1$. The matrices of K, 1, and 0 are exceptional, since they do not change when the basis is changed. For an example of an operator whose matrix does change with the basis, consider the operator R which subjects all vectors in the real cartesian plane to a reflection in the line $\xi_1 = \xi_2$. Under such a reflection, the vector $\xi_1 e_1 + \xi_2 e_2 \to \xi_2 e_1 + \xi_1 e_2$, while all vectors with $\xi_1 = \xi_2$ are unchanged; hence

$$Re_1 = e_2 = 0 \cdot e_1 + 1 \cdot e_2,$$

$$Re_2 = e_1 = 1 \cdot e_1 + 0 \cdot e_2,$$

and

$$(R_{kj}) = \begin{pmatrix} 0 & 1 \\ 1 & 0 \end{pmatrix}.$$

However, if the basis is $\{(1/\sqrt{2})(e_1 + e_2), (1/\sqrt{2})(e_1 - e_2)\}$, then

$$(R_{kj}) = \begin{pmatrix} 1 & 0 \\ 0 & -1 \end{pmatrix}.$$

The matrix associated with the product of two linear transformations S and T may be deduced by applying their product to a typical basis vector x_j. Since $STx_j = S(Tx_j)$, and

$$Tx_j = \sum_r T_{rj} x_r, \qquad Sx_r = \sum_i S_{ir} x_i,$$

it follows that

$$STx_j = \sum_i \left(\sum_r S_{ir} T_{rj} \right) x_i = \sum_i (ST)_{ij} x_i,$$

where

$$(ST)_{ij} = \sum_r S_{ir} T_{rj} \qquad (i, j = 1, 2, ..., n).$$

The last equation is the well-known rule for matrix elements of the product matrix ST in terms of the matrix elements of S and T. Hence the matrix representative of the product of two linear transformations is equal to the matrix product of the matrices representing the linear transformations.

If T is a nonsingular operator, the matrix representing T must also be nonsingular; hence[9] $\det T \neq 0$ (T nonsingular), where *det* denotes the determinant of T. On the other hand, $\det T = 0$, whenever T is singular.

The determinant of a product of two matrices may be computed by the rule [9]

$$\det(ST) = (\det S)(\det T) = \det TS,$$

which shows that a product of nonsingular matrices is also nonsingular.

The components of $x' = Tx$ relative to the basis $\{x_i\}$ may be obtained by equating the coefficients of x_k in the expression

$$x' = \sum_k \xi_k' x_k = \sum_k \sum_j T_{kj} \xi_j x_k .$$

It follows that

$$\xi_k' = \sum_j T_{kj} \xi_j .$$

If x and x' are written as column vectors, the last equation can be written

$$\begin{pmatrix} \xi_1' \\ \vdots \\ \xi_n' \end{pmatrix} = \begin{pmatrix} T_{11} & \cdots & T_{1n} \\ \vdots & & \vdots \\ T_{n1} & \cdots & T_{nn} \end{pmatrix} \begin{pmatrix} \xi_1 \\ \vdots \\ \xi_n \end{pmatrix},$$

which is the matrix representation of the operator equation $x' = Tx$.

Adjoints

The adjoint of a matrix is the matrix obtained by taking the complex conjugate of every element in the matrix and then interchanging rows and columns:

$$A^\dagger = \tilde{A}^*.$$

It follows that $(A^\dagger)^\dagger = A$, and from the rule for matrix multiplication that

$$(AB)^\dagger = B^\dagger A^\dagger.$$

Applying this rule to the matrix representation of $x' = Tx$ one obtains

$$(\xi_1'^* \ \dots \ \xi_n'^*) = (\xi_1{}^* \ \dots \ \xi_n{}^*) \begin{pmatrix} T_{11}^* & \cdots & T_{n1}^* \\ \vdots & & \vdots \\ T_{1n}^* & \cdots & T_{nn}^* \end{pmatrix}$$

or

$$(x')^\dagger \equiv (x^\dagger)' = (Tx)^\dagger = x^\dagger T^\dagger.$$

[9] Reference 2, pp. 304–305.

Thus, for every linear transformation represented by a matrix (T_{ij}), there is a corresponding linear transformation $T^\dagger$ on the dual space represented by the matrix adjoint to (T_{ij}).

Let x and y denote arbitrary vectors such that

$$x = \sum_i \xi_i x_i , \qquad y = \sum_i \eta_i x_i .$$

By the definition of a scalar product,

$$(x, Ty) = x^\dagger Ty = \Big(\sum_i \xi_i x_i , \sum_j \sum_k \eta_j T_{kj} x_k\Big) = \sum_i \sum_j \xi_i{}^* T_{ij} \eta_j$$

$$= (\xi_1{}^* \; \dots \; \xi_n{}^*) \begin{pmatrix} T_{11} & \cdots & T_{1n} \\ \vdots & & \vdots \\ T_{n1} & \cdots & T_{nn} \end{pmatrix} \begin{pmatrix} \eta_1 \\ \vdots \\ \eta_n \end{pmatrix}.$$

But $x^\dagger Ty$ can also be written $(T^\dagger x)^\dagger y$, so that one has the important relations

$$(x, Ty) = (T^\dagger x, y) = (y, T^\dagger x)^*.$$

If $T = AB$, then

$$(x, ABy) = (A^\dagger x, By) = (B^\dagger A^\dagger x, y).$$

The term *adjoint of a matrix* is also used in connection with an algorithm for computing the inverse of a nonsingular matrix. Let (a_{ij}) denote an $n \times n$ nonsingular matrix. The cofactor of the element a_{ij} is defined as

$$\text{cofactor of } a_{ij} \equiv A_{ij} = (-1)^{i+j} \det M_{ij} ,$$

where M_{ij} is the $n - 1 \times n - 1$ matrix obtained from A by deleting the ith row and jth column. The transpose of the $n \times n$ matrix of cofactors is called the *adjoint* of (a_{ij}),

$$\text{adj}(a_{ij}) = (\tilde{A}_{ij}),$$

and the *inverse* of (a_{ij}) is

$$(a_{ij})^{-1} = \frac{\text{adj}(a_{ij})}{\det(a_{ij})} .$$

In the following discussion the term "adjoint" will always refer to the operator in the dual space.

Normal Operators

Operators are often classified according to some specific relationship with their adjoints. A linear transformation is said to be *normal* if it commutes with its adjoint:

$$NN^\dagger - N^\dagger N = 0.$$

This condition is certainly satisfied if $N = N^\dagger$, and such operators are said to be *hermitian* or *self-adjoint*. If N is nonsingular, then N commutes with N^{-1}, so that an operator satisfying $N^\dagger = N^{-1}$ is normal. Operators of this type are said to be *unitary*. If the base field of the vector space consists of the real numbers, rather than the complex numbers, the complex conjugation included in the symbol † becomes unnecessary and only the transpose operation remains. Hermitian and unitary operators then become symmetric and orthogonal operators, respectively.

Unitary operators on an inner product space preserve inner products. For if x and y are subjected to a unitary transformation U, the scalar product of the transformed vectors is

$$(Ux, Uy) = (U^\dagger Ux, y) = (U^{-1}Ux, y) = (x, y),$$

by the unitary property $U^\dagger = U^{-1}$. For a real three-dimensional space, this means that the lengths and relative orientations of vectors are unchanged by an orthogonal transformation.

Similarity Transformations

Let T denote any linear transformation on an n-dimensional vector space, and let $\{x_i\}$ and $\{y_i\}$ be two bases for V, related by the nonsingular linear transformation A:

$$y_i = Ax_i \qquad (i = 1, 2, ..., n).$$

These equations define a change of basis $\{x_i\} \rightarrow \{y_i\}$, which induces a transformation[10] of all operators defined on V. In particular, the operator T is transformed into

$$T' = ATA^{-1}.$$

A transformation of this form is called a *similarity transformation.*

The matrix representing T also undergoes a similarity transformation[10] by the matrix representing A:

$$(T_{ij})' = (A_{ij})^{-1}(T_{ij})(A_{ij}).$$

It should be noted that the matrix of T' is referred to the y basis, whereas the matrices for T and A are referred to the x basis.

Similarity transformations preserve many important properties of linear transformations. For example, the determinant of a matrix is unaltered by a similarity transformation, since

$$\det T' = \det A^{-1}TA = \det AA^{-1}T = \det T.$$

---

[10] Reference 1, p. 84.

Another invariant is the trace of a (finite square) matrix, defined as the sum of the diagonal elements of the matrix:

$$\operatorname{tr} T = \sum_i T_{ii} .$$

The invariance of tr T under a similarity transformation can be deduced from the fact that the trace of AB is equal to the trace of BA:

$$\operatorname{tr} AB = \sum_i (AB)_{ii} = \sum_i \sum_k A_{ik} B_{ki} = \sum_k (BA)_{kk} = \operatorname{tr} BA.$$

It follows that

$$\operatorname{tr} T' = \operatorname{tr} A^{-1}TA = \operatorname{tr} AA^{-1}T = \operatorname{tr} T.$$

Direct Sums

An $n \times n$ matrix A is said to be the direct sum of the $n_1 \times n_1$ matrix A_1 and the $n_2 \times n_2$ matrix A_2 if A has the form

$$A = \begin{pmatrix} A_1 & 0 \\ 0 & A_2 \end{pmatrix},$$

where the zero in the upper right-hand corner represents an $n_1 \times n_2$ zero matrix, and the zero in the lower left-hand corner an $n_2 \times n_1$ zero matrix. The matrix for A is denoted

$$A = A_1 \oplus A_2 .$$

More generally, an $n \times n$ matrix is said to be the direct sum of the square matrices A_1, A_2, ..., A_N if all elements of A not contained in some A_i vanish. When this is the case,

$$A = A_1 \oplus A_2 \oplus \cdots \oplus A_N$$

and

$$N = \sum_{i=1}^{N} n_i \qquad (n_i = \dim A_i).$$

It is not difficult to show that if $A = A_1 \oplus \cdots \oplus A_N$, then

$$\operatorname{tr} A = \sum_{i=1}^{N} \operatorname{tr} A_i , \qquad \det A = \prod_{i=1}^{N} \det A_i .$$

Furthermore, if $B = B_1 \oplus \cdots \oplus B_N$ and $\dim A_i = \dim B_i$, $i = 1, 2, ..., N$, then

$$AB = A_1B_1 \oplus A_2B_2 \oplus \cdots \oplus A_NB_N .$$

4. Diagonalization of Commuting Matrices

Schur's Theorem

Let S be any linear transformation on an n-dimensional unitary space, and (S_{ij}) the matrix of S relative to an orthonormal basis $\{x_i\}$. Furthermore, let U denote a unitary operator, represented by the matrix (U_{ij}) relative to $\{x_i\}$, which sends the orginal basis into a new basis $\{y_i\}$. The change of basis $\{x_i\} \rightarrow \{y_i\} = \{Ux_i\}$ induces similarity transformations of S and (S_{ij}) with U and (U_{ij}):

$$USU^{\dagger} = T, \tag{1}$$

$$(U_{ij})^{\dagger}(S_{ij})(U_{ij}) = (T_{ij}). \tag{2}$$

For an arbitrary choice of U, the matrix (T_{ij}) will not, in general, be any simpler than (S_{ij}). However, according to an important theorem[11] of I. Schur, there exists, for any S, a unitary transformation U such that the matrix for T is triangular:

$$(T_{ij}) = \begin{pmatrix} \lambda_1 & T_{12} & T_{13} & \cdots & T_{1n} \\ 0 & \lambda_2 & T_{23} & \cdots & T_{2n} \\ 0 & 0 & \lambda_3 & \cdots & T_{3n} \\ \vdots & \vdots & \vdots & & \vdots \\ 0 & 0 & 0 & \cdots & \lambda_n \end{pmatrix}. \tag{3}$$

In this matrix, which is called the *Schur canonical form*, all elements below the principal diagonal are zero ($T_{ij} = 0$, for $j < i$). The elements along the principal diagonal ($\lambda_k = T_{kk}$) are called the *eigenvalues of S*. It follows that

(1) tr S = tr T = the sum of the eigenvalues.

(2) det S = det T = the product of the eigenvalues.

The eigenvalues of a linear transformation S are associated with the eigenvectors of S, defined as those *nonzero vectors* u_k satisfying

$$Su_k = \lambda_k u_k \,. \tag{4}$$

The scalar λ_k is said to be the eigenvalue associated with or belonging to the eigenvector u_k. It is possible that λ_k may belong to g_k linearly independent eigenvectors. If $g_k > 1$, the eigenvalue λ_k is said to be g_k-fold degenerate.

[11] For a proof of this theorem, see Reference 1, p. 144.

The $n \times 1$ matrices which represent the u_k in the y basis are

$$y_1 = \begin{pmatrix} 1 \\ 0 \\ 0 \\ \vdots \\ 0 \end{pmatrix}, \quad y_2 = \begin{pmatrix} 0 \\ 1 \\ 0 \\ \vdots \\ 0 \end{pmatrix}, \ldots, y_n = \begin{pmatrix} 0 \\ 0 \\ 0 \\ \vdots \\ 1 \end{pmatrix}, \tag{5}$$

as one may verify by operating with (T_{ij}) on the y_k. Thus the eigenvectors of S constitute an orthonormal set—in fact, a basis for the n-dimensional space.

The eigenvectors of S relative to the x basis may be obtained by applying (2) to a generic eigenvector y_k:

$$(U_{ij})^\dagger(S_{ij})(U_{ij})y_k = (T_{ij})y_k = \lambda_k y_k .$$

Multiplying from the left with (U_{ij}), one obtains

$$(S_{ij})[(U_{ij})y_k] = \lambda_k[(U_{ij})y_k],$$

which shows that the eigenvectors of S in the x basis are

$$(y_k)_x = (U_{ij})y_k . \tag{6}$$

It follows, from (5) and (6), that the $(y_k)_x$ are given by the n columns of the matrix (U_{ij}). Thus (4) in the x basis is

$$\begin{pmatrix} S_{11} & S_{12} & \cdots & S_{1n} \\ S_{21} & S_{22} & \cdots & S_{2n} \\ \vdots & \vdots & & \vdots \\ S_{n1} & S_{n2} & \cdots & S_{nn} \end{pmatrix} \begin{pmatrix} U_{1k} \\ U_{2k} \\ \vdots \\ U_{nk} \end{pmatrix} = \lambda_k \begin{pmatrix} U_{1k} \\ U_{2k} \\ \vdots \\ U_{nk} \end{pmatrix}, \tag{7}$$

or, more concisely,

$$[(S_{ij}) - \lambda_k I]U^{(k)} = 0, \tag{8}$$

where $U^{(k)}$ is the kth column of (U_{ij}).

The eigenvectors of S are, by definition, nonzero, so that $[(S_{ij}) - \lambda_k I]$ must be singular.[12] This requires that

$$\det[(S_{ij}) - \lambda_k I] = \begin{vmatrix} S_{11} - \lambda_k & S_{12} & \cdots & S_{1n} \\ S_{21} & S_{22} - \lambda_k & \cdots & S_{2n} \\ \vdots & \vdots & & \vdots \\ S_{n1} & S_{n2} & \cdots & S_{nn} - \lambda_k \end{vmatrix} = 0. \tag{9}$$

[12] If it is assumed that $[(S_{ij}) - \lambda_k I]$ is nonsingular, then (8) implies that $U^{(k)} = 0$, contrary to assumption.

This equation, variously known as the *secular*, *determinantal*, or *characteristic equation*, is a polynomial equation of the nth degree whose roots are the n eigenvalues of S. If one of these roots is inserted in (7), one obtains n linear equations for the n unknowns U_{ik}, $i = 1, 2, ..., n$. But the determinant of the coefficient matrix vanishes, so that only $n - 1$ of these equations are independent. One may, however, solve for $n - 1$ of the U_{ik} in terms of some fixed U_{ik}, say U_{nk}. The normalization condition

$$\sum_i | U_{ik} |^2 = 1$$

then determines $U_{1k}, U_{2k}, ..., U_{nk}$, except for an arbitrary phase factor of unit modulus. Repeating this procedure for each eigenvalue, one obtains the full matrix (U_{ij}).

The preceding analysis determines the eigenvalues and eigenvectors, but not their order of appearance in (T_{ij}) and (U_{ij}). If it desired to have a particular eigenvalue appear at the intersection of the kth row and kth column, care must be taken to have its associated eigenvector as the kth column of (U_{ij}).

The Schur canonical form of matrix can be used to obtain some important results concerning hermitian and unitary matrices.

Unitary Matrices

An operator U is unitary if $U^\dagger = U^{-1}$, so that

$$UU^\dagger = U^\dagger U = 1.$$

In matrix notation these relations lead to the orthogonality conditions

$$\sum_{k=1}^{n} U_{ik} U_{jk}^* = \delta_{ij}, \tag{10}$$

$$\sum_{k=1}^{n} U_{kj}^* U_{ik} = \delta_{ij}, \tag{11}$$

where $i, j = 1, 2, ..., n$. Equations (10) are equivalent to

$$\sum_k | U_{ik} |^2 = 1, \qquad \text{for} \quad i = j,$$

$$\sum_k U_{ik} U_{jk}^* = 0, \qquad \text{for} \quad i \neq j.$$

If the rows of U are interpreted as row vectors, these equations state that every row of U is normalized and orthogonal to every other row of U. Equations (11) may be used to show that every column of U is normalized and orthogonal to every other column.

A general $n \times n$ unitary matrix contains n^2 complex numbers, but not all of these are independent. The first row of U must be normalized and orthogonal to the remaining $n - 1$ rows, so that the unitary nature of U imposes n conditions on the first row. Similarly, the second row must be normalized and orthogonal to the remaining $n - 2$ rows, which give $n - 1$ additional constraints. Continuing this procedure, one finds that the most general $n \times n$ unitary matrix depends upon

$$n^2 - n - (n-1) - \cdots = n^2 - \sum_{k=0}^{n} k = \frac{n(n-1)}{2}$$

independent complex numbers, or $n(n - 1)$ real parameters.

The unitary property of a matrix U is preserved under a similarity transformation by a unitary matrix V. For if $U' = V^{-1}UV = V^{\dagger}UV$, then

$$\begin{aligned}(U')(U')^{\dagger} &= (V^{\dagger}UV)(V^{\dagger}UV)^{\dagger} = V^{\dagger}UVV^{\dagger}U^{\dagger}V \\ &= V^{\dagger}UVV^{-1}U^{-1}V = V^{\dagger}V = 1.\end{aligned}$$

Similarly, $(U')^{\dagger}(U') = 1$. Suppose now that V brings U to triangular form:

$$V^{\dagger}UV = \begin{pmatrix} u_{11} & u_{12} & \cdots & u_{1n} \\ 0 & u_{22} & \cdots & u_{2n} \\ 0 & 0 & \cdots & u_{3n} \\ \vdots & \vdots & & \vdots \\ 0 & 0 & \cdots & u_{nn} \end{pmatrix}.$$

Since $V^{\dagger}UV$ is still unitary, the rows and columns must satisfy the unitary conditions. In particular, the first column, considered as a vector, must be normalized to unity; hence

$$u_{11}u_{11}^* = 1,$$

or

$$u_{11} = e^{i\theta_1}.$$

Moreover, the first column must be orthogonal to the second column, so that

$$u_{11}^*u_{12} = e^{-i\theta_1}u_{12} = 0,$$

or

$$u_{12} = 0.$$

Normalization of the second column now yields $u_{22} = e^{i\theta_2}$. By a repeated application of the conditions for orthonormality to the remaining columns, it follows that

$$V^\dagger U V = \begin{pmatrix} e^{i\theta_1} & 0 & \cdots & 0 \\ 0 & e^{i\theta_2} & \cdots & 0 \\ 0 & 0 & \cdots & 0 \\ \vdots & \vdots & & \vdots \\ 0 & 0 & \cdots & e^{i\theta_n} \end{pmatrix} = (\lambda_k \, \delta_{kj}),$$

where λ_k denotes the kth diagonal element. This proves that

(1) Every unitary matrix can be brought to diagonal form by a similarity transformation with an appropriate unitary matrix.

(2) The eigenvalues of a unitary matrix are all of modulus unity.

Hermitian Operators

An operator is hermitian if it is self-adjoint:

$$H = H^\dagger.$$

In matrix notation this condition requires that

$$H_{ij} = H_{ji}^* .$$

The hermitian property is preserved under a similarity transformation by a unitary matrix U, since

$$(U^{-1}HU)^\dagger = (U^\dagger HU)^\dagger = U^\dagger H^\dagger (U^\dagger)^\dagger = U^\dagger HU.$$

If U is the unitary matrix which reduces H to triangular form, then, by the hermitian property, all elements above the principal diagonal must be equal to the complex conjugates of the corresponding elements below the diagonal. But the latter are all zero, so that

(1) Every hermitian matrix can be brought into diagonal form by an appropriate unitary matrix.

(2) The eigenvalues of a hermitian matrix are real numbers.

Theorem. Two hermitian matrices A and B can be simultaneously diagonalized by a unitary matrix V if and only if A and B commute.

Proof. If A and B can be simultaneously diagonalized, then, since diagonal matrices always commute,

$$(V^{\dagger}AV)(V^{\dagger}BV) = (V^{\dagger}BV)(V^{\dagger}AV),$$

or, upon left multiplication with V and right multiplication with $V^{\dagger}$,

$$AB = BA.$$

Suppose now that A and B commute. A unitary matrix can be found such that one of the given hermitian matrices, say A, is diagonal. Let V_A denote the unitary matrix which effects the diagonalization, $\{x_i\}$ the basis of eigenvectors, and a_i the eigenvalues of A which will be assumed to be g_i-fold degenerate. By permuting the rows of V_A, one can arrange for the diagonal matrix $V_A{}^{\dagger}AV_A$ to assume the block form

$$\begin{pmatrix} \begin{matrix} a_1 & 0 & \cdots & 0 \\ 0 & a_1 & \cdots & 0 \\ \vdots & \vdots & & \vdots \\ 0 & 0 & \cdots & a_1 \end{matrix} & & & \\ & \begin{matrix} a_2 & 0 & \cdots & 0 \\ 0 & a_2 & \cdots & 0 \\ \vdots & \vdots & & \vdots \\ 0 & 0 & \cdots & a_2 \end{matrix} & & \\ & & \ddots & \\ & & & \begin{matrix} a_N & 0 & \cdots & 0 \\ 0 & a_N & \cdots & 0 \\ \vdots & \vdots & & \vdots \\ 0 & 0 & \cdots & a_N \end{matrix} \end{pmatrix},$$

where all elements not on the principal diagonal are zero. The matrix is of dimension n, where $n = \sum g_i$. Evidently

$$V_A{}^{\dagger}AV_A = A_1 \oplus A_2 \oplus \cdots \oplus A_k = a_1 1_1 \oplus a_2 1_2 \oplus \cdots \oplus a_N 1_N,$$

where 1_i denotes a $g_i \times g_i$ unit matrix.

Consider now the matrix for B relative to the basis which diagonalizes A. By assumption $AB = BA$, so that

$$(x_i, ABx_j) = (x_i, BAx_j) = a_j(x_i, Bx_j)$$

and

$$(x_i, ABx_j) = (A^{\dagger}x_i, Bx_j) = (Ax_i, Bx_j) = a_i(x_i, Bx_j).$$

From these results one obtains

$$(a_i - a_j)(x_i, Bx_j) = 0.$$

Thus $B_{ij} = 0$ for $a_i \neq a_j$, but B_{ij} does not necessarily vanish when x_i and x_j are the eigenvectors corresponding to any of the degenerate eigenvalues. It follows that the B matrix has the form

$$V_A{}^\dagger B V_A = B_1 \oplus B_2 \oplus \cdots \oplus B_N,$$

where each B_i is of dimension $g_i \times g_i$. If $g_i = 1$ for all i, then B is diagonalized by V_A and the theorem is proved.

If all the g_i are not unity, one proceeds as follows. Each B_i is hermitian; hence there exists a unitary matrix V_i such that $V_i{}^\dagger B_i V_i$ is diagonal. The whole matrix B is diagonalized by

$$V_B = V_1 \oplus V_2 \oplus \cdots \oplus V_N,$$

since

$$V_B{}^\dagger B V_B = V_1{}^\dagger B_1 V_1 \oplus V_2{}^\dagger B_2 V_2 \oplus \cdots \oplus V_N{}^\dagger B_N V_N.$$

Moreover, the matrix V_B does not alter the diagonal form of $V_A{}^\dagger A V_A$, since

$$V_B{}^\dagger V_A{}^\dagger A V_A V_B = a_1 V_1{}^\dagger I_1 V_1 \oplus a_2 V_2{}^\dagger I_2 V_2 \cdots = a_1 I_1 \oplus \cdots \oplus a_n I_n = V_A{}^\dagger A V_A.$$

Thus $V = V_A V_B$ simultaneously diagonalizes A and B.

The method used to establish the preceding theorem can also be used to prove that any finite number of commuting hermitian matrices, or any finite number of commuting unitary matrices, can be simultaneously brought to diagonal form by a unitary matrix.

The theorem on commuting hermitian matrices is often stated in terms the hermitian operators which they represent.

Theorem. If $A_1, A_2, \ldots, A_N$ are N hermitian operators such that

$$[A_i, A_j] = 0,$$

for all i and j, then there exists a set of vectors which are simultaneous eigenvectors of all the given operators.

The Dirac Notation

When working with sets of commuting operators, it is convenient to employ the bra and ket notation of Dirac. In this notation, a vector which is a simultaneous eigenvector of the commuting operators

$A, B, C, \ldots$ is denoted by the *ket vector* $| a, b, c, \ldots\rangle$, where $a, b, c, \ldots$ are the eigenvalues of the given operators. The vector dual to $| a, b, c, \ldots\rangle$ is the *bra vector* $\langle a, b, c, \ldots |$. The scalar product of a bra vector $\langle a', b', c', \ldots |$ and a ket vector $| a, b, c, \ldots\rangle$ is written

$$\langle a', b', c', \ldots | a, b, c, \ldots\rangle = \langle a, b, c, \ldots | a', b', c', \ldots\rangle^*,$$

and the matrix elements of an arbitrary operator P are written

$$\langle a', b', c', \ldots | P | a, b, c, \ldots\rangle.$$

The operator P in this expression may be considered as operating on the ket vector, in which case the scalar product is $\langle a', \ldots |\{P| a, \ldots\rangle\}$. It may be also considered as operating on the bra (dual) vector, in which case the scalar product is $\{\langle a', \ldots |P^\dagger\}| a, \ldots\rangle$, where $\langle a', \ldots |P^\dagger = \{P| a', \ldots\rangle\}^\dagger$. These forms correspond to $(x, Py) = (P^\dagger x, y)$ in the previous notation.

APPENDIX II

Three-Dimensional Orthogonal Transformations

A nonsingular linear transformation R, defined with respect to an n-dimensional real vector space, is said to be orthogonal if $R^{-1} = \tilde{R}$. This condition implies that

$$R\tilde{R} = 1, \tag{1.a}$$

$$\tilde{R}R = 1. \tag{1.b}$$

If R is represented by an $n \times n$ matrix, (1.a) and (1.b) may be expanded to yield the orthogonality relations

$$\sum_{k=1}^{n} R_{ik}R_{jk} = \delta_{ij}\,, \tag{2.a}$$

$$\sum_{k=1}^{n} R_{ki}R_{kj} = \delta_{ij}\,, \tag{2.b}$$

where $i, j = 1, 2, ..., n$. Equation (2.a) states that if the rows of R are interpreted as n-dimensional vectors, each row is of unit length and orthogonal to every other row. Equation (2.b) shows that a similar remark applies to the columns of R. It follows that an $n \times n$ orthogonal matrix is determined by $\frac{1}{2}n(n - 1)$ independent real parameters.[1]

An important property of an orthogonal transformation is that it preserves the scalar product (ξ, η). For if $\xi' = R\xi$ and $\eta' = R\eta$ are the transforms of ξ and η, then

$$(\xi', \eta') = (R\xi, R\eta) = (\xi, \tilde{R}R\eta) = (\xi, \eta). \tag{3}$$

In particular, if ξ and η are orthogonal, then ξ' and η' are also orthogonal.

---

[1] See the discussion of unitary transformations in Appendix I.

If $\xi = \eta$, (3) states that

$$(\xi, \xi) = \sum_i \xi_i^2 = (\xi', \xi').$$

Thus orthogonal transformations preserve lengths and angles in the generalized sense.

A second property of orthogonal transformations follows upon taking the determinant of both sides of $R\tilde{R} = 1$:

$$\det R\tilde{R} = (\det R)^2 = 1,$$

where use has been made of the rule for the determinant of a matrix product, and the fact that $\det A = \det \tilde{A}$. It follows that

$$\det R = \pm 1. \tag{4}$$

Orthogonal transformations are classified as proper or improper, accordingly as the determinant is $+1$ or -1. Proper orthogonal transformations correspond to n-dimensional rotations; improper orthogonal transformations correspond to a rotation followed by a reflection.

Let the n-dimensional space be subjected to a succession of r orthogonal transformations R_1, R_2, ..., R_r, and let the product of these transformations be denoted

$$R = R_r R_{r-1} \cdots R_2 R_1. \tag{5}$$

Since each R_i is orthogonal, $\tilde{R}_i R_i = 1$, and

$$\tilde{R}R = \tilde{R}_1 \tilde{R}_2 \cdots \tilde{R}_r R_r \cdots R_2 R_1 = 1 = R\tilde{R}.$$

Hence the product of any number of orthogonal transformations is an orthogonal transformation. Furthermore, the determinant of each R_i is ± 1, so that a product of orthogonal transformations is proper or improper, accordingly as the product contains an even or odd number of improper transformations.

A proper orthogonal transformation in three dimensions may be interpreted as a rotation of a given cartesian-coordinate system (xyz) into a second $(x'y'z')$ cartesian system. The condition $\det R = +1$ requires the $(x'y'z')$ system to be right- or left-handed, accordingly as the (xyz) system is right- or left-handed. The following discussion will be restricted to proper orthogonal transformations and right-handed coordinate systems.

The matrix elements of a three-dimensional orthogonal transformation represent the direction cosines of the new axes relative to the original axes:

$$\cos(x_i', x_j) = R_{ij}. \tag{6}$$

where $(x_1x_2x_3) \equiv (xyz)$ and $(x_1'x_2'x_3') \equiv (x'y'z')$. Only three parameters are required to specify an orthogonal transformation in three dimensions, so that there must be six equations relating the nine direction cosines. These equations are provided by the orthogonality relations. In the special case where the rotation is about the direction of one of the original coordinate axes, the rotation matrices are easily written down:

$$R_x(\chi) = \begin{pmatrix} 1 & 0 & 0 \\ 0 & \cos\chi & \sin\chi \\ 0 & -\sin\chi & \cos\chi \end{pmatrix}, \tag{7}$$

$$R_y(\theta) = \begin{pmatrix} \cos\theta & 0 & -\sin\theta \\ 0 & 1 & 0 \\ \sin\theta & 0 & \cos\theta \end{pmatrix}, \tag{8}$$

$$R_z(\varphi) = \begin{pmatrix} \cos\varphi & \sin\varphi & 0 \\ -\sin\varphi & \cos\varphi & 0 \\ 0 & 0 & 1 \end{pmatrix}. \tag{9}$$

All three rotations are taken in the positive or right-hand screw sense; the matrices for the corresponding negative rotations are obtained by the transcription: $\chi, \theta, \varphi \to -\chi, -\theta, -\varphi$.

The matrices for R_x, R_y, and R_z, or any other orthogonal matrix, are applied to column vectors using the rule for matrix multiplication. Thus

$$\begin{pmatrix} x_1' \\ x_2' \\ x_3' \end{pmatrix} = \begin{pmatrix} R_{11} & R_{12} & R_{13} \\ R_{21} & R_{22} & R_{23} \\ R_{31} & R_{32} & R_{33} \end{pmatrix} \begin{pmatrix} x_1 \\ x_2 \\ x_3 \end{pmatrix}. \tag{10}$$

The matrices for R_x, R_y, and R_z reveal an important property of three-dimensional rotation matrices—the trace of each matrix is twice the cosine of the angle of rotation plus one. Now R_x, R_y, and R_z are special cases of the general three-dimensional rotation matrix and, since the trace is an invariant,

$$\mathrm{tr}\{R(\mathbf{n}\Phi)\} = 1 + 2\cos\Phi, \tag{11}$$

where $R(\mathbf{n}\Phi)$ is the matrix for a rotation through an angle Φ about a direction defined by the unit vector $\mathbf{n}$.

The nine matrix elements of $R(\mathbf{n}\Phi)$ can be expressed in terms of the angle of rotation Φ and the direction cosines of $\mathbf{n}$:

$$\begin{gathered} \mathbf{n} = (\cos\alpha, \cos\beta, \cos\gamma), \\ \cos^2\alpha + \cos^2\beta + \cos^2\gamma = 1. \end{gathered} \tag{12}$$

Thus there are only three independent parameters in the set $(\alpha, \beta, \gamma, \Phi)$. If $\mathbf{n}$ is defined in terms of its polar angles θ, φ, then

$$\cos\alpha = \sin\theta\cos\varphi, \qquad \cos\beta = \sin\theta\sin\varphi, \qquad \cos\gamma = \cos\theta, \tag{13}$$

and the matrix elements of $R(\mathbf{n}\Phi)$ can be expressed in terms of φ, θ, and Φ.

The rotation $R(\mathbf{n}\Phi)$ may be described as a rigid rotation of the (xyz) system about the direction $\mathbf{n}$ in such a way that the positive coordinate axes trace out conical sectors on the infinite cones defined by $\mathbf{n}$ and the positive axes; the semiangles of these cones are the direction angles α, β, γ, and the angle of rotation Φ is the angle between the initial and final planes of the conical sections thus generated (Fig. AII.1). The deduction of the matrix for $R(\mathbf{n}\Phi)$ by geometric considerations is straightforward but extremely tedious. There is, however, a procedure that involves much simpler computations and is more instructive.

Consider a coordinate system $(x'y'z')$ whose z' axis is parallel to $\mathbf{n}$. In this coordinate system, the matrix for $R(\mathbf{n}\Phi)$ has the simple form

$$R'(\mathbf{n}\Phi) = \begin{pmatrix} \cos\Phi & \sin\Phi & 0 \\ -\sin\Phi & \cos\Phi & 0 \\ 0 & 0 & 1 \end{pmatrix}. \tag{14}$$

The matrix $R'(\mathbf{n}\Phi)$ is the transform of $R(\mathbf{n}\Phi)$:

$$T^{-1}R(\mathbf{n}\Phi)T = R'(\mathbf{n}\Phi), \tag{15}$$

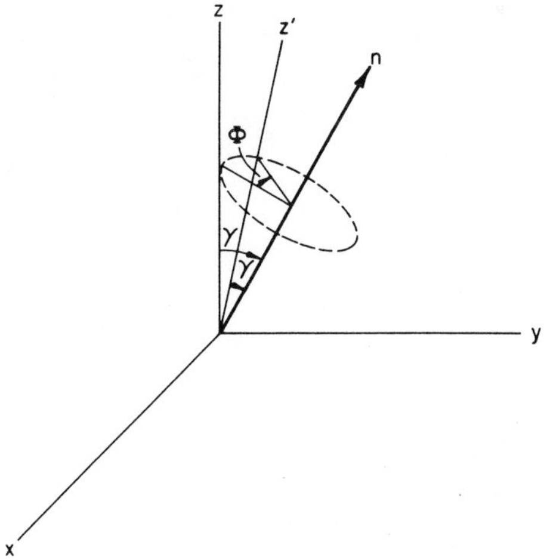

FIG. AII.1. Locus of the positive z axis under a rotation Φ about an axis defined by the unit vector $\mathbf{n}$. The positive x and y axes trace out analogous conical sections with $\mathbf{n}$ as their axis of symmetry, but with γ replaced by α and β, respectively.

where T is the orthogonal transformation which sends the (xyz) system into the $(x'y'z')$ system. If T can be determined, $R(\mathbf{n}\Phi)$ is given by

$$R(\mathbf{n}\Phi) = TR'(\mathbf{n}\Phi)T^{-1}. \tag{16}$$

The orthogonal transformation T is immediately apparent from Fig. AII.2: T consists of a rotation through π about an axis defined by

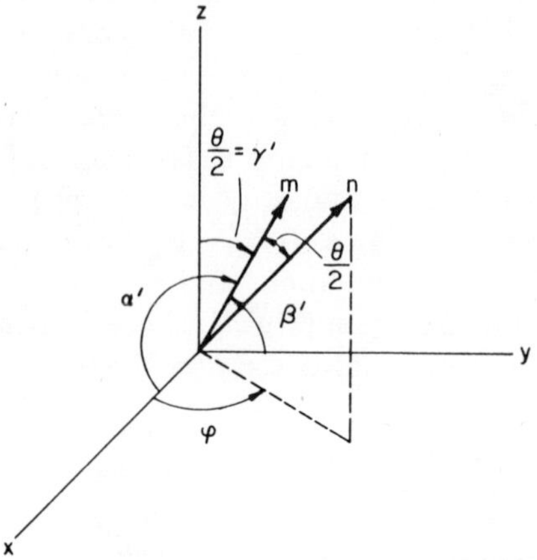

FIG. AII.2. The transformation T rotates the (xyz) system about $\mathbf{m}$ by an angle π, sending the z axis into the direction $\mathbf{n}$.

the unit vector $\mathbf{m}$ with direction angles $(\alpha', \beta', \gamma')$ given by

$$\cos\alpha' = \sin\frac{\theta}{2}\cos\varphi, \qquad \cos\beta' = \sin\frac{\theta}{2}\sin\varphi, \qquad \cos\gamma' = \cos\frac{\theta}{2}. \tag{17}$$

If $R(\mathbf{n}\Phi)$ is denoted $R(\varphi, \theta, \Phi)$, then

$$T = R(\varphi, \theta/2, \pi). \tag{18}$$

Furthermore, T^2 is a rotation by 2π, so that $T^2 = 1$. Since T is orthogonal and its own inverse, T must be symmetrical:

$$T = R(\varphi, \theta/2, \pi) = \tilde{R}(\varphi, \theta/2, \pi) = T^{-1}. \tag{19}$$

Thus

$$R(\mathbf{n}\Phi) = R(\varphi, \theta/2, \pi)R'(\mathbf{n}\Phi)R(\varphi, \theta/2, \pi). \tag{20}$$

The matrix elements of $R(\varphi, \theta/2, \pi)$ are easily determined. Since z' is in the direction $\mathbf{n}$, the last row of $R(\varphi, \theta/2, \pi)$ consists of $\cos\alpha$, $\cos\beta$, $\cos\gamma$, and since the matrix is symmetrical, the third column is also known. The matrix element $R_{11} = \cos(x_1', x_1)$ is determined by noting that both the initial and final x axes make an angle α' with the vector $\mathbf{m}$ (by the definition of a rotation), and that the angle of rotation is π; hence

$$\cos(x_1', x_1) = \cos 2\alpha' = \frac{\cos^2 \alpha}{1 + \cos \gamma} - 1,$$

where the last form is obtained by using (13) and (17). Similarly,

$$\cos(x_2', x_2) = \cos 2\beta' = \frac{\cos^2 \beta}{1 + \cos \gamma} - 1.$$

The remaining matrix element, $R_{12} = R_{21}$, can be obtained by using the orthogonality of the third row of $R(\varphi, \theta/2, \pi)$ with the first or second rows. Thus

$$R(\varphi, \theta/2, \pi) = \begin{pmatrix} \dfrac{\cos^2 \alpha}{1 + \cos \gamma} - 1 & \dfrac{\cos \alpha \cos \beta}{1 + \cos \gamma} & \cos \alpha \\ \dfrac{\cos \alpha \cos \beta}{1 + \cos \gamma} & \dfrac{\cos^2 \beta}{1 + \cos \gamma} - 1 & \cos \beta \\ \cos \alpha & \cos \beta & \cos \gamma \end{pmatrix}. \tag{21}$$

Substituting (14) and (21) into (20), one obtains

$$R(\mathbf{n}\Phi) = \begin{pmatrix} \sin^2 \alpha \cos \Phi + \cos^2 \alpha & \cos \gamma \sin \Phi + \cos \alpha \cos \beta(1 - \cos \Phi) & -\cos \beta \sin \Phi + \cos \alpha \cos \gamma(1 - \cos \Phi) \\ -\cos \gamma \sin \Phi + \cos \alpha \cos \beta(1 - \cos \Phi) & \sin^2 \beta \cos \Phi + \cos^2 \beta & \cos \alpha \sin \Phi + \cos \beta \cos \gamma(1 - \cos \Phi) \\ \cos \beta \sin \Phi + \cos \alpha \cos \gamma(1 - \cos \Phi) & -\cos \alpha \sin \Phi + \cos \beta \cos \gamma(1 - \cos \Phi) & \sin^2 \gamma \cos \Phi + \cos^2 \gamma \end{pmatrix}. \tag{22}$$

The matrix for $R(\mathbf{n}\Phi)$ is fundamental in the theory of proper orthogonal matrices in three dimensions. For if any proper orthogonal matrix A is given, the direction cosines of the axis of rotation and the angle of rotation may be obtained by equating the matrix elements of A to the corresponding matrix elements in $R(\mathbf{n}\Phi)$. The angle of rotation is determined from the trace relation:

$$1 + 2 \cos \Phi = a_{11} + a_{22} + a_{33}\,.$$

The proper rotation of an (xyz) system to a new $(x'y'z')$ system can also be expressed as a product of three rotations about axes defined by unit vectors $\mathbf{a}$, $\mathbf{b}$, and $\mathbf{c}$:

$$R(\mathbf{n}\Phi) = R(\mathbf{c}\psi)R(\mathbf{b}\theta)R(\mathbf{a}\varphi). \tag{23}$$

If the factorization on the right side of (23) is to be expressible in terms of three independent parameters, it is necessary that two successive rotations take place about different axes. This restriction also holds for the associative groupings into a product of two factors. For example, **a** cannot be parallel to **b**, and the axis of rotation of the product $R(\mathbf{b}\theta)R(\mathbf{a}\varphi)$ cannot be parallel to **c**. On the other hand, it is possible for **a** to be parallel to **c**, since the independence of φ and ψ is ensured by the noncommutivity of finite rotations. Even with these restrictions, there are many ways in which $R(\mathbf{n}\Phi)$ can be expressed as a product of three factors. Whichever factorization is selected, Φ and **n** may be determined by the method indicated above.

One of the most useful factorizations is the Euler decomposition. Let $(x'y'z')$ be the axes of the (xyz) system after the rotation $R(\mathbf{n}\Phi)$, and let the line determined by the intersection of the $x'y'$ plane with the xy plane be denoted N, as shown in Fig. AII.3. The line N, called the *line of nodes*,

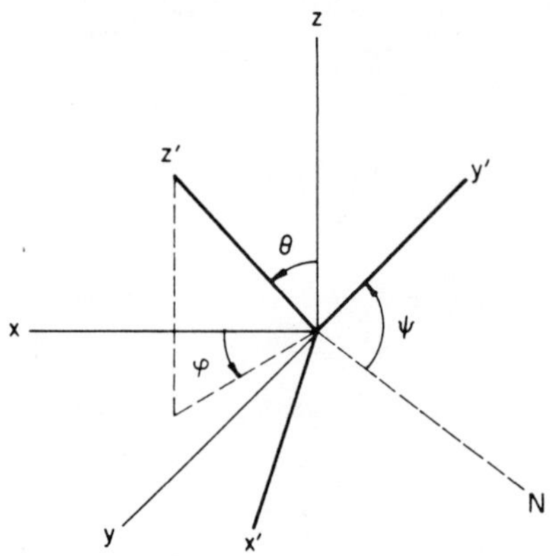

FIG. AII.3. The Euler angles φ, θ, and ψ.

is perpendicular to z and z'. The Euler angles φ, θ, ψ are defined as follows:

(1) A rotation about the z axis through an angle φ, sending the (xyz) system into the (x_1y_1z) system.

(2) A rotation about the y_1 axis through an angle θ, sending the (x_1y_1z) system into the (x_2y_1z') system.

(3) A rotation about the z' axis through an angle ψ, sending the (x_2y_1z') system into the $(x'y'z')$ system.

The angles θ and φ are the polar angles of z', so that

$$0 \leqslant \theta \leqslant \pi, \qquad 0 \leqslant \varphi \leqslant 2\pi, \qquad 0 \leqslant \psi \leqslant 2\pi.$$

The matrices for $R_z(\varphi)$, $R_{y_1}(\theta)$, and $R_{z'}(\psi)$ may be obtained from (8) and (9); their product

$$R_{z'}(\psi)R_{y_1}(\theta)R_z(\varphi)$$

gives the matrix for a three-dimensional rotation in terms of Euler's angles. Upon carrying out the matrix multiplications, one finds

$$R_{z'}(\psi)R_{y_1}(\theta)R_z(\varphi)$$
$$= \begin{pmatrix} \cos\psi\cos\theta\cos\varphi - \sin\psi\sin\varphi & \cos\psi\cos\theta\sin\varphi + \sin\psi\cos\varphi & -\cos\psi\sin\theta \\ -\sin\psi\cos\theta\cos\varphi - \cos\psi\sin\varphi & -\sin\psi\cos\theta\sin\varphi + \cos\psi\cos\varphi & \sin\psi\sin\theta \\ \sin\theta\cos\varphi & \sin\theta\sin\varphi & \cos\theta \end{pmatrix}. \tag{24}$$

The angle of rotation in terms of the Euler angles may be obtained by equating $1 + 2\cos\Phi$ to the trace of (24). One finds, after some trigonometric reductions,

$$\cos\frac{\Phi}{2} = \pm\cos\frac{\theta}{2}\cos\frac{1}{2}(\varphi + \psi).$$

In the special case $\theta = \psi = 0$, the angle of rotation is φ, so that the positive sign must be chosen. The direction cosines of the axis of rotation may be determined by equating corresponding matrix elements of (22) and (24). The final results are

$$\begin{aligned} \cos\alpha\sin\tfrac{1}{2}\Phi &= \sin\tfrac{1}{2}\theta\sin\tfrac{1}{2}(\psi - \varphi), \\ \cos\beta\sin\tfrac{1}{2}\Phi &= \sin\tfrac{1}{2}\theta\cos\tfrac{1}{2}(\psi - \varphi), \\ \cos\gamma\sin\tfrac{1}{2}\Phi &= \cos\tfrac{1}{2}\theta\sin\tfrac{1}{2}(\psi + \varphi), \\ \cos\tfrac{1}{2}\Phi &= \cos\tfrac{1}{2}\theta\cos\tfrac{1}{2}(\psi + \varphi). \end{aligned} \tag{25}$$

APPENDIX III

Exponential Operators

1. Definition and Elementary Properties

The analysis of many problems in mathematics and physics is facilitated by the use of functions of operators and matrices. One of the most important matrix functions is the exponential function, defined by the power series expansion

$$e^A = \sum_{r=0}^{\infty} \frac{A^r}{r!}, \tag{1.1}$$

where $A^0 = 1$. It can be shown (*1*) that this series converges for all A.

The exponential function of a matrix possesses the following properties:

(1) If B is any matrix which commutes with A, then

$$[e^A, B] = 0, \qquad [e^A, e^B] = 0, \qquad e^{A+B} = e^A e^B. \tag{1.2}$$

The first and second relations follow from the fact that, if $[A, B] = 0$, $[A^r, B^s] = 0$ $(r, s = 0, 1, 2, ...)$, so that every integral power of B commutes with every term in the series expansion for e^A. The last equation of (1.2) can be verified by comparing the series expansions for e^A and e^B. It must be emphasized, however, that

$$e^{A+B} \neq e^A e^B, \qquad \text{if} \quad [A, B] \neq 0.$$

(2) If t is a scalar variable, and A is a matrix independent of t, then

$$\frac{d}{dt} e^{tA} = Ae^{tA}. \tag{1.3}$$

This relation follows from a term-by-term differentiation of the power series for e^{tA}:

$$\frac{d}{dt}\left\{\sum_{r=0}^{\infty}\frac{t^r A^r}{r!}\right\} = \sum_{r=1}^{\infty}\frac{t^{r-1}A^r}{(r-1)!} = A\sum_{r=0}^{\infty}\frac{t^r A^r}{r!}.$$

On the other hand, if A is a function of the variable t, then

$$\frac{d}{dt}e^{A(t)} \neq \frac{dA}{dt}e^{A(t)} \quad \text{or} \quad e^{A(t)}\frac{dA}{dt} \quad \text{unless} \quad \left[A, \frac{dA}{dt}\right] = 0.$$

(3) If S is a nonsingular matrix, $(S^{-1}AS)^n = S^{-1}A^nS$, so that

$$S^{-1}e^A S = \sum_{r=0}^{\infty}\frac{1}{r!}(S^{-1}A^rS) = \sum_{r=0}^{\infty}\frac{1}{r!}(S^{-1}AS)^r = e^{S^{-1}AS}. \tag{1.4}$$

An important application of (1.4) results when S is interpreted as the matrix which reduces A to the triangular form of Schur's theorem[1]:

$$S^{-1}AS = T; \qquad T_{ij} = 0, \qquad \text{when} \quad j < i.$$

For if T is triangular, then T^n ($n = 1, 2, \ldots$) is also triangular, and this implies that

$$S^{-1}e^A S = \exp(S^{-1}AS) = e^T$$

is triangular.

If the matrix can be diagonalized, then e^A can also be diagonalized. Indeed, if $S^{-1}AS = (A_i\,\delta_{ij})$, then

$$S^{-1}e^A S = (e^{A_i}\,\delta_{ij}),$$

which shows that the diagonal elements of $S^{-1}e^AS$ are the exponential functions of the eigenvalues of A. This property also holds in the case where $S^{-1}AS$ is triangular. For the diagonal elements of T^n are T^n_{11}, T^n_{22}, ..., so that the diagonal elements of e^T are $e^{T_{11}}, e^{T_{22}}, \ldots$. But the latter are the eigenvalues of e^T and their product is the determinant of e^T:

$$\det e^T = e^{T_{11}}e^{T_{22}}\cdots = e^{T_{11}+T_{22}\cdots} = e^{\operatorname{tr} T}.$$

Since the trace and determinant are invariant under a similarity transformation, it follows that

$$\det e^A = e^{\operatorname{tr} A}. \tag{1.5}$$

[1] Cf. Appendix I, Section 4.

Equation (1.5) shows that e^A is always nonsingular. In fact, the inverse of e^A is

$$(e^A)^{-1} = e^{-A}, \tag{1.6}$$

since

$$e^A e^{-A} = e^{-A} e^A = e^{(A-A)} = e^0 = 1.$$

If $A = iH$, where H is hermitian, then the adjoint of e^{iH} is

$$\left\{\sum_{r=0}^{\infty} \frac{(iH)^r}{r!}\right\}^\dagger = \left\{\sum_{r=0}^{\infty} \frac{(-iH)^r}{r!}\right\} = e^{-iH}.$$

Thus e^{iH} is unitary if H is hermitian. A similar argument can be used to prove that e^A is orthogonal when A is skew-symmetric.

The preceding results also hold for exponential operators; the matrix forms for exponential operators appear upon introducing a basis and representing the operators by matrices.

The series expansion for the exponential function of a matrix A can be reduced to a polynomial in A if the integral powers of A obey simple recurrence relations. This is illustrated by the following examples:

1. Let

$$A = i\theta \begin{pmatrix} 0 & 1 \\ 1 & 0 \end{pmatrix},$$

so that $A^2 = -\theta^2 1$, $A^3 = -i\theta^3 A$, $A^4 = \theta^4 1$, ... Inserting these results into (1.1), one obtains

$$e^A = 1 \cos\theta + iA \sin\theta = \begin{pmatrix} \cos\theta & i\sin\theta \\ i\sin\theta & \cos\theta \end{pmatrix}.$$

2. Let A be the $n \times n$ matrix

$$A = \begin{pmatrix} 0 & 1 & 0 & 0 & \cdots & 0 \\ 0 & 0 & 1 & 0 & \cdots & 0 \\ 0 & 0 & 0 & 1 & \cdots & 0 \\ \vdots & \vdots & \vdots & \vdots & & \vdots \\ 0 & 0 & 0 & 0 & \cdots & 1 \\ 0 & 0 & 0 & 0 & \cdots & 0 \end{pmatrix}.$$

It is easily verified that $A^n = 0$; hence

$$e^A = 1 + A + \frac{A^2}{2!} + \cdots + \frac{A^{n-1}}{(n-1)!}.$$

In particular, when $n = 3$,

$$A = \begin{pmatrix} 0 & 1 & 0 \\ 0 & 0 & 1 \\ 0 & 0 & 0 \end{pmatrix}, \qquad A^2 = \begin{pmatrix} 0 & 0 & 1 \\ 0 & 0 & 0 \\ 0 & 0 & 0 \end{pmatrix}, \qquad A^3 = 0,$$

$$e^A = I + A + \tfrac{1}{2}A^2 = \begin{pmatrix} 1 & 1 & \frac{1}{2} \\ 0 & 1 & 1 \\ 0 & 0 & 1 \end{pmatrix}.$$

3. A very interesting example is provided by the skew-symmetric matrix

$$A = \begin{pmatrix} 0 & \cos\gamma & -\cos\beta \\ -\cos\gamma & 0 & \cos\alpha \\ \cos\beta & -\cos\alpha & 0 \end{pmatrix},$$

with

$$\cos^2\alpha + \cos^2\beta + \cos^2\gamma = 1.$$

The square of A is

$$A^2 = \begin{pmatrix} -\sin^2\alpha & \cos\alpha\cos\beta & \cos\alpha\cos\gamma \\ \cos\alpha\cos\beta & -\sin^2\beta & \cos\beta\cos\gamma \\ \cos\alpha\cos\gamma & \cos\beta\cos\gamma & -\sin^2\gamma \end{pmatrix},$$

but $A^3 = -A$, $A^4 = -A^2$, $A^5 = A$, ..., so that

$$e^{\Phi A} = I + A\sin\Phi + (1 - \cos\Phi)A^2.$$

Upon inserting the matrices for A and A^2 into the right-hand member of the last equation, it is easily shown that

$$e^{\Phi A} = R(\mathbf{n}\Phi), \qquad \mathbf{n} = (\cos\alpha, \cos\beta, \cos\gamma),$$

where $R(\mathbf{n}\Phi)$ is the three-dimensional rotation matrix derived in Appendix II.

2. Expansion of e^{A+B}

The decomposition of e^{A+B} into a product of two or more simpler exponential functions is a problem of some difficulty (*2*) when $[A, B] \neq 0$. It is not difficult, however, to obtain a formal expansion for e^{A+B} in terms of "transformed powers" of B. This expansion is quite useful when B can be regarded as a small correction or perturbation on A.

The expansion is most readily obtained by introducing an auxiliary scalar parameter s, and defining $Q(s)$ by

$$Q(s) = e^{s(A+B)}. \tag{2.1}$$

Evidently

$$Q(0) = 1, \qquad Q(1) = e^{A+B}, \qquad \frac{dQ}{ds} = (A+B)Q. \tag{2.2}$$

The differential equation for $Q(s)$ can be written

$$e^{sA}\frac{d}{ds}(e^{-sA}Q) = BQ,$$

or, upon multiplying from the left with e^{-sA}, as

$$\frac{d}{ds}(e^{-sA}Q) = e^{-sA}BQ. \tag{2.3}$$

Integrating this equation from zero to s, one obtains

$$Q(s) = e^{sA}\left\{1 + \int_0^s e^{-s'A}BQ(s')\,ds'\right\}. \tag{2.4}$$

Equation (2.4) can be used to obtain an expression for $Q(s')$ by replacing s with s' and s' with s''. Inserting the expression for $Q(s')$ into the integrand of (2.4) yields

$$Q(s) = e^{sA}\left\{1 + \int_0^s e^{-s'A}Be^{s'A}\,ds' + \int_0^s e^{-s'A}Be^{s'A}\left[\int_0^{s'} e^{-s''A}BQ(s'')\,ds''\right]ds'\right\}. \tag{2.5}$$

Iterating this process, one finds that

$$\begin{aligned} Q(s) = e^{sA}\Big\{1 &+ \int_0^s e^{-s'A}Be^{s'A}\,ds' + \int_0^s e^{-s'A}Be^{s'A}\,ds' \int_0^{s'} e^{-s''A}Be^{s''B}\,ds'' \\ &+ \cdots + \int_0^s e^{-s'A}Be^{s'A}\,ds' \int_0^{s'} e^{-s''A}Be^{s''A}\,ds'' \\ &\cdots \int_0^{s^{(n-1)}} \exp(-s^{(n)}A)B\exp(s^{(n)}A)\,ds^{(n)} + \cdots\Big\}. \end{aligned} \tag{2.6}$$

The expansion for e^{A+B} follows upon putting $s = 1$.

Equation (2.6) expresses $\exp[s(A+B)]$ as a power series in B. If $B = 0$, $Q(s)$ correctly reduces to e^{sA}. If $A = 0$, the multiple integrals are easily evaluated, and one obtains the series

$$1 + sB + \frac{s^2}{2!}B^2 + \cdots = e^{sB}.$$

Moreover, if $[A, B] = 0$, then all factors in B can be removed from the integrals, and $Q(s)$ gives the correct factorization $e^{sA}e^{sB}$.

Except for the limiting cases just noted, the integrations indicated in (2.6) are not easily carried out. However, if one introduces the matrix representatives of A and B, the integrations become quite simple. It will be assumed that the chosen representation diagonalizes A, and that the eigenvalues of A are nondegenerate:

$$A = (A_k\,\delta_{kj}), \qquad e^{sA} = (e^{sA_k}\,\delta_{kj}), \qquad B = (B_{kj}).$$

A particular term of (2.6) is said to be of the nth order if it involves n integrations. The order of a given term is equal to the number of times B occurs in that term. For example, the first-order term is

$$e^{sA}\int_0^s e^{-s'A}Be^{s'A}\,ds'$$

and its matrix elements are given by

$$\sum_l\sum_m\sum_n e^{sA_j}\,\delta_{jl}\int_0^s e^{-s'A_l}\,\delta_{lm}B_{mn}e^{s'A_n}\,\delta_{nk}\,ds'$$
$$= e^{sA_j}\int_0^s e^{-s'A_j}B_{jk}e^{s'A_k}\,ds' = B_{jk}\frac{e^{sA_j}-e^{sA_k}}{A_j-A_k}\,.$$

Similar computations lead to the following expansion for the matrix elements of $e^{s(A+B)}$ up to terms of the third order:

$$\begin{aligned}
[e^{s(A+B)}]_{jk} &= e^{sA_j}\,\delta_{jk} + B_{jk}\frac{e^{sA_j}-e^{sA_k}}{A_j-A_k}\\
&\quad+\sum_l \frac{B_{jl}B_{lk}}{A_k-A_l}\left\{\frac{e^{sA_k}-e^{sA_j}}{A_k-A_j}-\frac{e^{sA_l}-e^{sA_k}}{A_l-A_k}\right\}\\
&\quad+\sum_q\sum_r\frac{B_{jq}B_{qr}B_{rk}}{A_k-A_r}\left\{\frac{e^{sA_k}-e^{sA_j}}{(A_k-A_j)(A_k-A_q)}-\frac{e^{sA_q}-e^{sA_j}}{(A_q-A_j)(A_k-A_q)}\right.\\
&\quad\left.-\frac{e^{sA_r}-e^{sA_j}}{(A_r-A_q)(A_r-A_j)}+\frac{e^{sA_q}-e^{sA_j}}{(A_r-A_q)(A_q-A_j)}\right\}+\cdots. \qquad (2.7)
\end{aligned}$$

REFERENCES

1. Paul R. Halmos, "Finite-Dimensional Vector Spaces," 2nd ed., Chap. IV. Van Nostrand, Princeton, New Jersey, 1958.
2. R. P. Feynman, *Phys. Rev.* **84**, 108 (1951).

APPENDIX IV

The Difference Equation of Laplace

The general linear homogeneous difference equation of the nth order with coefficients that are linear functions of the independent variable may be written

$$\sum_{r=0}^{n} (a_r x + b_r) f(x + r) = 0, \tag{1}$$

and is known as the difference equation of Laplace. The domain of the independent variable x is a discrete set of points $x = x_0, x_1, \ldots, x_N$, and it will be assumed that successive values of x differ by unity.

The solution of (1) can be represented as a contour integral:

$$f(x) = \frac{1}{2\pi i} \int_c s^{x-1} v(s) \, ds, \tag{2}$$

where the contour of integration may be open or closed. To proceed further, it is necessary to deduce expressions for $f(x + r)$ and $xf(x + r)$ from (2).

The function $f(x + r)$ is obtained from (2) by replacing x with $x + r$:

$$f(x + r) = \frac{1}{2\pi i} \int_c s^{x+r-1} v(s) \, ds. \tag{3}$$

Alternatively, one may obtain $f(x + r)$ by replacing $v(s)$, in (2), with $s^r v(s)$.

To obtain an expression for $xf(x + r)$, multiply (2) by x, and perform an integration by parts:

$$xf(x) = \frac{1}{2\pi i} \{s^x v(s)\}_c - \frac{1}{2\pi i} \int_c s^x \frac{d}{ds} v(s) \, ds. \tag{4}$$

Replacing $v(s)$ with $s^r v(s)$, one obtains

$$xf(x + r) = \frac{1}{2\pi i}\{s^{x+r}v(s)\}_c - \frac{1}{2\pi i}\int_c s^x \frac{d}{ds}[s^r v(s)]\, ds. \tag{5}$$

Substituting (3) and (5) in (1) gives

$$\frac{1}{2\pi i}\sum_r s^x[a_r s^r v(s)]_c - \frac{1}{2\pi i}\sum_r \int_c s^x \left\{\frac{d}{ds}[a_r s^r v(s)] - b_r s^{r-1}v(s)\right\} ds = 0.$$

It follows that (2) will be a solution of (1) provided that

$$\sum_r \left\{\frac{d}{ds}[a_r s^r v(s)] - b_r s^{r-1}v(s)\right\} = 0 \tag{6}$$

and

$$I(x, s) = \left\{s^x \sum_r a_r s^r v(s)\right\}_c = 0. \tag{7}$$

If the contour of integration is open, then (7) will be satisfied if $I(x, s)$ vanishes at both limits. If the contour is closed, $I(x, s)$ must return to its initial value. For each independent pair of limits of integration, or every (independent) contour of integration, one obtains a particular solution of (1).

Equation (6) may be rewritten

$$\frac{d}{ds}\ln v = \frac{\sum (b_r - ra_r)s^r}{\sum a_r s^{r+1}}, \tag{8}$$

and reduces to

$$\frac{d}{ds}\ln v = \frac{b_0 + (b_1 - a_1)s + (b_2 - 2a_2)s^2}{s(a_0 + a_1 s + a_2 s^2)}, \tag{9}$$

when $n = 2$.

For equation (3.28) in Chapter 2, $x = m$, and

$$\begin{aligned} a_2 &= 1, & b_2 &= I + 2, \\ a_1 &= 2\cot\theta, & b_1 &= 2\cot\theta - m'\csc\theta, \\ a_0 &= -1, & b_0 &= I. \end{aligned}$$

Substituting in (9) one obtains

$$\frac{d}{ds}\ln v = \frac{I - 2sm'\csc\theta + Is^2}{s(s^2 + 2s\cot\theta - 1)}.$$

The right side of this equation may be decomposed into partial fractions to give

$$\frac{d}{ds}\ln v = -\frac{I}{s} + \frac{I - m'}{(s - a_+)} + \frac{I + m'}{(s - a_-)}, \tag{10}$$

where

$$a_+ = \tan\frac{\theta}{2}, \qquad a_- = -\cot\frac{\theta}{2}$$

are the roots of

$$s^2 + 2s\cot\theta - 1 = 0.$$

From (10) it follows that

$$v(s) = s^{-I}(s - a_+)^{I-m'}(s - a_-)^{I+m'},$$

$$I(x, s) = \{s^{m-I}(s - a_+)^{I-m'+1}(s - a_-)^{I+m'+1}\}_c,$$

$$F_{mm'} = \frac{1}{2\pi i}\int_c \frac{(s - a_+)^{I-m'}(s - a_-)^{I+m'}}{s^{I-m+1}}.$$

REFERENCE

L. M. Milne-Thomson, "The Calculus of Finite Differences," Chap. XV. Macmillan, New York, 1933.

APPENDIX V

Trace Calculations

A number of theoretical calculations require a knowledge of the traces of the component spin operators and their binary products.

The invariance of the trace operation under a similarity transformation permits the use of any convenient basis to provide a matrix representation for the spin operators, for example, the basis which diagonalizes $\mathbf{I}^2$ and I_z, or the basis which diagonalizes $\mathbf{I}_j^2$ and I_{zj}, $j = 1, 2, \ldots, N$. However, one can derive some useful trace relations from the assumptions that the component operators are nonzero, hermitian, defined with respect to a finite-dimensional vector space, and satisfy the commutation rules

$$I_x I_y - I_y I_x = iI_z \,, \tag{1}$$

$$I_y I_z - I_z I_y = iI_x \,, \tag{2}$$

$$I_z I_x - I_x I_z = iI_y \,. \tag{3}$$

Consider first the case of a single particle. Taking the traces of the left- and right-hand members of (1) through (3) one obtains

$$\operatorname{tr} I_x = \operatorname{tr} I_y = \operatorname{tr} I_z = 0, \tag{4}$$

upon making use of the symmetric property tr AB = tr BA. It follows that for any (ordinary) vector $\mathbf{n}$,

$$\operatorname{tr} \mathbf{n} \cdot \mathbf{I} = 0. \tag{5}$$

The traces of I_x^2, I_y^2, and I_z^2 cannot vanish. For suppose that tr $I_z^2 = 0$. Since I_z is hermitian, the matrix for I_z can be diagonalized and all eigenvalues must be real numbers. When the matrix for I_z is diagonal, so is the matrix for I_z^2. Thus tr $I_z^2 = 0$ requires the sum of the squares of the eigenvalues of I_z to vanish, which can be true only if each eigenvalue of I_z is zero. This would imply that I_z is the zero operator, contrary to assumption. Hence $\operatorname{tr} I_z^2 \neq 0$. Similar remarks apply to $\operatorname{tr} I_x^2$ and $\operatorname{tr} I_y^2$. In fact,

$$\operatorname{tr} I_x^2 = \operatorname{tr} I_y^2 = \operatorname{tr} I_z^2. \tag{6}$$

To prove (6), multiply (1) from the right with I_z, (2) from the left with I_x, and (3) from the left with I_y, obtaining

$$I_xI_yI_z - I_yI_xI_z = iI_z^2,$$
$$I_xI_yI_z - I_xI_zI_y = iI_x^2,$$
$$I_yI_zI_x - I_yI_xI_z = iI_y^2.$$

Equations (6) follow at once upon noting that $\operatorname{tr} I_yI_xI_z = \operatorname{tr} I_xI_zI_y$, $\operatorname{tr} I_xI_yI_z = \operatorname{tr} I_yI_zI_x$, by the symmetric property of the trace operation. An analogous calculation can be used to show that

$$\operatorname{tr} I_xI_y = \operatorname{tr} I_xI_z = \operatorname{tr} I_yI_z = 0. \tag{7}$$

The preceding trace relations can be used to prove that I_x, I_y, and I_z are linearly independent. For suppose that nonzero constants c_x, c_y, and c_z exist such that

$$c_xI_x + c_yI_y + c_zI_z = 0.$$

Multiplying from the left (or right) with I_x and taking the trace of the resulting equation, one obtains $c_x \operatorname{tr} I_x^2 = 0$. Since $\operatorname{tr} I_x^2 \neq 0$, $c_x = 0$. Similarly, $c_y = c_z = 0$, so that the component operators are linearly independent.

The square of the angular momentum of a single particle may be written

$$\mathbf{I}^2 = I_x^2 + I_y^2 + I_z^2 = I(I+1)1, \tag{8}$$

where 1 is a $(2I+1)$-dimensional identity matrix. It follows that

$$\operatorname{tr} \mathbf{I}^2 = I(I+1)(2I+1), \tag{9}$$

$$\operatorname{tr} I_x^2 = \operatorname{tr} I_y^2 = \operatorname{tr} I_z^2 = \tfrac{1}{3}I(I+1)(2I+1), \tag{10}$$

$$\operatorname{tr} I^+I^- = \tfrac{2}{3}I(I+1)(2I+1). \tag{11}$$

The generalization of the preceding results to multispin systems is not difficult. Let $\mathbf{I}_j = (I_{xj}, I_{yj}, I_{zj})$ denote the spin vector for the jth particle ($j = 1, 2, ..., N$). The components of the total angular momentum

$$\mathbf{I} = (I_x, I_y, I_z) = \sum_j \mathbf{I}_j \tag{12}$$

satisfy (1) through (3), so that (4) through (7) are of general applicability. Moreover, the components of $\mathbf{I}_j$ also satisfy the commutation relations (1) through (3), so that

$$\operatorname{tr} I_{xj} = \operatorname{tr} I_{yj} = \operatorname{tr} I_{zj} = \operatorname{tr} \mathbf{n} \cdot \mathbf{I}_j = 0, \tag{13}$$

$$\operatorname{tr} I_{xj}^2 = \operatorname{tr} I_{yj}^2 = \operatorname{tr} I_{zj}^2, \tag{14}$$

$$\operatorname{tr} I_{xj} I_{yj} = \operatorname{tr} I_{xj} I_{zj} = \operatorname{tr} I_{yj} I_{zj} = 0. \tag{15}$$

However, (8) through (11) are not valid for multispin systems. The reason is that in a multispin system one deals with Kronecker products of spin operators. For example, I_{zj} is an abbreviation for

$$1_1 \otimes 1_2 \cdots 1_{j-1} \otimes I_{zj} \otimes 1_{j+1} \cdots \otimes 1_N,$$

where 1_r is a $(2I_r + 1)$-dimensional identity matrix defined with respect to the vector space of spin r alone (cf. Chapter 4). For any Kronecker product $A \otimes B \cdots$,

$$\operatorname{tr} A \otimes B \otimes \cdots = (\operatorname{tr} A)(\operatorname{tr} B) \cdots,$$

as shown in Chapter 4. Now, the trace of any component of $\mathbf{I}_j$ vanishes when computed over the spin space of particle j, so that

$$\operatorname{tr} 1_1 \otimes 1_2 \cdots 1_{j-1} \otimes I_{\lambda j} \otimes 1_{j+1} \cdots \otimes 1_N = 0 \qquad (\lambda = x, y, \text{ or } z)$$

as required by equations (13). Similar remarks apply to the traces of mixed products $I_{\lambda j} I_{\mu k}$, which vanish unless $\lambda = \mu$ and $j = k$.

The trace of $I_{\lambda j}^2$ over the space of spin j alone is given by (10) with I replaced by I_j. However, when the trace of $I_{\lambda j}^2$ is computed with respect to the whole space, it is necessary to include the product of the traces of identity operators for the remaining spaces. Thus

$$\operatorname{tr} I_{\lambda j}^2 = \tfrac{1}{3} I_j (I_j + 1) \dim S, \tag{16}$$

where

$$\dim S = \prod_{j=1}^{N} (2I_j + 1) \tag{17}$$

is the dimension of the space of the composite system. The traces of all binary products are now given by

$$\operatorname{tr} I_{\lambda j} I_{\mu k} = \tfrac{1}{3} \dim S \{I_j (I_j + 1)\}\, \delta_{\lambda\mu}\, \delta_{jk}, \tag{18}$$

where

$$\lambda, \mu = x, y, z; \qquad j, k = 1, 2, ..., N.$$

Upon setting $\lambda = \mu$, and summing over μ, one obtains

$$\operatorname{tr} \mathbf{I}_j \cdot \mathbf{I}_k = \dim S\{I_j(I_j + 1)\}\, \delta_{jk}\,. \tag{19}$$

As a first application of the trace relations for multispin systems, consider the general hamiltonian

$$\mathscr{H} = -\left\{\sum_j \gamma_j(1 - \sigma_j)\mathbf{H}(t) \cdot \mathbf{I}_j + \sum_{j<k}\sum J_{jk}\mathbf{I}_j \cdot \mathbf{I}_k\right\}.$$

It follows, from (13) and (19), that

$$\operatorname{tr} \mathscr{H} = 0. \tag{20}$$

As a second application, consider the trace of the square of the total angular momentum. Since

$$\mathbf{I}^2 = \sum_j \mathbf{I}_j^2 + 2 \sum_{j<k}\sum \mathbf{I}_j \cdot \mathbf{I}_k\,,$$

(19) shows that

$$\operatorname{tr} \mathbf{I}^2 = \dim S\left\{\sum_j I_j(I_j + 1)\right\}. \tag{21}$$

The trace of $\mathbf{I}^2$ can also be evaluated as (cf. Section 3.B, Chapter 4)

$$\operatorname{tr} \mathbf{I}^2 = \sum_I g_I I(I + 1)(2I + 1), \tag{22}$$

where g_I is the multiplicity of thc total spin quantum number I. It follows that

$$\sum_I g_I I(I + 1)(2I + 1) = \prod_{j=1}^{N} (2I_j + 1)\left\{\sum_{j=1}^{N} I_j(I_j + 1)\right\}. \tag{23}$$

Finally, consider the trace of I^+I^-. Since

$$I^+I^- = \left(\sum_j I_j^+\right)\left(\sum_j I_j^-\right) = \sum_j \sum_k (I_{xj}I_{xk} + I_{yj}I_{yk} + iI_{yj}I_{xk} - iI_{xj}I_{yk}),$$

it follows that

$$\operatorname{tr} I^+I^- = \tfrac{2}{3} \dim S \sum_j I_j(I_j + 1). \tag{24}$$

APPENDIX VI

Numerical Data for Some Two-Group Systems

The following tables give the resonance frequencies and relative intensities of the A_2B, A_3B, A_4B, A_2B_2, and A_3B_2 systems for a number of values of J/δ. All resonance frequencies are given in units of the internal chemical shift $\delta = \omega_A - \omega_B$, with $\omega_A > \omega_B$. In the A_2B_2 case, the origin has been taken at $\frac{1}{2}(\omega_A + \omega_B)$ and only the positive half of the (symmetrical) spectrum is given; in all other cases the origin is at ω_B.

In general, the study of complex spectra is materially simplified with the assistance of high-speed computing devices. The reader interested in such matters should consult the following references:

1. J. D. Swalen and C. A. Reilly, *J. Chem. Phys.* **37**, 21 (1962). "Analysis of Complex NMR Spectra. An Iterative Method."
2. D. R. Whitman, *J. Chem. Phys.* **36**, 2085 (1962). "Computer Assignment Technique for Analysis of High Resolution NMR Spectra."
3. S. Castellano and A. A. Bothner-By, *J. Chem. Phys.* **41**, 3863 (1964). "Analysis of NMR Spectra by Least Squares."
4. R. C. Ferguson and D. W. Marquardt, *J. Chem. Phys.* **41**, 2087 (1964). "Computer Analysis of NMR Spectra: Magnetic Equivalence Factoring."

Line Frequencies And Relative Intensities
For The A_2B Spin System

	J/δ	Intensity	Frequency	J/δ	Intensity	Frequency
A_1	0.00	2.00000	1.00000	0.05	1.89640	1.02628
A_2		2.00000	1.00000		1.90386	1.02494
A_3		2.00000	1.00000		2.10361	0.97506
A_4		2.00000	1.00000		2.09615	0.97622
B_1		1.00000	0.00000		1.10361	0.04872
B_2		1.00000	0.00000		0.99254	-0.00250
B_3		1.00000	0.00000		0.90386	-0.05122
B_4		1.00000	0.00000		1.00000	0.00000
M		0.00000	2.00000		0.00000	2.00250
A_1	0.10	1.78632	1.05523	0.15	1.67123	1.08701
A_2		1.81568	1.04951		1.73556	1.07336
A_3		2.21366	0.95049		2.32866	0.92664
A_4		2.18430	0.95474		2.26433	0.93537
B_1		1.21368	0.09477		1.32877	0.13799
B_2		0.97064	-0.00997		0.93568	-0.02237
B_3		0.81570	-0.10474		0.73567	-0.16037
B_4		1.00000	0.00000		1.00000	0.00000
M		0.00002	2.00997		0.00011	2.02237
A_1	0.20	1.55300	1.12170	0.25	1.43377	1.15936
A_2		1.66324	1.09619		1.59826	1.11776
A_3		2.44667	0.90381		2.56548	0.88224
A_4		2.33643	0.91789		2.40100	0.90212
B_1		1.44700	0.17830		1.56623	0.21564
B_2		0.88976	-0.03959		0.83552	-0.06149
B_3		0.66357	-0.21789		0.59900	-0.27712
B_4		1.00000	0.00000		1.00000	0.00000
M		0.00034	2.03959		0.00074	2.06149
A_1	0.30	1.31579	1.20000	0.35	1.20117	1.24355
A_2		1.54004	1.13788		1.48796	1.15645
A_3		2.68284	0.86212		2.79660	0.84355
A_4		2.45859	0.88788		2.50981	0.87500
B_1		1.68421	0.25000		1.79883	0.28145
B_2		0.77575	-0.08788		0.71321	-0.11855
B_3		0.54141	-0.33788		0.49020	-0.40000
B_4		1.00000	0.00000		1.00000	0.00000
M		0.00137	2.08788		0.00223	2.11855

A_2B

	J/δ	Intensity	Frequency	J/δ	Intensity	Frequency
A_1	0.40	1.09175	1.28990	0.45	0.98894	1.33890
A_2		1.44142	1.17343		1.39984	1.18882
A_3		2.90496	0.82657		3.00656	0.81118
A_4		2.55529	0.86332		2.59566	0.85272
B_1		1.90825	0.31010		2.01107	0.33610
B_2		0.65033	-0.15322		0.58910	-0.19163
B_3		0.44471	-0.46332		0.40434	-0.52772
B_4		1.00000	0.00000		1.00000	0.00000
M		0.00329	2.15322		0.00450	2.19163
A_1	0.50	0.89366	1.39039	0.55	0.80641	1.44415
A_2		1.36270	1.20268		1.32953	1.21511
A_3		3.10054	0.79732		3.18647	0.78489
A_4		2.63151	0.84307		2.66335	0.83426
B_1		2.10634	0.35961		2.19359	0.38085
B_2		0.53097	-0.23346		0.47688	-0.27842
B_3		0.36850	-0.59307		0.33665	-0.65926
B_4		1.00000	0.00000		1.00000	0.00000
M		0.00580	2.23346		0.00712	2.27842
A_1	0.60	0.72727	1.50000	0.65	0.65603	1.55772
A_2		1.29991	1.22621		1.27345	1.23610
A_3		3.26433	0.77379		3.33436	0.76390
A_4		2.69169	0.82621		2.71695	0.81882
B_1		2.27273	0.40000		2.34397	0.41728
B_2		0.42737	-0.32621		0.38258	-0.37655
B_3		0.30831	-0.72621		0.28306	-0.79382
B_4		1.00000	0.00000		1.00000	0.00000
M		0.00840	2.32621		0.00960	2.37655
A_1	0.70	0.59227	1.61714	0.75	0.53542	1.67805
A_2		1.24982	1.24490		1.22868	1.25272
A_3		3.39704	0.75510		3.45294	0.74728
A_4		2.73950	0.81203		2.75968	0.80578
B_1		2.40773	0.43286		2.46458	0.44695
B_2		0.34245	-0.42917		0.30674	-0.48383
B_3		0.26050	-0.86203		0.24032	-0.93078
B_4		1.00000	0.00000		1.00000	0.00000
M		0.01069	2.42917		0.01164	2.48383

A_2B

	J/δ	Intensity	Frequency	J/δ	Intensity	Frequency
A_1	0.80	0.48487	1.74031	0.85	0.43998	1.80376
A_2		1.20978	1.25969		1.19284	1.26589
A_3		3.50269	0.74031		3.54691	0.73411
A_4		2.77778	0.80000		2.79405	0.79465
B_1		2.51513	0.45969		2.56002	0.47124
B_2		0.27509	-0.54031		0.24714	-0.59841
B_3		0.22222	-1.00000		0.20595	-1.06965
B_4		1.00000	0.00000		1.00000	0.00000
M		0.01245	2.54031		0.01311	2.59841
A_1	0.90	0.40014	1.86827	0.95	0.36477	1.93372
A_2		1.17766	1.27142		1.16401	1.27636
A_3		3.58623	0.72858		3.62120	0.72364
A_4		2.80871	0.78969		2.82196	0.78508
B_1		2.59986	0.48173		2.63523	0.49128
B_2		0.22249	-0.65796		0.20076	-0.71879
B_3		0.19129	-1.13969		0.17804	-1.21008
B_4		1.00000	0.00000		1.00000	0.00000
M		0.01363	2.65796		0.01403	2.71879
A_1	1.00	0.33333	2.00000	2.00	0.08579	3.41421
A_2		1.15174	1.28078		1.04595	1.31784
A_3		3.65235	0.71922		3.90354	0.68216
A_4		2.83395	0.78078		2.94338	0.73205
B_1		2.66667	0.50000		2.91421	0.58579
B_2		0.18160	-0.78078		0.03984	-2.14626
B_3		0.16605	-1.28078		0.05662	-2.73205
B_4		1.00000	0.00000		1.00000	0.00000
M		0.01432	2.78078		0.01067	4.14626
A_1	3.00	0.03699	4.88600	4.00	0.02034	6.37228
A_2		1.02125	1.32621		1.01212	1.32928
A_3		3.95651	0.67379		3.97543	0.67072
A_4		2.97225	0.71221		2.98365	0.70156
B_1		2.96302	0.61400		2.97966	0.62772
B_2		0.01574	-3.59822		0.00822	-5.07384
B_3		0.02775	-4.21221		0.01635	-5.70156
B_4		1.00000	0.00000		1.00000	0.00000
M		0.00650	5.59822		0.00423	7.07384

A_2B

	J/δ	Intensity	Frequency	J/δ	Intensity	Frequency
A_1	5.00	0.01281	7.86421	10.00	0.00309	15.34847
A_2		1.00781	1.33073		1.00197	1.33268
A_3		3.98425	0.66927		3.99605	0.66732
A_4		2.98925	0.69493		2.99717	0.68115
B_1		2.98719	0.63579		2.99691	0.65153
B_2		0.00501	-6.55914		0.00112	-14.02961
B_3		0.01075	-7.19493		0.00283	-14.68115
B_4		1.00000	0.00000		1.00000	0.00000
M		0.00294	8.55914		0.00086	16.02961

	J/δ	Intensity	Frequency
A_1	∞	0.00000	∞
A_2		1.00000	1.33333
A_3		4.00000	0.66667
A_4		3.00000	0.66667
B_1		3.00000	0.66667
B_2		0.00000	-∞
B_3		0.00000	-∞
B_4		1.00000	0.00000
M		0.00000	∞

Line Frequencies And Relative Intensities
For The A_3B Spin System

	J/δ	Intensity	Frequency	J/δ	Intensity	Frequency
A_1	0.00	3.00000	1.00000	0.05	2.83863	1.02697
A_2		4.00000	1.00000		3.80099	1.02552
A_3		3.00000	1.00000		2.86104	1.02429
A_4		3.00000	1.00000		3.16141	0.97448
A_5		4.00000	1.00000		4.19900	0.97571
A_6		3.00000	1.00000		3.13899	0.97678
A_7		2.00000	1.00000		1.90012	1.02562
A_8		2.00000	1.00000		2.09988	0.97562
B_1		1.00000	0.00000		1.16137	0.07303
B_2		1.00000	0.00000		1.03765	0.02054
B_3		1.00000	0.00000		0.94000	-0.02928
B_4		1.00000	0.00000		0.86101	-0.07678
B_5		2.00000	0.00000		2.09988	0.02438
B_6		2.00000	0.00000		1.90012	-0.02562
M_1		0.00000	2.00000		0.00001	1.97946
M_2		0.00000	2.00000		0.00000	2.02928

	J/δ	Intensity	Frequency	J/δ	Intensity	Frequency
A_1	0.10	2.65465	1.05826	0.15	2.45004	1.09441
A_2		3.60767	1.05164		3.42481	1.07761
A_3		2.74271	1.04687		2.64269	1.06748
A_4		3.34525	0.94836		3.54948	0.92239
A_5		4.39218	0.95313		4.57449	0.93252
A_6		3.25724	0.95678		3.35710	0.93949
A_7		1.80099	1.05249		1.70332	1.08059
A_8		2.19901	0.95249		2.29668	0.93059
B_1		1.34535	0.14174		1.54996	0.20559
B_2		1.04698	0.03184		1.02522	0.03358
B_3		0.86506	-0.06668		0.78262	-0.11151
B_4		0.74276	-0.15678		0.64290	-0.23949
B_5		2.19901	0.04751		2.29668	0.06941
B_6		1.80099	-0.05249		1.70332	-0.08059
M_1		0.00009	1.96816		0.00049	1.96643
M_2		0.00005	2.06668		0.00021	2.11151

A_3B

	J/δ	Intensity	Frequency	J/δ	Intensity	Frequency
A_1	0.20	2.22942	1.13589	0.25	2.00000	1.18301
A_2		3.25567	1.10263		3.10198	1.12600
A_3		2.55833	1.08598		2.48717	1.10242
A_4		3.76904	0.89737		3.99641	0.87400
A_5		4.74226	0.91402		4.89345	0.89758
A_6		3.44115	0.92450		3.51186	0.91144
A_7		1.60777	1.10990		1.51493	1.14039
A_8		2.39223	0.90990		2.48507	0.89039
B_1		1.77058	0.26411		2.00000	0.31699
B_2		0.97375	0.02559		0.89802	0.00797
B_3		0.69889	-0.16302		0.61841	-0.22045
B_4		0.55885	-0.32450		0.48814	-0.41144
B_5		2.39223	0.09010		2.48507	0.10961
B_6		1.60777	-0.10990		1.51493	-0.14039
M_1		0.00155	1.97441		0.00359	1.99203
M_2		0.00052	2.16302		0.00098	2.22045

	J/δ	Intensity	Frequency	J/δ	Intensity	Frequency
A_1	0.30	1.77058	1.23589	0.35	1.54997	1.29441
A_2		2.96425	1.14721		2.84216	1.16592
A_3		2.42703	1.11690		2.37606	1.12960
A_4		4.22266	0.85279		4.43912	0.83408
A_5		5.02745	0.88310		5.14475	0.87040
A_6		3.57143	0.90000		3.62177	0.88993
A_7		1.42530	1.17202		1.33930	1.20474
A_8		2.57470	0.87202		2.66070	0.85474
B_1		2.22942	0.36411		2.45004	0.40559
B_2		0.80634	-0.01899		0.70780	-0.05474
B_3		0.54398	-0.28310		0.47702	-0.35026
B_4		0.42857	-0.50000		0.37823	-0.58993
B_5		2.57470	0.12798		2.66070	0.14526
B_6		1.42530	-0.17202		1.33930	-0.20474
M_1		0.00676	2.01899		0.01092	2.05474
M_2		0.00155	2.28310		0.00218	2.35026

A_3B

	J/δ	Intensity	Frequency	J/δ	Intensity	Frequency
A_1	0.40	1.34535	1.35826	0.45	1.16137	1.42697
A_2		2.73493	1.18205		2.64151	1.19571
A_3		2.33271	1.14071		2.29570	1.15042
A_4		4.63898	0.81795		4.81807	0.80429
A_5		5.24658	0.85929		5.33451	0.84958
A_6		3.66448	0.88102		3.70088	0.87310
A_7		1.25722	1.23852		1.17927	1.27329
A_8		2.74278	0.83852		2.82073	0.82329
B_1		2.65465	0.44174		2.83863	0.47303
B_2		0.61041	-0.09857		0.51986	-0.14965
B_3		0.41790	-0.42134		0.36637	-0.49579
B_4		0.33552	-0.68102		0.29912	-0.77310
B_5		2.74278	0.16148		2.82073	0.17671
B_6		1.25722	-0.23852		1.17927	-0.27329
M_1		0.01568	2.09857		0.02056	2.14965
M_2		0.00281	2.42134		0.00342	2.49579

	J/δ	Intensity	Frequency	J/δ	Intensity	Frequency
A_1	0.50	1.00000	1.50000	0.55	0.86101	1.57678
A_2		2.56066	1.20711		2.49106	1.21652
A_3		2.26399	1.15892		2.23669	1.16637
A_4		4.97487	0.79289		5.10993	0.78348
A_5		5.41025	0.84108		5.47545	0.83363
A_6		3.73205	0.86603		3.75888	0.85967
A_7		1.10557	1.30902		1.03616	1.34564
A_8		2.89443	0.80902		2.96384	0.79564
B_1		3.00000	0.50000		3.13899	0.52322
B_2		0.43934	-0.20711		0.36995	-0.27009
B_3		0.32180	-0.57313		0.28343	-0.65297
B_4		0.26795	-0.86603		0.24112	-0.95967
B_5		2.89443	0.19098		2.96384	0.20436
B_6		1.10557	-0.30902		1.03616	-0.34564
M_1		0.02513	2.20711		0.02906	2.27009
M_2		0.00396	2.57313		0.00443	2.65297

A_3B

	J/δ	Intensity	Frequency	J/δ	Intensity	Frequency
A_1	0.60	0.74276	1.65678	0.65	0.64290	1.73949
A_2		2.43135	1.22425		2.38022	1.23057
A_3		2.21309	1.17291		2.19261	1.17869
A_4		5.22503	0.77575		5.32257	0.76943
A_5		5.53162	0.82709		5.58012	0.82131
A_6		3.78208	0.85394		3.80225	0.84875
A_7		0.97101	1.38310		0.91002	1.42134
A_8		3.02899	0.78310		3.08998	0.77134
B_1		3.25724	0.54322		3.35710	0.56051
B_2		0.31141	-0.33780		0.26268	-0.40955
B_3		0.25046	-0.73496		0.22214	-0.81881
B_4		0.21792	-1.05394		0.19775	-1.14875
B_5		3.02899	0.21690		3.08998	0.22866
B_6		0.97101	-0.38310		0.91002	-0.42134
M_1		0.03221	2.33780		0.03453	2.40955
M_2		0.00482	2.73496		0.00513	2.81881

	J/δ	Intensity	Frequency	J/δ	Intensity	Frequency
A_1	0.70	0.55885	1.82450	0.75	0.48814	1.91144
A_2		2.33645	1.23573		2.29893	1.23995
A_3		2.17476	1.18380		2.15914	1.18834
A_4		5.40507	0.76427		5.47489	0.76005
A_5		5.62210	0.81620		5.65857	0.81166
A_6		3.81987	0.84403		3.83533	0.83972
A_7		0.85308	1.46033		0.80000	1.50000
A_8		3.14692	0.76033		3.20000	0.75000
B_1		3.44115	0.57550		3.51186	0.58856
B_2		0.22240	-0.48473		0.18921	-0.56283
B_3		0.19777	-0.90426		0.17676	-0.99111
B_4		0.18013	-1.24403		0.16467	-1.33972
B_5		3.14692	0.23967		3.20000	0.25000
B_6		0.85308	-0.46033		0.80000	-0.50000
M_1		0.03608	2.48473		0.03697	2.56283
M_2		0.00537	2.90426		0.00553	2.99111

A_3B

	J/δ	Intensity	Frequency	J/δ	Intensity	Frequency
A_1	0.80	0.42857	2.00000	0.85	0.37823	2.08993
A_2		2.26671	1.24340		2.23896	1.24622
A_3		2.14541	1.19238		2.13330	1.19600
A_4		5.53414	0.75660		5.58460	0.75378
A_5		5.69035	0.80762		5.71816	0.80400
A_6		3.84895	0.83578		3.86100	0.83216
A_7		0.75061	1.54031		0.70470	1.58122
A_8		3.24939	0.74031		3.29530	0.73122
B_1		3.57143	0.60000		3.62177	0.61007
B_2		0.16186	-0.64340		0.13927	-0.72609
B_3		0.15859	-1.07918		0.14284	-1.16831
B_4		0.15105	-1.43578		0.13900	-1.53216
B_5		3.24939	0.25969		3.29530	0.26878
B_6		0.75061	-0.54031		0.70470	-0.58122
M_1		0.03729	2.64340		0.03717	2.72609
M_2		0.00564	3.07918		0.00570	3.16831

	J/δ	Intensity	Frequency	J/δ	Intensity	Frequency
A_1	0.90	0.33552	2.18102	0.95	0.29912	2.27310
A_2		2.21497	1.24854		2.19416	1.25044
A_3		2.12257	1.19926		2.11303	1.30219
A_4		5.62777	0.75146		5.66488	0.74956
A_5		5.74259	0.80074		5.76413	0.79871
A_6		3.87171	0.82882		3.88127	0.82574
A_7		0.66207	1.62268		0.62250	1.66466
A_8		3.33793	0.72268		3.37750	0.71466
B_1		3.66448	0.61898		3.70088	0.62690
B_2		0.12055	-0.81059		0.10496	-0.89665
B_3		0.12912	-1.25838		0.11714	-1.34928
B_4		0.12829	-1.62882		0.11873	-1.72574
B_5		3.33793	0.27732		3.37750	0.28534
B_6		0.66207	-0.62268		0.62250	-0.66466
M_1		0.03671	2.81059		0.03600	2.89665
M_2		0.00572	3.25838		0.00570	3.34928

A_3B

	J/δ	Intensity	Frequency	J/δ	Intensity	Frequency
A_1	1.00	0.26795	2.36603	2.00	0.05855	4.30278
A_2		2.17604	1.25201		2.04352	1.25878
A_3		2.10452	1.20484		2.03259	1.22974
A_4		5.69694	0.74799		5.92525	0.74122
A_5		5.78319	0.79516		5.93683	0.77026
A_6		3.88982	0.82288		3.96396	0.79129
A_7		0.58579	1.70711		0.21115	2.61803
A_8		3.41421	0.70711		3.78885	0.61803
B_1		3.73205	0.63397		3.94145	0.69722
B_2		0.09191	-0.98406		0.01503	-2.86433
B_3		0.10663	-1.44091		0.02713	-3.35284
B_4		0.11018	-1.82288		0.03604	-3.79129
B_5		3.41421	0.29289		3.78885	0.38197
B_6		0.58579	-0.70711		0.21115	-1.61803
M_1		0.03511	2.98406		0.01620	4.86433
M_2		0.00566	3.44091		0.00345	5.35284

	J/δ	Intensity	Frequency	J/δ	Intensity	Frequency
A_1	3.00	0.02434	6.28388	4.00	0.01320	8.27492
A_2		2.01884	1.25750		2.01042	1.25621
A_3		2.01548	1.23734		2.00898	1.24087
A_4		5.96729	0.74250		5.98178	0.74379
A_5		5.97075	0.76266		5.98324	0.75913
A_6		3.98248	0.77872		3.98970	0.77200
A_7		0.10263	3.58114		0.05972	4.56155
A_8		3.89737	0.58114		3.94029	0.56155
B_1		3.97566	0.71612		3.98680	0.72508
B_2		0.00550	-4.82526		0.00278	-6.80605
B_3		0.01173	-5.32010		0.00646	-7.30313
B_4		0.01752	-5.77872		0.01030	-7.77200
B_5		3.89737	0.41886		3.94029	0.43845
B_6		0.10263	-2.58114		0.05972	-3.56155
M_1		0.00837	6.82526		0.00502	8.80605
M_2		0.00204	7.32010		0.00132	9.30313

A_3B

	J/δ	Intensity	Frequency	J/δ	Intensity	Frequency
A_1	5.00	0.00826	10.26970	10.00	0.00197	20.25961
A_2		2.00660	1.25524		2.00161	1.25288
A_3		2.00585	1.24289		2.00151	1.24665
A_4		5.98841	0.74476		5.99714	0.74712
A_5		5.98916	0.75711		5.99724	0.75335
A_6		3.99323	0.76783		3.99822	0.75914
A_7		0.03884	5.54951		0.00993	10.52494
A_8		3.96116	0.54951		3.99007	0.52494
B_1		3.99174	0.73030		3.99803	0.74039
B_2		0.00166	-8.79463		0.00036	-18.77210
B_3		0.00407	-9.29276		0.00098	-19.27163
B_4		0.00677	-9.76783		0.00178	-19.75914
B_5		3.96116	0.45049		3.99007	0.47506
B_6		0.03884	-4.54951		0.00993	-9.52494
M_1		0.00333	10.79463		0.00089	20.77210
M_2		0.00091	11.29276		0.00027	21.27163

	J/δ	Intensity	Frequency
A_1	∞	0.00000	∞
A_2		2.00000	1.25000
A_3		2.00000	1.25000
A_4		6.00000	0.75000
A_5		6.00000	0.75000
A_6		4.00000	0.75000
A_7		0.00000	∞
A_8		4.00000	0.50000
B_1		4.00000	0.75000
B_2		0.00000	−∞
B_3		0.00000	−∞
B_4		0.00000	−∞
B_5		4.00000	0.50000
B_6		0.00000	−∞
M_1		0.00000	∞
M_2		0.00000	∞

Line Frequencies and Relative Intensities
For the A_4B Spin System

	J/δ	Intensity	Frequency	J/δ	Intensity	Frequency
A_1	0.00	4.00000	1.00000	0.05	3.77635	1.02769
A_2		6.00000	1.00000		5.69080	1.02614
A_3		6.00000	1.00000		5.71290	1.02481
A_4		4.00000	1.00000		3.82119	1.02368
A_5		4.00000	1.00000		4.22364	0.97386
A_6		6.00000	1.00000		6.30918	0.97519
A_7		6.00000	1.00000		6.28708	0.97632
A_8		4.00000	1.00000		4.17880	0.97732
A_9		6.00000	1.00000		5.68918	1.02628
A_{10}		6.00000	1.00000		5.71156	1.02494
A_{11}		6.00000	1.00000		6.31081	0.97506
A_{12}		6.00000	1.00000		6.28843	0.97622
B_1		1.00000	0.00000		1.22365	0.09731
B_2		1.00000	0.00000		1.08555	0.04347
B_3		1.00000	0.00000		0.97791	-0.00748
B_4		1.00000	0.00000		0.89172	-0.05597
B_5		1.00000	0.00000		0.82120	-0.10232
B_6		3.00000	0.00000		3.31082	0.04872
B_7		3.00000	0.00000		2.97762	-0.00250
B_8		3.00000	0.00000		2.71157	-0.05122
B_9		2.00000	0.00000		2.00000	0.00000
M_1		0.00000	2.00000		0.00001	1.95653
M_2		0.00000	2.00000		0.00001	2.00748
M_3		0.00000	2.00000		0.00001	2.05597
M_4		0.00000	2.00000		0.00000	2.00250

A_4B

	J/δ	Intensity	Frequency	J/δ	Intensity	Frequency
A_1	0.10	3.50205	1.06161	0.15	3.17686	1.10302
A_2		5.37234	1.05393		5.05901	1.08213
A_3		5.45639	1.04856		5.23382	1.07038
A_4		3.67942	1.04453		3.56705	1.06257
A_5		4.49771	0.94607		4.82171	0.91787
A_6		6.62722	0.95144		6.93873	0.92962
A_7		6.54334	0.95547		6.76507	0.93743
A_8		4.32050	0.95863		4.43268	0.94310
A_9		5.35896	1.05523		5.01369	1.08701
A_{10}		5.44704	1.04951		5.20667	1.07336
A_{11}		6.64097	0.95049		6.98596	0.92664
A_{12}		6.55289	0.95474		6.79299	0.93537
B_1		1.49795	0.18839		1.82314	0.27198
B_2		1.12970	0.07286		1.11786	0.08683
B_3		0.91620	-0.02963		0.82661	-0.06568
B_4		0.77716	-0.12273		0.66761	-0.19863
B_5		0.67950	-0.20863		0.56732	-0.31810
B_6		3.64104	0.09477		3.98631	0.13799
B_7		2.91192	-0.00997		2.80703	-0.02237
B_8		2.44711	-0.10474		2.20701	-0.16037
B_9		2.00000	0.00000		2.00000	0.00000
M_1		0.00024	1.92714		0.00143	1.91317
M_2		0.00020	2.02963		0.00084	2.06568
M_3		0.00008	2.12273		0.00027	2.19863
M_4		0.00007	2.00997		0.00034	2.02237

A_4B

	J/δ	Intensity	Frequency	J/δ	Intensity	Frequency
A_1	0.20	2.81009	1.15311	0.25	2.42191	1.21270
A_2		4.76329	1.10923		4.49381	1.13380
A_3		5.04459	1.08973		4.88578	1.10643
A_4		3.47758	1.07799		3.40585	1.09111
A_5		5.18513	0.89077		5.56674	0.86620
A_6		7.22981	0.91027		7.49086	0.89357
A_7		6.95271	0.92201		7.10926	0.90889
A_8		4.52184	0.93007		4.59318	0.91904
A_9		4.65900	1.12170		4.30132	1.15936
A_{10}		4.98971	1.09619		4.79478	1.11776
A_{11}		7.33999	0.90381		7.69645	0.88224
A_{12}		7.00929	0.91789		7.20299	0.90212
B_1		2.18991	0.34689		2.57809	0.41230
B_2		1.04679	0.08454		0.92811	0.06580
B_3		0.72349	-0.11443		0.61937	-0.17443
B_4		0.56913	-0.28215		0.48391	-0.37198
B_5		0.47816	-0.43007		0.40682	-0.54404
B_6		4.34100	0.17830		4.69868	0.21564
B_7		2.66929	-0.03959		2.50654	-0.06149
B_8		1.99071	-0.21789		1.79701	-0.27712
B_9		2.00000	0.00000		2.00000	0.00000
M_1		0.00478	1.91546		0.01134	1.93420
M_2		0.00212	2.11443		0.00399	2.17443
M_3		0.00058	2.28215		0.00097	2.37198
M_4		0.00101	2.03959		0.00223	2.06149

A_4B

	J/δ	Intensity	Frequency	J/δ	Intensity	Frequency
A_1	0.30	2.03928	1.28197	0.35	1.68730	1.36047
A_2		4.25523	1.15483		4.04925	1.17193
A_3		4.75355	1.12056		4.64388	1.13236
A_4		3.34788	1.10225		3.30063	1.11173
A_5		5.93969	0.84517		6.28026	0.82807
A_6		7.71755	0.87944		7.90988	0.86764
A_7		7.23888	0.89775		7.34590	0.88827
A_8		4.65073	0.90962		4.69758	0.90149
A_9		3.94737	1.20000		3.60352	1.24355
A_{10}		4.62012	1.13788		4.46389	1.15645
A_{11}		8.04851	0.86212		8.38978	0.84355
A_{12}		7.37575	0.88788		7.52941	0.87500
B_1		2.96072	0.46803		3.31270	0.51453
B_2		0.78405	0.03122		0.63805	-0.01787
B_3		0.52272	-0.24417		0.43781	-0.32216
B_4		0.41185	-0.46698		0.35168	-0.56625
B_5		0.34927	-0.65962		0.30242	-0.77649
B_6		5.05263	0.25000		5.39648	0.28145
B_7		2.32725	-0.08788		2.13963	-0.11855
B_8		1.62425	-0.33788		1.47059	-0.40000
B_9		2.00000	0.00000		2.00000	0.00000
M_1		0.02103	1.96878		0.03244	2.01787
M_2		0.00619	2.24417		0.00843	2.32216
M_3		0.00139	2.46698		0.00179	2.56625
M_4		0.00412	2.08788		0.00670	2.11855

A_4B

	J/δ	Intensity	Frequency	J/δ	Intensity	Frequency
A_1	0.40	1.38197	1.44721	0.45	1.12836	1.54094
A_2		3.87529	1.18524		3.73096	1.19528
A_3		4.55305	1.14214		4.47773	1.15023
A_4		3.26180	1.11983		3.22960	1.12678
A_5		6.57446	0.81476		6.81881	0.80472
A_6		8.07068	0.85786		8.20405	0.84977
A_7		7.43436	0.88017		7.50769	0.87322
A_8		4.73607	0.89443		4.76797	0.88824
A_9		3.27526	1.28990		2.96681	1.33890
A_{10}		4.32425	1.17343		4.19950	1.18882
A_{11}		8.71487	0.82657		9.01968	0.81118
A_{12}		7.66587	0.86332		7.78699	0.85272
B_1		3.61803	0.55279		3.87164	0.58406
B_2		0.50668	-0.07967		0.39740	-0.15217
B_3		0.36581	-0.40705		0.30606	-0.49768
B_4		0.30171	-0.66902		0.26028	-0.77470
B_5		0.26393	-0.89443		0.23203	-1.01324
B_6		5.72474	0.31010		6.03319	0.33610
B_7		1.95100	-0.15322		1.76730	-0.19163
B_8		1.33413	-0.46332		1.21301	-0.52772
B_9		2.00000	0.00000		2.00000	0.00000
M_1		0.04357	2.07967		0.05283	2.15217
M_2		0.01046	2.40705		0.01215	2.49768
M_3		0.00214	2.66902		0.00243	2.77470
M_4		0.00988	2.15322		0.01351	2.19163

A_4B

	J/δ	Intensity	Frequency	J/δ	Intensity	Frequency
A_1	0.50	0.92352	1.64039	0.55	0.76051	1.74442
A_2		3.61272	1.20268		3.51651	1.20804
A_3		4.41512	1.15693		4.36288	1.16249
A_4		3.20270	1.13278		3.18005	1.13799
A_5		7.01702	0.79732		7.17604	0.79196
A_6		8.31437	0.84307		8.40569	0.83751
A_7		7.56877	0.86722		7.61994	0.86201
A_8		4.79464	0.88278		4.81712	0.87794
A_9		2.68098	1.39039		2.41923	1.44415
A_{10}		4.08808	1.20268		3.98858	1.21511
A_{11}		9.30161	0.79732		9.55941	0.78489
A_{12}		7.89451	0.84307		7.99006	0.83426
B_1		4.07648	0.60961		4.23949	0.63058
B_2		0.31080	-0.23346		0.24401	-0.32187
B_3		0.25706	-0.59307		0.21707	-0.69240
B_4		0.22587	-0.88278		0.19718	-0.99288
B_5		0.20536	-1.13278		0.18288	-1.25294
B_6		6.31902	0.35961		6.58077	0.38085
B_7		1.59290	-0.23346		1.43065	-0.27842
B_8		1.10549	-0.59307		1.00994	-0.65926
B_9		2.00000	0.00000		2.00000	0.00000
M_1		0.05947	2.23346		0.06345	2.32187
M_2		0.01345	2.59307		0.01436	2.69240
M_3		0.00265	2.88278		0.00282	2.99288
M_4		0.01740	2.23346		0.02136	2.27842

A_4B

	J/δ	Intensity	Frequency	J/δ	Intensity	Frequency
A_1	0.60	0.63148	1.85208	0.65	0.52921	1.96262
A_2		3.43838	1.21186		3.37482	1.21455
A_3		4.31908	1.16713		4.28216	1.17102
A_4		3.16084	1.14254		3.14443	1.14653
A_5		7.30336	0.78814		7.40564	0.78545
A_6		8.48153	0.83287		8.54482	0.82898
A_7		7.66306	0.85746		7.69962	0.85347
A_8		4.83622	0.87361		4.85256	0.86973
A_9		2.18182	1.50000		1.96810	1.55772
A_{10}		3.89972	1.22621		3.82035	1.23610
A_{11}		9.79297	0.77379		10.00308	0.76390
A_{12}		8.07507	0.82621		8.15083	0.81882
B_1		4.36852	0.64792		4.47079	0.66238
B_2		0.19310	-0.41602		0.15439	-0.51479
B_3		0.18447	-0.79501		0.15781	-0.90036
B_4		0.17316	-1.10468		0.15294	-1.21792
B_5		0.16378	-1.37361		0.14744	-1.49473
B_6		6.81818	0.40000		7.03190	0.41728
B_7		1.28210	-0.32621		1.14775	-0.37655
B_8		0.92493	-0.72621		0.84917	-0.79382
B_9		2.00000	0.00000		2.00000	0.00000
M_1		0.06517	2.41602		0.06515	2.51479
M_2		0.01492	2.79501		0.01521	2.90036
M_3		0.00294	3.10468		0.00302	3.21792
M_4		0.02521	2.32621		0.02881	2.37655

A_4B

	J/δ	Intensity	Frequency	J/δ	Intensity	Frequency
A_1	0.70	0.44774	2.07545	0.75	0.38234	2.19010
A_2		3.32290	1.21641		3.28024	1.21766
A_3		4.25087	1.17430		4.22420	1.17709
A_4		3.13032	1.15006		3.11812	1.15319
A_5		7.48836	0.78359		7.55582	0.78234
A_6		8.59793	0.82570		8.64278	0.82291
A_7		7.73081	0.84994		7.75759	0.84681
A_8		4.86662	0.86622		4.87882	0.86304
A_9		1.77681	1.61714		1.60626	1.67805
A_{10}		3.74944	1.24490		3.68605	1.25272
A_{11}		10.19112	0.75510		10.35882	0.74728
A_{12}		8.21849	0.81203		8.27903	0.80578
B_1		4.55226	0.67455		4.61766	0.68490
B_2		0.12484	-0.61730		0.10210	-0.72286
B_3		0.13593	-1.00801		0.11787	-1.11761
B_4		0.13581	-1.33238		0.12123	-1.44789
B_5		0.13338	-1.61622		0.12118	-1.73804
B_6		7.22319	0.43286		7.39374	0.44695
B_7		1.02736	-0.42917		0.92021	-0.48383
B_8		0.78151	-0.86203		0.72097	-0.93078
B_9		2.00000	0.00000		2.00000	0.00000
M_1		0.06390	2.61730		0.06184	2.72286
M_2		0.01526	3.00801		0.01515	3.11761
M_3		0.00305	3.33238		0.00306	3.44789
M_4		0.03207	2.42917		0.03492	2.48383

A_4B

	J/δ	Intensity	Frequency	J/δ	Intensity	Frequency
A_1	0.80	0.32939	2.30623	0.85	0.28613	2.42355
A_2		3.24494	1.21847		3.21553	1.21895
A_3		4.20135	1.17946		4.18165	1.18151
A_4		3.10751	1.15599		3.09823	1.15849
A_5		7.61132	0.78153		7.65740	0.78105
A_6		8.68087	0.82054		8.71344	0.81849
A_7		7.78071	0.84401		7.80078	0.84151
A_8		4.88945	0.86015		4.89876	0.85750
A_9		1.45461	1.74031		1.31995	1.80376
A_{10}		3.62933	1.25969		3.57853	1.26589
A_{11}		10.50805	0.74031		10.64073	0.73411
A_{12}		8.33333	0.80000		8.38215	0.79465
B_1		4.67061	0.69377		4.71387	0.70145
B_2		0.08445	-0.83092		0.07060	-0.94105
B_3		0.10288	-1.22885		0.09035	-1.34151
B_4		0.10874	-1.56431		0.09799	-1.68151
B_5		0.11055	-1.86015		0.10124	-1.98250
B_6		7.54539	0.45969		7.68005	0.47124
B_7		0.82528	-0.54031		0.74142	-0.59841
B_8		0.66667	-1.00000		0.61785	-1.06965
B_9		2.00000	0.00000		2.00000	0.00000
M_1		0.05928	2.83092		0.05647	2.94105
M_2		0.01490	3.22885		0.01456	3.34151
M_3		0.00304	3.56431		0.00301	3.68151
M_4		0.03734	2.54031		0.03932	2.59841

A_4B

	J/δ	Intensity	Frequency	J/δ	Intensity	Frequency
A_1	0.90	0.25046	2.54186	0.95	0.22080	2.66098
A_2		3.19085	1.21920		3.16999	1.21928
A_3		4.16458	1.18327		4.14972	1.18480
A_4		3.09007	1.16075		3.08286	1.16279
A_5		7.69599	0.78080		7.72858	0.78072
A_6		8.74145	0.81673		8.76568	0.81520
A_7		7.81830	0.83925		7.83366	0.83721
A_8		4.90697	0.85508		4.91424	0.85284
A_9		1.20043	1.86827		1.09431	1.93372
A_{10}		3.53296	1.27142		3.49204	1.27636
A_{11}		10.75867	0.72858		10.86360	0.72364
A_{12}		8.42614	0.78969		8.46587	0.78508
B_1		4.74954	0.70814		4.77920	0.71402
B_2		0.05962	-1.05291		0.05081	-1.16623
B_3		0.07981	-1.45538		0.07089	-1.57031
B_4		0.08867	-1.79940		0.08057	-1.91790
B_5		0.09303	-2.10508		0.08576	-2.22784
B_6		7.79957	0.48173		7.90569	0.49128
B_7		0.66746	-0.65796		0.60227	-0.71879
B_8		0.57386	-1.13969		0.53413	-1.21008
B_9		2.00000	0.00000		2.00000	0.00000
M_1		0.05354	3.05291		0.05062	3.16623
M_2		0.01416	3.45538		0.01371	3.57031
M_3		0.00296	3.79940		0.00290	3.91790
M_4		0.04090	2.65796		0.04210	2.71879

Line Frequencies And Relative Intensities For The A_2B_2 Spin System

	J/δ	Intensity	Frequency	J/δ	Intensity	Frequency
A_1	0.00	2.00000	0.50000	0.05	1.80099	0.55249
A_2		2.00000	0.50000		1.81445	0.54988
A_3		2.00000	0.50000		1.98413	0.50274
A_4		2.00000	0.50000		1.98654	0.50224
A_5		2.00000	0.50000		2.21487	0.45013
A_6		2.00000	0.50000		2.19901	0.45249
A_7		4.00000	0.50000		4.00000	0.50000
M_1		0.00000	1.50000		0.00000	1.45512
M_2		0.00000	1.50000		0.00000	1.55487
A_1	0.10	1.60777	0.60990	0.15	1.42530	0.67202
A_2		1.65527	0.59915		1.51843	0.64741
A_3		1.92969	0.51188		1.83459	0.52860
A_4		1.95243	0.50792		1.90650	0.51543
A_5		2.46251	0.40113		2.73999	0.35400
A_6		2.39223	0.40990		2.57470	0.37202
A_7		4.00000	0.50000		4.00000	0.50000
M_1		0.00007	1.42094		0.00037	1.39803
M_2		0.00003	1.61896		0.00012	1.69144
A_1	0.20	1.25722	0.73852	0.25	1.10557	0.80902
A_2		1.40074	0.69445		1.29754	0.74024
A_3		1.70049	0.55381		1.53606	0.58805
A_4		1.85526	0.52322		1.80516	0.52998
A_5		3.04200	0.30975		3.35787	0.26928
A_6		2.74278	0.33852		2.89443	0.30902
A_7		4.00000	0.50000		4.00000	0.50000
M_1		0.00122	1.38678		0.00288	1.38732
M_2		0.00028	1.77148		0.00050	1.85828
A_1	0.30	0.97101	0.88310	0.35	0.85308	0.96033
A_2		1.20752	0.78486		1.12774	0.82843
A_3		1.35451	0.63145		1.17049	0.68371
A_4		1.75801	0.53474		1.71648	0.53694
A_5		3.67373	0.23322		3.97544	0.20182
A_6		3.02899	0.28310		3.14692	0.26033
A_7		4.00000	0.50000		4.00000	0.50000
M_1		0.00547	1.39941		0.00885	1.42247
M_2		0.00075	1.95105		0.00099	2.04909

A_2B_2

	J/δ	Intensity	Frequency	J/δ	Intensity	Frequency
A_1	0.40	0.75061	1.04031	0.45	0.66207	1.12268
A_2		1.05648	0.87113		0.99244	0.91313
A_3		0.99634	0.74418		0.84015	0.81197
A_4		1.68151	0.53644		1.65329	0.53340
A_5		4.25184	0.17500		4.49640	0.15242
A_6		3.24939	0.24031		3.33793	0.22268
A_7		4.00000	0.50000		4.00000	0.50000
M_1		0.01262	1.45563		0.01634	1.49778
M_2		0.00121	2.15176		0.00138	2.25850
A_1	0.50	0.58579	1.20711	0.55	0.52012	1.29330
A_2		0.93449	0.95459		0.88162	0.99567
A_3		0.70542	0.88607		0.59229	0.96550
A_4		1.63173	0.52814		1.61632	0.52111
A_5		4.70725	0.13356		4.88597	0.11786
A_6		3.41421	0.20711		3.47988	0.19330
A_7		4.00000	0.50000		4.00000	0.50000
M_1		0.01956	1.54777		0.02217	1.60447
M_2		0.00154	2.36881		0.00162	2.48227
A_1	0.60	0.46356	1.38102	0.65	0.41475	1.47006
A_2		0.83322	1.03648		0.78863	1.07713
A_3		0.49884	1.04935		0.42232	1.13682
A_4		1.60632	0.51270		1.60092	0.50330
A_5		5.03592	0.10480		5.16124	0.09390
A_6		3.53644	0.18102		3.58525	0.17006
A_7		4.00000	0.50000		4.00000	0.50000
M_1		0.02402	1.66685		0.02520	1.73402
M_2		0.00168	2.59853		0.00169	2.71725
A_1	0.70	0.37253	1.56023	0.75	0.33590	1.65139
A_2		0.74740	1.11773		0.70915	1.15833
A_3		0.35985	1.22725		0.30881	1.32007
A_4		1.59935	0.49322		1.60086	0.48270
A_5		5.26595	0.08474		5.35366	0.07701
A_6		3.62747	0.16023		3.66410	0.15139
A_7		4.00000	0.50000		4.00000	0.50000
M_1		0.02579	1.80521		0.02588	1.87979
M_2		0.00167	2.83819		0.00163	2.96110

A_2B_2

	J/δ	Intensity	Frequency	J/δ	Intensity	Frequency
A_1	0.80	0.30400	1.74340	0.85	0.27613	1.83615
A_2		0.67356	1.19900		0.64034	1.23979
A_3		0.26696	1.41484		0.23246	1.51118
A_4		1.60483	0.47195		1.61071	0.46113
A_5		5.42746	0.07044		5.48990	0.06481
A_6		3.69600	0.14340		3.72387	0.13615
A_7		4.00000	0.50000		4.00000	0.50000
M_1		0.02562	1.95724		0.02508	2.03712
M_2		0.00158	3.08579		0.00151	3.21209
A_1	0.90	0.25169	1.92956	0.95	0.23016	2.02355
A_2		0.60929	1.28072		0.58020	1.32184
A_3		0.20386	1.60880		0.17954	1.70745
A_4		1.61804	0.45033		1.62637	0.43965
A_5		5.54302	0.05996		5.58894	0.05774
A_6		3.74831	0.12956		3.76984	0.12355
A_7		4.00000	0.50000		4.00000	0.50000
M_1		0.02436	2.11909		0.02359	2.20283
M_2		0.00143	3.33985		0.00135	3.46893
A_1	1.00	0.21115	2.11803	2.00	0.05972	4.06155
A_2		0.55292	1.36316		0.23917	2.23552
A_3		0.15950	1.80693		0.03365	3.84835
A_4		1.63556	0.42914		1.81161	0.27475
A_5		5.62808	0.05205		5.90634	0.02232
A_6		3.78885	0.11803		3.94029	0.06155
A_7		4.00000	0.50000		4.00000	0.50000
M_1		0.02267	2.28812		0.00894	4.14542
M_2		0.00127	3.59923		0.00029	6.35862
A_1	3.00	0.02721	6.04138	4.00	0.01544	8.03113
A_2		0.12550	3.16867		0.07557	4.13014
A_3		0.01441	5.88705		0.00797	7.91160
A_4		1.89741	0.19571		1.93738	0.15066
A_5		5.95830	0.01434		5.97655	0.01061
A_6		3.97279	0.04138		3.98456	0.03113
A_7		4.00000	0.50000		4.00000	0.50000
M_1		0.00431	6.09710		0.00250	8.07287
M_2		0.00008	9.25143		0.00003	12.19240

A_2B_2

	J/δ	Intensity	Frequency	J/δ	Intensity	Frequency
A_1	5.00	0.00993	10.02494	10.00	0.00250	20.01249
A_2		0.05002	5.10556		0.01311	10.05380
A_3		0.00506	9.92780		0.00125	19.96286
A_4		1.95828	0.12207		1.98897	0.06212
A_5		5.98500	0.00843		5.99625	0.00418
A_6		3.99007	0.02494		3.99750	0.01249
A_7		4.00000	0.50000		4.00000	0.50000
M_1		0.00163	10.05831		0.00041	20.02916
M_2		0.00001	15.15543		0.00000	30.07878

	J/δ	Intensity	Frequency
A_1	∞	0.00000	∞
A_2		0.00000	∞
A_3		0.00000	∞
A_4		2.00000	0.00000
A_5		6.00000	0.00000
A_6		4.00000	0.00000
A_7		4.00000	0.50000
M_1		0.00000	∞
M_2		0.00000	∞

Line Frequencies And Relative Intensities
For The A_3B_2 Spin System

	J/δ	Intensity	Frequency	J/δ	Intensity	Frequency
A_1	0.00	3.00000	1.00000	0.05	2.69081	1.05383
A_2		4.00000	1.00000		3.61692	1.05103
A_3		3.00000	1.00000		2.73116	1.04862
A_4		3.00000	1.00000		2.97284	1.00301
A_5		4.00000	1.00000		3.97054	1.00244
A_6		3.00000	1.00000		2.98175	1.00202
A_7		3.00000	1.00000		3.33633	0.94894
A_8		4.00000	1.00000		4.41251	0.95147
A_9		3.00000	1.00000		3.28708	0.95365
A_{10}		2.00000	1.00000		1.80771	1.05122
A_{11}		2.00000	1.00000		1.98508	1.00250
A_{12}		2.00000	1.00000		2.20721	0.95128
$A1_3$		12.00000	1.00000		12.00000	1.00000
B_1		2.00000	0.00000		2.30919	0.07117
B_2		2.00000	0.00000		2.07388	0.02035
B_3		2.00000	0.00000		1.87457	-0.03027
B_4		2.00000	0.00000		1.73116	-0.07484
B_5		2.00000	0.00000		2.33634	0.07478
B_6		2.00000	0.00000		2.07618	0.02071
B_7		2.00000	0.00000		1.88577	-0.02824
B_8		2.00000	0.00000		1.71292	-0.07865
B_9		4.00000	0.00000		4.19229	0.02378
B_{10}		4.00000	0.00000		4.20721	0.02494
B_{11}		4.00000	0.00000		3.80771	-0.02494
B_{12}		4.00000	0.00000		3.79279	-0.02628
M_1		0.00000	3.00000		0.00000	3.00753
M_2		0.00000	-1.00000		0.00001	2.03370
M_3		0.00000	2.00000		0.00001	2.07930
M_4		0.00000	2.00000		0.00001	1.98376
M_5		0.00000	2.00000		0.00001	1.93067
M_6		0.00000	-1.00000		0.00001	-0.90788
M_7		0.00000	-1.00000		0.00001	-1.10997
M_8		0.00000	-1.00000		0.00000	-1.10713
M_9		0.00000	-1.00000		0.00000	-1.00250

A_3B_2

	J/δ	Intensity	Frequency	J/δ	Intensity	Frequency
A_1	0.10	2.37259	1.11554	0.15	2.06044	1.18515
A_2		3.27099	1.10331		2.96460	1.15583
A_3		2.51488	1.09415		2.33849	1.13642
A_4		2.87275	1.01419		2.67892	1.03669
A_5		3.88909	1.00910		3.77276	1.01810
A_6		2.94153	1.00635		2.89540	1.01089
A_7		3.75441	0.89675		4.25941	0.84548
A_8		4.83939	0.90666		5.25994	0.86651
A_9		3.54341	0.91410		3.76534	0.88053
A_{10}		1.63141	1.10474		1.47134	1.16037
A_{11}		1.94128	1.00997		1.87135	1.02237
A_{12}		2.42736	0.90523		2.65754	0.86201
A_{13}		12.00000	1.00000		12.00000	1.00000
B_1		2.62741	0.13446		2.93957	0.18985
B_2		2.10145	0.03312		2.09490	0.04139
B_3		1.70399	-0.07185		1.50530	-0.12517
B_4		1.51492	-0.14891		1.33864	-0.22187
B_5		2.75454	0.14803		3.26018	0.21763
B_6		2.08504	0.03059		2.00081	0.02642
B_7		1.75615	-0.06110		1.62624	-0.09634
B_8		1.45659	-0.16410		1.23466	-0.25553
B_9		4.36860	0.04526		4.52866	0.06463
B_{10}		4.42732	0.04951		4.65731	0.07336
B_{11}		3.63136	-0.04951		3.47111	-0.07336
B_{12}		3.57264	-0.05523		3.34246	-0.08701
M_1		0.00000	3.03050		0.00000	3.06992
M_2		0.00012	2.08438		0.00046	2.15113
M_3		0.00007	2.16435		0.00025	2.25086
M_4		0.00014	1.98485		0.00062	2.00257
M_5		0.00028	1.87525		0.00170	1.83716
M_6		0.00015	-0.83304		0.00093	-0.77767
M_7		0.00008	-1.03960		0.00034	-1.08802
M_8		0.00003	-1.22710		0.00010	-1.35793
M_9		0.00005	-1.00997		0.00023	-1.02237

A_3B_2

	J/δ	Intensity	Frequency	J/δ	Intensity	Frequency
A_1	0.20	1.76808	1.26235	0.25	1.50515	1.34650
A_2		2.69509	1.20794		2.45798	1.25940
A_3		2.19304	1.17551		2.07115	1.21162
A_4		2.38893	1.07329		2.03210	1.12573
A_5		3.64181	1.02684		3.51396	1.03278
A_6		2.85171	1.01431		2.81489	1.01593
A_7		4.83922	0.79765		5.45443	0.75560
A_8		5.65470	0.83149		6.00914	0.80158
A_9		3.95330	0.85208		4.11024	0.82793
A_{10}		1.32714	1.21789		1.19800	1.27712
A_{11}		1.77953	1.03959		1.67103	1.06149
A_{12}		2.89400	0.82170		3.13245	0.78436
A_{13}		12.00000	1.00000		12.00000	1.00000
B_1		3.23193	0.23765		3.49485	0.27850
B_2		2.06969	0.04859		2.03914	0.05772
B_3		1.29841	-0.18985		1.10080	-0.26494
B_4		1.19341	-0.29372		1.07188	-0.36458
B_5		3.84190	0.28112		4.46083	0.33638
B_6		1.81624	0.00549		1.55627	-0.03374
B_7		1.50233	-0.13251		1.38730	-0.16890
B_8		1.04671	-0.35208		0.88977	-0.45293
B_9		4.67286	0.08211		4.80200	0.09788
B_{10}		4.89333	0.09619		5.13097	0.11776
B_{11}		3.32648	-0.09619		3.19652	-0.11776
B_{12}		3.10600	-0.12170		2.86755	-0.15936
M_1		0.00000	3.12702		0.00000	3.20264
M_2		0.00110	2.23263		0.00192	2.32740
M_3		0.00057	2.33486		0.00102	2.41329
M_4		0.00159	2.03565		0.00300	2.08245
M_5		0.00597	1.81900		0.01443	1.82212
M_6		0.00329	-0.74357		0.00803	-0.73162
M_7		0.00082	-1.15385		0.00144	-1.23542
M_8		0.00019	-1.49787		0.00030	-1.64545
M_9		0.00067	-1.03959		0.00149	-1.06149

A_3B_2

	J/δ	Intensity	Frequency	J/δ	Intensity	Frequency
A_1	0.30	1.27627	1.43681	0.35	1.08169	1.53240
A_2		2.24844	1.31026		2.06194	1.36075
A_3		1.96723	1.24498		1.87783	1.27580
A_4		1.65864	1.19428		1.31588	1.27769
A_5		3.40196	1.03427		3.31352	1.03091
A_6		2.78667	1.01562		2.76641	1.01355
A_7		6.05064	0.72076		6.58156	0.69328
A_8		6.31618	0.77641		6.57539	0.75540
A_9		4.24027	0.80737		4.34769	0.78976
A_{10}		1.08283	1.33788		0.98039	1.40000
A_{11}		1.55150	1.08788		1.42642	1.11855
A_{12}		3.36842	0.75000		3.59766	0.71855
A_{13}		12.00000	1.00000		12.00000	1.00000
B_1		3.72374	0.31319		3.91831	0.34260
B_2		2.01299	0.07067		1.99743	0.08789
B_3		0.92371	-0.34911		0.77185	-0.44096
B_4		0.96842	-0.43467		0.87963	-0.50419
B_5		5.06234	0.38227		5.59901	0.41896
B_6		1.26810	-0.09126		0.99756	-0.16545
B_7		1.28190	-0.20532		1.18499	-0.24194
B_8		0.75974	-0.55737		0.65231	-0.66476
B_9		4.91717	0.11212		5.01961	0.12500
B_{10}		5.36568	0.13788		5.59319	0.15645
B_{11}		3.08008	-0.13788		2.97593	-0.15645
B_{12}		2.63158	-0.20000		2.40235	-0.24355
M_1		0.00001	3.29657		0.00002	3.40739
M_2		0.00276	2.43386		0.00342	2.55055
M_3		0.00157	2.48456		0.00222	2.54866
M_4		0.00464	2.14115		0.00627	2.20992
M_5		0.02652	1.84628		0.03976	1.88964
M_6		0.01483	-0.74134		0.02232	-0.77084
M_7		0.00207	-1.33084		0.00254	-1.43831
M_8		0.00038	-1.79940		0.00045	-1.95871
M_9		0.00275	-1.08788		0.00447	-1.11855

A_3B_2

	J/δ	Intensity	Frequency	J/δ	Intensity	Frequency
A_1	0.40	0.91886	1.63246	0.45	0.78380	1.73623
A_2		1.89490	1.41118		1.74410	1.46185
A_3		1.80014	1.30430		1.73203	1.33064
A_4		1.03032	1.37367		0.80666	1.47960
A_5		3.25156	1.02335		3.21495	1.01267
A_6		2.75314	1.01004		2.74568	1.00541
A_7		7.02442	0.67235		7.37932	0.65669
A_8		6.79072	0.73790		6.96805	0.72330
A_9		4.43649	0.77460		4.51012	0.76146
A_{10}		0.88942	1.46332		0.80868	1.52772
A_{11}		1.30067	1.15322		1.17820	1.19163
A_{12}		3.81650	0.68990		4.02213	0.66390
A_{13}		12.00000	1.00000		12.00000	1.00000
B_1		4.08114	0.36754		4.21620	0.38877
B_2		1.99530	0.10876		2.00663	0.13215
B_3		0.64529	-0.53916		0.54154	-0.64250
B_4		0.80267	-0.57334		0.73541	-0.64226
B_5		6.04688	0.44761		6.40536	0.46977
B_6		0.77108	-0.25371		0.59450	-0.35314
B_7		1.09579	-0.27907		1.01323	-0.31703
B_8		0.56351	-0.77460		0.48989	-0.88646
B_9		5.11058	0.13668		5.19133	0.14728
B_{10}		5.80991	0.17343		6.01313	0.18882
B_{11}		2.88284	-0.17343		2.79967	-0.18882
B_{12}		2.18350	-0.28990		1.97787	-0.33890
M_1		0.00003	3.53278		0.00006	3.67016
M_2		0.00394	2.67609		0.00418	2.80930
M_3		0.00298	2.60672		0.00385	2.66034
M_4		0.00769	2.28709		0.00879	2.37122
M_5		0.05108	1.94941		0.05905	2.02250
M_6		0.02866	-0.81730		0.03307	-0.87768
M_7		0.00291	-1.55613		0.00302	-1.68283
M_8		0.00048	-2.12253		0.00052	-2.29017
M_9		0.00659	-1.15322		0.00901	-1.19163

A_3B_2

	J/δ	Intensity	Frequency	J/δ	Intensity	Frequency
A_1	0.50	0.67218	1.84307	0.55	0.57995	1.95246
A_2		1.60713	1.51304		1.48239	1.56495
A_3		1.67178	1.35496		1.61820	1.37742
A_4		0.63702	1.59307		0.50982	1.71207
A_5		3.20005	1.00000		3.20204	0.98627
A_6		2.74285	1.00000		2.74356	0.99406
A_7		7.65848	0.64503		7.87721	0.63631
A_8		7.11376	0.71107		7.23363	0.70076
A_9		4.57143	0.75000		4.62277	0.73995
A_{10}		0.73699	1.59307		0.67329	1.65926
A_{11}		1.06193	1.23346		0.95377	1.27842
A_{12}		4.21268	0.64039		4.38718	0.61915
A_{13}		12.00000	1.00000		12.00000	1.00000
B_1		4.32782	0.40693		4.42005	0.42255
B_2		2.02969	0.15693		2.06166	0.18216
B_3		0.45715	-0.75000		0.38863	-0.86083
B_4		0.67612	-0.71107		0.62358	-0.77988
B_5		6.68659	0.48696		6.90614	0.50043
B_6		0.46188	-0.46107		0.36363	-0.57533
B_7		0.93656	-0.35611		0.86541	-0.39652
B_8		0.42857	-1.00000		0.37724	-1.11495
B_9		5.26301	0.15693		5.32671	0.16574
B_{10}		6.20108	0.20268		6.37294	0.21511
B_{11}		2.72539	-0.20268		2.65905	-0.21511
B_{12}		1.78732	-0.39039		1.61282	-0.44415
M_1		0.00007	3.81718		0.00008	3.97185
M_2		0.00421	2.94918		0.00410	3.09486
M_3		0.00478	2.71107		0.00580	2.76021
M_4		0.00960	2.46107		0.01010	2.55566
M_5		0.06340	2.10611		0.06474	2.19791
M_6		0.03536	-0.94918		0.03590	-1.02948
M_7		0.00301	-1.81718		0.00288	-1.95812
M_8		0.00051	-2.46107		0.00050	-2.63477
M_9		0.01160	-1.23346		0.01424	-1.27842

$\underline{A_3B_2}$

	J/δ	Intensity	Frequency	J/δ	Intensity	Frequency
A_1	0.60	0.50354	2.06394	0.65	0.43997	2.17717
A_2		1.36828	1.61775		1.26374	1.67155
A_3		1.57026	1.39813		1.52721	1.41720
A_4		0.41427	1.83505		0.34184	1.96085
A_5		3.21663	0.97215		3.24000	0.95812
A_6		2.74690	0.98781		2.75213	0.98140
A_7		8.04950	0.62972		8.18647	0.62468
A_8		7.33265	0.69201		7.41487	0.68453
A_9		4.66600	0.73107		4.70264	0.72319
A_{10}		0.61662	1.72621		0.56611	1.79382
A_{11}		0.85473	1.32621		0.76517	1.37655
A_{12}		4.54546	0.60000		4.68793	0.58272
A_{13}		12.00000	1.00000		12.00000	1.00000
B_1		4.49646	0.43606		4.56003	0.44783
B_2		2.10005	0.20717		2.14250	0.23150
B_3		0.33288	-0.97433		0.28730	-1.08999
B_4		0.57674	-0.84875		0.53484	-0.91773
B_5		7.07832	0.51114		7.21461	0.51978
B_6		0.29082	-0.69419		0.23635	-0.81639
B_7		0.79920	-0.43843		0.73766	-0.48192
B_8		0.33400	-1.23107		0.29736	-1.34819
B_9		5.38338	0.17379		5.43389	0.18118
B_{10}		6.52865	0.22621		6.66873	0.23610
B_{11}		2.59981	-0.22621		2.54690	-0.23610
B_{12}		1.45455	-0.50000		1.31207	-0.55772
M_1		0.00009	4.13263		0.00010	4.29832
M_2		0.00387	3.24564		0.00359	2.40089
M_3		0.00686	2.80871		0.00799	2.85725
M_4		0.01036	2.65415		0.01040	2.75591
M_5		0.06394	2.29607		0.06177	2.39919
M_6		0.03520	-1.11675		0.03373	-1.20957
M_7		0.00270	-2.10478		0.00245	-2.25644
M_8		0.00047	-2.81089		0.00046	-2.98911
M_9		0.01681	-1.32621		0.01921	-1.37655

A_3B_2

	J/δ	Intensity	Frequency	J/δ	Intensity	Frequency
A_1	0.70	0.38680	2.29186	0.75	0.34208	2.40776
A_2		1.16788	1.72640		1.07993	1.78234
A_3		1.48837	1.43476		1.45322	1.45091
A_4		0.28623	2.08859		0.24290	2.21766
A_5		3.26911	0.94448		3.30171	0.93141
A_6		2.75867	0.97494		2.76609	0.96853
A_7		8.29662	0.62076		8.38625	0.61767
A_8		7.48362	0.67808		7.54147	0.67248
A_9		4.73387	0.71616		4.76065	0.70985
A_{10}		0.52101	1.86203		0.48064	1.93078
A_{11}		0.68491	1.42917		0.61347	1.48383
A_{12}		4.81546	0.56714		4.92916	0.55305
A_{13}		12.00000	1.00000		12.00000	1.00000
B_1		4.61320	0.45814		4.65793	0.46724
B_2		2.18709	0.25488		2.23240	0.27714
B_3		0.24982	-1.20737		0.21879	-1.32616
B_4		0.49716	-0.98686		0.46315	-1.05617
B_5		7.32371	0.52686		7.41208	0.53276
B_6		0.19509	-0.94097		0.16336	-1.06723
B_7		0.68057	-0.52704		0.62769	-0.57379
B_8		0.26613	-1.46616		0.23935	-1.58485
B_9		5.47900	0.18797		5.51936	0.19422
B_{10}		6.79409	0.24490		6.90588	0.25272
B_{11}		2.49963	-0.24490		2.45737	-0.25272
B_{12}		1.18454	-0.61714		1.07084	-0.67805
M_1		0.00010	4.46801		0.00010	4.64101
M_2		0.00327	3.56011		0.00294	3.72286
M_3		0.00911	2.90628		0.01023	2.95611
M_4		0.01030	2.86039		0.01010	2.96717
M_5		0.05882	2.50621		0.05548	2.61631
M_6		0.03183	-1.30685		0.02974	-1.40776
M_7		0.00221	-2.41249		0.00197	-2.57243
M_8		0.00043	-3.16918		0.00039	-3.35086
M_9		0.02138	-1.42917		0.02328	-1.48383

A_3B_2

	J/δ	Intensity	Frequency	J/δ	Intensity	Frequency
A_1	0.80	0.30422	2.52470	0.85	0.27200	2.64250
A_2		0.99926	1.83936		0.92530	1.89745
A_3		1.42133	1.46576		1.39232	1.47940
A_4		0.20864	2.34759		0.18117	2.47806
A_5		3.33609	0.91903		3.37101	0.90738
A_6		2.77405	0.96223		2.78228	0.95608
A_7		8.46000	0.61521		8.52134	0.61322
A_8		7.59049	0.66758		7.63231	0.66328
A_9		4.78375	0.70416		4.80379	0.69901
A_{10}		0.44444	2.00000		0.41190	2.06965
A_{11}		0.55019	1.54031		0.49428	1.59841
A_{12}		5.03026	0.54031		5.12004	0.52876
A_{13}		12.00000	1.00000		12.00000	1.00000
B_1		4.69578	0.47531		4.72800	0.48250
B_2		2.27734	0.29820		2.32114	0.31805
B_3		0.19290	-1.44609		0.17115	-1.56694
B_4		0.43238	-1.12566		0.40444	-1.19534
B_5		7.48451	0.53774		7.54450	0.54200
B_6		0.13858	-1.19464		0.11894	-1.32284
B_7		0.57883	-0.62213		0.53379	-0.67202
B_8		0.21625	-1.70416		0.19621	-1.82401
B_9		5.55556	0.20000		5.58810	0.20535
B_{10}		7.00537	0.25969		7.09382	0.26589
B_{11}		2.41956	-0.25969		2.38569	-0.26589
B_{12}		0.96974	-0.74031		0.87997	-0.80376
M_1		0.00010	4.81677		0.00009	4.99486
M_2		0.00263	3.88875		0.00233	4.05745
M_3		0.01132	3.00692		0.01236	3.05880
M_4		0.00982	3.07590		0.00949	3.18630
M_5		0.05203	2.72888		0.04863	2.84344
M_6		0.02762	-1.51165		0.02556	-1.61801
M_7		0.00173	-2.73580		0.00152	-2.90224
M_8		0.00036	-3.53398		0.00034	-3.71836
M_9		0.02489	-1.54031		0.02622	-1.59841

A_3B_2

	J/δ	Intensity	Frequency	J/δ	Intensity	Frequency
A_1	0.90	0.24439	2.76106	0.95	0.22061	2.88025
A_2		0.85753	1.95657		0.79545	2.01667
A_3		1.36587	1.49193		1.34172	1.50344
A_4		0.15884	2.60881		0.14046	2.73969
A_5		3.40561	0.89648		3.43928	0.88631
A_6		2.79061	0.95010		2.79889	0.94431
A_7		8.57286	0.61159		8.61654	0.61024
A_8		7.66821	0.65946		7.69923	0.65606
A_9		4.82126	0.69433		4.83657	0.69005
A_{10}		0.38258	2.13969		0.35609	2.21008
A_{11}		0.44497	1.65796		0.40151	1.71879
A_{12}		5.19972	0.50827		5.27046	0.50872
A_{13}		12.00000	1.00000		12.00000	1.00000
B_1		4.75561	0.48894		4.77940	0.49475
B_2		2.36326	0.33670		2.40337	0.35418
B_3		0.15274	-1.68856		0.13706	-1.81080
B_4		0.37900	-1.26523		0.35577	-1.33531
B_5		7.59471	0.54568		7.63713	0.54889
B_6		0.10315	-1.45154		0.09029	-1.58055
B_7		0.49238	-0.72339		0.45439	-0.77618
B_8		0.17874	-1.94433		0.16343	-2.06505
B_9		5.61743	0.21031		5.64391	0.21492
B_{10}		7.17245	0.27142		7.24240	0.27636
B_{11}		2.35531	-0.27142		2.32803	-0.27636
B_{12}		0.80028	-0.86827		0.72954	-0.93372
M_1		0.00009	5.17493		0.00008	5.35673
M_2		0.00206	4.22868		0.00181	4.40218
M_3		0.01334	3.11180		0.01425	3.16594
M_4		0.00913	3.29812		0.00876	3.41117
M_5		0.04536	2.95961		0.04228	3.07711
M_6		0.02360	-1.72643		0.02178	-1.83661
M_7		0.00133	-3.07141		0.00116	-3.24304
M_8		0.00031	-3.90388		0.00028	-4.09042
M_9		0.02727	-1.65796		0.02806	-1.71879

A_3B_2

	J/δ	Intensity	Frequency	J/δ	Intensity	Frequency
A_1	1.00	0.20000	3.00000	2.00	0.05051	5.44949
A_2		0.73859	2.07772		0.21674	3.42349
A_3		1.31962	1.51402		1.10843	1.61552
A_4		0.12515	2.87056		0.02886	5.44949
A_5		3.47168	0.87687		3.82280	0.78246
A_6		2.80704	0.93872		2.91365	0.86329
A_7		8.65386	0.60911		8.91359	0.60202
A_8		7.72619	0.65302		7.92684	0.62521
A_9		4.85005	0.68614		4.95677	0.64575
A_{10}		0.33211	2.28078		0.11325	3.73205
A_{11}		0.36319	1.78078		0.07967	3.14626
A_{12}		5.33334	0.50000		5.82843	0.41421
A_{13}		12.00000	1.00000		12.00000	1.00000
B_1		4.80000	0.50000		4.94949	0.55051
B_2		2.44131	0.37056		2.82828	0.55051
B_3		0.12361	-1.93356		0.02989	-4.42822
B_4		0.33453	-1.40560		0.12613	-2.84275
B_5		7.67326	0.55173		7.92048	0.57651
B_6		0.07969	-1.70972		0.01661	-4.27096
B_7		0.41955	-0.83030		0.10837	-2.09052
B_8		0.14995	-2.18614		0.04323	-4.64575
B_9		5.66789	0.21922		5.88675	0.26795
B_{10}		7.30470	0.28078		7.80708	0.31784
B_{11}		2.30348	-0.28078		2.09190	-0.31784
B_{12}		0.66667	-1.00000		0.17157	-2.41421
M_1		0.00008	5.54001		0.00002	9.36148
M_2		0.00159	4.57772		0.00014	8.32247
M_3		0.01508	3.22118		0.01773	4.48850
M_4		0.00838	3.52530		0.00345	5.91671
M_5		0.03942	3.19570		0.01237	5.65545
M_6		0.02010	-1.94827		0.00550	-4.32247
M_7		0.00101	-3.41688		0.00008	-7.14395
M_8		0.00026	-4.27788		0.00005	-8.13425
M_9		0.02863	-1.78078		0.02135	-3.14626

A_3B_2

	J/δ	Intensity	Frequency	J/δ	Intensity	Frequency
A_1	3.00	0.02222	7.93273	4.00	0.01240	10.42443
A_2		0.09497	4.86824		0.05225	6.34128
A_3		1.05170	1.64241		1.02984	1.65270
A_4		0.01272	7.98019		0.00715	10.49496
A_5		3.91785	0.75671		3.95328	0.74681
A_6		2.95387	0.82687		2.97172	0.80613
A_7		8.96163	0.60087		8.97836	0.60049
A_8		7.96693	0.61651		7.98116	0.61228
A_9		4.98000	0.63104		4.98855	0.62348
A_{10}		0.05550	5.21221		0.03270	6.70156
A_{11}		0.03148	4.59822		0.01644	6.07384
A_{12}		5.92603	0.38600		5.95932	0.37228
A_{13}		12.00000	1.00000		12.00000	1.00000
B_1		4.97778	0.56727		4.98760	0.57557
B_2		2.92485	0.61473		2.95883	0.64610
B_3		0.01306	-6.93522		0.00738	-9.44082
B_4		0.06437	-4.31234		0.03871	-5.79493
B_5		7.96503	0.58430		7.98044	0.58819
B_6		0.00704	-6.79502		0.00382	-9.30628
B_7		0.04329	-3.49680		0.02242	-4.94837
B_8		0.02000	-7.13104		0.01145	-9.62348
B_9		5.94451	0.28779		5.96730	0.29844
B_{10}		7.91303	0.32621		7.95087	0.32928
B_{11}		2.04249	-0.32621		2.02424	-0.32928
B_{12}		0.07397	-3.88600		0.04068	-5.37228
M_1		0.00001	13.29181		0.00000	17.25465
M_2		0.00003	12.23370		0.00001	16.19014
M_3		0.01268	5.89592		0.00888	7.34788
M_4		0.00176	8.37860		0.00103	10.85923
M_5		0.00578	8.15260		0.00340	10.65358
M_6		0.00239	-6.78116		0.00132	-9.26067
M_7		0.00001	-11.04852		0.00000	-15.00146
M_8		0.00001	-12.07443		0.00000	-16.04188
M_9		0.01301	-4.59822		0.00846	-6.07384

A_3B_2

	J/δ	Intensity	Frequency	J/δ	Intensity	Frequency
A_1	5.00	0.00789	12.91948	10.00	0.00195	25.40967
A_2		0.03284	7.82550		0.00784	15.29514
A_3		1.01933	1.65763		1.00491	1.66437
A_4		0.00458	13.00345		0.00115	25.51929
A_5		3.96996	0.74206		3.99243	0.73555
A_6		2.98097	0.79284		2.99477	0.76436
A_7		8.98615	0.60031		8.99656	0.60008
A_8		7.98788	0.60977		7.99698	0.60484
A_9		4.99260	0.61887		4.99811	0.60952
A_{10}		0.02150	8.19493		0.00566	15.68115
A_{11}		0.01001	7.55914		0.00224	15.02961
A_{12}		5.97437	0.36421		5.99382	0.34847
A_{13}		12.00000	1.00000		12.00000	1.00000
B_1		4.99211	0.58052		4.99805	0.59033
B_2		2.97422	0.66448		2.99390	0.69995
B_3		0.00471	-11.94489		0.00113	-24.45469
B_4		0.02576	-7.28374		0.00693	-14.75966
B_5		7.98753	0.59053		7.99690	0.59524
B_6		0.00241	-11.81261		0.00061	-24.32398
B_7		0.01352	-6.41896		0.00293	-13.85965
B_8		0.00741	-12.11887		0.00189	-24.60952
B_9		5.97841	0.30507		5.99435	0.31885
B_{10}		7.96850	0.33073		7.99211	0.33268
B_{11}		2.01562	-0.33073		2.00394	-0.33268
B_{12}		0.02563	-6.86421		0.00618	-14.34847
M_1		0.00000	21.23157		0.00000	41.18362
M_2		0.00001	20.16446		0.00000	40.11449
M_3		0.00643	8.81865		0.00202	16.25956
M_4		0.00068	13.34751		0.00019	25.82388
M_5		0.00221	13.15498		0.00054	25.65960
M_6		0.00083	-11.74843		0.00020	-24.22411
M_7		0.00000	-18.97363		0.00000	-38.91917
M_8		0.00000	-20.02148		0.00000	-39.97870
M_9		0.00588	-7.55914		0.00172	-15.02961

A_3B_2

	J/δ	Intensity	Frequency
A_1	∞	0.00000	∞
A_2		0.00000	∞
A_3		1.00000	1.66667
A_4		0.00000	∞
A_5		4.00000	0.73333
A_6		3.00000	0.73333
A_7		9.00000	0.60000
A_8		8.00000	0.60000
A_9		5.00000	0.60000
A_{10}		0.00000	∞
A_{11}		0.00000	∞
A_{12}		6.00000	0.33333
A_{13}		12.00000	1.00000
B_1		5.00000	0.60000
B_2		3.00000	0.73333
B_3		0.00000	−∞
B_4		0.00000	−∞
B_5		8.00000	0.60000
B_6		0.00000	−∞
B_7		0.00000	−∞
B_8		0.00000	−∞
B_9		6.00000	0.33333
B_{10}		8.00000	0.33333
B_{11}		2.00000	-0.33333
B_{12}		0.00000	−∞
M_1		0.00000	−∞
M_2		0.00000	−∞
M_3		0.00000	−∞
M_4		0.00000	−∞
M_5		0.00000	−∞
M_6		0.00000	−∞
M_7		0.00000	−∞
M_8		0.00000	−∞
M_9		0.00000	−∞

Author Index

Numbers in parentheses are reference numbers and indicate that an author's work is referred to although his name is not cited in the text. Numbers in italic show the page on which the complete reference is listed.

Y

Z

Subject Index

A

B

C